Airplane Design

Part VII: Determination of Stability, Control and Performance Characteristics: FAR and Military Requirements

Dr. Jan Roskam
Ackers Distinguished Professor of Aerospace Engineer
The University of Kansas, Lawrence

2006

1440 Wakarusa Drive, Suite 500 • Lawrence, Kansas 66049, U.S.A.

PUBLISHED BY
Design, Analysis and Research Corporation (*DARcorporation*)
1440 Wakarusa Drive, Suite 500
Lawrence, Kansas 66049
U.S.A.
Phone: (785) 832-0434
Fax: (785) 832-0524
e-mail: info@darcorp.com
http://www.darcorp.com

Library of Congress Catalog Card Number: 97-68580

ISBN-13: 978-1-884885-54-9
ISBN-10: 1-884885-54-3

In all countries, sold and distributed by
Design, Analysis and Research Corporation
1440 Wakarusa Drive, Suite 500
Lawrence, Kansas 66049
U.S.A.

Printed in the United States of America
First Printing, 1986
Second Printing, 1989
Third Printing, 2002
Fourth Printing, 2006

TABLE OF CONTENTS

COURTESY: SAAB

TABLE OF SYMBOLS

The Table of Symbols is organized as follows:

IMPORTANT NOTES:

1. All aerodynamic coefficients and derivatives are defined in the stability axis system, unless stated to the contrary!
2. All rate derivatives are with respect to:

   $(\text{rate})\bar{c}/2U_1$ or $(\text{rate})b/2U_1$ depending on

   whether they are longitudinal or lateral-directional derivatives.
3. All speed derivatives are with respect to: u/U_1
4. Appendices contain separate symbol listings.

1. GENERAL SYMBOLS

Symbol	Definition	Dimension
$\bar{a}$	average deceleration during the groundrun	ft/sec^2
a_{lat}	lateral acceleration	ft/sec^2
a_{vert}	vertical acceleration	ft/sec^2
A	Wing aspect ratio	-----
A_h	Horizontal tail aspect ratio	-----
b	wing span	ft
b_f	flapped wing span	ft

$\bar{c}$	wing mean geometric chord, m.g.c.	ft
c_j	specific fuel consumption	lbs/lbs/hr
c_p	specific fuel consumption	lbs/hp/hr
$\bar{c}_{subscript}$	mean geometric chord of the surface corresponding to subscript area	ft
c_β	gear cornering coefficient, see page 47	lbs/deg
C_{D_o}	Zero lift drag coefficient	-----
C_{D_1}	Airplane steady state drag coefficient	-----
C_{D_u}	Airplane drag-due-to-speed derivative	-----
CGR	Climb gradient	rad
C_h	Hingemoment coefficient	-----
C_{h_o}	Hingemoment coefficient at zero angle of attack	-----
C_{h_α}	Hingemoment derivative due to angle of attack	1/rad
C_{h_β}	Hingemoment derivative due to sideslip angle	1/rad
C_{h_δ}	Hingemoment derivative due to control surface defl.	1/rad
C_{l_p}	Rolling moment due to roll rate derivative	1/rad
C_{l_r}	Rolling moment due to yaw rate derivative	1/rad
C_{l_β}	Rolling moment due to sideslip derivative	1/rad
$C_{l_{\beta_B}}$	Rolling moment due to sideslip derivative in the body axis system	1/rad
$C_{l_{\delta_a}}$	Rolling moment due to aileron derivative	1/rad
$C_{l_{\delta_{cpt}}}$	Rolling moment due to cockpit controller derivative, see Eqn.(2.63)	1/rad
$C_{l_{\delta_r}}$	Rolling moment due to rudder derivative	1/rad
$C_{l_{\delta_s}}$	Rolling moment due to spoiler derivative	1/rad

$C_L = W/\bar{q}S$	Airplane lift coefficient level flight	-----
C_{L_o}	Airplane lift coefficient at zero angle of attack	-----
C_{L_1}	Airplane steady state lift coefficient	-----
C_{L_q}	Lift due to pitchrate derivative	1/rad
C_{L_α}	Airplane lift curve slope	1/rad
$C_{L_{\delta_{ctrl}}}$	Airplane lift due to control surface deflection deriv.	1/rad
$C_{L_{\delta_e}}$	Airplane lift due to elevator deflection deriv.	1/rad
$C_{L_{wf}}$	Lift coefficient of the wing + fuselage	-----
$c_{m_{ac_f}}$	section pitching moment coefficient including flaps, about the section a.c.	-----
$C_{m_{ac_{wf}}}$	Pitching moment coefficent about the wing/fuselage aerodynamic center	-----
C_m	Airplane pitching moment coefficient	-----
C_{m_o}	Airplane pitching moment coefficient at zero angle of attack	-----
C_{m_α}	Airplane static longitudinal stability deriv.	1/rad
$C_{m_{\delta_{ctrl}}}$	Airplane pitching moment due to control surface deflection derivative	1/rad
$C_{m_{\delta_e}}$	Airplane pitching moment due to elevator deriv.	1/rad
C_{m_q}	Airplane pitching moment due to pitchrate deriv.	1/rad
C_{n_p}	Yawing moment due to rollrate derivative	1/rad
C_{n_r}	Yawing moment due to yawrate derivative	1/rad
C_{n_β}	Yawing moment due to sideslip derivative	1/rad
$C_{n_{\beta_B}}$	Yawing moment due to sideslip in the body fixed axis system	1/rad
$C_{n_{\delta_a}}$	Yawing moment due to aileron derivative	1/rad

$C_{n_{\delta_r}}$	Yawing moment due to rudder derivative	1/rad
C_{ride}	Ride comfort index	-----
$C_{T_{x_1}}$	Airplane steady state thrust coefficient	-----
$C_{T_{x_u}}$	Airplane thrust-due-to-speed derivative	-----
C_{y_p}	Sideforce due to rollrate derivative	1/rad
C_{y_r}	Sideforce due to yawrate derivative	1/rad
C_{y_β}	Sideforce due to sideslip derivative	1/rad
$C_{y_{\delta_a}}$	Sideforce due to aileron deflection deriv.	1/rad
$C_{y_{\delta_r}}$	Sideforce due to rudder deflection deriv.	1/rad
d_T	thrust moment arm in pitch about the airplane c.g.	ft
$D = C_D\bar{q}S$	Airplane drag	lbs
e	Oswald's efficiency factor	-----
E	Endurance	hrs
f_{mp}	range factor, page 134	-----
f_{TO}	obstacle height factor, see page 119	-----
F_a	Lateral cockpit control force	lbs
F_r	Directional cockpit control force	lbs
F_s	Longitudinal cockpit control force	lbs
F_{T_y}	Sideforce component due to thrust	lbs
g=32.2	acceleration of gravity	ft/sec^2
G	gearing ratio	rad/ft
h	altitude	ft
h_L	obstacle height for landing	ft

Symbol	Definition	Dimension
h_{TO}	obstacle height for takeoff	ft
HM	Hingemoment	ftlbs
I_{xx}	Rolling moment of inertia about the c.g.	$slugft^2$
I_{yy}	Pitching moment of inertia about the c.g.	$slugft^2$
$I_{yy_{mg}}$	Pitching moment of inertia about the main gear to runway contact point	$slugft^2$
I_{zz}	Yawing moment of inertia about the c.g.	$slugft^2$
K	See Eqn.(4.7), p.109	-----
K_1	Gust parameter, see p.107	-----
K_2	Gust parameter, see pages 107 and 108	-----
K_a, K_r	Proportionality constant for cockpit control force coupling of aileron to rudder and vice versa	lbs/rad
l_h	distance of the horizontal tail aerodynamic center to the airplane c.g.	ft
$L = C_L\bar{q}S$	Airplane lift	lbs
L.E.	Leading Edge	-----
L_h	Lift acting on the horizontal tail at the hor. tail aerodynamic center	lbs
L_v	Gust length in y-dir.	ft
L_w	Gust length in z-dir.	ft
L_{wf}	Lift acting on wing + fuselage at the wing/fuselage aerodynamic center	lbs
L_p	$C_{l_p}\bar{q}_1Sb^2/2I_{xx}U_1$	1/sec
L_r	$C_{l_r}\bar{q}_1Sb^2/2I_{xx}U_1$	1/sec
L_T	Rolling moment due to thrust	ftlbs
L_β	$C_{l_\beta}\bar{q}_1Sb/I_{xx}$	1/sec

$m=W/g$	airplane mass	slugs
$M_{ac_{wf}}$	Pitching moment about the wing/fuselage aerodynamic center	ftlbs
M_q	$C_{m_q}\bar{q}_1 S\bar{c}^2/2I_{yy}U_1$	1/sec
M_α	$C_{m_\alpha}\bar{q}_1 S\bar{c}/I_{yy}$	$1/sec^2$
M_α	$C_{m_\alpha}\bar{q}_1 S\bar{c}^2/2I_{yy}U_1$	1/sec
n	load factor (L/W)	-----
$\bar{n}$	load factor function, see page 32	-----
n_α	load factor derivative with respect to angle of attack	1/rad
$N_{1,2,3}$	Numerator determinants defined in Table 2.1	
N_D	Yawing moment due to asymmetric drag	ftlbs
N_r	$C_{n_r}\bar{q}_1 Sb^2/2I_{zz}U_1$	1/sec
N_T	Yawing moment due to asymmetric thrust	ftlbs
N_β	$C_{n_\beta}\bar{q}_1 Sb/I_{zz}$	$1/sec^2$
p	roll rate	deg/sec
P_{mg}	Vertical reaction force on the main gear	lbs
P_{ng}	Vertical reaction force on the nose gear	lbs
P_{reqd}	$T_{reqd}U_1/550$, power reqd	hp
P_s	Specific excess power	ft/sec
$\bar{q}$	dynamic pressure	psf

Q_1	Steady state pitch rate	rad/sec
R	Range	nm or sm
RC	Rate of climb	ft/min or ft/sec
RD	Rate of descent	ft/min or ft/sec
R_e/R_r	Rigid-to-elastic ratio	-----
R_L	Loop radius	ft
R_t	Turn radius	ft
s_{AIR}	Air distance in landing	ft
s_{FL}	Landing fieldlength	ft
s_L	Landing distance	ft
s_{LG}	Landing ground distance	ft
s_{TO}	Takeoff distance	ft
s_{TOG}	Takeoff ground distance	ft
S	wing area	ft^2
$S.M._{free}$	Static margin, stick free	-----
$S_{subscript}$	Surface area correspon-ding to subscript area	ft^2
t	time	sec
T	installed thrust	lbs
$\bar{T}$	Average thrust (p.117)	lbs
T_{reqd}	W/(L/D), Thrust reqd	lbs
T_R	Roll time constant	sec
T_2	Time to double amplitude	sec
$\dot{u}$	airplane forward acceleration, also:	ft/sec^2
$\dot{u}$	bleed rate	ft/sec^2
U	forward speed	ft/sec
$\dot{U}$	forward acceleration	ft/sec^2
U_1	Steady state speed	fps
V	Speed	fps
V_A	Approach speed	fps

V_s	Stall speed	fps
$V_{s_{PA}}$	Stall speed in power approach	fps
V_{TD}	Touchdown speed	fps
W	Airplane weight	lbs
$\dot{W}_F$	Fuel flow rate	lbs/sec
$\bar{x}_{ac_A}$	airplane aerodynamic center location in fractions of wing m.g.c.	-----
x_{ac_h}	horiz. tail aerodynamic center location relative to leading edge of the wing m.g.c.	ft
$x_{ac_{wf}}$	location of wing/fuselage aerodynamic center relative to leading edge of wing m.g.c.	ft
$\bar{x}_{cg}$	airplane center of gravity location in fractions of wing m.g.c.	-----
x_{ng}	distance from nose gear to leading edge of wing m.g.c.	ft
x_{mg}	distance from main gear to leading edge of wing m.g.c.	ft
y_{mg}	lateral distance from the main gear to the c.g.	ft
Y_{ng}	Lateral ground friction force on nose gear	lbs
Y_{mg}	Lateral ground friction force on main gear	lbs
Y_r	$C_{y_r}\bar{q}_1 Sb/2mU_1$	ft/sec
Y_β	$C_{y_\beta}\bar{q}_1 S/m$	ft/sec^2
z_D	vertical distance from drag force to the c.g.	ft
z_{mg}	vertical distance from the c.g. to the main gear to ground contact point	ft

z_T	vertical distance from the thrustline to the c.g.	ft
Z_α	$-\bar{q}_1 S(C_{L_\alpha} + C_{D_1})/m$	ft/sec^2

2. GREEK SYMBOLS

α	angle of attack	deg or rad
α_g	angle of attack on the ground	deg or rad
α_δ	angle of attack effectiveness due to control surface deflection	-----
β	sideslip angle	deg or rad
β_{cross}	crosswind induced sideslip	deg or rad
$\beta_{ng\ or\ mg}$	gear slip angle	deg or rad
γ	flight path angle	deg or rad
$\dot{\gamma}$	rate of change of flight path angle	rad/sec
γ_2	angle defined on p.121	deg or rad
$\gamma_{2_{min}}$	angle defined on p.122	deg or rad
Λ_{le}	leading edge sweep angle	deg or rad
δ	control surface deflection angle	deg or rad
δ_{cpt}	cockpit control deflection	deg or rad
Δ	Denominator determinant defined in Table 2.1, also: incremental value of ...	
ε	downwash angle at the horizontal tail	deg or rad
η_h	ratio of dynamic pressure at hor. tail to free stream	-----
Θ	pitch attitude angle	deg or rad
λ	taper ratio, also engine bypass ratio	-----
μ_g	tire-to-ground friction coefficient	-----
μ'	see p.121	-----
ρ	air density	$slug/ft^3$

σ_v	rms lateral gust velocity	fps
σ_w	rms vert. gust velocity	fps
ξ	damping ratio	-----
τ_R	roll time constant, also: T_R	sec
ϕ	bank angle	deg or rad
ϕ_T	thrust inclination angle	deg or rad
$\dot{\psi}$	Airplane turnrate	deg/sec or rad/sec
ψ_A	Airplane crab angle	deg or rad
ψ_{steer}	Nose gear steering angle	deg or rad
ω_n	undamped natural freq.	rad/sec

3. SUBSCRIPTS

1	Steady state
2	takeoff safety speed
3	speed at obstacle
a	aileron
abs	absolute
cl	climb
cr	cruise
cross	crosswind
e	elevator
end	end
fg	front gear
h	horizontal tail
in	initial
lat	lateral
mc	minimum control
mg	main gear
man	maneuver
max	maximum
min	minimum
ng	nose gear

o	sealevel
r	rudder
reqd	required
rg	rear gear
s	stall, also: stability axes
sb	speedbrake
t	tab
tg	tail gear
v	vertical tail
w	wing
wf	wing + fuselage
A	Approach
B	Body axes
D	Dutch Roll
E	Empty
F	Fuel
GL	Glide
L	Landing, also: Left
P	Phugoid
PL	Payload
R	Roll Also: Right
S	Spiral
SP	Short Period
T	Throttle
TO	Takeoff

4. Acronyms

AEO	All engines operating
ASW	Anti submarine warfare
BFL	Balanced fieldlength
CGR	Climb gradient
LOF	Liftoff
NADC	Naval Air Development Center
OEI	One engine inoperative
P.D.	Preliminary design
rms	root mean square
SHP	Shaft horsepower

ACKNOWLEDGEMENT

Writing a book on airplane design is impossible without the supply of a large amount of data. In this particular volume, the author has used a large number of photographs and threeview data from the following companies:

Aerospatiale
Beech Aircraft Corp.
The Boeing Company
British Aerospace Corp.
Cessna Aircraft Company
Fairchild Republic Co.
Gates Learjet Corporation
Fokker Aircraft Co.
Piper Aircraft Corporation
General Dynamics Corporation
Grumman Aerospace Corp.
Gulfstream Aerospace Corp.
Lockheed Aircraft Corp.
McDonnell Douglas Corp.
SAAB
Rinaldo Piaggio, SpA.

The author wishes to thank these companies for kindly allowing the use of this information: it makes this book much more attractive.

A significant amount of airplane design information has been accumulated by the author over many years from the following magazines:

Interavia (Swiss, monthly)
Flight International (British, weekly)
Business and Commercial Aviation (USA, monthly)
Aviation Week and Space Technology (USA, weekly)
Journal of Aircraft (USA, AIAA, monthly)

The author wishes to acknowledge the important role played by these magazines in his own development as an aeronautical engineer. Aeronautical engineering students and graduates should read these magazines regularly.

1. INTRODUCTION

The purpose of this series of books on Airplane Design is to familiarize aerospace engineering students with the design methodology and design decision making involved in the process of designing airplanes.

The series of books is organized as follows:

Part I:	PRELIMINARY SIZING OF AIRPLANES
Part II:	PRELIMINARY CONFIGURATION DESIGN AND INTEGRATION OF THE PROPULSION SYSTEM
PART III:	LAYOUT DESIGN OF COCKPIT, FUSELAGE, WING AND EMPENNAGE: CUTAWAYS AND INBOARD PROFILES
PART IV:	LAYOUT DESIGN OF LANDING GEAR AND SYSTEMS
PART V:	COMPONENT WEIGHT ESTIMATION
PART VI:	PRELIMINARY CALCULATION OF AERODYNAMIC, THRUST AND POWER CHARACTERISTICS
PART VII:	DETERMINATION OF STABILITY, CONTROL AND PERFORMANCE CHARACTERISTICS: FAR AND MILITARY REQUIREMENTS
PART VIII:	AIRPLANE COST ESTIMATION: DESIGN, DEVELOPMENT, MANUFACTURING AND OPERATING

In this part (Part VII) frequent use is made of most other parts in this series on Airplane Design: Refs 1-7.

In Parts I and II so-called Class I methods for sizing airplanes to performance, stability and control requirements were presented. These methods are compatible with Preliminary Design Sequence I as outlined in Steps 1-16 in Part II. A flowchart which relates Class I methods and P.D. Sequence I to Class II methods and P.D. Sequence II is presented in Table 1.1.

The purpose of Part VII is to present Class II preliminary design methods for determining stability, control and performance characteristics of airplanes. These methods are compatible with Steps 17-36 of Preliminary Design Sequence II as outlined also in Part II.

The objective of these methods is to assure that:

1. the mission requirements of the airplane (as stated in the mission specification) are satisfied

2. the airworthiness regulations (as stated in References 8, 9 and 10) are met

Table 1.1 Flowchart of the Preliminary Design Process

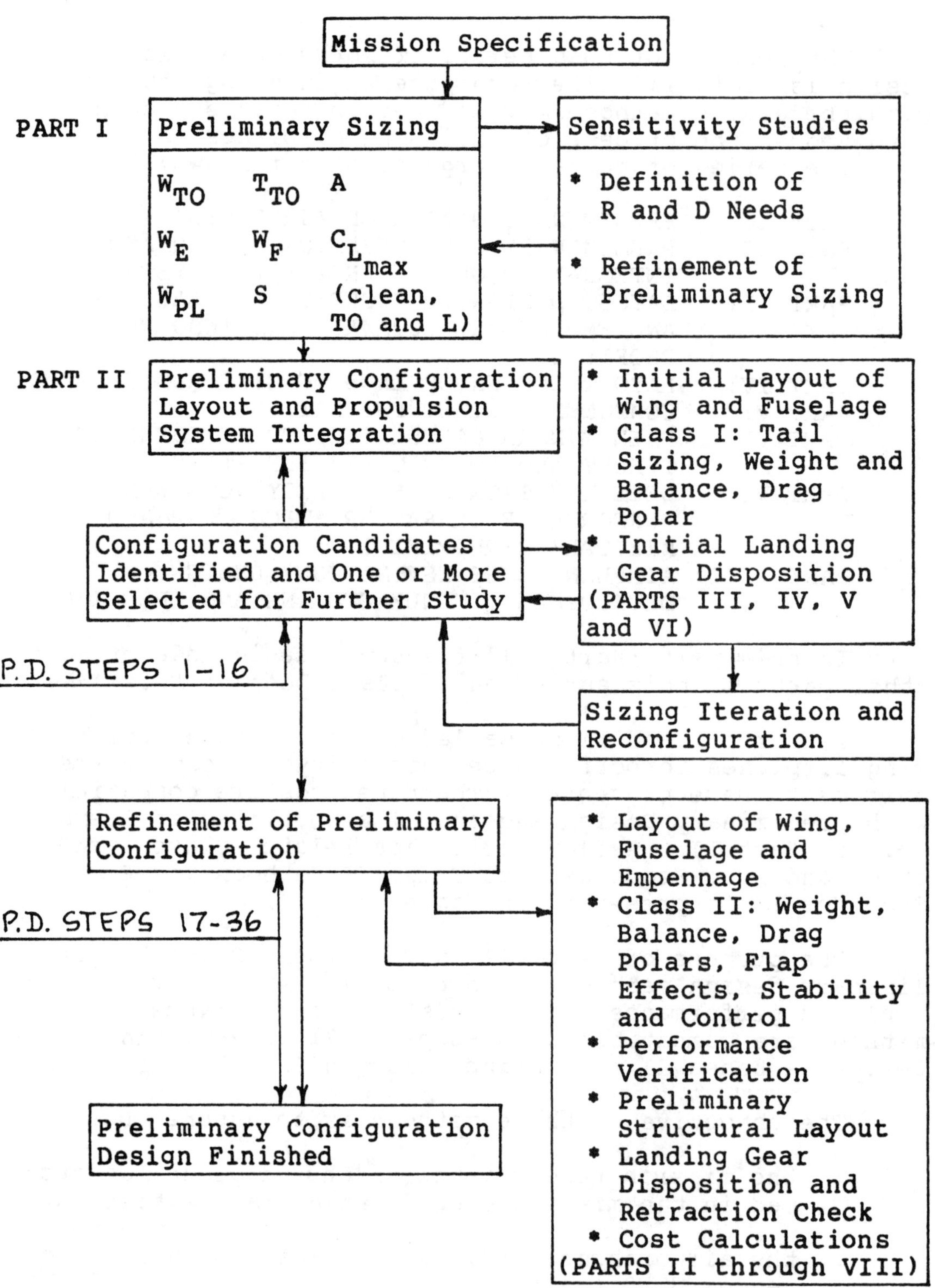

Airplanes must be controllable, maneuverable and trimmable to be safe as well as useful. Chapter 2 presents methods for assessing the controllability, the maneuverability and the trimmability capabilities of new airplane designs.

Stability is a requirement for all airplanes*. Methods for predicting the static and dynamic stability characteristics of airplanes are found in Chapter 3.

To be useful most airplanes must possess ride qualities such that the crew can carry out its functions and such that passengers are not made uncomfortable. The subject of ride qualities is taken up in Chapter 4.

All airplanes must satisfy specific performance objectives which are normally defined in a statement of mission requirements. For an airplane to be airworthy, it must also meet certain safety related performance requirements. Methods for computing the performance capabilities of airplanes are discussed in Chapter 5.

Airworthiness regulations have a major impact on the design and development of airplanes. Therefore, the most important aspects of civil and military stability, control and performance airworthiness requirements (regulations) are presented in Appendices A and B.

Part VII is not intended as a textbook on airplane performance, stability and control. It is designed as a reference manual for students to ascertain that their designs will meet mission performance as well as stability and control requirements. For a detailed presentation of airplane performance, stability and control theory and methods References 11 and 12 are recommended.

Frequently, the mission specification of an airplane will identify which regulations form the certification base for an airplane. If that is not the case it is recommended that Table 1.2 be used to identify the type of airplane which is being designed. With this information, Table 1.3 can then be used to identify which regulations apply to the design.

---

* Stability can be satisfied in an open or closed loop manner. If stability is satisfied 'open loop' it is referred to as 'inherent stability'. If stability is satisfied 'closed loop' it is referred to as 'de facto stability'.

A most important aspect of airplane design is to ensure that the airplane has not only satisfactory performance characteristics but also acceptable flying qualities following one or more failures of flight crucial components. To analyze the effect of failures of flight crucial components, the regulations must be interpreted in terms of the so-called airworthiness code as well as in terms of minimum acceptable levels of flying qualities. Appendix C contains a brief outline of the methodology used in determining the required levels of flying qualities in case of flight crucial failures.

TABLE 1.2 AIRPLANE TYPES

1. Homebuilt Propeller Driven Airplanes
2. Single Engine Propeller Driven Airplanes
3. Twin Engine Propeller Driven Airplanes
4. Agricultural Airplanes
5. Business Jets
6. Regional Turbopropeller Driven Airplanes
7. Transport Jets
8. Military Trainers
9. Fighters
10. Military Patrol, Bomb and Transport Airplanes
11. Flying Boats, Amphibious and Float Airplanes
12. Supersonic Cruise Airplanes

TABLE 1.3 RELATION BETWEEN AIRPLANE TYPE AND APPLICABLE AIRWORTHINESS REQUIREMENTS (REGULATIONS)

Airplane Type (See Table 1.2)	Passenger Limit	Weight Limit	Regulations
1	none	none	Experimental: FAR 21
2,3,4,5,11,12	<9	12,500	Normal Category: FAR 23, Appendix A
3,6,7,12	<19	<19,000	Commuter Category: FAR 23, Appendix A, see page 207
5,6,7,11,12	>19	none	FAR 25: Appendix A
8,9,10	none	none	Military: Appendix B

2. CONTROLLABILITY, MANEUVERABILITY AND TRIM

The purpose of this chapter is to present Class II methods for analyzing the controllability, maneuverability and trimmability of a newly designed airplane. These methods are compatible with Step 24 in Preliminary Design Sequence II as outlined in Chapter 2 of Part II.

The objectives of the methods in this chapter are to assure that:

1. the airplane has sufficient control power to maintain steady state, straight line flight
2. the airplane can be safely maneuvered from one steady state flight condition to another
3. cockpit control force levels are acceptable under all expected conditions, including those caused by configuration changes
4. the airplane can be trimmed in certain flight conditions

The qualitative statements 1-4 are only one component of what constitutes good flying qualities (handling qualities) of airplanes. These <u>qualitative</u> statements are translated in terms of <u>quantitative</u> requirements in the airworthiness requirements of References 8 and 9. These airworthiness requirements will be referred to as the REGULATIONS.

Which regulations apply to a given new airplane design depends on the projected use of that airplane. Certification according to more than one regulation is possible at the option of the designer. Broadly speaking, the regulations are applied as indicated in Table 1.3 of Chapter 1.

The material in this chapter is organized as follows:

2.1 Longitudinal controllability and trim
2.2 Directional and lateral controllability and trim
2.3 Minimum control speed
2.4 Maneuvering flight (acrobatic maneuvers)
2.5 Control during the takeoff groundrun
2.6 Control during the landing groundrun
2.7 Roll performance
2.8 High speed characteristics
2.9 Aeroelastic characteristics

It is essential to gain insight into how the various regulatory requirements for control, maneuvering and trim fit into the airplane design process. For that reason, the material in most sections is presented in the following general sequence:

1. identification of the applicable airworthiness regulation(s)
2. relationship to the stability and control checks performed as part of the preliminary layout design steps described in Chapter 2 of Part II: P.D. Sequences I and II (mostly Steps 11 and 24)
3. presentation of a model for analyzing controllability, trimmability and/or maneuverability
4. a step-by-step procedure for determining whether or not the airplane meets the control, trim and/or maneuvering requirements of the regulations

In this chapter, frequent use is made of the following terms:

* control surface
* trim surface
* trim
* trim diagram

Definitions of these terms are as follows:

Definition: A control surface is a surface used by the pilot to attain airplane moment equilibrium and/or to maneuver the airplane from one flight condition to another flight condition.

Definition: A trim surface is a surface used by the pilot to attain zero required cockpit control force while retaining moment equilibrium.

Definition: When an airplane is in moment equilibrium while the cockpit control force is zero, the airplane is trimmed.

Definition: A trim diagram is used to determine the conditions for which moment equilibrium (not necessarily with zero cockpit control forces) can be attained.

For detailed discussion(s) of airplane stability and control characteristics Reference 12 should be consulted.

2.1 LONGITUDINAL CONTROLLABILITY AND TRIM

2.1.1 Applicable Regulations

Civil: FAR 23.143, 23.145, 23.161, FAR 25.143, FAR 25.145, 25.161, see: Appendix A.

Military: Mil-F-8785C, Par.3.2, see Appendix B.

2.1.2 Relationship to Preliminary Design

See Part II, Chapter 2 (in particular Step 24), Chapter 8 and Chapter 11.

2.1.3 Mathematical Model for Analyzing Longitudinal Controllability and Trim

The regulations essentially require that any airplane, when trimmed in a given flight condition at a given airspeed:

A. can be maneuvered safely and easily to another speed

B. can be controlled safely and easily when a configuration change is made

The words *'safely'* and *'easily'* as used here are defined in the regulations in terms of control forces which may not be exceeded and/or in terms of control power levels which must be available.

The words *'configuration change'* are meant to imply any of the following events:

1. Change in center of gravity location
2. Change in thrust (or power) setting (voluntary or failure)
3. Hard-over failure of any control or trim surface
4. Change in landing gear position (up or down)
5. Change in flap position (up, take-off, approach or landing)
6. Change in speed brake position (retracted or deployed)
7. Store release (i.e. bomb or payload drop): symmetrical and asymmetrical
8. Weapons firing (i.e. moment due to recoil force)
9. Combat damage

Whether or not these events must be assumed to occur

simultaneously is stated in the applicable regulations!

For purposes of Class II analyses, longitudinal controllability is considered satisfied if:

1. Sufficient control power is available to cope with all required configuration changes

2. Sufficient control power is available to allow the airplane to be maneuvered from one flight speed to another

3. Cockpit control forces required in the use of control power to satisfy controllability are within the limits prescribed in the regulations

Figure 2.1 depicts the forces and moments which act on an airplane in a symmetrical, wings level, steady state, straight line flight condition.

The following three equations of motion apply to this case:

1. The Drag Equation:

$$C_{L_1}\sin\gamma = C_{D_1} + T\cos(\phi_T + \alpha) \tag{2.1}$$

2. The (One-g) Lift Equation:

$$C_{L_1}\cos\gamma = \{C_{L_o} + C_{L_\alpha}\alpha + \sum_{i=n}^{i=1}(C_{L_{\delta_{ctrl_i}}}\delta_{ctrl_i}\} + (T/\bar{q}S)\sin(\phi_T + \alpha) \tag{2.2}$$

3. The Pitching Moment Equation:

$$0 = (C_{m_o} + C_{m_\alpha}\alpha + \sum_{i=n}^{i=1}(C_{m_{\delta_{ctrl_i}}}\delta_{ctrl_i}\} + (Td_T/\bar{q}S\bar{c}) \tag{2.3}$$

For any given flight condition (i.e. known $\bar{q}$) at any given thrust setting (i.e. known T) the usual variables in these equations are:

α, γ and one of the i control surface deflections, δ_{ctrl_i}.

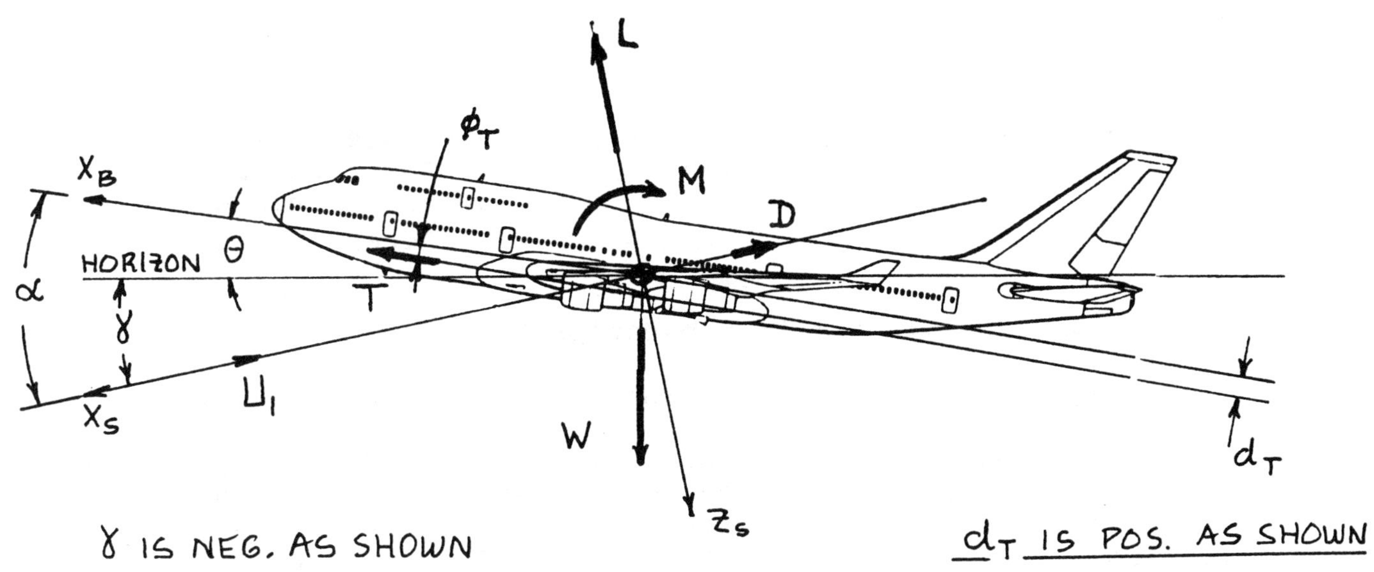

Figure 2.1 Forces and Moments Acting on an Airplane in Symmetrical, Wings Level, Steady State, Straight Line Flight

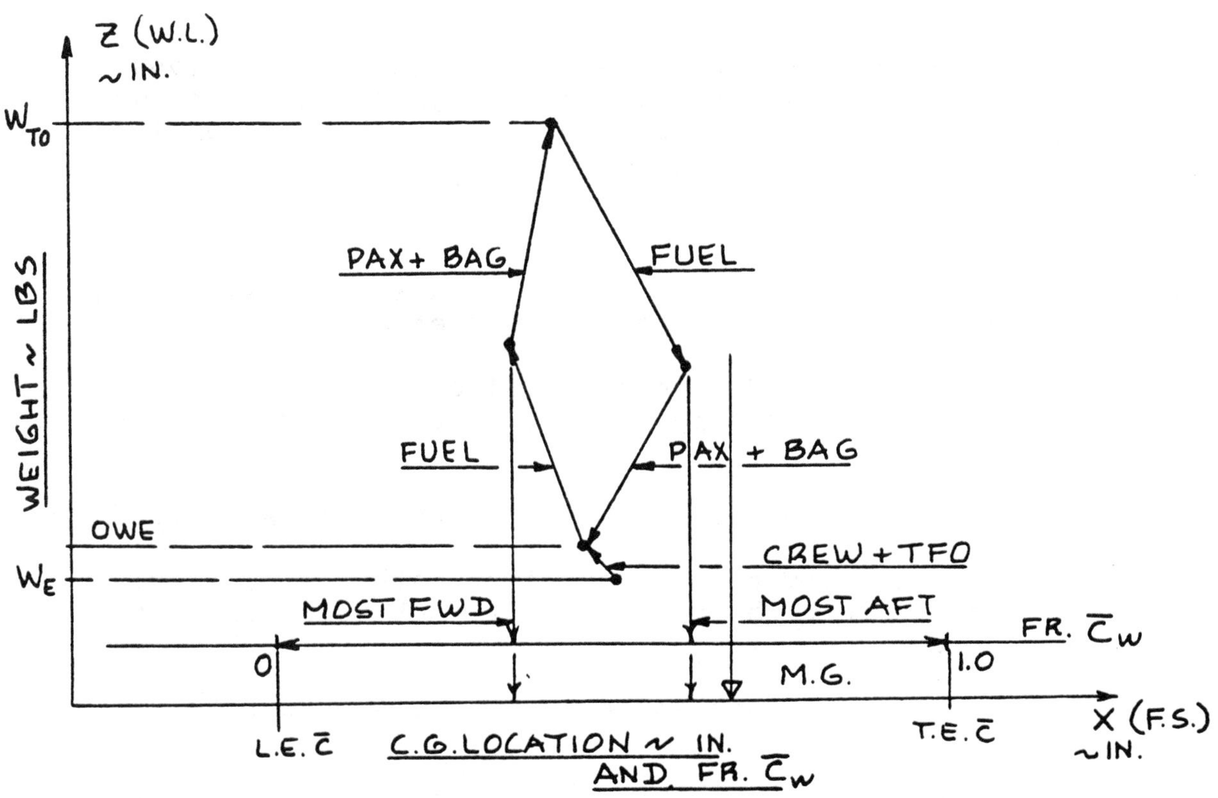

Figure 2.2 Example of a Weight/C.G. Envelope

The numerical solutions for these variables must be 'tested' against acceptability criteria. These acceptability criteria normally consist of allowable bounds on the numerical values of α, γ and δ_{ctrl_i}. Acceptability criteria are presented in Subsection 2.1.4.

Methods for computing airplane drag coefficient, C_D and installed thrust, T in Eqn.(2.1) are given in Chapters 4 and 6 of Part VI. The reader is reminded of the fact that the drag coefficient in Eqn.(2.1) is the so-called 'trimmed' drag coefficient! That means: C_D includes the drag effect of all control surface deflections necessary to achieve moment equilibrium and trim.

Methods for computing the stability and control derivatives in Equations (2.2) and (2.3) are provided in Chapter 10 of Part VI.

The reason for using the 'Sum' terms in Equations (2.2) and (2.3) explicitly is to recognize the fact that many airplanes use two (or more) different types of longitudinal controls. Frequently, one of these controls is used for primary longitudinal control while the other is used for longitudinal trim.

A detailed justification for Equations (2.1) through (2.3) is given in Reference 12 (Chapter 5).

In preliminary design, the following assumptions are made to enable a rapid resolution of the controllability issue:

1. The drag equation (2.1) is inherently satisfied.

   For any given desired flight path angle, γ this means that the throttles are set to balance the drag equation.

2. The flight path angle, γ is small enough to use: $\cos\gamma = 1.0$.

The consequence of these assumptions is that only Equations (2.2) and (2.3) are needed to determine controllability! This can be done with the help of the airplane trim diagram. The trim diagram allows a graphical solution of Equations (2.2) and (2.3) while accounting for all eight configuration changes mentioned before. A method for constructing airplane trim diagrams is presented in Part VI, Chapter 8.

Class II analysis of longitudinal trim is usually accomplished by writing an equation for the cockpit control force required to hold the aerodynamic controls in a position such that Eqns (2.2) and (2.3) are satisfied. Such an equation is called the stick- (or wheel-) force equation and it takes the following form:

$$F_s = G(HM) + F_{s_{artificial}} \tag{2.4}$$

where: G is the control system gearing ratio. For a discussion and definition of control system gearing ratios, see Part IV, Chapter 4 and Reference 12, Chapter 5. Typical numerical values for gearing ratios are given in Table 4.1 of Part VI.

HM is the control surface hingemoment, normally expressed in ftlbs and computed from:

$$HM = C_h\bar{q}(S\bar{c})_{control\ surface} \tag{2.5}$$

where: C_h is the control surface hingemoment coefficient. This hingemoment coefficient depends on the detail design of the control surfaces of the airplane. Section 10.4 of Part VI contains methods for estimating hingemoment coefficients and their derivatives.

$F_{s_{artificial}}$ is the incremental cockpit control force due to such items as: downsprings, bobweights and other 'feel'-systems. For a discussion of such devices, see Reference 12, Chapter 5 and Part IV, Chapter 4.

In these Class II methods the mathematical coupling which exists between Equations (2.1) through (2.4) is neglected. For an exact approach to the question of controllability and trim the reader is referred to the generalized matrix approach to trim as described in Section 5.6 of Reference 12.

2.1.4 Step-by-Step Procedure for Analyzing Longitudinal Controllability and Trim

The following step-by-step procedure is suggested to determine the longitudinal controllability and trim characteristics of an airplane during preliminary design:

Step 1: Determine which regulations apply to the design: see Table 1.3 and Subsection 2.1.1.

Step 2: The regulations define pairs of flight conditions so that the airplane must be controllable and maneuverable within each pair. Tabulate these flight conditions.

Step 3: The regulations define for which airplane weights the various controllability and trim requirements must be met. Tabulate these weights.

Note: It is important to also determine the airplane configuration and/or change in configuration associated with each pair of flight conditions: see items 1-9 on page 7. Tabulate the airplane configurations and/or the change in configuration as stipulated by the regulations.

Step 4: For the flight conditions and configurations defined in Steps 2 and 3 determine and tabulate: Mach number, M, dynamic pressure,

$\bar{q}$ and center of gravity location(s), $\bar{x}_{cg}$.

Note: the center of gravity location associated with any given configuration follows from the weight/c.g. envelope developed with the method of Chapter 10 in Part II. A typical example of such a weight/c.g. envelope is shown in Figure 2.2.

Step 5: For the conditions defined in Steps 2, 3 and 4 construct the airplane trim diagram. This can be done with the help of Section 8.3 in Part VI. Chapter 12 of Part VI should also be consulted. Figure 2.3 shows an example trim diagram for a conventional airplane.

Notes: 1.) Before the trim diagram can be constructed, a decision must have been made relative to the type and size of longitudi-

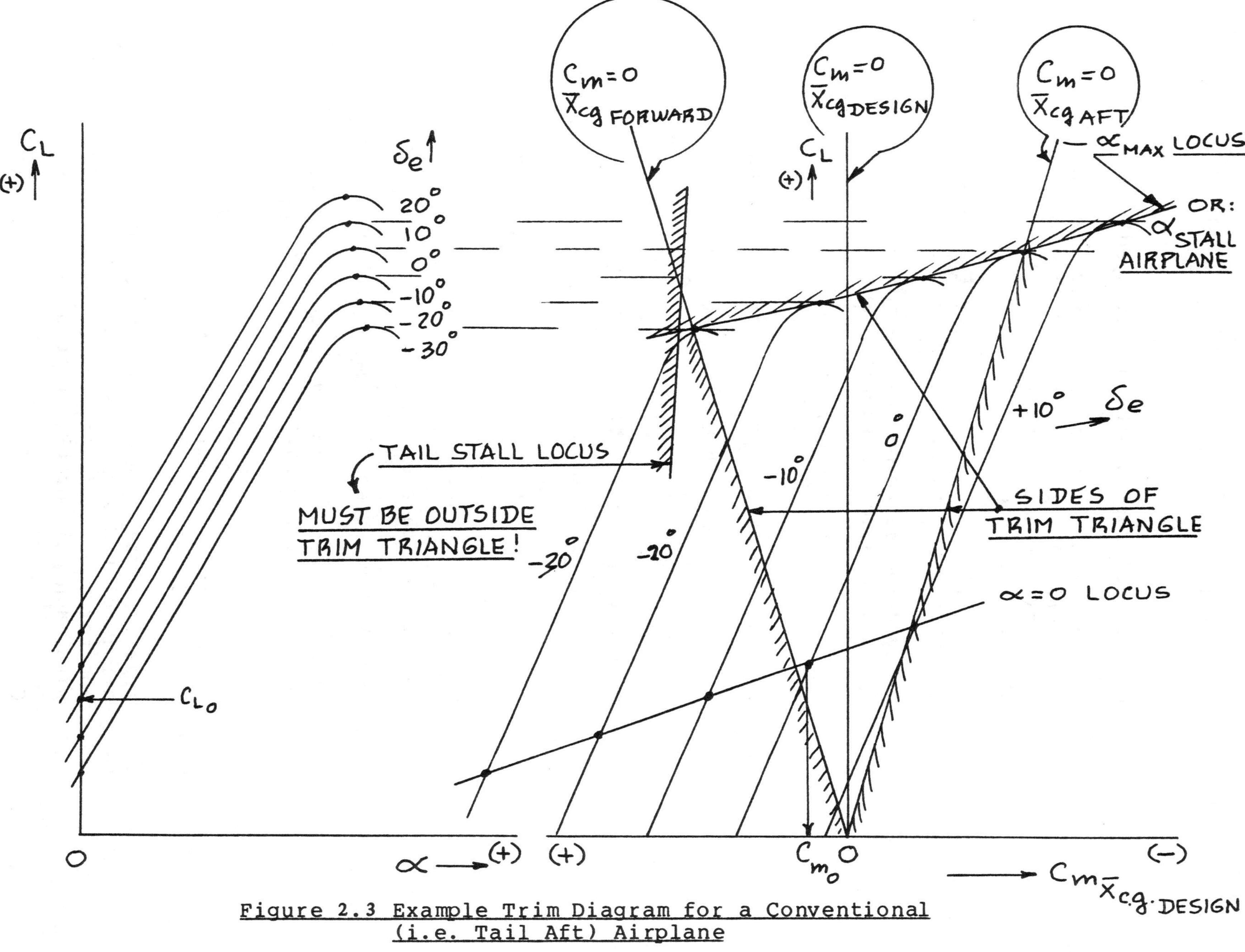

Figure 2.3 Example Trim Diagram for a Conventional (i.e. Tail Aft) Airplane

nal control surfaces to be employed!

2.) The method for constructing airplane trim diagrams in Part VI applies to conventional, pure canard as well as three-surface airplanes.

3.) The c.g. location associated with the vertical $C_m=0$ line in Figure 2.3 is normally selected to be the one for a typical 'design' mission of the airplane.

4.) The boundaries of the trim-triangle as shown in the example of Fig.2.3 are:

a) the $C_m=0$ lines for the most forward and for the most aft c.g. locations which in turn follow from the weight/c.g. envelope of Figure 2.2.

b) the α_{max} locus. This locus follows from either the airplane stall angle of attack or from the airplane angle of attack for which the stick pusher is set to trigger.

5.) Make sure that the effect of configuration changes 2-9 of page 7 are taken into account. This is particularly important in the case of thrust-induced-pitching-moment coefficient $Td_T/\bar{q}S\bar{c}$ and flaps.

Configuration events 2-9 (page 7) can be interpreted as a change in C_{m_o} and/or C_{L_o}.

<u>Step 6:</u> From the trim diagram of Step 5 determine whether or not equilibrium flight is possible within each pair of flight conditions.

This is accomplished by first computing the airplane lift coefficient for the initial and for the end flight condition associated with each pair of flight conditions from:

$$C_{L_{in}} = W/\bar{q}_{in}S \qquad (2.6)$$

and from:

$$C_{L_{end}} = W/\bar{q}_{end}S \tag{2.7}$$

Second, in Figure 2.3 enter these lift coefficients into the trim diagram at the appropriate center of gravity line.

Step 7: Determine whether or not the results of Step 6 are acceptable. Criteria for acceptability can be:

1. the control surface deflections are within the control power capabilities designed into the airplane. Typical control deflection ranges may be found in various issues of Reference 13.

2. the angle of attack (or the lift coefficient) is below airplane stall.

3. the tail and/or the canard are not stalled inside the 'trim-triangle'.

NOTE: if one or more of these acceptability criteria are violated, the design must be adjusted until they are satisfied. Such design adjustments may consist of increases in control surface sizes, a change in airfoil(s) and/or rebalancing of the configuration.

In marginal cases a decision to scrap the design and start from scratch may be the only good choice!!

Step 8: Determine whether the flight control system of the airplane is of the reversible or irreversible type.

If reversible, proceed to Step 9. If irreversible, proceed to Step 12.

Note: airplanes with irreversible flight control systems usually require artificial control force feel systems. The design and analysis of such systems is beyond the scope of this text. Chapter 5 of Reference 12 may be consulted for further information on this subject.

Step 9: Using Eqns (2.4) and (2.5), compute the trim surface deflection required to set the cockpit control force equal to zero for the initial flight condition.

To do this requires that a preliminary decision as to the sizing and location of trim control surfaces has been made. If not, now is the time to make this decision.

An example of how the trim control surface deflection for $F_s=0$ may be computed will

be given for the case of an airplane with an elevator as the primary control surface and an elevator tab as the trim control surface. The reader will have to adjust this analysis to suit his own control system.

For an airplane with an elevator as the primary control surface and an elevator tab as the trim control surface the stick force equation (2.4) may be specialized to:

$$F_s = F_{s_{artificial}} + G\bar{q}\eta_h S_e \bar{c}_e [C_{h_o} + C_{h_\alpha}\{\alpha(1 - d\varepsilon/d\alpha) + $$

$$+ i_h - \varepsilon_o\} + C_{h_{\delta_e}}\delta_e + C_{h_{\delta_t}}\delta_t] \qquad (2.8)$$

Setting F_s equal to zero the required tab deflection to trim the airplane is found from:

$$\delta_t = \qquad (2.9)$$

$$[\{-F_{s_{artificial}}/(G\bar{q}_{in}\eta_h S_e \bar{c}_e)\} - [C_{h_o} + C_{h_\alpha}\{\alpha\ (1 - d\varepsilon/d\alpha) + $$

$$+ i_h - \varepsilon_o\} + C_{h_{\delta_e}}\delta_e]]/C_{h_{\delta_t}}$$

where: α and δ_e both follow from the trim diagram, Figure 2.3 at the appropriate value of $C_{L_{in}}$ and at the appropriate combination of c.g. location and airplane configuration!

G, the gearing ratio depends on the detail design of the flight control system. Typical values are found in Table 4.1 of Part IV.

i_h is the stabilizer incidence setting, fixed

or vaiable, depending on the design of the control system.

all hingemoment coefficients in Eqns (2.8) and (2.9) can be computed with the methods Section 10.4, Part VI.

the value of $F_{s_{artificial}}$ depends on the detail design of the flight control system. In airplanes without artificial feel gadgetry such as a bobweight, a downspring, a springtab or a feel system, this force should be set equal to zero.

Note: The tab deflection magnitude as determined from Eqn.(2.9) should not exceed 25 degrees!

If the airplane is equipped with a different type of flight control system than that assumed in this example, the reader must redevelop Equation (2.8) accordingly. A detailed treatment of the many possible types of flight control systems is beyond the scope of this text. The reader is referred to Part IV, Chapter 4 for many practical examples of different primary and trim control systems. A general analytical treatment of the cockpit control force behavior of various types of systems is given in Reference 12, Chapter 5.

Step 10: For the final (end) flight condition find the cockpit control force with Eqn.(2.8),

PROVIDED: $C_{L_{end}}$ and $\bar{q}_{end}$ are used instead

of $C_{L_{in}}$ and $\bar{q}_{in}$, to find α and δ_e!

NOTES: 1.) The value for δ_t in this case is that obtained exactly from Eqn.(2.8) if the regulations do not allow retrimming of the airplane between the two flight conditions!

2.) The cockpit control force required to cope with one or more configuration changes (listed as 2-9 on page 7) may also be computed from Eqn.(2.8).

Step 11: Check the cockpit control force against the magnitude allowed by the regulation(s). If the cockpit control force exceeds the value allowed, a redesign of the flight control system may be required. Methods for 'tailoring control forces by tabs, balances and control surface design are discussed in Part III, Chapter 3 and in Reference 12, Chapter 5.

NOTE: The method presented here neglects coupling between Equations (2.1) through (2.4). For purposes of preliminary design this method is usually adequate. For a more complete approach to the solution of airplane trim problems the reader should consult Section 5.5 of Ref.12.

Step 12: Document the results obtained, including any design changes made as a result of not meeting (or exceeding!) any of the airworthiness regulations.

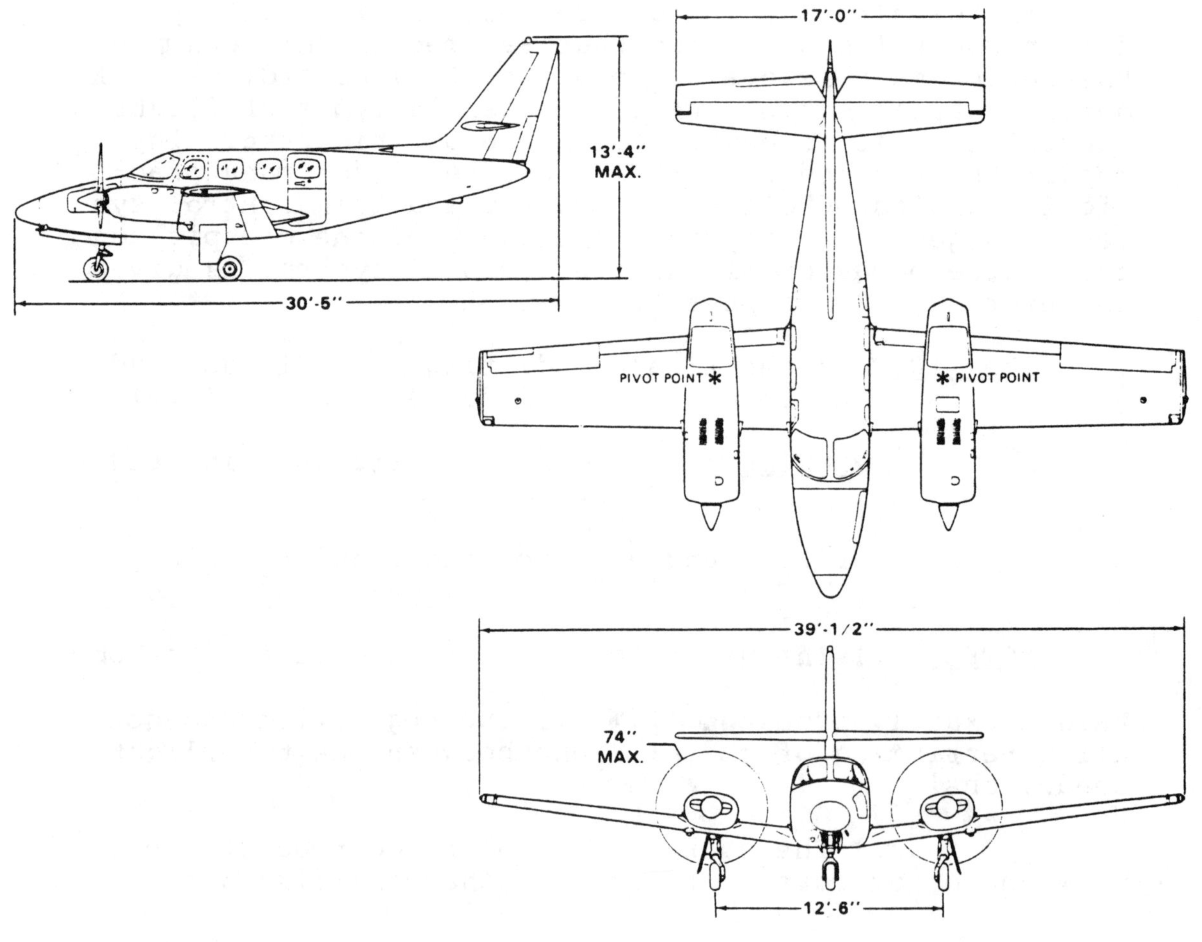

2.2 DIRECTIONAL AND LATERAL CONTROLLABILITY AND TRIM

2.2.1 Applicable Regulations

Civil: FAR 23.143, 23.147, 23.161, FAR 25.143,
FAR 25.147, 25.161, see: Appendix A.

Military: Mil-F-8785C, Par.3.3, see Appendix B.

2.2.2 Relationship to Preliminary Design

See Part II, Chapter 2 (in particular Step 24), Chapter 8 and Chapter 11.

2.2.3 Mathematical Model for Analyzing Directional and Lateral Controllability and Trim

The regulations essentially require that any airplane, when trimmed in a given flight condition at a given airspeed:

A. can make turns at a specified bank angle into and away from one or more inoperative engines

B. can make sudden changes in heading while keeping the wings approximately level

The magnitudes of required bank angles and changes in heading angle are specified differently in each regulation, depending on the type of airplane.

In addition, the regulations specify the airplane configuration for which directional and lateral controllability must be satisfied. Configuration definitions usually include such items as:

1. Center of gravity location
2. Thrust or power setting (voluntary or failure)
3. Hard-over failure of any control or trim surface
4. Landing gear position (up or down)
5. Flap position (up, take-off, approach or landing)
6. Speed brake position (retracted or deployed)
7. Weapons loading (mostly asymmetrical loadings)
8. Weapons firing (mostly asymmetrical firing)
9. Combat damage

The regulations determine the various combinations of these configuration items which must be considered.

For purposes of Class II analyses, directional and lateral controllability is considered satisfied if:

1. Sufficient control power is present to perform the required turns and heading changes in all required configurations

2. Cockpit control forces required in the use of control power to satisfy controllability are within the limits prescribed in the regulations

The making of turns and changes of heading is assumed to place at such a slow rate that controllability can be verified by examining:

a. the numerical values of the lateral-directional motion variables: β, δ_a and δ_r

and:

b. the numerical values of the lateral-directional cockpit control forces

for 'before' and 'after' flight conditions (initial and end).

The following three equations of motion apply to this case:

$$-C_L \sin\phi \cos\gamma = (F_{T_y})/\bar{q}S + C_{y_\beta}\beta + C_{y_{\delta_a}}\delta_a + C_{y_{\delta_r}}\delta_r \qquad (2.10)$$

$$0 = (L_T)/\bar{q}Sb + C_{l_\beta}\beta + C_{l_{\delta_a}}\delta_a + C_{l_{\delta_r}}\delta_r \qquad (2.11)$$

$$0 = (N_T + N_D)/\bar{q}Sb + C_{n_\beta}\beta + C_{n_{\delta_a}}\delta_a + C_{n_{\delta_r}}\delta_r \qquad (2.12)$$

The numerical solutions to these equations must be 'tested' against acceptability criteria. These acceptability criteria normally consist of allowable bounds on the numerical values of the motion variables in these equations. These acceptability criteria are given in Subsection 2.2.4.

For any given flight condition (i.e. known $\bar{q}$) at any given thrust setting (i.e. known F_{y_T}, L_T, N_T and N_D) the usual variables in these equations are:

β, δ_a and δ_r, which assumes that the bank angle, o

is determined by the 'initial' and 'end' conditions of the turns and/or the associated heading changes if the latter are to be made within a specified time.

The numerical solutions to these equations must be 'tested' against acceptability criteria. These acceptability criteria normally consist of allowable bounds on the numerical values of β, δ_a and δ_r. Acceptability criteria are presented in Subsection 2.2.4.

Methods for computing the stability and control derivatives which appear in Equations (2.10) - (2.12) are presented in Chapter 10 of Part VI.

Methods for computing installed thrust (from which F_{y_T}, L_T and N_T may be found) are presented in Chapter 6 of Part VI.

The yawing moment due to drag, N_D is found from the drag due to windmilling powerplants. Drag coefficients for windmilling jet engines and propellers may be computed with the method of Chapter 4, Part VI.

The lateral-directional cockpit control forces may be found from the following equations:

$$F_a = G_a \bar{q} S_a \bar{c}_a (C_{h_{\delta_a}} \delta_a + C_{h_{\delta_{a_t}}} \delta_{a_t}) + K_a \delta_r \tag{2.13}$$

$$F_r = G_r \bar{q} S_r \bar{c}_r (C_{h_{\delta_r}} \delta_r + C_{h_{\delta_{r_t}}} \delta_{r_t} + C_{h_{r_\beta}} \beta) + K_r \delta_a \tag{2.14}$$

The hingemoment derivatives in Equations (2.13) and (2.14) may be found with the methods of Ch.10, Part VI.

The reader should assume that the β-hingemoment derivative in Eqn.(2.14) is similar to the α-hingemoment derivatives of Chapter 10, Part VI. Likewise, the δ_a- and δ_r-hingemoment derivatives in Eqns (2.13) and (2.14) are similar to the δ-hingemoment derivatives of Chapter 10, Part VI.

Typical values for the gearing ratios, G_a and G_r may be found in Table 4.1 of Part IV.

The rudder-aileron interconnect terms, K_a and K_r are normally present only in airplanes with unsatisfactory control behavior. Ideally these terms should be zero.

2.2.4 Step-by-Step Procedure for Analyzing Directional and Lateral Controllability and Trim

Directional and lateral controllability can be verified with the following step-by-step procedure:

Step 1: Determine which regulations apply to the design: see Table 1.3 and Subsection 2.2.1.

Step 2: The regulations define flight conditions for which it must be possible to carry out turning and sudden heading change maneuvers. Identify these flight conditions.

When changes of bank angle are involved from positive to negative (right to left) values, identify one as the 'initial' and the other as the 'end' flight condition.

Note: It is important to also determine the airplane configuration and/or change in configuration associated with each flight condition: see items 1-9 on page 19.

Tabulate the flight condition and airplane configuration data as stipulated by the regulations.

Step 3: For the flight conditions defined in Step 2, determine: Mach number, M, dynamic pressure, $\bar{q}$ and center of gravity location, $\bar{x}_{cg}$. See the note under Step 4 in Subsection 2.1.4.

Step 4: For the conditions defined in Steps 2 and 3 determine the stability, control and other airplane characteristics required to solve the lateral-directional equations of motion: (2.10) - (2.12).

Notes: 1) methods for calculating stability and control derivatives are given in Ch.10 of Part VI. Methods for determining installed thrust (or power) are given in Ch.6 of Part VI.

2) which engines are to be considered inoperative is defined in the regulations. The magnitude and sign of F_{y_T}, L_T, N_T and N_D

depend on which engines are inoperative!!

Step 5: From solutions to Eqns (2.10) - (2.12) as defined by Eqns (2.15) - (2.17) in Table 2.1 determine whether or not turning maneuvers can be made which satisfy the regulations.

Note: The regulations may be considered to be satisfied if the magnitudes of the following variables are within acceptable bounds:

1. lateral control surface deflection(s), δ_a
2. directional control surface deflection(s), δ_r
3. sideslip angle, β

For a control surface deflection to be 'acceptable' means that it must be within the stall limits of that surface. Typical acceptability criteria are:

Lateral: $|\delta_a| < 25$ deg.

Directional: $|\delta_r| < 25$ deg. for single hinge rudder
< 35 deg. for double hinge rudder

For a sideslip angle to be 'acceptable' it must be sufficiently small so that the airplane drag is not significantly increased and so that the directional stability of the airplane has not significantly deteriorated due to vertical tail stall. Typical acceptability criteria are:

Sideslip angle for drag: $|\beta| < 5$ deg.

Sideslip angle for directional stability: $|\beta| < 12$ deg.

NOTE: If one or more of these acceptability criteria are violated, the design must be adjusted until they are satisfied. Such design adjustments may consist of increases in control surface sizes, addition of other types of control surfaces and/or a change (size and/or location) of the vertical tail.

In marginal cases a decision to scrap the design and start from scratch may be the only good choice!

Step 6: Determine whether the flight control system of the airplane is of the reversible or irreversible type.

Table 2.1 Solutions for Eqns.(2.10) - (2.12) of Page 20

$\beta = N_1/\Delta$ (2.15) $\delta_a = N_2/\Delta$ (2.16) $\delta_r = N_3/\Delta$ (2.17)

with:

$$N_1 = \begin{vmatrix} -(C_{L_1}\sin\phi\cos\gamma + F_{T_{Y_1}}/\bar{q}_1 S) & C_{y_{\delta_a}} & C_{y_{\delta_r}} \\ -L_{T_1}/\bar{q}_1 Sb & C_{l_{\delta_a}} & C_{l_{\delta_r}} \\ (-N_{T_1} - N_{D_1})/\bar{q}_1 Sb & C_{n_{\delta_a}} & C_{n_{\delta_r}} \end{vmatrix} \quad (2.18)$$

$$N_2 = \begin{vmatrix} C_{y_\beta} & -(C_{L_1}\sin\phi\cos\gamma + F_{T_{Y_1}}/\bar{q}_1 S) & C_{y_{\delta_r}} \\ C_{l_\beta} & -L_{T_1}/\bar{q}_1 Sb & C_{l_{\delta_r}} \\ C_{n_\beta} & -(N_{T_1} + N_{D_1})/\bar{q}_1 Sb & C_{n_{\delta_r}} \end{vmatrix} \quad (2.19)$$

$$N_3 = \begin{vmatrix} C_{y_\beta} & C_{y_{\delta_a}} & -(C_{L_1}\sin\phi\cos\gamma + F_{T_{Y_1}}/\bar{q}_1 S) \\ C_{l_\beta} & C_{l_{\delta_a}} & -L_{T_1}/\bar{q}_1 Sb \\ C_{n_\beta} & C_{n_{\delta_a}} & -(N_{T_1} + N_{D_1})/\bar{q}_1 Sb \end{vmatrix} \quad (2.20)$$

$$\Delta = \begin{vmatrix} C_{y_\beta} & C_{y_{\delta_a}} & C_{y_{\delta_r}} \\ C_{l_\beta} & C_{l_{\delta_a}} & C_{l_{\delta_r}} \\ C_{n_\beta} & C_{n_{\delta_a}} & C_{n_{\delta_r}} \end{vmatrix} \quad (2.21)$$

NOTE: The subscript 1 indicates steady state flight!

If reversible, proceed to Step 7. If irreversible, proceed to Step 10.

Note: airplanes with irreversible flight control systems usually require artificial control force feel systems. The design and analysis of such systems is beyond the scope of this text. Chapter 5 of Reference 12 may be consulted for further information on this subject.

Step 7: Using Eqns (2.13) and (2.14), compute the trim surface deflections, δ_{a_t} and δ_{r_t} required to set both cockpit control forces, F_a and F_r equal to zero for the 'initial' flight condition.

Acceptable values for the trim-tab deflections are:

$$|\delta_{(a \text{ or } r)_t}| < 20 \text{ degrees}$$

Step 8: For the 'end' flight condition(s), use Eqns (2.13) and (2.14) to compute the cockpit control forces, F_a and F_r.

Note: be sure to use the trim surface values obtained from Step 7!

Step 9: Check the cockpit control force values against the magnitudes allowed by the regulation.

If any cockpit control force exceeds the value allowed, a redesign of the flight control system may be required. Methods for tailoring control forces by tabs, balances and control surface design are discussed in Part III, Chapter 3 and in Reference 12, Chapter 5.

Step 10: Document the results obtained, including any design changes made as a result of not meeting (or exceeding!) any of the airworthiness regulations.

NOTE: The method presented here neglects coupling between Equations (2.10) through (2.14). A generalized approach to the solution of airplane trim problems is presented in Chapter 5 of Reference 12.

2.3 MINIMUM CONTROL SPEED

2.3.1 Applicable Regulations

Civil: FAR 23.149, FAR 25.149, see Appendix A.

Military: Mil-F-8785C, Par. 3.3.9.2, see Appendix B.

2.3.2 Relationship to Preliminary Design

See Part II, Chapter 2 (in particular Step 24), Chapter 8 and Chapter 11.

2.3.3 Mathematical Model for Analyzing Minimum Control Speed

The regulations essentially require that any airplane, when experiencing failure of its most critical engine:

1. can be brought under control in such a manner that straight line flight is possible with zero sideslip or with a bank angle of no more than five degrees toward the operating engine

2. does not require more than:

   civil airplanes: 150 lbs of rudder pedal force

   military airplanes: a) 180 lbs of rudder pedal force
   b) the roll control force specified in Table X of Par.3.3.4.3, Appendix B

3. can do so at a speed called the minimum control speed, V_{mc} which must satisfy the following conditions:

   For take-off with one engine inoperative

   civil airplanes: $V_{mc} < 1.2V_s$

   military airplanes: $V_{mc} < V_{min_{TO}}$, where in preliminary design: $V_{min_{TO}} = 1.1V_{s_{TO}}$

   For landing with one or two engines inoperative

   civil airplanes: $V_{mc} > V_A$

military airplanes: $V_{mc} > 1.4V_{min}$, where V_{min} is defined in Section 6.2 of Appendix B

In addition, the regulations specify the airplane configuration for which the minimum control speed capability must be satisfied. As a general rule, configuration changes and/or power (thrust) changes are not allowed.

For purposes of Class II analyses, controllability is considered satisfied if:

1. Sufficient control power is present to cope with the stated requirements
2. Cockpit control forces required in the use of control power to satisfy controllability are within the limits prescribed in the regulations

Equations (2.15) through (2.17), see Table 2.1, are normally used to determine the magnitude of sideslip angle, rudder angle and aileron angle needed to keep the airplane in straight line flight and with a favorable bank angle of 5 degrees.

Equations (2.13) and (2.14) are used next to determine the cockpit control forces needed to keep the rudder and aileron deflections at the values required by Equations (2.15) through (2.17).

2.3.4 Step-by-Step Procedure for Determining the Minimum Control Speed

In preliminary design the minimum control speed capability of an airplane can be verified with the following step-by-step procedure:

Step 1: Determine which regulations apply to the design: see Table 1.3 and Subsection 2.3.1.

Step 2: The regulations define flight conditions and airplane configurations for which the regulations apply. Identify these flight conditions and configurations and determine the corresponding airplane weight, W.

Step 3: For the flight conditions and configurations of Step 2, determine: Mach Number, M, dynamic pressure, $\bar{q}$, lift coefficient, C_L

and center of gravity location, $\bar{x}_{cg}$.

<u>Step 4:</u> For the conditions defined in Steps 2 and 3, determine the required stability and control derivatives as well as the asymmetric engine side force, rolling moment and yawing moment (including any drag induced effects): see Equations (2.10) - (2.12).

<u>Step 5:</u> Using Equations (2.15) through (2.17), find the values of sideslip angle, aileron angle and rudder angle required at V_{mc}. The regulations allow the use of a bank angle of no more than 5 degrees toward the operating engine(s).

<u>Step 6:</u> Determine whether or not the results of Step 5 are acceptable.

Criteria for acceptability can be:

1. The sideslip angle, β must not be so large that the added drag due to sideslip would cause the airplane to violate the minimum climb requirements of Section 5.3
2. The aileron and/or rudder deflection angles are less than those values for which wing and/or vertical tail stall might result. Typical maximum acceptable angles are:

Ailerons: $<$ 25 degrees or whatever corresponds to no more than 75 percent of available lateral control power in the flight condition and airplane configuration being considered

Rudder: $<$ 25 degrees for single hingeline rudders
$<$ 35 degrees for double hingeline rudders

If the airplane violates any of these acceptability criteria, the design must be adjusted until the regulatory requirements are satisfied. This may involve changing control surface sizes, changing vertical tail size and location and/or re-arranging the most critical engines.

In marginal cases the decision to scrap the design and start from scratch may be the appropriate choice!!

If the airplane is equipped with a reversible flight control system in the roll and yaw axes proceed to Step 7. If not, proceed to Step 10.

<u>Step 7:</u> Determine the hingemoment coefficients and derivatives contained in Equations (2.13) and (2.14).

<u>Step 8:</u> Calculate the lateral and directional cockpit control forces needed to hold the aileron and rudder surfaces at deflection values corresponding to those obtained in Step 5. Use Equations (2.13) and (2.14).

<u>Note:</u> the values for the trim-tab deflections must be those corresponding to the trimmed flight condition prior to engine failure.

<u>Step 9:</u> Determine whether or not the roll control and rudder control forces of Step 8 are acceptable. The rudder control forces are normally the most critical ones!

Criteria for acceptability are given in the applicable regulations. A summary of the allowable rudder pedal forces is given under Subsection 2.3.3.

<u>Step 10:</u> Document the results obtained, including any design changes made as a result of not meeting (or exceeding!) any of the airworthiness regulations.

<u>NOTE:</u> The method presented here neglects coupling between Equations (2.10) through (2.14). A generalized approach to the solution of the lateral-directional trim problem is given in Chapter 5 of Reference 12.

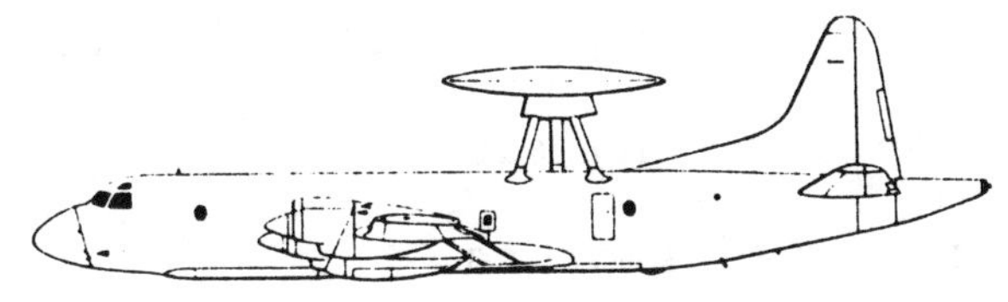

2.4 MANEUVERING FLIGHT

2.4.1 Applicable Regulations

Civil: FAR 23.151 (acrobatic and utility category only), FAR 23.155, see Appendix A.
Note: there are no sustained maneuvering requirements in FAR 25!

Military: Mil-F-8785C, Par. 3.2.2.2, see Appendix B.

2.4.2 Relationship to Preliminary Design

Maneuvering flight requirements are accounted for in the initial sizing process to assure that:

1. The powerplant installation can overcome the extra drag incurred during maneuvers: see Part I, Chapter 3.

2. The maximum trimmed lift capability of the airplane is consistent with the maneuvering demands. See Part I, Chapter 3 and Part II, Chapter 7.

Note: these maneuvering requirements are of great importance to the design of fighters and acrobatic and utility category airplanes.

2.4.3 Mathematical Model for Analyzing Maneuvering Flight

The regulations essentially require that:

1. the airplane must be able to attain certain specified load factors: instantaneous or sustained.

2. the longitudinal cockpit control force per unit load factor increase (stick-force per 'g') shall be bounded by maximum as well as by minimum allowable values. Reversal in the stick-force per 'g' gradient is not allowed.

To satisfy the first item requires that the airplane be capable of achieving a value of maximum lift coefficient which is consistent with the required load factor. There are two types of required load factors:

A) Instantaneous load factors

and

B) Sustained load factors.

A) Instantaneous load factors

Three conditions must be satisfied to achieve a specified instantaneous load factor, n_{reqd}:

A1) The available lift condition,
A2) The available control power condition

and

A3) The cockpit control force condition.

A1) The available lift condition

The available lift condition is:

$$n_{reqd} < C_{L_{max}} \bar{q}S/W \qquad (2.22)$$

where: n_{reqd} is the load factor which must be attained according to the mission specification and/ or according to the applicable regulation.

$C_{L_{max}}$ must be interpreted as the maximum trimmed lift coefficient of which the airplane is capable in the given flight condition. The magnitude of $C_{L_{max}}$ depends on the wing design and on the type and size of flaps used, on the type of longitudinal control used and on the center of gravity location. Methods to estimate maximum trimmed lift coefficients are given in Section 8.3 of Part VI.

A2) The available control power condition

The available control power condition is:

$$\delta_{e_{reqd}} = \delta_{e_{trim}} + (\partial\delta_e/\partial n)n_{reqd} \qquad (2.23)$$

where: $\delta_{e_{trim}}$ is the elevator deflection required to trim the airplane in the steady state flight condition before the maneuver was initiated. It is computed with the procedure of sub-section 2.1.4.

$\partial\delta_e/\partial n$ is the elevator versus load-factor gradient. It may be computed from:

$$\partial\delta_e/\partial n = \qquad (2.24)$$

$$\{-C_{L_\alpha} C_{m_q}(\bar{c}g/2U_1{}^2)\bar{n} - C_{m_\alpha} C_{L_1}\}/(C_{L_\alpha} C_{m_{\delta_e}} - C_{L_{\delta_e}} C_{m_\alpha})$$

with: $\bar{n} = n$ for symmetrical pull-up maneuvers

$\bar{n} = (1 + 1/n^2)$ for turning maneuvers

The stability and control derivatives in Eqn.(2.24) may be computed with the methods of Chapter 10, Part VI.

n_{reqd} is defined under Eqn.(2.22)

<u>Note:</u> the condition: $\delta_{e_{reqd}} < \delta_{e_{available}}$ must always be satisfied, where: $\delta_{e_{available}}$ is that value of elevator deflection which is geometrically available: also called the maximum available elevator throw.

<u>A3) The cockpit control force condition</u>

This condition demands that the level of required cockpit control force needed to perform an instantaneous maneuver must be less than values specified in the regulations:

$$F_s = F_{s_1} + (\partial F_s/\partial n)n_{reqd} \quad (2.25)$$

where: F_{s_1} is the cockpit control force required to 'hold' the steady state. If the airplane is in complete trim in the steady state, $F_{s_1} = 0$.

n_{reqd} is defined under Eqn.(2.22)

The 'stick-force-per-g', $\partial F_s/\partial n$ is found from

an equation, the terms in which depend strongly on the type of control system employed. For an airplane which uses an elevator for primary control, and no bobweight, Ref.12 shows that the following equation determines the stick-force per 'g':

$$\partial F_{s_e}/\partial n = \eta_h \bar{q} S_e \bar{c}_e G_e * \quad (2.26)$$

$$*\{C_{L_1}(C_{h_{\delta_e}}/C_{m_{\delta_e}})(SM_{free}) + (gl_h/U_1^2)(C_{h_\alpha} - C_{h_{\delta_e}}/\alpha_{\delta_e})\}$$

where: l_h is the distance of the horizontal tail aerodynamic center to the airplane center of gravity

SM_{free} is the static margin stick free which may be determined from:

$$SM_{free} = \bar{x}_{ac_A} - \bar{x}_{cg} + \qquad (2.27)$$

$$+ \{(C_{m_{\delta_e}} C_{h_\alpha})/(C_{L_{\alpha_A}} C_{h_{\delta_e}})\}(1 - d\varepsilon/d\alpha)$$

where: all terms are defined in the list of symbols. They may be determined with the help of Part VI.

Note: For an airplane which uses another type of primary longitudinal controller (other than an elevator), the reader should re-develop the appropriate equations in this Section to reflect the actual control system used.

B) Sustained load factors

Four conditions must be satisfied to achieve a specified magnitude of sustained load factor:

B1) The available lift condition,
B2) The available control power condition,
B3) The cockpit control force condition

and

B4) The available thrust condition.

Conditions B1 through B3 are identical to conditions A1 through A3 which were discussed before.

B4) The available thrust condition

This condition is discussed in Section 5.7.

2.4.4 Step-by-step Procedure for Determining Maneuvering Flight Ability

The following step-by-step procedure is suggested to check maneuvering flight ability in preliminary design.

Step 1: Read the regulations and determine which regulations apply to the design.

Step 2: The regulations define flight conditions and airplane configurations for which the regulations apply. Identify these flight conditions and configurations and determine the corresponding airplane weight, W.

Step 3: For the flight conditions and configurations of Step 2, determine: Mach Number, M, dynamic pressure, $\bar{q}$, lift coefficient, C_L and center of gravity location, $\bar{x}_{cg}$.

Step 4: This step concerns the available lift condition as given by A1) or B1) in sub-section 2.4.3.

For the flight conditions and for the configurations of Steps 2 and 3 determine the maximum achievable load factor from:

$$n_{max} = C_{L_{max}} \bar{q}S/W \tag{2.28}$$

The maximum lift coefficient, $C_{L_{max}}$ in Eqn.(2.28) is that 'trimmed' value which applies to the airplane configuration (flaps up or down) as well as to the flight condition (particularly the Mach number) being analyzed. Methods for determining trimmed maximum lift coefficients are presented in Section 8.3 of Part VI.

Compare n_{max} from Eqn.(2.28) with n_{reqd} from Eqn.(2.22) and determine whether or not the airplane can satisfy its maneuvering requirements from a maximum lift viewpoint.

Step 5: This step concerns the available control power condition, as given in A2) or B2) in sub-section 2.4.3.

For the conditions defined in Steps 2 and 3, determine the required stability, control and hingemoment derivatives as well as other terms identified in Eqns (2.23) and (2.24).

Part VI contains methods for estimating all required parameters.

Compute the amount of elevator required to attain the specified load factor from Eqns (2.23) and (2.24).

The amount of elevator deflection required to attain the specified load factor should not exceed the available elevator travel, nor should it exceed that amount which would cause the tail to stall.

Step 6: This step concerns the required cockpit control force level as given in A3) or B3) in sub-section 2.4.3.

For the conditions defined in Steps 2 and 3, determine the required stability, control, hingemoment derivatives as well as other terms identified in Eqns (2.25) and (2.26).

Compute the stick-force required to pull the specified load factor from Eqns (2.25) and (2.26). Compare the computed magnitude of stick-force with those specified in the regulations.

Step 7: This step concerns the available thrust condition of B4) in sub-section 2.4.3.

Using the methods of Section 5.7, determine whether sufficient thrust is available to maintain (sustain) the required load factor.

Step 8: Determine whether or not the results of Steps 4, 5, 6 and 7 are acceptable. If not, inspect the applicable equations for 'clues' as to what design changes may be needed to 'fix' the problem. It may very well be that major changes in the design of the wing and/ or the flight control system are required!

If the available thrust condition of Step 7 is not met, an increase in thrust may be required. This could cause a major change in the design of the airplane!

Step 9: Document the results obtained, including any design changes made as a result of not meeting (or exceeding!) any of the mission specifications and/or regulations.

2.5 CONTROL DURING THE TAKEOFF GROUNDRUN

2.5.1 Applicable Regulations

Civil: FAR 23.143, 23.51, 23.231, 23.233 and 23.235, see Appendix A.

FAR 25.107, 25.143, 25.149, 25.231, 25.233, 25.235 and 25.237, see Appendix A.

Military: MIL-F-8785C, Section 3.3 (in particular 3.3.7 and 3.2.3.3), see Appendix B.

2.5.2 Relationship to Preliminary Design

See Chapter 11, Part II.

2.5.3 Mathematical Model for Analyzing Control During the Takeoff Groundrun

The regulations essentially require that any airplane shall be safely controllable and maneuverable during take-off ground operations.

The words 'safely' and 'easily' as used here imply the following:

1. Sufficient control power must exist to effect take-off rotation: this applies to airplanes with tricycle as well well as to airplanes with taildragger landing gears.

2. Sufficient control power must exist to lift the tail early in the takeoff run for airplanes with tailwheels. Following this, there must be sufficient control power to effect lift-off.

3. Directional control and lateral control must be sufficient to allow for straight line taxiing as well as for straight line takeoff runs in cross winds as specified in the regulations.

4. The control forces required to accomplish 1,2 and 3 shall be sufficiently small. Also, nu unusual pilot control technique shall be required.

The regulations also imply that these characteristics be satisfied under the most adverse conditions of:

1. center of gravity location
2. power setting (voluntary or failure)

3. flap position as required for takeoff
4. weapons or payload disposition as required by the airplane mission

Class II analysis of control during takeoff is normally accomplished by uncoupling the longitudinal control problem from the directional/lateral control problem:

2.5.3.1 Mathematical model for analyzing longitudinal control during the takeoff groundrun

2.5.3.2 Mathematical model for analyzing directional and lateral control during the takeoff groundrun

2.5.3.1 Mathematical model for analyzing longitudinal control during the takeoff groundrun

Figure 2.4 shows the forces and moments which act on an airplane during the take-off run. Note the difference between:

a) Tricycle Gear Configurations
b) Taildragger Gear Configurations
c) Tandem Gear Configurations

The following mathematical model is presented for airplanes with conventional (that is tail-aft) configurations and with a tricycle landing gear.

NOTA BENE: The reader should modify this mathematical model to reflect the actual airplane configuration and landing gear layout of his airplane.

The following example applies to conventional airplanes equipped with a tricycle landing gear. Figure 2.5 defines all forces, moments and moment arms.

NOTA BENE: All aerodynamic quantities in Figure 2.5 must be determined in the presence of ground effect! See Part VI for methods to do this.

The longitudinal equations of motion which govern the controllability of the airplane on the ground are:

$$T\cos(\alpha_g + \phi_T) - \mu_g(P_{mg} + P_{ng}) - D = (W/g)\dot{u} \qquad (2.29)$$

$$T\sin(\alpha_g + \phi_T) + L_{wf} + L_h + P_{mg} + P_{ng} - W = 0 \qquad (2.30)$$

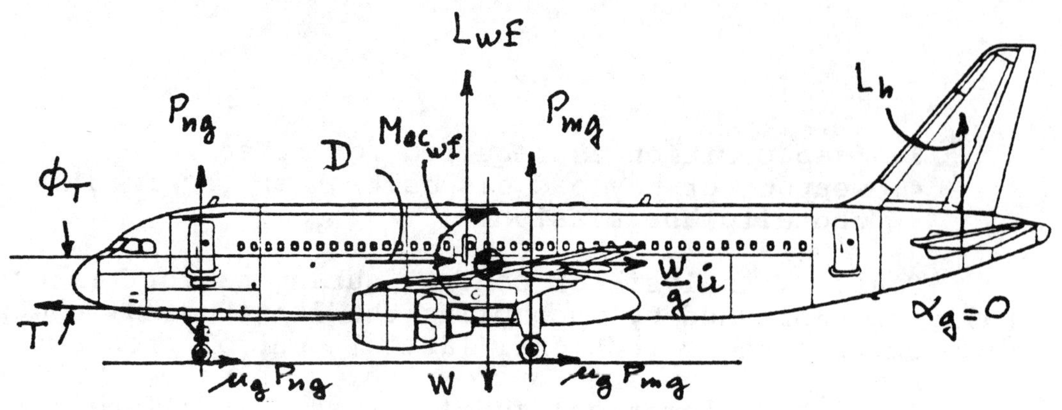

2.4a Tricycle Landing Gear

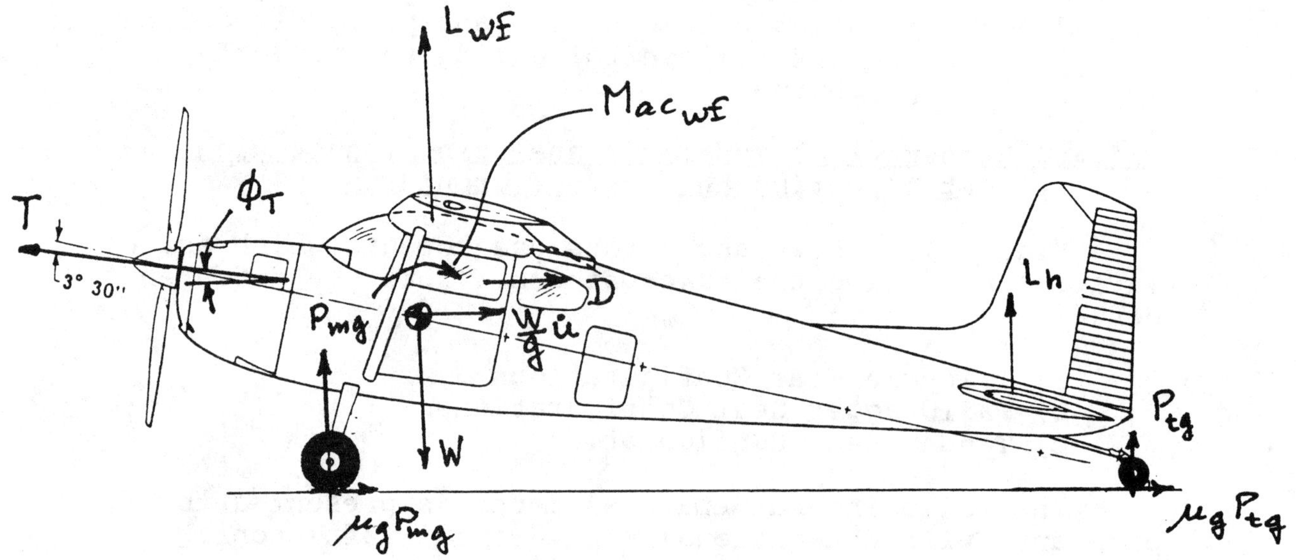

2.4b Taildragger Landing Gear

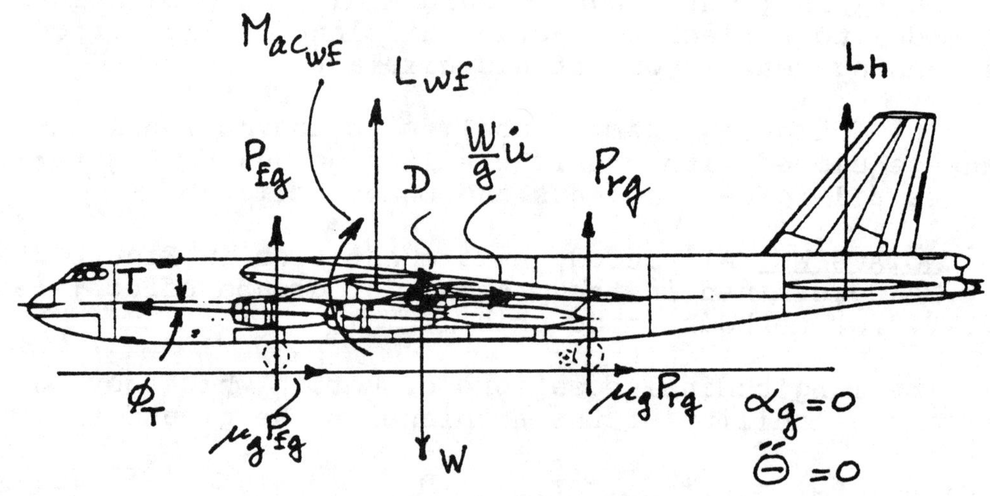

2.4c Tandem Landing Gear

Figure 2.4 Longitudinal Forces and Moments Acting on an Airplane During the Takeoff Groundrun

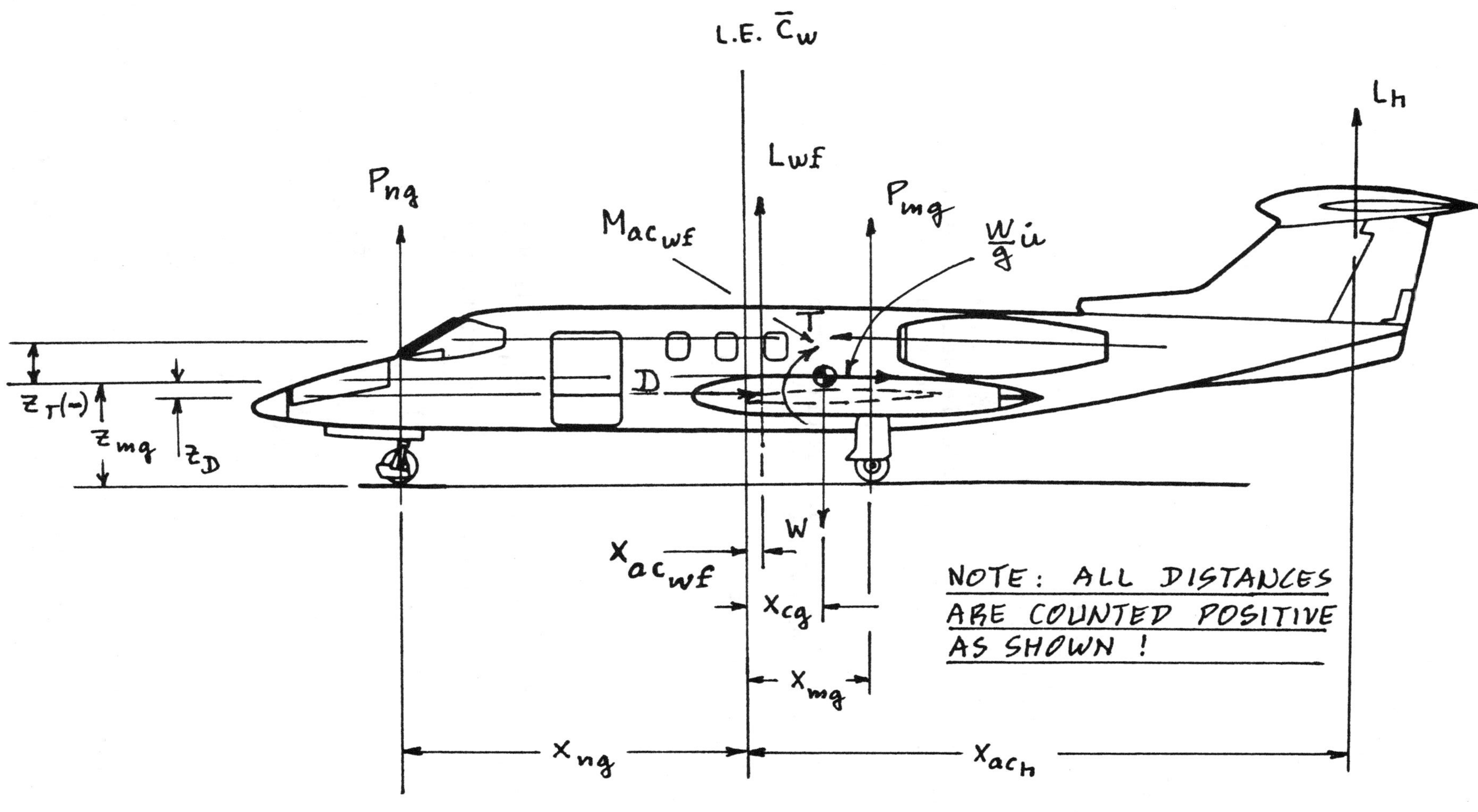

Figure 2.5 Forces, Moments and Moment Arms for Longitudinal Control During the Takeoff Groundrun

$$M_{ac_{wf}} - T(z_{mg} - z_T) - W(x_{mg} - x_{cg}) + P_{ng}(x_{ng} + x_{cg}) +$$

$$+ L_{wf}(x_{mg} - x_{ac_{wf}}) + D(z_{mg} - z_D) + (W/g)\dot{u}z_{mg} +$$

$$- L_h(x_{ac_h} - x_{mg}) = I_{yy_{mg}}\ddot{\theta} \qquad (2.31)$$

where: T is the installed thrust during the take-off run. It varies with speed during the take-off run and is determined with the method of Part VI, Ch.6.

α_g is the angle of attack during the groundrun. This angle is usually very small except at the instant before liftoff.

ϕ_T is the thrust inclination angle

μ_g is the wheel-ground rolling friction coefficient. During take-offs use:

for concrete or asphalt: $\mu_g = 0.02$

for hard turf: $\mu_g = 0.04$

for short grass: $\mu_g = 0.05$

for long grass: $\mu_g = 0.10$

for soft ground: $\mu_g = 0.10$ to 0.30

Note: these values are recommended for use on civil airplanes. For military airplanes consult Appendix B.

P_{mg} and P_{ng} are the ground reaction forces. It is assumed that the nosewheel is no longer in touch with the ground (i.e. $P_{ng}=0$), at the instant that the rotation has been initiated.

D is the airplane drag in ground effect:

$$D = (C_D)\bar{q}S \qquad (2.32)$$

with: C_D the drag coefficient on the ground. This drag coefficient follows from the airplane drag polar on the ground as discussed in Part VI, Chapter 4.

$\bar{q}$ is the dynamic pressure. It varies during the take-off run.

W is the weight. This is not necessarily the airplane maximum take-off weight. It is up to the designer to determine the most critical combination of weight and center of gravity location, x_{cg}. The weight versus c.g. diagram of Ch.10 of Part II should be used.

$\dot{u}$ is the forward acceleration along the runway.

L_{wf} is the wing-fuselage lift in ground effect:

$$L_{wf} = C_{L_{wf}}\bar{q}S \qquad (2.33)$$

with: $C_{L_{wf}}$ the airplane lift coefficient during the ground roll, in ground effect. Its value will be constant before initiation of the rotation. The methods of Pt VI, Chapter 8 can be used to determine this lift coefficent.

NOTE: The relative location of L_{wf} to the main landing gear is important. If it too far forward, the airplane will have a tendency to rapidly autorotate after the pilot has initiated the rotation by pulling the cockpit control aft. This autorotation is caused by the rapid increase in L_{wf} as the angle of attack begins to increase. The designer should attempt to locate L_{wf} as close as possible to but forward of the main gear!

L_h is the tail lift during the ground roll:

$$L_h = C_{L_h}\bar{q}_hS_h \qquad (2.34)$$

with: C_{L_h} the horizontal tail lift coefficient during the ground roll. It must be evaluated in ground effect. It will be constant (and usually negative due to the preset negative incidence angle on the stabilizer) before initiation of rotation.

Upon initiation of rotation the tail lift coefficient becomes large and negative. The negative tail lift in ground effect may be computed with the methods of Part VI, Chapter 8.

$\bar{q}_h$ is the dynamic pressure at the horizontal tail. It varies during the take-off roll and is related to $\bar{q}$ by:

$$\bar{q}_h = \eta_h \bar{q} \tag{2.35}$$

The dynamic pressure ratio at the tail, η_h is found from Part VI, p.269.

$M_{ac_{wf}}$ is the wing-fuselage pitching moment about the wing-fuselage aerodynamic center in ground effect and with the flaps in the take-off position:

$$M_{ac_{wf}} = C_{m_{ac_{wf}}} \bar{q} S \bar{c} \tag{2.36}$$

with: $C_{m_{ac_{wf}}}$ the wing-fuselage pitching moment coefficient about the wing-fuselage aerodynamic center and with the flaps in the take-off position. This coefficient may be determined with the methods of Part VI, Chapter 8. It must be computed in ground effect.

If the reader does not wish to employ the rather laborious methods of Part VI, the following approximation may be employed:

$$C_{m_{ac_{wf}}} = 1.1(b_f/b)c_{m_{ac_f}} \tag{2.37}$$

where: the factor 1.1 accounts for ground effect

b_f/b is the flap-span to wing-span ratio

$c_{m_{ac_f}}$ is the airfoil pitching moment coefficient with the flap down (in this case in the take-off position). Methods for determining the effect of flaps on airfoil $c_{m_{ac}}$ are given in subsection 8.2.2.1 of Part VI.

z_{mg} is defined in Figure 2.5.

z_T is defined in Figure 2.5.

x_{mg} is defined in Figure 2.5.

x_{cg} is defined in Figure 2.5.

$x_{ac_{wf}}$ is defined in Figure 2.5.

z_D is defined in Figure 2.5. It is usually taken at the wing-fuselage aerodynamic center.

x_{ac_h} is defined in Figure 2.5.

$I_{yy_{mg}}$ is the pitching moment of inertia about the main gear contact point. It may be computed from:

$$I_{yy_{mg}} = \qquad (2.38)$$

$$I_{yy} + (W/g)\{z_{mg}^2 + (x_{mg} - x_{cg})^2\}$$

with: I_{yy} the airplane moment of inertia as determined from Part V, Chapter 3 or, more appropriately for Class II methods from Part V, Chapter 10

$\ddot{\theta}$ is the pitch angular acceleration at the instant of initiation of rotation. In preliminary design it is suggested to use:

For large transports: $\ddot{\theta}$ = 6 to 8 deg/sec^2

For small transports: $\ddot{\theta}$ = 8 to 10 deg/sec^2

For light airplanes
and for fighters: $\ddot{\theta}$ = 10 to 12 deg/sec^2

Equations (2.29) through (2.31) are normally solved for the amount of horizontal tail area required to achieve take-off rotation at the rotation speed, V_{rot}:

$$S_h = \frac{-z_T T + z_D D + W\left(x_{mg} - x_{cg} + \mu_g z_{mg}\right) - L_{wf}\left(x_{mg} - x_{ac_{wf}} + \mu_g z_{mg}\right) - C_{m_{ac_{wf_g}}} \bar{q}_{rot} S\bar{c} + I_{yy_{mg}} \ddot{\Theta}}{\bar{q}_{rot}\left(x_{mg} - x_{ac_h} + \mu_g z_{mg}\right) C_{L_{h_{max}}}} \tag{2.39}$$

The rotation speed is defined relative to the stall speed in the regulations: Appendix A or Appendix B.

Values for maximum lift coefficient for the horizontal tail depend on the tail design and on the ground effect (ground proximity) of the tail during the rotation process. If the reader does not wish to employ the rather laborious methods of Part VI to estimate $C_{L_{h_{max}}}$ it is suggested to use:

$C_{L_{h_{max}}} = -0.35(A_h)^{1/3}$ for fixed stabilizer with 30 percent chord elevator

$= -0.8$ for a controllable stabilizer with a fixed elevator at zero deflection

$= -1.2$ for a controllable stabilizer with a 30 percent chord elevator deflected for maximum down lift

<u>Note:</u> higher values for maximum downlift on the tail are possible with negative camber, negative slots and/or blowing over the lower surface.

2.5.3.2 Mathematical model for analyzing lateral-directional control during the take-off groundrun

The regulations essentially require that controllability during the take-off run is such as to ensure that:

1) Positive steering is possible
2) Wing-over is impossible
3) The airplane does not slide off the runway

Wet and/or slick runway surfaces coupled with strong crosswinds can cause anyone of these problems. The regulations specify the magnitude of crosswinds which each airplane category must be able to cope with.

Figure 2.6 shows the forces and moments which are important to these ground operation problems. To satisfy items 1), 2) and 3) it is necessary for the designer to show that the following three runway constraints are satisfied:

Runway Constraint 1:

The lateral ground friction force on the nosegear should not reverse sign. For positive sideslip due to crosswind (as shown in Figure 2.6), it is required that:

$$Y_{ng} > 0 \qquad (2.40)$$

If condition (2.40) is violated, nosewheel steering becomes ineffective.

Runway Constraint 2:

The normal force (= vertical ground reaction) on either main gear should not become zero. For positive sideslip due to crosswind it is required that:

$$P_{mg_L} > 0 \text{ and } P_{mg_R} > 0, \qquad (2.41)$$

where:

$$P_{mg_L} + P_{mg_R} = P_{mg} \qquad (2.42)$$

If either of the conditions (2.41) is violated, the airplane will start to 'wing-over'.

Runway Constraint 3:

The sum of all lateral ground friction forces should

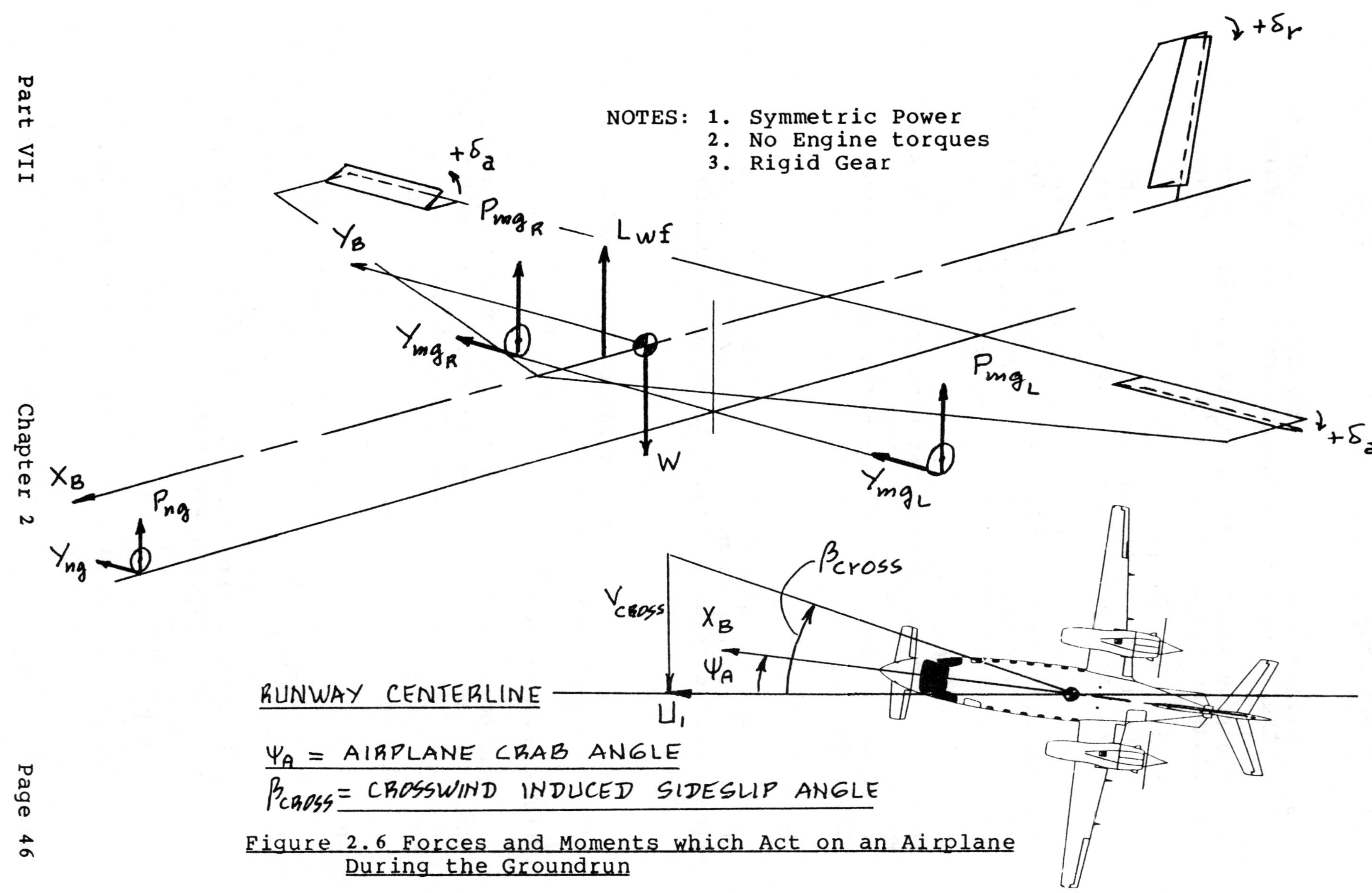

Figure 2.6 Forces and Moments which Act on an Airplane During the Groundrun

not reverse sign. For positive sideslip due to crosswind it is required that:

$$Y_{ng} + Y_{mg_L} + Y_{mg_R} > 0 \tag{2.43}$$

If condition (2.43) is violated, the airplane will begin to slide off the runway.

Note: As soon as the take-off rotation process as described in sub-section 2.5.3.1 is completed, the runway constraints loose their validity: the airplane is flying.

The magnitudes of the lateral gear forces, Y_{ng} and $Y_{mg_{(L \text{ or } R)}}$, depend on the values of the vertical gear reactions: P_{ng} and $P_{mg_{(L \text{ or } R)}}$ and on the so-called gear cornering coefficient.

The vertical gear reactions, P_{ng} and P_{mg} (and the airplane forward acceleration, $\dot{u}$) may be computed from from Equations (2.29) through (2.31) by setting:

a) Thrust equal to takeoff thrust

b) L_h to a value corresponding to the primary longitudinal control deflection used during the take-off roll (prior to initiation of rotation!).

c) $\ddot{\theta} = 0$

The relationship between the lateral gear forces, Y_{ng} and $Y_{mg_{(L \text{ or } R)}}$, the so-called cornering coefficient, c_β and the vertical gear reactions, P_{ng} and $P_{mg_{(L \text{ or } R)}}$ are normally writtent as follows:

$$Y_{ng} = c_\beta P_{ng} \tag{2.44}$$

$$Y_{mg_{(L \text{ or } R)}} = c_\beta P_{mg_{(L \text{ or } R)}} \tag{2.45}$$

The cornering coefficient itself is a function of the gear slip angles, $\beta_{ng \text{ or } mg}$ which are defined in

Figure 2.7. They can be expressed as:

for the main gear: $\beta_{mg} = \psi_A$ (2.46)

for the nose gear: $\beta_{ng} = \psi_A + U_{steer}$ (2.47)

where: ψ_A is the airplane crab angle.

ψ_{steer} is the nosegear steering angle.

Note: These relations assume a steerable nose-gear and a non-steerable main gear!

In preliminary design it is conservative to write:

For dry surfaces:

for the main gear: $c_\beta = 0.025\psi_A$ (2.48)

for the nose gear: $c_\beta = 0.025(\psi_A + \psi_{steer})$ (2.49)

For slick surfaces:

for the main gear: $c_\beta = 0.005\psi_A$ (2.50)

for the nose gear: $c_\beta = 0.005(\psi_A + \psi_{steer})$ (2.51)

For purposes of preliminary design it is acceptable to assume that the maximum possible value for the cornering coefficients are:

$c_\beta = 0.70$ for dry surfaces

$= 0.15$ for slick surfaces

In checking the runway constraint conditions (2.40) and (2.43) these maximum allowable values should be kept in mind!

Figure 2.7 illustrates the relationships between the cornering coefficients and the gear slip angle.

To find the actual values of the lateral gear forces, the lateral-directional equations of motion are needed. The steady state lateral-directional equations of motion for a straight line track along the runway are:

$$\{(C_{y_\beta})(\beta_{cross} - \psi_A) + C_{y_{\delta_a}}\delta_a + C_{y_{\delta_r}}\delta_r\}\bar{q}S + Y_{ng} +$$

$$+ Y_{mg_L} + Y_{mg_R} = 0 \qquad (2.52)$$

$$\{(C_{l_\beta})(\beta_{cross} - \psi_A) + C_{l_{\delta_a}}\delta_a + C_{l_{\delta_r}}\delta_r\}\bar{q}Sb + P_{mg_L}y_{mg} +$$

$$- P_{mg_R}y_{mg} - Y_{ng}z_{ng} - (Y_{mg_L} + Y_{mg_R})z_{mg} = 0 \qquad (2.53)$$

$$\{(C_{n_\beta})(\beta_{cross} - \psi_A) + C_{n_{\delta_a}}\delta_a + C_{n_{\delta_r}}\delta_r\}\bar{q}Sb +$$

$$+ Y_{ng}(x_{ng} + x_{cg}) - (Y_{mg_L} + Y_{mg_R})(x_{mg} - x_{cg}) = 0 \qquad (2.54)$$

The x- and z- distances in these equations are defined in Figure 2.6. They are consistent with Figure 2.5.

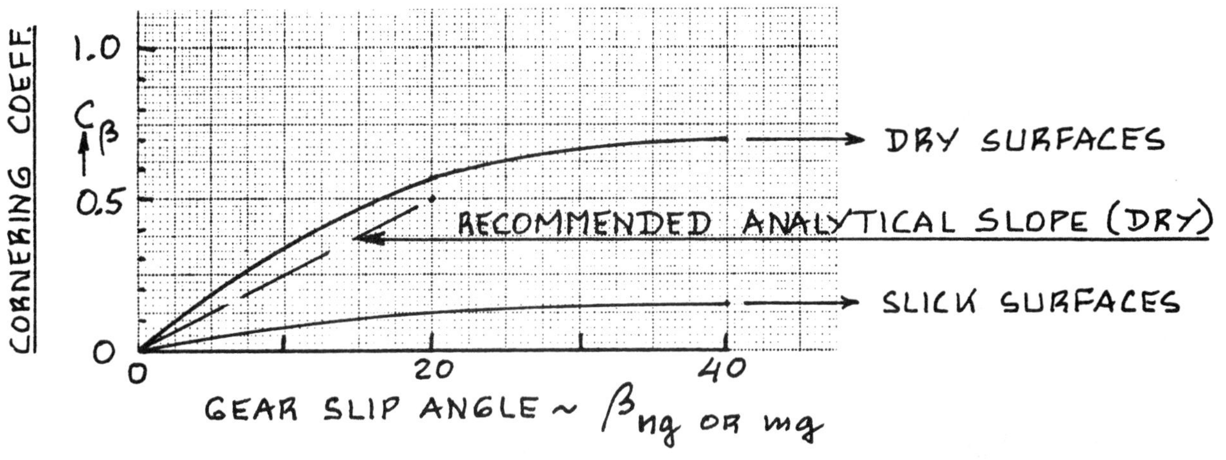

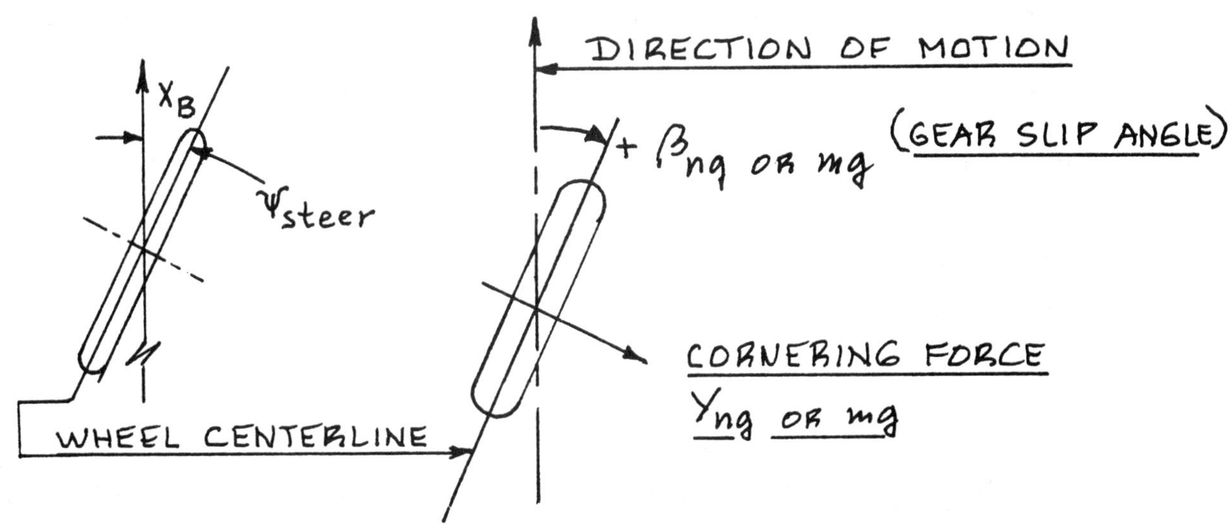

Figure 2.7 Gear Slip Angle, Gear Steering Angle, and Cornering Coefficients

Assumptions made in setting up these equations are:

1. The airplane does not bank (gear is rigid in the vertical direction).

2. All gears are rigid in torsion.

3. The tire induced torque on the gears can be neglected.

4. The engine induced torque in roll and in yaw can be neglected.

5. The dynamic pressure is a constant value between zero and that value corresponding to liftoff.

   The change in dynamic pressure during the takeoff groundrun is accounted for by solving Equations (2.52) - (2.54) for a range of values of dynamic pressure.

By using Equations (2.42), and (2.44) through (2.49) it is possible to cast Equations (2.52) - (2.54) in the following, more tractable form:

$$\{(C_{y_\beta})(\beta_{cross} - \psi_A) + C_{y_{\delta_A}}\delta_a + C_{y_{\delta_r}}\delta_r\}\bar{q}S + $$
$$+ 0.025(\psi_A + \psi_{steer})P_{ng} + 0.025\psi_A P_{mg} = 0 \qquad (2.55)$$

$$\{(C_{l_\beta})(\beta_{cross} - \psi_A) + C_{l_{\delta_a}}\delta_a + C_{l_{\delta_r}}\delta_r\}\bar{q}Sb + $$
$$+ 2P_{mg_L}y_{mg} - P_{mg}y_{mg} - 0.025(\psi_A + \psi_{steer})P_{ng}z_{ng} + $$
$$- 0.025\psi_A P_{mg}z_{mg} = 0 \qquad (2.56)$$

$$\{(C_{n_\beta})(\beta_{cross} - \psi_A) + C_{n_{\delta_a}}\delta_a + C_{n_{\delta_r}}\delta_r\}\bar{q}Sb + $$
$$+ 0.025(\psi_A + \psi_{steer})P_{ng}(x_{ng} - x_{cg}) + $$
$$- 0.025\psi_A P_{mg}(x_{mg} + x_{cg}) = 0 \qquad (2.57)$$

The following observations are in order:

A. The crosswind, V_{cross}, is specified by the mission specification and/or by the regulations. From the crosswind and the airplane speed along the runway, U_1:

$$\beta_{cross} = \arctan(V_{cross}/U_1) \qquad (2.58)$$

B. The variables in Equations (2.55) - (2.57) are:

1. The runway crab angle, ψ_A
2. The left vertical main gear reaction, P_{mg_L}
3. The lateral control deflection angle, δ_a
4. The rudder deflection angle, δ_r
5. The nosegear steering angle, ψ_{steer}

There are five variables and three equations. Thus, two variables must be specified. Usually the assumption is made that the pilot will select the nosegear steering angle, ψ_{steer} and the aileron deflection angle, δ_a to obtain the desired straight line track along the runway without winging over. The other variables are then completely determined by Eqns (2.55)-(2.57). Based on assumed values for ψ_{steer} and δ_a, and the solved variables ψ_A, P_{mg_L} and δ_r the designer must then make sure that the constraints 1 - 3 are not violated. Subsection 2.5.4 contains a procedure for these calculations.

2.5.4 Step-by-Step Procedure for Analyzing Control During the Take-off Groundrun

2.5.4.1 Step-by-step procedure for analyzing longitudinal control during the take-off groundrun

The following step-by-step procedure is suggested to verify the longitudinal controllability of an airplane during take-off:

Step 1: Read the regulations and determine which regulations apply to the design.

Step 2: The regulations define the speeds at which take-off rotation must be possible. Determine these speeds.

Step 3: The mission of the airplane defines the most severe field conditions in terms of altitude, temperature and surface conditions. This determines the atmospheric density to be used in the analysis. The field condition also deter mines the wheel-ground rolling friction coefficient, μ_g which should be used: see page 40 for guidelines.

Step 4: Determine the most critical weight versus c.g. locations for which take-off rotation must be possible.

Step 5: Determine all forces and coefficients needed to find the horizontal tail area required to rotate, from Eqn.(2.39). Make sure that ground effect is accounted for!

NOTE: If the airplane is not a conventional tricycle gear airplane it will be necessary to rewrite Equations (2.29) through (2.31)!

Step 6: Using Eqn.(2.39), find S_h as a function of speed, plot this relationship and mark the desired take-off rotation speed. Next, perform a sensitivity analysis to determine the sensitivity of the solution to such parameters as:

z_T, the vertical thrustline location.

$C_{m_{ac_{wf}}}$, the pitching moment coefficient of wing-fuselage with flaps in the take-off position. Determine the effect of flap type and flap size on the solution for S_h.

$C_{L_{h_{max}}}$, the maximum available lift coefficient of the horizontal tail.

Compare the value of S_h required for takeoff rotation with the value required from other considerations such as: control, trim and stability). Decide on a course of action.

IMPORTANT NOTE: It turns out that the horizontal tail of many airplanes is determined by the take-off rotation requirement rather than by stability or by trim requirements. If that is the case a sensitivity analysis will allow for rapid decision making relative to changes in the design to bring this tail sizing requirement in better balance with the other tail sizing requirements.

Step 7: Document the results obtained, including any design changes made.

2.5.4.2 Step-by-step procedure for analyzing lateral-directional control during the take-off groundrun

Step 1: Read the regulations and determine which regulations apply to the design.

Step 2: The regulations define the crosswind magnitudes which the airplane must be able to cope with. Note these!

Step 3: Compute the stability and control derivatives identified in Eqns (2.55) - (2.57). The methods of Part VI can be used to do this.

Step 4: For a range of speeds between zero and V_{rot} determine the vertical gear reactions, P_{ng} and P_{mg} from Eqns (2.29) - (2.31) but using conditions a,b and c as stated on page 47.

Note: The nosegear reaction depends strongly on the longitudinal control deflections used during the take-off roll. The longitudinal trim control (usually the stabilizer incidence angle) must be set at an angle consistent with the requirement for take-off rotation: this usually means a negative angle!!
The primary longitudinal control deflection may be assumed to be that giving the most favorable steering (usually full nose down).

Step 5: With the help of the specified crosswind determine the crosswind angle, β_{cross} from Equation (2.58). This must be done for a range of speeds consistent with Step 4.

Step 6: Select values for the nosegear steering angle, ψ_{steer} and for the aileron angle, δ_a.

With the help of Eqns (2.55) - (2.57) determine the airplane crab angle, ψ_A, the left vertical gear reaction, P_{mg_L} and the rudder angle, δ_r.

Step 7: With the results of Step 6, compute all gear reactions which appear in the runway constraint conditions 1, 2 and 3. See whether or not these constraints are satisfied. If not, different initial assumptions for ψ_A and δ_a may be tried as long as these new values are feasible. It may be, that the airplane cannot cope with the required cross wind conditions. In that case, possible design solutions are:

1. A larger vertical tail: more directional stability and perhaps more rudder control power.

2. Larger values for y_{mg} (larger distance between the main gears. This can have major redesign implications!

3. Incorporate a crosswind main gear into the airplane. See Part IV, Chapter 2 for implications!

4. Sometimes a smaller crosswind capability has to be accepted despite the fact that this will hurt the operational flexibility of the airplane.

Step 8: Document the results obtained, including any design changes made.

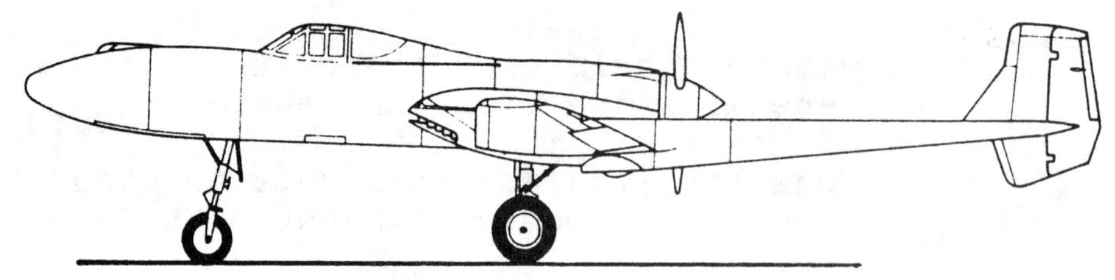

2.6 CONTROL DURING THE LANDING GROUNDRUN

2.6.1 Applicable Regulations:

Civil: FAR 23.231, see Appendix A.

FAR 25.231, 233, 237, see Appendix A.

Military: MIL-F-8785C, Section 3.3 (inparticular 3.2.3.3), see Appendix B.

2.6.2 Relationship to Preliminary Design

See Chapter 11, Part II.

2.6.3 Mathematical Model for Analyzing Control During the Landing Groundrun

The mathematical model to be used in this case is essentially that of Section 2.5.3 with the following additions:

1. The thrust, T should be investigated for flight idle as well as for reversed thrust if the airplane is equipped with a thrust reverser system.

2. Application of brakes should now be considered. The rolling friction coefficient, μ_g encountered during braking depends on brake design. For typical values, consult Part IV, pages 60 and 61.

3. Application of wing mounted spoilers can reduce the wing-fuselage lift very considerably thus changing L_{wf} in Eqns. (2.30) and (2.31).

4. The airplane may touch down in a 'crabbed' position. The crab-angle, ψ_A depends on the value of crosswind and on the touchdown speed, V_L:

   $$\psi_A = \arctan(V_{cross}/V_L) \tag{2.59}$$

5. The longitudinal control deflections are those most favorable for positive nosegear steering.

2.6.4 Step-by-Step Procedure for Analyzing Control During the Landing Groundrun

Use the procedures of Section 2.5.4 with the exception, that airplane speed ranges from V_L down to zero.

2.7 ROLL PERFORMANCE

2.7.1 Applicable Regulations

Civil: FAR 23.157 and FAR 25.147, see Appendix A.

Military: MIL-F-8785C, Section 3.3, see Appendix B.

2.7.2 Relationship to Preliminary Design

Part II, Chapter 2 (see Step 24), and Chapter 6.

2.7.3 Mathematical Model for Analyzing Roll Performance

The regulations essentially require that any airplane, when trimmed in a given flight condition at a given airspeed and in a given configuration:

1. can be maneuvered safely and easily from one bank angle to another (rolled) within some specified time period (Except FAR 25.147)

2. has roll time constant values which are within certain limits (Military only)

The words 'safely' and 'easily' as used here are defined in the regulations in terms of lateral cockpit control forces which may not be exceeded while achieving the bank angles and roll rates which must be obtained within some specified amount of time. In addition, the regulations imply that reversals in bank angle and roll rate may not occur outside well defined boundaries.

The words 'airplane configuration' imply one or more of the following as defined in the regulations:

1. center of gravity location
2. power setting (voluntary or failure)
3. landing gear position (up or down)
4. flap position (up, take-off, approach or landing)
   Note: in some instances asymmetric flap deployment has to be considered.
5. asymmetric fuel distribution
6. asymmetric weapons or payload disposition

When in doubt about the specific meaning of civil roll performance requirements, the author suggests to use the corresponding military specification.

Class II analysis of roll performance is normally accomplished with solutions of the so-called single-degree-of-freedom differential rolling equation:

$$\ddot{\phi} = L_p\dot{\phi} + L_{\delta_{cpt}}\delta_{cpt} \tag{2.60}$$

where: ϕ is the bank angle in rad

$\dot{\phi} = p$ is the roll rate in rad/sec

L_p is the dimensional roll damping derivative, which is defined as:

$$L_p = (C_{l_p}\bar{q}Sb^2)/(2I_{xx_s}U_1) \tag{2.61}$$

in which: C_{l_p} is the dimensionless roll damping derivative. Part VI, Chapter 10 gives a method for estimating C_{l_p}

S is the wing area in ft^2

b is the wing span in ft

U_1 is the steady state speed in fps

I_{xx_s} is the rolling moment of inertia in $slugft^2$ in the stability axis system. Methods for computing the moments of inertia in an arbitrary body axis system are provided in Chapters 3 and 10 of Part V. Transformation of airplane moments of inertia to the stability axes system can be accomplished with the help of Appendix D.

$L_{\delta_{cpt}}$ is the dimensional roll control power derivative. It is defined as:

$$L_{\delta_{cpt}} = (C_{l_{\delta_{cpt}}}\bar{q}Sb)/I_{xx_s} \tag{2.62}$$

$C_{l_{\delta_{cpt}}}$ is the lateral control power derivative. Read on to see how it may be computed.

δ_{cpt} is the lateral cockpit control deflection in degrees, in radians or in inches depending on the type of cockpit controller in use. The cockpit controller is normally geared to the lateral control surfaces. Many airplanes employ more than one type of lateral control surface. If an airplane uses both ailerons and spoilers and if a linear gearing is assumed between the cockpit controller and the lateral control surface it is possible to write:

$$C_{l_{\delta_{cpt}}} \delta_{cpt_{max}} = C_{l_{\delta_a}} \delta_{a_{max}} + C_{l_{\delta_s}} \delta_{s_{max}} \qquad (2.63)$$

where: $C_{l_{\delta_a}}$ is the aileron control power derivative in 1/deg or in 1/rad. It may be computed with the method of Chapter 10 in Part VI.

$\delta_{a_{max}}$ is the maximum available aileron deflection in degrees or in radians

$C_{l_{\delta_s}}$ is the spoiler control power derivative in 1/deg or in 1/rad. It may be computed with the method of Chapter 10 in Part VI.

δ_s is the maximum available spoiler deflection in degrees or in radians.

$\delta_{cpt_{max}}$ represents the maximum available deflection of the lateral cockpit controller in inches or in radians. This quantity follows from the detail design of the cockpit as discussed in Chapter 2 of Part III. Maximum allowable deflections for sticks and wheels are defined in Chapter 2, Part III. Once $\delta_{cpt_{max}}$ has been determined, Eqn.(2.63) can be used to solve for $C_{l_{\delta_{cpt}}}$.

It must be possible for the pilot to move the lateral cockpit controller (stick, wheel or other) to a position consistent with the required roll performance. This means that the accompanying cockpit control force should not exceed the capabilities of the pilot. The magnitudes of allowable lateral control forces are defined in the regulations. The lateral cockpit control force may be estimated from:

$$F_{s_{lat}} = \text{Sum}\,(G_i HM_i) + F_{s_{lat_{artificial}}} \tag{2.64}$$

where: G_i is the gearing ratio in rad/in or in rad/ft associated with the ith lateral control surface

HM_i is the hingemoment in ftlbs associated with the ith lateral control surface. Such hingemoments may be estimated from:

$$HM_i = C_{h_i}\bar{q}S_i\bar{c}_i \tag{2.65}$$

where: C_{h_i} is the hingemoment coefficient associated with the ith lateral control surface. Methods for estimating hingemoment coefficients are given in Chapter 10 of Part VI.

S_i is the reference area of the ith lateral control surface

$\bar{c}_i$ is the m.g.c. of the ith lateral control surface

$F_{s_{lat_{artificial}}}$ is the lateral cockpit controller force produced by the lateral force-feel system. For a discussion of force-feel systems, see Ref.12, Chapter 5.

2.7.4 Step-by-Step Procedure for Analyzing Roll Performance

In preliminary design, the roll performance capabilities of an airplane can be verified with the following step-by-step procedure:

Step 1: Read the regulations and determine which regulations apply to the design.

Step 2: The regulations define flight conditions and airplane configurations for which certain roll performance standards are to be met. Identify these flight conditions.

Note: Also determine the airplane configuration for which the regulations apply.

<u>Step 3:</u> For the flight conditions defined in Step 2, determine: Mach number, M, dynamic pressure, $\bar{q}$ and the rolling moment of inertia (in stability axes!).

<u>Step 4:</u> For the conditions defined in Steps 2 and 3 determine the roll damping derivative, C_{l_p}.

<u>NOTE:</u> for airplanes subject to aeroelastic deformations, read Section 2.9!

<u>Step 5:</u> For the conditions defined in Steps 2 and 3 determine the roll control power derivative due to lateral cockpit control, $C_{l_{\delta_{cpt}}}$.

This derivative depends on the type of roll control system used. For an airplane which uses ailerons and/or spoilers, Eqn.(2.63) may be used. If a differential stabilizer is used, the appropriate term must be added to Eqn.(2.63). Methods for estimating control power derivatives due to ailerons, spoilers and differential stabilizer are given in Chapter 10 of Part VI.

Acceptable values for control surface deflections depend on aerodynamic considerations. Suggested 'not-to-exceed' values for lateral control surface deflections are:

Ailerons: $\delta_{a_{max}} < 25$ degrees

Spoilers: $\delta_{s_{max}} < 60$ degrees

Differential stabilizer: $\delta_{i_h} < 15$ degrees

<u>NOTE:</u> for airplanes subject to aeroelastic deformations, read Section 2.9!

<u>Step 6:</u> Determine the roll angle performance capability of the airplane from:

$$\phi(t) = \{(-L_{\delta_{cpt}}\delta_{cpt})t/L_p\} + [(L_{\delta_{cpt}}\delta_{cpt})/\{(L_p)^2\}](e^{L_p t} - 1) \qquad (2.66)$$

where: $\phi(t)$ is the bank angle reached at t seconds after full movement of the lateral cockpit controller, δ_{cpt}. Note that Eqn.(2.66) is based on the assumption that the control input can be thought of as a 'perfect' step input.

t is the time elapsed from full movement of the cockpit controller, δ_{cpt} to the time at which the bank angle is to be measured.

<u>IMPORTANT NOTE:</u> in most regulations, the values for $\phi(t)$ and the corresponding value of t are given. Therefore, Eqn.(2.66) can be used by the designer to solve for that value of the control power derivative, $L_{\delta_{cpt}}$ which is needed to satisfy the regulation. With that information the designer can decide how to change the lateral control surface sizes and locations until the regulation is satisfied.

<u>Step 7:</u> Calculate the airplane roll time constant, τ_R from:

$$\tau_R = -1/L_p \tag{2.67}$$

where L_p is found from Equation (2.61).

If the airplane is to have acceptable roll performance, the roll time constant must be below some maximum allowable value. Maximum allowable values for the roll time constant are presented in the military regulations: Appendix B, Table VII, page 297.

<u>Important Note:</u> The civil regulations do not require specific values of the roll time constant. Accepted design practice in the U.S.A. is to use the appropriate military specifications (Airplane class, flight phase and handling quality level) whenever the civil regulations fail to provide specific design guidance.

<u>Step 8:</u> Document the results obtained, including any design changes made.

2.8 HIGH SPEED CHARACTERISTICS

2.8.1 Applicable Regulations

Civil: FAR 23.253 and FAR 25.253, see Appendix A.

Military: MIL-F-8785C, Section 3.2, in particular Sub-sections 3.2.3.6 and 3.2.3.7, see Appendix B.

2.8.2 Relationship to Preliminary Design

Part II, Chapter 8, in particular Step 8.4.

2.8.3 Mathematical Model for Analyzing High Speed Characteristics

The regulations essentially require that any airplane, when inadvertently placed in a flight condition between the maximum allowable operating speed and the design dive speed, must be able to be recovered to a normal operating flight condition without the use of exceptional pilot skills and without exceeding reasonable cockpit control force levels.

To satisfy these requirements it is usually sufficient in preliminary design to show that no reversals occur in control force versus speed gradients within the speed range prescribed in the regulations.

Calculation of the control force versus speed gradients can be done with the method of Section 3.1.3 with the proviso that all derivatives and coefficients must be evaluated at the high Mach numbers required by the regulations. This cannot normally be done without the availability of windtunnel data and/or advanced aerodynamic panel codes.

Note: Another way around the high speed handling problem is to prevent the airplane from becoming exposed to certain Mach number ranges. This can be done by the addition of 'flight envelope protection' systems, such as on the Airbus 320.

2.8.4 Step-by-Step Procedure for Analyzing High Speed Characteristics

The step-by-step procedure for analyzing high speed characteristics is similar to that of Section 3.1.4. All stability derivatives and coefficients must be evaluated at the high Mach numbers required by the regulations.

2.9 AEROELASTIC CONSIDERATIONS

The analysis methods and procedures presented in Sections 2.1 through 2.8 are based on the assumption that designer has available ALL values for aerodynamic coefficients, control power derivatives and stability derivatives which reflect the ACTUAL airplane behavior in a particular flight condition.

In Sections 2.1 through 2.8 frequent reference is made to the methods for estimating aerodynamic coefficients, control power derivatives and stability derivatives in Part VI. The reader MUST keep in mind that these methods are VALID ONLY for RIGID airplanes. Most high performance airplanes, including fighters and transports are often far from rigid: they exhibit significant aeroelastic behavior!

Therefore it becomes necessary to evaluate the aerodynamic coefficients, the control power derivatives and the stability derivatives not only as a function of Mach number, but also as a function of dynamic pressure. It is the dynamic pressure which (at any combination of angle of attack and Mach number) determines the severity of aeroelastic distortions.

Calculating aeroelastic effects requires rather detailed knowledge of the airplane structural properties: in particular the EI (bending stiffness) and GJ (torsional stiffness) distribution about the airplane elastic axes. In the early design phase such knowledge may not yet be available. Therefore, in the early preliminary design phase, use is made of so-called elastic-to-rigid ratios. These ratios are used to 'guestimate' the ELASTIC AIRPLANE value of a coefficient (or derivative) from a known value of that coefficient (or derivative) for the corresponding RIGID AIRPLANE. A typical example is:

$$C_{L_{\alpha_{elastic}}} = (R_e/R_r)C_{L_{\alpha_{rigid}}} \qquad (2.68)$$

where: $C_{L_{\alpha_{rigid}}}$ is the lift-curve slope of the rigid airplane as computed with the methods of Part VI.

R_e/R_r is the elastic-to-rigid ratio which may be computed with the methods of Ch. 8, Reference 12, provided the required structural stiffness information and elastic axes locations are available.

In preliminary design, these ratios are frequently 'guestimated' on the basis of computed data on similar configurations. Chapter 8 of Reference 12 provides examples of elastic airplane versus rigid airplane derivatives. The reader may use these to arrive at an 'educated' guestimate of R_e/R_r for a newly designed airplane. Care must be exercised in doing this: the data in Reference 12 apply to transport airplanes only!

Figure 2.8 shows an example application of these ideas.

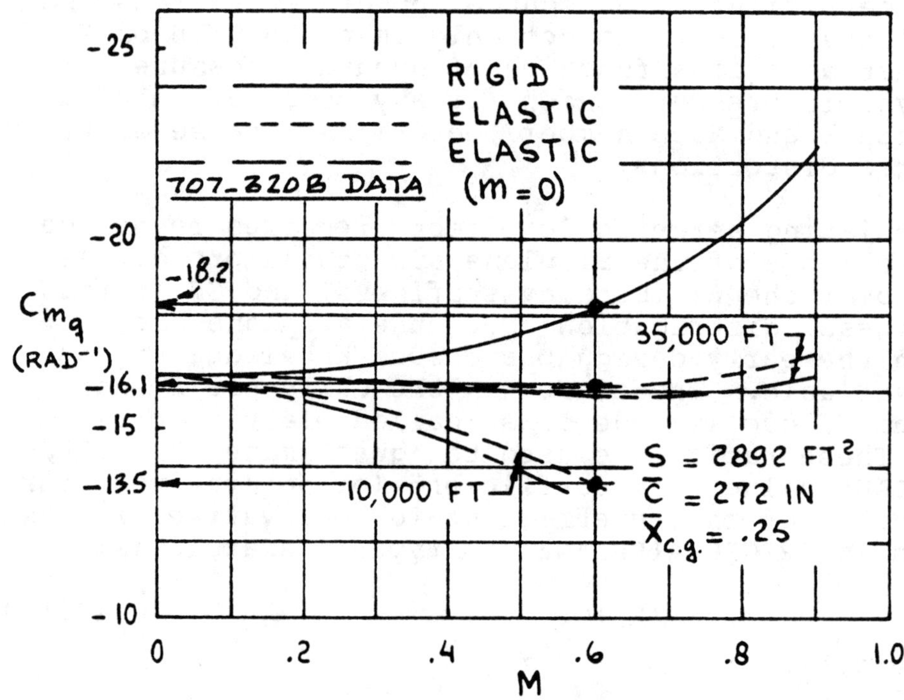

AT M = 0.6 AND 10,000 FT $R_e/R_r = -13.5/-18.2 = 0.74$

" " AND 35,000 FT $R_e/R_r = -16.1/-18.2 = 0.88$

Figure 2.8 Example of Extraction of R_e/R_r Values from Elastic Airplane Derivative Data

3. STABILITY: STATIC AND DYNAMIC

The purpose of this chapter is to present Class II methods for analyzing the static and dynamic stability characteristics of airplanes. These methods are compatible with Step 24 in Preliminary Design Sequence II as outlined in Chapter 2 of Part II.

The designer must decide at the outset whether his airplane should be designed with:

1. Inherent stability OR WITH: 2. De-facto stability.

Definition 1: Airplanes with 'inherent stability' do not require any form of 'closed loop' stability augmentation.

The Cessna 172 and the Fokker F-50 are examples of such airplanes.

As a general rule, low to moderate performance airplanes are designed with inherent stability.

Definition 2: Airplanes with 'de-facto stability' require static and/or dynamic stability augmentation.

The F-18 and the X-29 are examples of such airplanes. Both are inherently unstable and rely on a feedback system to achieve theirs de-facto stability: they cannot be controlled without feedback!

As a general rule very high performance airplanes are designed with de-facto stability.

Most moderate to high performance airplanes (B-727, DC-10, C- 141) have inherent static stability but are deficient in inherent dynamic stability. Such airplanes are typically equipped with feedback systems to assure that they have de-facto dynamic stability.

The B-727 and the DC-10 have yaw dampers to assure that the dutch roll damping ratio is sufficiently large. The C-141 also has a pitch damping system to assure that the short period damping ratio is sufficiently large.

QUESTION: What drives airplane designers toward de-facto (or artificial) stability?

ANSWERS: 1. For fighters: Enhanced maneuverability!

2. For transports: Savings in tail areas and weight as well as savings in drag! These savings must be traded against greater complexity of the flight control system and its sensors.

Reliability and maintainability issues also play an important role in the design decision making process between inherent and de-facto stability.

IMPORTANT COMMENT: The choice between inherent stability and de-facto stability is made by the designer (together with the customer) and NOT by the regulations!

The objective of the methods in this chapter is to assure that the airplane meets all the regulatory static and dynamic stability requirements which are placed on an airplane. These regulatory requirements are placed on an airplane to ensure that it is airworthy. Airworthiness in this case implies that the airplane possesses safe, 'minimum' handling characteristics.

To ensure safe, minimum handling characteristics the civil and the military regulations specify certain minimum allowable frequency, damping, time constant and response parameters.

A problem with many civil stability regulations (see (Appendix A) is that they are frequently cast in language which is not easily translated in numerical statements. This makes them difficult to use by designers!

However, the military regulations (see Appendix B) are written in terms of very specific numerical design objectives. For that reason, the military regulations are commonly used in the preliminary design process of BOTH civil and military airplanes.

The military regulations (Appendix B) define static, dynamic and control-response characteristics in three levels. These levels can be summarized as follows:

LEVEL 1: Flying qualities which are clearly adequate for any given mission flight phase.

LEVEL 2: Flying qualities which are adequate to complete the mission flight phase but some increase in pilot workload or degradation in mission effectiveness, or both, exists.

LEVEL 3: Flying qualities such that the airplane can

be controlled safely, but pilot workload is excessive or mission effectiveness is inadequate, or both. HOWEVER: the airplane can be safely landed.

IMPORTANT DESIGN GUIDELINES FOR CIVIL AND FOR MILITARY AIRPLANES:

1. Inherently stable airplanes must be designed to LEVEL 1 requirements.

2. De-facto stable airplanes must be designed to LEVEL 1 requirements with the feedback augmentation system in the normal state.

3. After failures occur in the flight control system the degraded handling quality levels which are tolerated depend on the probability, P (per flight) with which the failures occur.

HANDLING QUALITY LEVEL which is tolerated:	Civil Airplanes	Military Airplanes
LEVEL 2	$P < 10^{-4}$	for $P < 10^{-2}$
LEVEL 3	$P < 10^{-6}$	for $P < 10^{-4}$

The airplane designer must be aware of the fact that a penalty paid for 'de-facto' stability is that stability augmentation systems use control power to achieve their objective. It is up to the designer to assure that the required levels of control power are indeed designed into the airplane during the preliminary design process.

The material in this chapter is organized as follows:

3.1 Static longitudinal stability
3.2 Static lateral and directional stability
3.3 Dynamic longitudinal stability
3.4 Dynamic lateral-directional stability
3.5 Dynamic coupling
3.6 Stall characteristics
3.7 Spinning
3.8 Aeroelastic considerations

Reference 12 can be used as a source for derivations and applications of the theory of airplane static and dynamic stability and control: open and closed loop.

3.1 STATIC LONGITUDINAL STABILITY

3.1.1 Applicable Regulations

Civil: FAR 23.171, 23.173, 23.175, and 23.253, see Appendix A.

FAR 25.171, 25.173, 25.175, 25.253, and 25.255, see Appendix A.

Military: Mil-F-8785C, Sub-section 3.2.1 and Paragraph 3.2.2.2, see Appendix B.

3.1.2 Relationship to Preliminary Design

See Part II, Chapter 11.

3.1.3 Mathematical Model for Analyzing Static Longitudinal Stability

The regulations essentially require that the airplane must possess the following characteristics:

1.) With the airplane trimmed at speeds which are specified in the regulations, a PULL must be required to obtain AND maintain speeds below the trim speed. Conversely, a PUSH must be required to obtain AND maintain speeds above the trim speed.

2.) The speed must return to within some specified percentage of the trim speed if the cockpit control is released from the push or pull condition(s) implied by 1.).

3.) The stick-force speed gradient must not be less than that specified in the regulations.

Figure 3.1 illustrates these concepts.

It is clear that a mathematical model for analysis of these characteristics must relate the stick force to speed relative to any given trim speed. Since the mathematical relationship between stick force and speed depends on the type of control system employed (as shown in Eqn.(2.8)) the designer must decide on the type of flight control system to be used in his airplane.

In the following it is assumed that the airplane is equipped with an elevator as the primary longitudinal controller. The stabilizer angle is assumed to have the

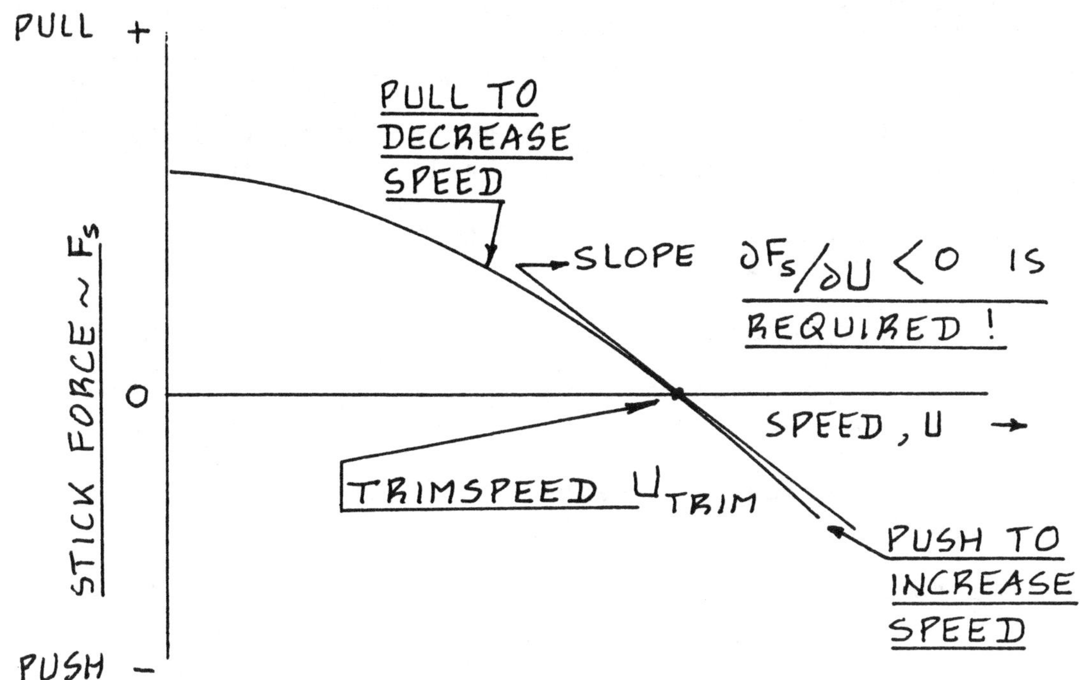

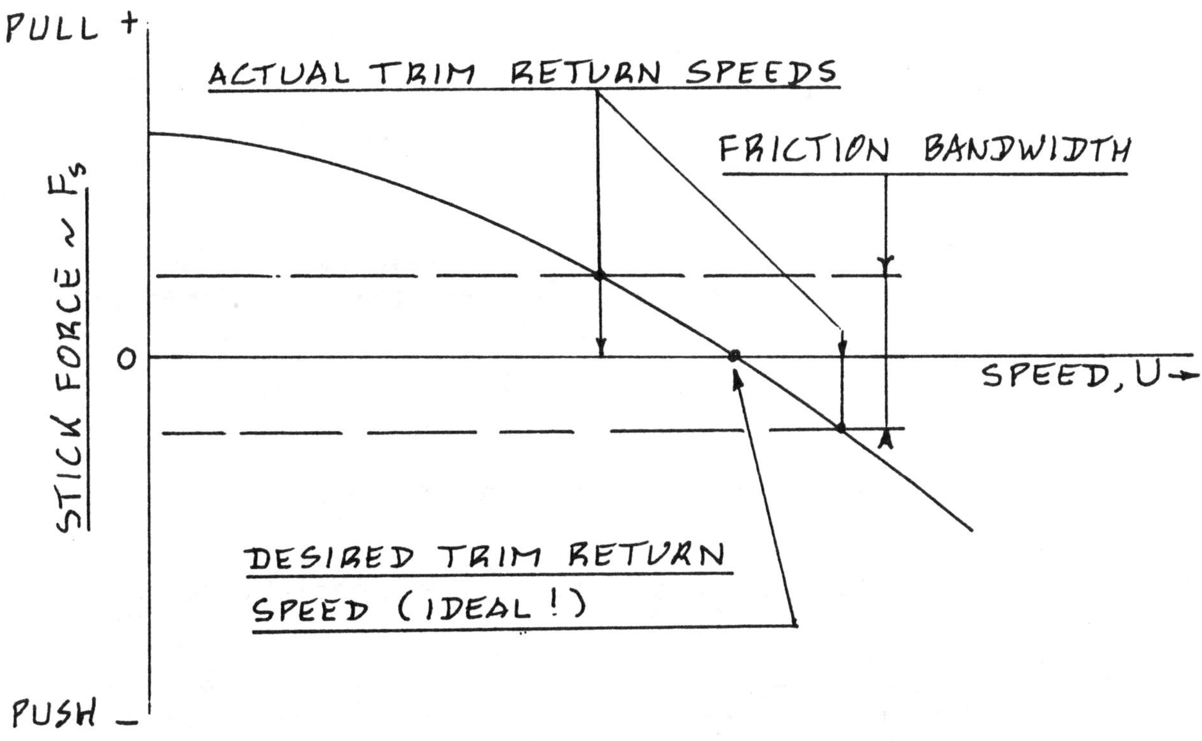

Figure 3.1 Stick-force Versus Speed and Return-to-Trim-Speed Characteristics

stick force trim function. In that case, Reference 12, Chapter 5 shows that the following relations hold:

1. For the stick force needed to maintain a speed U, relative to a given trimspeed, U_{trim}:

$$F_s = \eta_h G S_e \bar{c}_e (W/S) x \tag{3.1}$$

$$x (C_{h_{\delta_e}} / C_{m_{\delta_e}}) (S.M._{free}) \{1 - (U/U_{trim})^2$$

2. For the stick-force-speed-gradient at the trimspeed:

$$(\partial F_s / \partial U)_{trim} = -(2/U_{trim}) x \tag{3.2}$$

$$x \eta_h G S_e \bar{c}_e (W/S) (C_{h_{\delta_e}} / C_{m_{\delta_e}}) (S.M._{free})$$

where: $S.M._{free}$ is the stick-free static margin of the airplane. This quantity may be found from the following approximation:

$$S.M._{free} = \bar{x}_{ac_A} - \bar{x}_{cg} + \tag{3.3}$$

$$+ (C_{m_{\delta_e}} / C_{L_\alpha}) (C_{h_\alpha} / C_{h_{\delta_e}}) (1 - d\varepsilon/d\alpha)$$

with: $\bar{x}_{ac_A}$ the airplane aerodynamic center as found from Part VI, Sub-section 8.2.5.2

$\bar{x}_{cg}$ the airplane c.g. location in fractions of the wing m.g.c.

All other quantities have been previously defined.

<u>NOTE 1:</u> As long as the hingemoment derivative $C_{h_{\delta_e}}$ has the normal (negative) sign, the stick-force as found from Equation (3.1) and the stick-force-speed-gradient as found from Equation (3.2) have the correct sign, provided the airplane has a POSITIVE STATIC MARGIN!

<u>NOTE 2:</u> The reader should modify these equations if the flight control system of his airplane is different

than the one assumed here. For guidance on how to do this the reader should consult Chapter 5 of Reference 12.

3.1.4 Step-by-Step Procedure for Analyzing Static Longitudinal Stability

Step 1: Determine which regulations apply to the design: see Table 3.1 and Subsection 3.1.1.

Step 2: The regulations define the flight conditions and the airplane configurations for which the stability requirements must be met. Tabulate these flight conditions and these configurations.

Step 3: For the flight conditions and for the airplane configurations of Step 2 determine the Mach number, the dynamic pressure and the center of gravity locations.

Step 4: For the flight conditions and for the airplane configurations of Steps 2 and 3 determine all derivatives and coefficients used in Equations (3.1) through (3.3).

Step 5: Calculate the stick-force-speed gradient from Eqn.(3.2) and check its value against that allowed in the applicable regulation. If the required gradient is not achieved, determine which parameters need to be adjusted. Note: in many cases a satisfactory gradient can be achieved only by moving the aft allowable center of gravity forward! This has obvious implications to the utility of the airplane!

Step 6: Document the results obtained, including any design changes made.

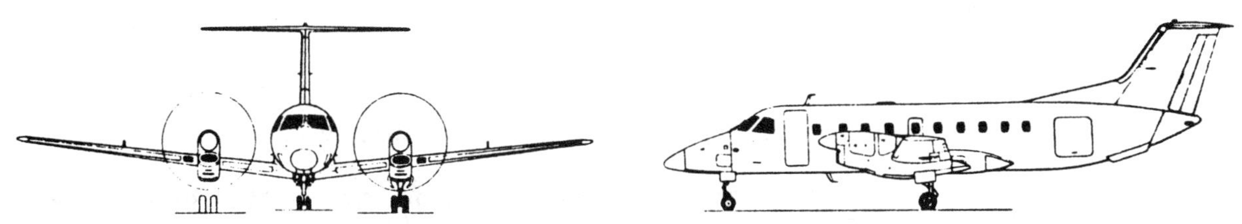

3.2 STATIC LATERAL AND DIRECTIONAL STABILITY

3.2.1 Applicable Regulations

Civil: FAR 23.171 and FAR 23.177, see Appendix A.

FAR 25.171 and FAR 25.177, see Appendix A.

Military: Mil-F-8785C, Sub-section 3.3.6, see Appendix B.

3.2.2 Relationship to Preliminary Design

See Part II, Chapter 11.

3.2.3 Mathematical Model for Analyzing Static Lateral and Directional Stability

The regulations essentially require that the airplane must possess the following characteristics:

1.) When the airplane is put in a sideslip (skid) condition it shall have the tendency to return to the original (zero sideslip) condition.

2.) The rudder pedal force required to put the airplane in a sideslip condition shall be such that the pedal-force-gradient is does not reverse its sign.

3.) When the airplane is put in a positive sideslip (skid), it must have the tendency to raise the right wing.

Figure 3.2 illustrates these concepts. The conditions for which these requirements are satisfied are now presented.

1.) This condition is referred to as the condition for positive directional stability:

a) For irreversible control systems:

$$C_{n_\beta} > 0 \qquad (3.4)$$

The directional stability derivative, C_{n_β} may be computed with the method of Section 10.2.4 of Part VI. From those methods it will be clear that directional stability strongly de-

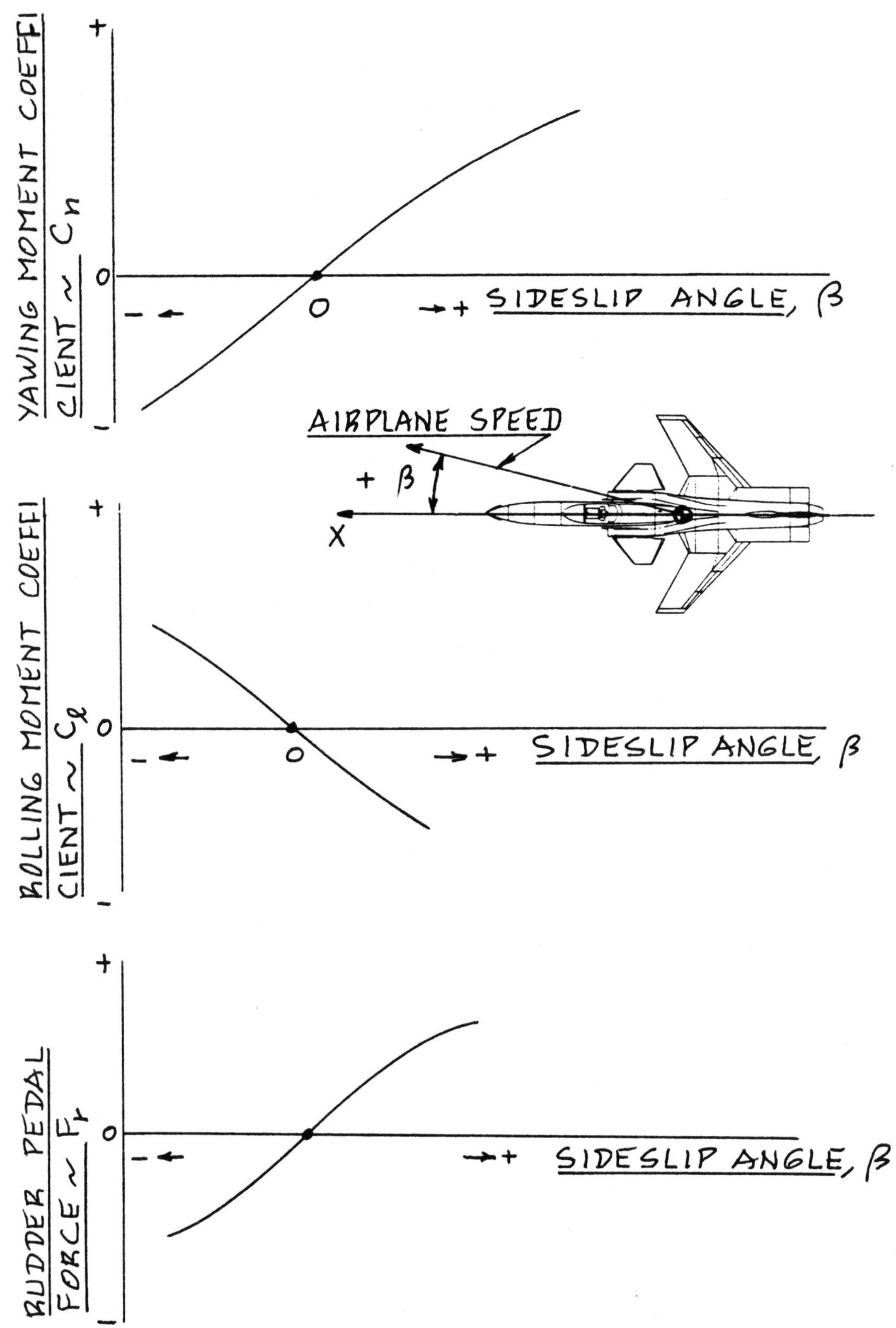

Figure 3.2 Requirements for Lateral and Directional Static Stability

pends on the size and shape of the fuselage and on the size, shape and location of the vertical tail.

b) For reversible control systems:

$$C_{n_{\beta_{free}}} = C_{n_{\beta_{fixed}}} + \\ + C_{n_{\delta_r}}(C_{h_{\beta_v}}/C_{h_{\delta_r}}) \tag{3.5}$$

where: $C_{n_{\beta_{fixed}}} = C_{n_\beta}$ of Eqn.(3.4)

$C_{n_{\delta_r}}$ is the rudder control power derivative. It may be computed with the method of Section 10.3.8 of Part VI.

$C_{h_{\beta_v}}$ is the rudder hingemoment derivative due to sideslip. It is physically equivalent to the elevator hingemoment derivative due to elevator deflection, $C_{h_{\delta_e}}$ and may be computed with the help of Sect.10.4 of Pt VI.

$C_{h_{\delta_r}}$ is the rudder hingemoment derivative due to rudder deflection. It is physically equivalent to the elevator hingemoment derivative due to elevator deflection, $C_{h_{\delta_e}}$ and may be computed with the method of Section 10.4 of Pt VI.

2.) This condition is satisfied if:

$$\partial F_r/\partial\beta > 0 \tag{3.6}$$

It is shown in Chapter 5 of reference 12 that this in turn is satisfied if:

$$C_{n_{\beta_{free}}} > 0 \tag{3.7}$$

Note therefore that for this type of airplane the detail design of the flight control system becomes (again) important!

3.) This condition is satisfied as long as:

$$C_{l_\beta} < 0 \qquad (3.8)$$

The lateral stability derivative, C_{l_β} may be determined with the method of Section 10.2.4 of Part VI. The method makes it clear that this derivative depends mainly on three factors:

a) wing geometric dihedral angle
b) wing position on the fuselage (high or low)
c) wing sweep angle and lift coefficient

3.2.4 Step-by-Step Procedure for Analyzing Static Lateral and Directional Stability

Step 1: Determine which regulations apply to the design: see Table 1.3 and Subsection 3.2.1.

Step 2: The regulations define the flight conditions and the airplane configurations for which the static lateral-directional stability requirements must be satisfied. Tabulate these flight conditions and these configurations.

Step 3: For the flight conditions and for the airplane configurations of Step 2 determine the Mach number, the dynamic pressure and the center of gravity locations.

Step 4: For the conditions and configurations of Steps 2 and 3 determine the derivatives used in Equations (3.4) through (3.8).

Step 5: Using Equations (3.4) through (3.8) determine whether or not these stability conditions are satisfied. If not, determine how the design must be modified to meet the requirements.

NOTE: It may very well be that the airplane needs a larger vertical tail or that the geometric dihedral angle of the wing will have to be changed to meet the regulations.

Step 6: Document the results obtained, including any design changes made.

3.3 DYNAMIC LONGITUDINAL STABILITY

3.3.1 Applicable Regulations

Civil: FAR 23.181 and FAR 25.181, see Appendix A.

Military: Mil-F-8785C, Par.3.2.2, see Appendix B.

3.3.2 Relationship to Preliminary Design

See Part II, Step 24 in Chapter 2. Also, read Chapter 11 in Part II.

3.3.3 Mathematical Model for Analyzing Dynamic Longitudinal Stability

The civil regulations in Appendix A are vague about specific requirements for frequency and damping characteristics. For that reason the military regulations of Appendix B are used to check whether or not a civil airplane design meets the intent of the civil regulations.

The civil and military requirements for dynamic stability must be met with the cockpit controls held fixed as well as with the cockpit controls kept free. The analysis of dynamic stability with the controls held free is beyond the scope of preliminary design since it requires detailed design data on the flight control system. For that reason, only the 'controls fixed' case is considered here. An analytical approach to the analysis of dynamic stability with controls free is given in Reference 12.

The military regulations (Appendix B) specify ranges of acceptable values for the following dynamic stability parameters of the airplane phugoid (P) and short-period (SP) modes of perturbed motion:

1. Undamped natural frequency: $\omega_{n_{SP}}$

2. Damping ratio: ξ_P and ξ_{SP}

Because phugoid frequency is primarily determined by airplane speed, there is no requirement for it.

The required numerical magnitudes for frequency and damping behavior of airplanes depends on:

1. Airplane Type: this is recognized by classifying airplanes in four classes:

   Class I, II, III or IV: see Appendix B.

2. Flight Phase: this is recognized by classifying flight conditions into three flight phases:

Phase: A, B, and C: see Appendix B.

The following characterization is typical of the modal breakdown for most airplanes in most flight conditions:

Mode	Undamped Natural Frequency	Damping Ratio	Most Important Motion Variables
Phugoid	Low	Low	Speed and Pitch Attitude Angle
Short Period	High	Moderately High	Angle of Attack, Pitch Attitude Angle

The damping characteristics of the phugoid mode of motion primarily affects the pilot's ability to control airspeed with the longitudinal controls. The phugoid damping ratio must not be too low.

The frequency and damping characteristics of the short period mode of motion primarily affects the pilot's ability to control pitch attitude angle. The short period frequency must not be too low, nor too high. The short period damping ratio must not be too low.

The phugoid and short period frequencies and damping ratios can be found from a solution of the three-degree-of-freedom, small perturbation equations of motion of an airplane. General methods (so-called Class III methods) for solving such equations are presented in Chapter 6 of Reference 12. In preliminary design it is acceptable to employ approximations for the phugoid and for the short-period behavior of an airplane. The Class II methods to be presented next are based on such approximate methods. The justification for these Class II methods is also discussed in Chapter 6 of Reference 12.

3.3.3.1 Class II method for analysis of phugoid characteristics

The following Class II method is suggested for determining phugoid undamped natural frequency and damping ratio:

$$\omega_{n_P} = (1.414g/U_1) \qquad (3.9)$$

$$\xi_P = \{g/(2C_{L_1}U_1\omega_{n_P})\}(C_{D_u} + 2C_{D_1} - C_{T_{x_u}} - 2C_{T_{x_1}}) \qquad (3.10)$$

where: U_1 is the steady state speed for the flight condition for which the dynamic stability of the airplane is being analyzed.

ρ is the air density for the flight condition being analyzed.

C_{L_1} is the steady state lift coefficient in the flight condition being analyzed.

C_{D_u} and $C_{T_{x_u}}$ are the drag-due-to-speed and thrust-due-to-speed derivatives. These derivatives may be computed with the methods of Ch.10 of Part VI.

C_{D_1} and $C_{T_{x_1}}$ are the steady state drag and thrust coefficients. These may be computed with the methods of Ch.10 of Part VI.

Observe that the phugoid frequency depends only on airplane speed! The phugoid damping ratio depends on the steady state drag and thrust as well as on the variation of drag and thrust with speed (Mach number!). Also observe, that the phugoid damping ratio is inversely proportional to the airplane lift-to-drag ratio, C_{L_1}/C_{D_1}.

3.3.3.2 Class II method for analysis of short period characteristics

The following Class II method is suggested for determination of the short period undamped natural frequency and damping ratio:

$$\omega_{n_{SP}} = \{(Z_\alpha M_q/U_1) - M_\alpha\}^{1/2} \qquad (3.11)$$

$$\xi_{SP} = -\{M_q + (Z_\alpha/U_1) + M_{\dot{\alpha}}\}/2\omega_{n_{SP}} \qquad (3.12)$$

where: the dimensional derivatives: Z_α, M_α, $M_{\dot{\alpha}}$ and M_q

are all defined in the list of symbols. These derivatives are functions of several dimensional derivatives which can be determined with the methods of Chapter 10, Part VI.

U_1 is the steady state speed corresponding to the flight condition for which dynamic stability is being analyzed.

It turns out that for many airplanes, in many flight conditions, the combination $(Z_\alpha M_q/U_1)$ in Eqn.(3.11) is small compared to M_α. The significance of this is that the short period undamped natural frequency is determined mostly by the magnitude of the derivative M_α.

<u>IMPORTANT OBSERVATION ON EQN.(3.11):</u>

The derivative M_α depends directly on the center of gravity location of the airplane, because:

$$C_{m_\alpha} = C_{L_\alpha}(\bar{x}_{cg} - \bar{x}_{ac_A}) \tag{3.13}$$

<u>Therefore:</u> the short period undamped natural frequency of an airplane depends primarily on the distance between the center of gravity and the airplane aerodynamic center (stick-fixed neutral point!).

The reader is reminded of the fact that the c.g. location at any given airplane weight depends on the loading state of the airplane as reflected by the airplane weight-c.g. excursion diagram of Chapter 10 in Part II.

<u>IMPORTANT OBSERVATION ON EQN.(3.12):</u>

This equation predicts that the short period damping ratio of an airplane will always be positive! This is <u>NOT</u> correct. If this equation predicts the damping ratio to be less than 0.1, the reader is advised to use the Class III method of Chapter 6 of Reference 12.

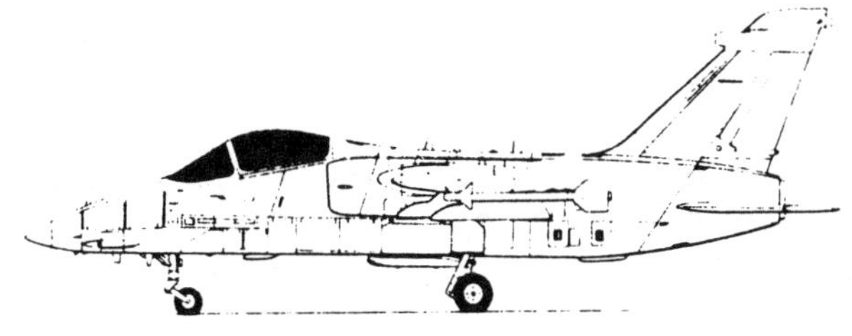

3.3.4 Step-by-Step Procedure for Analyzing Dynamic Longitudinal Stability

Step 1: Determine which regulations apply to the design: see Table 1.3 and Subsection 3.3.1.

Step 2: Determine from the description of airplane Classes in Appendix B which airplane Class (I, II, III or IV) best 'fits' the design.

Step 3: Determine for which flight conditions and for which airplane configurations the dynamic stability must be verified. Determine which flight phase category (A, B or C) is associated with each flight condition. The definition of flight phase categories is given in Appendix B.

Tabulate this information.

For inexperienced readers the following guidelines may be useful:

Flight conditions:

For purposes of preliminary design, the most critical flight conditions may be determined from the 'design' flight envelope. Figure 3.3 gives examples of 'design' flight envelopes for a civil and for a military airplane. The 'design' flight envelope normally follows from the airplane mission specification and from the Class II performance calculations which have been performed as part of Step 28 as described in Chapter 2 of Part II. Methods for Class II performance calculations are presented in Chapter 5.

Figure 3.3 shows the most critical flight conditions for which the dynamic stability should be verified at the early design stage.

Airplane configurations:

For purposes of preliminary design, the most critical airplane configurations occur at the most forward and at the most aft center of gravity locations. These c.g. locations follow from the weight-c.g. excursion diagram of Chapter 10 in Part II.

To decide on other critical configuration effects, the reader should check items 1-9 on page 7 and determine which of these effects apply to his design.

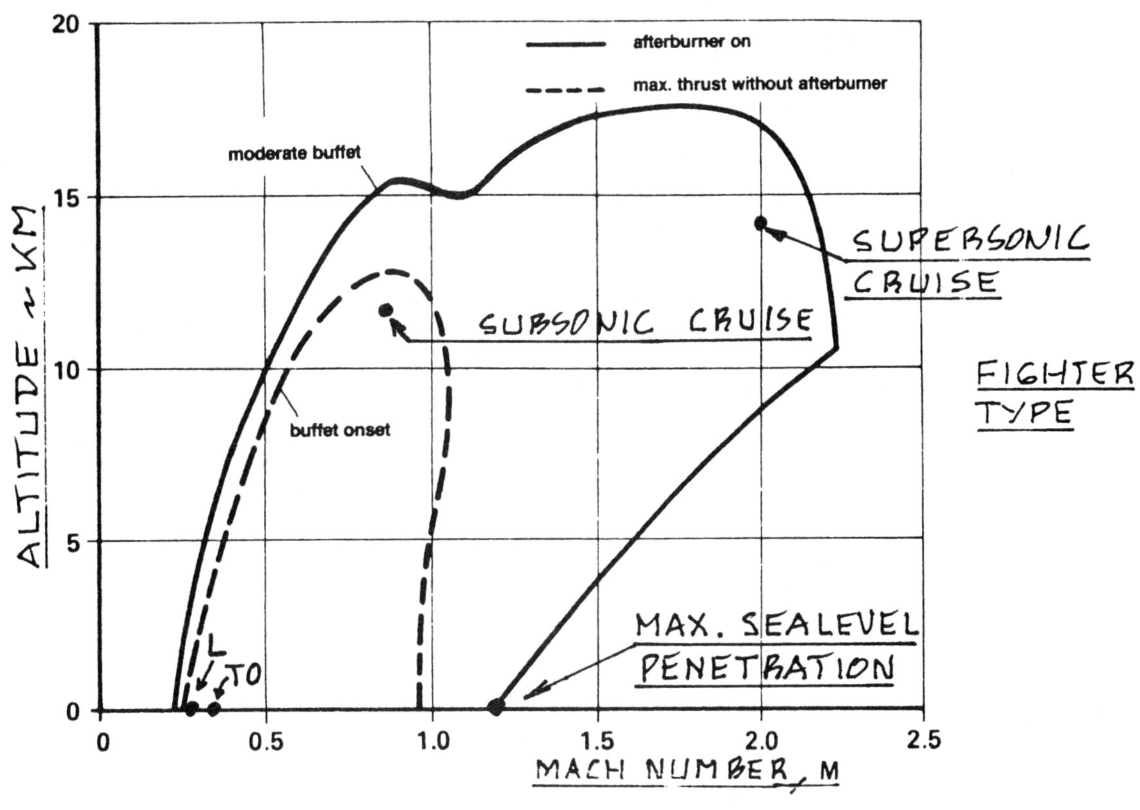

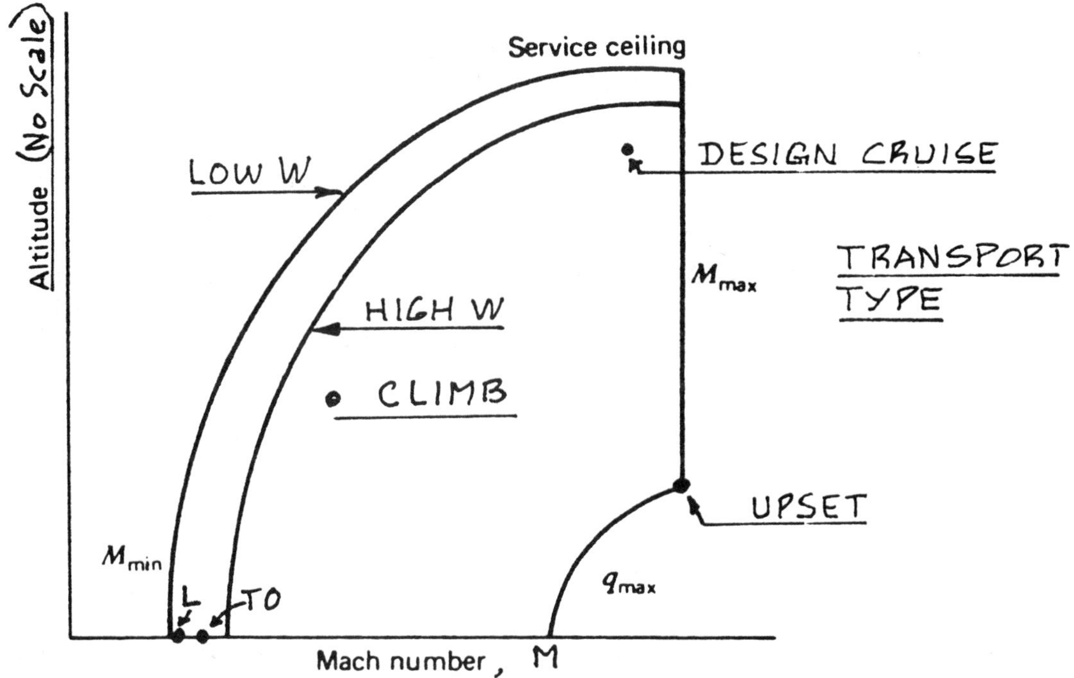

Figure 3.3 Examples of Civil Transport and Military Fighter Flight Envelopes with Indication of Flight Conditions Requiring Static and Dynamic Stability Calculations in Preliminary Design

Step 4: For the flight conditions and for the airplane configurations defined in Step 3, calculate the derivatives and other parameters which appear in Eqns (3.9) through (3.12).

Since the allowable short-period frequency ranges in Appendix B depend on the load-factor-to-angle-of-attack derivative n_{α}, also compute:

$$n_{\alpha} = \bar{q}SC_{L_{\alpha}}/W \tag{3.14}$$

These 'input' data should all be tabulated!

Step 5: Decide whether the airplane being designed is to be 'inherently stable' or 'de-facto' stable.

Definitions for these types of stability are given on page 65.

If the airplane is to be 'inherently stable' proceed to Step 6.

If the airplane is to be 'de-facto stable' proceed to Step 8.

The choice between 'inherent' and 'de-facto' stability is made by the designer and not by the regulations!

Step 6: Determine the phugoid damping ratios associated with the flight conditions and airplane configurations of Step 3. Use Eqn.(3.10).

Determine the LEVEL 1 phugoid damping ratio requirements from Paragraph 3.2.1.2, in Appendix B.

Decide whether or not the airplane meets the LEVEL 1 requirements. If not, determine from Eqn.(3.10) what (if any) design changes should be made to satisfy the LEVEL 1 requirements OR put the airplane in the 'de-facto' stable category and proceed to Step 8.

Note: in most cases it will be found to be impractical to modify airplane phugoid damping through airplane design changes. The reasons are that phugoid damping depends mostly on drag and on installed thrust characteristics. These in turn are normally dictated by performance considerations! Therefore, airplanes with deficient inherent phugoid damping are usually equipped with speed-to-thrust-feedback, speed-to-speedbrake feedback and/or with pitch-attitude-feedback. Chapter 13 of Reference 12 contains detailed discussions of such systems.

<u>Step 7:</u> Determine the short period frequencies and damping ratios associated with the flight conditions and airplane configurations of Step 3. Use Eqns.(3.11) and (3.12).

Determine the LEVEL 1 short period frequency and damping ratio requirements with the help of Figures B1 through B3 and Table IV in Appendix B. Compute n_α with Eqn.(3.14).

Decide whether or not the airplane meets the LEVEL 1 requirements. If not, use Eqns (3.11) and (3.12) to determine what design changes should be made to the airplane.

<u>Note 1:</u> By performing a derivative sensitivity analysis on Equations (3.11) and (3.12) the reader will find that the short period frequency is very sensitive to C_{m_α} (thus, according to Eqn.(3.13) to c.g. location!). It is also found that for a given short period frequency, the short period damping ratio is very sensitive to C_{m_q} (in other words to tail moment arm as shown in Section 10.2.7 of Part VI!).

<u>Note 2:</u> From a practical viewpoint, the only derivative over which the designer has much influence at this stage of the design is C_{m_α}. Eqn.(3.13) shows that this derivative may be altered by changes in the center of gravity location. The designer may therefore wish to 'taylor' the c.g. range of the airplane such as to bring the short period frequency range 'in line' with the requirements. Such c.g. range 'tailoring' will result in modification of the weight and balance of the airplane as discussed in Chapter 10 of Part II.

Another option is to put the airplane in the 'de-facto stable' category and proceed to Step 9.

Step 8: Carry out the instructions in the first two paragraphs of Step 6: the result is the inherent phugoid damping ratio, ξ_P. Note from

Appendix B, Par.3.2.1.2 that the Level 1, minimum required phugoid damping ratio is: $\xi_P = 0.04$. If the inherent phugoid damping

ratio is insufficient, augmentation can be accomplished with speedbrake or throttle (i.e. thrust) feedback to speed. The required feedback gains can be found as follows:

1. For speed feedback to a speedbrake:

Compute the required increment in the speed-damping derivative, C_{D_u} from:

$$\Delta C_{D_u} = \{(0.08 C_{L_1} U_1 \omega_{n_P})/g\} - C_{D_u} - 2C_{D_1} + $$

$$+ C_{T_{x_u}} + 2C_{T_{x_1}} \tag{3.15}$$

Compute the speedbrake feedback gain from:

$$k_{u/\delta_{sb}} = \Delta C_{D_u} / (U_1 C_{D_{\delta_{sb}}}) \tag{3.16}$$

The magnitude of this gain should not exceed a value of 150 degrees of speedbrake deflection per unit of u/U_1.

The drag-due-to-speedbrake derivative $C_{D_{\delta_{sb}}}$

may be computed using the 'spoiler drag' method of Sub-section 4.12.1 in Part VI.

For speed feedback to throttle:

Compute the required increment in $C_{T_{x_u}}$ from:

$$\Delta C_{T_{x_u}} = - \{(0.08 C_{L_1} U_1 \omega_{n_P})/g\} - C_{D_u} - 2C_{D_1} + $$

$$+ C_{T_{x_u}} + 2C_{T_{x_1}} \tag{3.17}$$

Compute the throttle feedback gain from:

$$k_{u/\delta_T} = \Delta C_{T_{x_u}} / (U_1 C_{T_{\delta_T}}) \qquad (3.18)$$

The magnitude of this feedback gain should not exceed a value which corresponds to more than 15 percent increase in thrust for a sheargust of 25 fps.

The thrust-coefficient-due-to-throttle derivative, $C_{T_{\delta_T}}$ follows from taking the slope of thrust coefficient versus throttle position of the engine, remembering that:

$$C_T = T/\bar{q}S \qquad (3.19)$$

where: T is the installed thrust of the engine. It may be found with the method of Chapter 6 in Part VI.

For more detailed methods of synthesizing speed-damping feedback systems, refer to Chapter 13 of Reference 12.

Step 9: For the appropriate flight conditions and for the airplane configurations of Step 2 AND for the n_α values of Step 3, find the allowable short period frequency values from Figures B.1 through B.3 in Appendix B.

Decide which frequency levels the airplane should have for each flight condition. Such a frequency level is called: $\omega_{n_{SP_{de\text{-}facto}}}$.

Compute the 'de-facto' level of static stability at which the airplane should operate from:

$$(C_{m_\alpha})_{de\text{-}facto} = \qquad (3.20)$$

$$\{(Z_\alpha M_q/U_1) - (\omega_{n_{SP_{de\text{-}facto}}})^2\}(I_{yy}/\bar{q}S\bar{c})$$

Find the angle-of-attack feedback gain, k_α from:

$$k_{\alpha} = \{(C_{m_{\alpha}})_{\text{de-facto}} - C_{m_{\alpha}}\}/C_{m_{\delta_e}} \qquad (3.21)$$

where: $C_{m_{\alpha}}$ is the inherent value of the static longitudinal stability derivative of the airplane. This value will normally be positive (unstable) for a 'de-facto' stable airplane!

The value for k_{α} should not be larger than 5 degrees of elevator deflection per degree of angle of attack. If k_{α} does not satisfy this condition, the longitudinal control power level, $C_{m_{\delta_e}}$ must be increased until it does.

<u>Note:</u> if the feedback is around the stabilizer instead of around the elevator, replace the elevator derivative by the stabilizer derivative in Equation (3.16).

<u>Step 10:</u> For the appropriate flight conditions and for the airplane configurations of Step 3, find the minimum allowable damping ratios at which the airplane should operate by using Table IV in Appendix B. This damping ratio level is called: $\xi_{SP_{\text{de-facto}}}$.

Compute the 'de-facto' level of C_{m_q} at which the airplane should operate from:

$$C_{m_{q_{\text{de-facto}}}} = \{-(2\omega_{n_{SP_{\text{de-facto}}}} \xi_{SP_{\text{de-facto}}}) + - (Z_{\alpha}/U_1) - M_{\alpha}\}(2I_{yy}U_1)/(\bar{q}S\bar{c}^2) \qquad (3.22)$$

Compute the pitchrate feedback gain from:

$$k_q = \{(C_{m_{q_{\text{de-facto}}}} - C_{m_q})(\bar{c}/2U_1)\}/C_{m_{\delta_e}} \qquad (3.23)$$

The magnitude of this gain should not exceed 2 deg/deg/sec. If it does, the airplane needs more control power.

<u>Step 11:</u> Document the results obtained, including any design changes made.

3.4 DYNAMIC LATERAL-DIRECTIONAL STABILITY

3.4.1 Applicable Regulations

Civil: FAR 23.181 and FAR 25.181, see Appendix A.

Military: Mil-F-8785C, Par.3.3.1, see Appendix B.

3.4.2 Relationship to Preliminary Design

See Part II, Step 24 in Chapter 2.

3.4.3 Mathematical Model for Analyzing Lateral-Directional Dynamic Stability

Because the civil regulations in Appendix A are vague about specific requirements of frequency, damping and time-constant characteristics it is customary to use the military regulations of Appendix B to verify whether or not a new civil airplane design meets the intent of the regulations.

The civil and military requirements for dynamic stability must be met with the cockpit controls held fixed as well as with the cockpit controls kept free. The analysis of dynamic stability with the controls held free is beyond the scope of preliminary design since it requires detailed design data on the flight control system. For that reason, only the 'controls fixed' case is considered here. An analytical approach to the analysis of dynamic stability with controls free is given in Reference 12.

The military regulations (Apppendix B) specify ranges of acceptable values for the following dynamic stability parameters:

For the spiral mode: minimum allowable time-to-double the amplitude, T_{2_S}

For the dutch roll mode: minimum allowable undamped natural frequency, ω_{n_D}

minimum allowable damping ratio, ξ_D

minimum allowable real root part value: $\omega_{n_D}\xi_D$

For the roll mode: see Section 2.7.

The following characterization is typical of the

modal breakdown for most airplanes in most flight conditions:

Mode	Undamped Natural Frequency	Damping Ratio	Time Constant	Most Important Motion Variables
Spiral	N.A.	N.A.	Large, Unstable	Heading and bank angles
Dutch Roll	Moderately High	Low	N.A.	Sideslip and bank angles
Roll	N.A.	N.A.	Small	Bank angle

Note: Roll mode requirements are discussed in Section 2.7

The spiral behavior primarily affects the pilot's ability to maintain wings level flight, particularly when in IFR conditions.

The dutch roll behavior tends to make passengers sick if it is undamped. If the dutch roll mode has a high degree of bank angle participation, it can interfere with a pilot's ability to carry out rapid rolling maneuvers and/or bank angle tracking maneuvers.

The spiral and dutch roll mode behavior can be obtained from a solution of the three-degree-of-freedom, small perturbation equations of motion of an airplane. General methods (so-called Class III methods) for solving such equations are given in Chapter 6 of Reference 12. In preliminary design it is acceptable to employ approximations for the spiral and for the dutch roll behavior of an airplane. The Class II methods to be presented in Subsections 3.4.3.1 and 3.4.3.2 are based on such approximate methods. The justification for these Class II methods is also discussed in Chapter 6 of Reference 12.

3.4.3.1 Class II method for analysis of the spiral characteristics

There is no requirement for a stable spiral root. In fact, too much spiral stability is considered undesirable in most airplanes. An acceptable Class II condition for spiral stability is:

$$L_{\beta}N_{r} - N_{\beta}L_{r} > 0 \qquad (3.24)$$

If this spiral stability condition is violated (as

is often the case), an acceptable Class II method for predicting the time-to-double the amplitude in the spiral mode is:

$$T_{2_S} = (L_\beta \ln 2)/(N_\beta L_r - L_\beta N_r) \qquad (3.25)$$

All dimensional stability derivatives in Equations (3.24) and (3.25) are defined in the list of symbols. The corresponding dimensionless derivatives may be computed with the methods of Chapter 10 in Part VI.

3.4.3.2 Class II method for analysis of the dutch roll characteristics

The following Class II method is suggested for the calculation of the dutch roll undamped natural frequency and damping ratio:

$$\omega_{n_D} = [\{Y_\beta N_r + N_\beta(U_1 - Y_r)\}/U_1]^{1/2} \qquad (3.26)$$

$$\xi_D = -\{N_r + (Y_\beta/U_1)\}/2\omega_{n_D} \qquad (3.27)$$

All dimensional stability derivatives in Equations (3.26) and (3.27) are defined in the list of symbols. The corresponding dimensionless derivatives may be computed with the methods of Chapter 10, Part VI.

IMPORTANT OBSERVATION ON EQUATION (3.27):

This equation predicts that the dutch roll damping ratio will always be positive. This is NOT correct! The problem is that this dutch roll approximation ignores the effects of the derivatives C_{l_β}, C_{l_p} and C_{n_p}.

If this equation predicts the damping ratio to be less than 0.05, it is suggested that the reader use the Class III method of Chapter 6, Reference 12 to predict the actual dutch roll damping ratio.

3.4.4 Step-by-Step Procedure for Analyzing Dynamic Lateral-Directional Stability

Step 1: Determine which regulations apply to the design: see Table 1.3 and Subsection 3.4.1.

Step 2: Determine from the description of airplane Classes in Appendix B which airplane Class (I, II, III or IV) best 'fits' the design.

Step 3: Determine for which flight conditions and for which airplane configurations the dynamic stability must be verified. Determine which flight phase category (A, B or C) is associated with each flight condition. The definition of flight phase categories is given in Appendix B.

Tabulate this information.

NOTE: Be sure to read the guidelines stated under Step 3 in Subsection 3.3.4 (pages 80-81)!

Step 4: For the flight conditions and for the airplane configurations defined in Step 3, calculate the derivatives and other parameters which appear in Eqns. (3.24) through (3.27).

Step 5: Decide whether the airplane is to be 'inherently' stable or 'de-facto' stable.

Definitions for these types of stability are given on pages 65-67.

If the airplane is to be 'inherently stable' proceed to Step 6.

If the airplane is to be 'de-facto' stable, proceed to Step 8.

The choice between 'inherent' and 'de-facto' stability is made by the designer and not by the regulations!

Step 6: Determine whether or not the airplane is spirally stable with the help of Eqn.(3.24).

Case 1: Stable spiral

If the airplane is found to be spirally stable, it may in fact be too spirally stable!

Since specific levels of spiral stability are not required by the regulations, the designer should check how much of a change in the derivative L_{β} (i.e. $C_{l_{\beta}}$) is needed to obtain neutral spiral stability. The required change in L_{β} can normally be achieved through a change in the wing geometric dihedral angle. The required change in the wing geometric dihedral angle can be obtained with Eqn.(10.34) on p.392 of Part VI. Recalculate L_{β} as required!

Case 2: Unstable spiral

If the airplane is found to be unstable in the spiral mode, use Eqn.(3.25) to find the spiral 'time-to-double' the amplitude.

From the regulations determine whether or not the Level 1 requirements are met. If not, use Eqn.(3.25) to determine that value of L_{β} (and $C_{l_{\beta}}$) for which the Level 1 requirement is met. Use Eqn.(10.34) on p.392 of Part VI to determine the change in wing geometric dihedral angle needed to get the required Level 1 value of T_{2_S}. Recalculate L_{β} as required!

IMPORTANT NOTE: When it is decided to change the wing geometric dihedral angle, make sure that the lateral landing gear clearance criterion of Figure 9.1b, page 221 of Part II is not violated!

Step 7: Use Equations (3.26) and (3.27) to find the dutch roll characteristics of the airplane.

From the regulations determine whether or not Level 1 requirements are met. If not, use Eqns.(3.26) and (3.27) to find 'compatible' values for N_r and N_{β} so that the Level 1 requirements are met.

NOTE 1: The reader will usually find that the undamped natural frequency of Eqn.(3.26) is 'driven' by N_{β}, while the damping ratio of Eqn. (3.27) is 'driven' by N_r.

NOTE 2: from Part VI, Equations (10.43) and (10.88) the reader will be able to verify that N_r and N_β BOTH depend on:

1. Vertical tail size
2. Vertical tail moment arm
3. Vertical tail lift-curve-slope and therefore on vertical tail planform geometry

'Compatible' values for N_r and N_β are required because of these relationships.

Make the necessary changes in the design and check that the spiral condition has not been significantly affected. If it has, an iteration between Steps 6 and 7 will be needed.

Step 8: Using Equations (3.25) - (3.27) determine the spiral and dutch roll characteristics of the airplane. Check these characteristics against the requirements of Appendix B, Tables VI and VIII and determine the level of handling qualities for the airplane.

It will now be necessary to determine what type of feedback is required to 'augment' the airplane such that it meets the Level 1 requirements. When it does, it is referred to as a 'de-facto' stable airplane. The following requirements for feedback may arise:

1) sideslip angle feedback: this changes C_{y_β}, C_{l_β} and C_{n_β}

2) yawrate feedback: this changes C_{y_r}, C_{l_r} and C_{n_r}

3) rollrate feedback: this changes C_{y_p}, C_{l_p} and C_{n_p}

The usual procedure is:

Step 8.1: Find those values of N_r, N_β and L_β

which meet Level 1 requirements for the dutch roll and spiral characteristics as expressed by Equations (3.25) - (3.27).

NOTES: 1) Use Eqn.(3.26) to find the value of N_β which meets Level 1 frequency requirement

2) Use Eqn.(3.27) to find the value of N_r which

meets Level 1 damping requirements: using the 'new' frequency value!

3) Use Eqn.(3.25) to find the value of L_β which

meets Level 1 time-to-double-spiral-amplitude.

Step 8.2: By subtraction, determine the 'increment', (Δ = de-facto - inherent) in each derivative which must be generated by the feedback system.

Step 8.3: Estimate the feedback gains and judge them by an acceptability criterion.

The feedback gains may be estimated from:

$$k_{\beta/\delta_r} = (C_{n_{\beta_{de\text{-}facto}}} - C_{n_{\beta_{inherent}}})/C_{n_{\delta_r}} \tag{3.28}$$

$$k_{r/\delta_r} = (C_{n_{r_{de\text{-}facto}}} - C_{n_{r_{inherent}}})b/(2U_1C_{n_{\delta_r}}) \tag{3.29}$$

$$k_{\beta/\delta_a} = (C_{l_{\beta_{de\text{-}facto}}} - C_{l_{\beta_{inherent}}})/C_{l_{\delta_a}} \tag{3.30}$$

Gains estimated from Eqns.(3.28) - (3.30) are judged acceptable in preliminary design if they satisfy the following inequalities:

$$(k_{\beta/\delta_r})\beta_{expected} < 0.3\delta_{r_{available}} \tag{3.31}$$

$$(k_{r/\delta_r})r_{expected} < 0.3\delta_{r_{available}} \tag{3.32}$$

$$(k_{\beta/\delta_a})\beta_{expected} < 0.3\delta_{a_{available}} \tag{3.33}$$

The 'expected values of the sideslip and yawrate perturbations in Equations (3.29) - (3.32) depend on the type of airplane being designed. The following guidelines are suggested:

Airplane Type	$\beta_{expected}$	$r_{expected}$
Transports	5 deg	10 deg/sec
Fighters	10 deg	20 deg/sec
Light airplanes	10 deg	20 deg/sec

The reader is referred to Chapter 6 of Reference 12 for the development of the theory behind these gain estimations.

If the gain acceptability criteria are violated, the airplane does not have sufficient control power to be augmented to Level 1 requirements. The designer should incorporate the necessary design changes to increase the appropriate control power levels. Control power equations in Section 10.3 of Part VI should be used to determine which design changes are feasible. In some cases it will be found necessary to introduce new control surfaces and/or to scrap the design and start from scratch!

Step 9: Document the results obtained, including any design changes made.

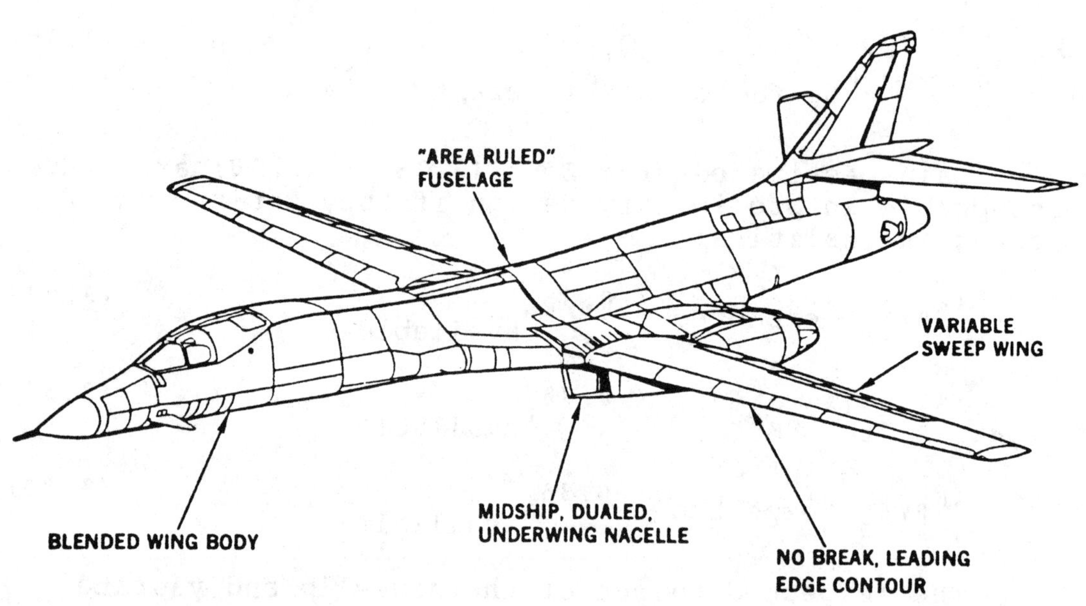

3.5 DYNAMIC COUPLING

3.5.1 Applicable Regulations

Civil: There are no specific regulations governing dynamic coupling phenomena. However, the FAR's can be interpreted as requiring that no dynamic coupling phenomena may exist which make normal piloting difficult.

Note: the only type of civil airplanes which conceivably might encounter dynamic coupling phenomena are aerobatic type airplanes.

Military: Mil-F-8785C, Par.3.4.3, see Appendix B

Notes: 1) Roll-rate coupling into pitch and yaw degrees of freedom occurs in fighter type airplanes during combat roll rate maneuvers.

2) Pitch-rate coupling into the lateral-directional degrees of freedom occurs in fighter type airplanes during rolling pull-up or during rolling push-over maneuvers.

3.5.2 Relationship to Preliminary Design

Dynamic coupling was not addressed in Part II.

3.5.3 Mathematical Model for Analyzing Dynamic Coupling

Two types of dynamic coupling phenomena will be addressed:

3.5.3.1 Roll-rate coupling

3.5.3.2 Pitch-rate coupling

3.5.3.1 Roll-rate coupling

As shown in Chapter 7 of Reference 12, when roll-rate coupling is divergent, violent excursions in angle of attack and/or in sideslip angle may occur during combat roll-rate maneuvers. These excursions can be so violent, that structural failure occurs.

A theoretical model for determining whether or not an airplane will experience roll-rate coupling induced instabilities is discussed in Chapter 7 of Reference 12. Based on this mathematical model the following condition for stability can be derived:

$$[\{(M_q N_r/M_\alpha) + D_1 + (N_\beta/M_\alpha)C_1\}^2 +$$

$$- 4C_1 D_1(N_\beta/M_\alpha)] < 0 \qquad (3.34)$$

where: all dimensional derivatives are defined in the list of symbols.

$$C_1 = (I_{xx} - I_{zz})/I_{yy} \qquad (3.35)$$

$$D_1 = (I_{yy} - I_{xx})/I_{zz} \qquad (3.36)$$

The moments of inertia in Eqns (3.35) and (3.36) must be determined in the airplane stability axes system!!

3.5.3.2 Pitch-rate coupling

No suitable Class II mathematical model is available for the analysis of pitch-rate coupling into the lateral-directional degrees of freedom. For a Class III method, the reader is referred to Chapter 7 of Reference 12.

3.5.4 Step-by-Step Procedure for Analyzing Roll-rate Coupling

Step 1: Read the applicable regulation, see 3.5.1.

Step 2: From the operational flight envelope of the airplane, determine the flight conditions and airplane configurations for which roll-rate coupling must be analyzed.

Note: flight conditions which are critical for roll coupling are usually those at moderate to high altitude.

Step 3: For the flight conditions and airplane configurations of Step 2 determine the dimensional derivatives which occur in Eqn.(3.34)

Note: for a highly augmented airplane, these derivatives must include the effect of the stability augmentation system.

Step 4: Using Eqn.(3.34) determine whether or not the airplane has roll-rate coupling instability. If not, proceed to Step 8, otherwise proceed to Step 5.

Step 5: Determine the minimum roll-rate for which roll-rate coupling instability instability occurs from the method of Chapter 7, Ref.12.

Step 6: Determine the maximum roll rate of which the airplane is capable from:

$$|p_{max}| = |-(L_{\delta_a} \delta_{a_{max}})/L_p| \qquad (3.37)$$

where: all dimensional stability derivatives are defined in the list of symbols.

If the airplane maximum roll rate from Eqn.(3.37) is less than that of Step 5, proceed to Step 8, if not, proceed to Step 7.

Step 7: Investigate with the help of Eqn.(3.34) what values the derivatives must have to assure that the airplane is stable against roll-rate coupling. These new values are the so-called 'augmented' (or 'de-facto') values which these derivatives must have to prevent roll coupling instability.

With the help of Equations (3.28) - (3.30), determine the required feedback gains.

Next, using the acceptability criteria as expressed by Eqns (3.31) - (3.33) determine whether or not sufficient control power is available in the airplane. If not, introduce the necessary design changes.

Step 8: Document the results obtained as well as any design changes made.

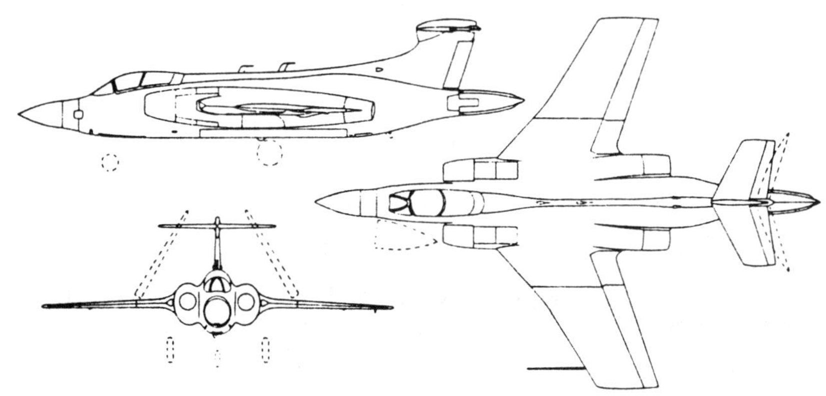

3.6 STALL CHARACTERISTICS

3.6.1 Applicable Regulations

Civil: **FAR 23.201, 23.203, 23.205 and 23.207, see Appendix A.**

FAR 25.201, 25.203, 25.205 and 25.207, see Appendix A.

Military: Mil-F-8785C, Par.3.4.2, see Appendix B

3.6.2 Relationship to Preliminary Design

See Step 6 in Preliminary Design Sequence I, p.12, Chapter 2 in Part II. Also see Chapter 7 in Part II and Subsection 5.1.4 in Part III.

3.6.3 Mathematical Model for Analyzing Stall Characteristics

Stall characteristics must be shown to satisfy the regulations for stalls starting from the following types of flight condition:

1. Wings level flight
2. Turning flight, including accelerated stalls
3. Engine-out stalls

The regulations essentially require that the airplane possess the following desirable tendencies when put in an approach to any of these stalls:

A. No sudden, uncontrollable pitch-up

B. Adequate roll control and no more wing drop than specified in the regulations

C. Adequate directional control

D. Adequate stall warning

E. Resistance to spin departure.

There are no closed form Class II methods for assuring satisfactory stall characteristics, with the exception of item E.

The following fundamental characteristics will normally lead to acceptable stall behavior relative to A-D.

1. Spanwise lift distributions which are conducive to wing root stall instead of to wing tip stall. Read the suggestions on wing design in Chapter 4 of Part III.

2. Wingtip mounted roll control devices when used to 25 percent of maximum available should not produce wing tip stall.

3. The location of the horizontal tail relative to the wing should satisfy the 'no-pitch-up' design criteria of Subsection 5.1.4 in Part III, or if not, the appropriate stick-shaker and stick pusher systems must be installed.

4. The rudder should not be blanked by a stalled wing wake emanating from the wing root or from any other sources of separated flow (such as from nacelles or from leading edge strakes). Read the suggestions on empennage design in Chapter 5 of Part III.

Methods for determining spanwise lift distributions are presented in References 14 and 15.

As for item E, an airplane has been found to be resistant to spin departure as long as its so-called $C_{n_{\beta_{dyn}}}$ is positive:

$$C_{n_{\beta_{dyn}}} = \{C_{n_{\beta_B}} + - (I_{zz_B}/I_{xx_B})C_{l_{\beta_B}}(\tan\alpha)\}\cos\alpha > 0 \qquad (3.38)$$

3.6.4 Step-by-Step Procedure for Analyzing Stall Characteristics

Step 1: Read the applicable regulations, see Table 1.3 and Section 3.6.1.

Step 2: From the regulations determine the flight conditions and airplane configurations for which satisfactory stall characteristics must be shown.

Step 3: For the flight conditions and airplane configurations of Step 2 determine the spanwise lift distribution for a range of angles of attack. Also determine the spanwise variation of section (= airfoil) maximum lift coefficient. Be sure to account for the effect of Reynold's Number!!

This is readily done with the method of Subsub-section 8.1.3.4 (pages 256-257), Pt VI.

1. The span location where tangency occurs between the two spanwise distributions is the span location where the wing will begin to stall. This span location must be close to the wing root for satisfactory stall characteristics.

   If stall occurs close to the tip, the wing design should be changed. Possible design changes are:

   a) addition of twist (or wash-out)
   b) change to airfoils capable of higher maximum lift coefficient values at the appropriate Reynold's Numbers.
   c) a variation of b) is to add leading edge droop to the outboard wing.

2. The angle of attack where tangency of item one first occurs is the value of WING angle of attack for which the stall will occur. Remember that the airplane angle of attack differs from the wing angle of attack by the wing incidence angle!

3. If the decision is made to 'live' with outboard wing stall, a stick-shaker and/ or a stick-pusher may have to be installed. In such an event, the value of lift coefficient corresponding to that at which the stick-pusher is triggered must be used as the effective value of wing maximum lift coefficient.

<u>Step 4:</u> Determine the airplane pitch-up characteristics with the guidelines of Subsection 5.1.4 of Part III. If a stick-pusher is required, see item 3.) under Step 3.

<u>Step 5:</u> Determine whether directional control at the stall is available by sketching in the location of the separated wing-root wake at the

tail location of the airplane: see Fig.5.13 in Part III.

Step 6: For the conditions of Step 2, compute the body axis directional and lateral stability derivatives as well as the moments of inertia in Eqn.(3.38) and verify whether the corresponding spin departure resistance criterion is met. If not, introduce the required design changes.

Note: these design changes can take the form of a larger or relocated vertical tail (or tails), a change in wing geometric dihedral and/or a change in mass distribution.

Step 7: Document the results obtained as well as any design changes made.

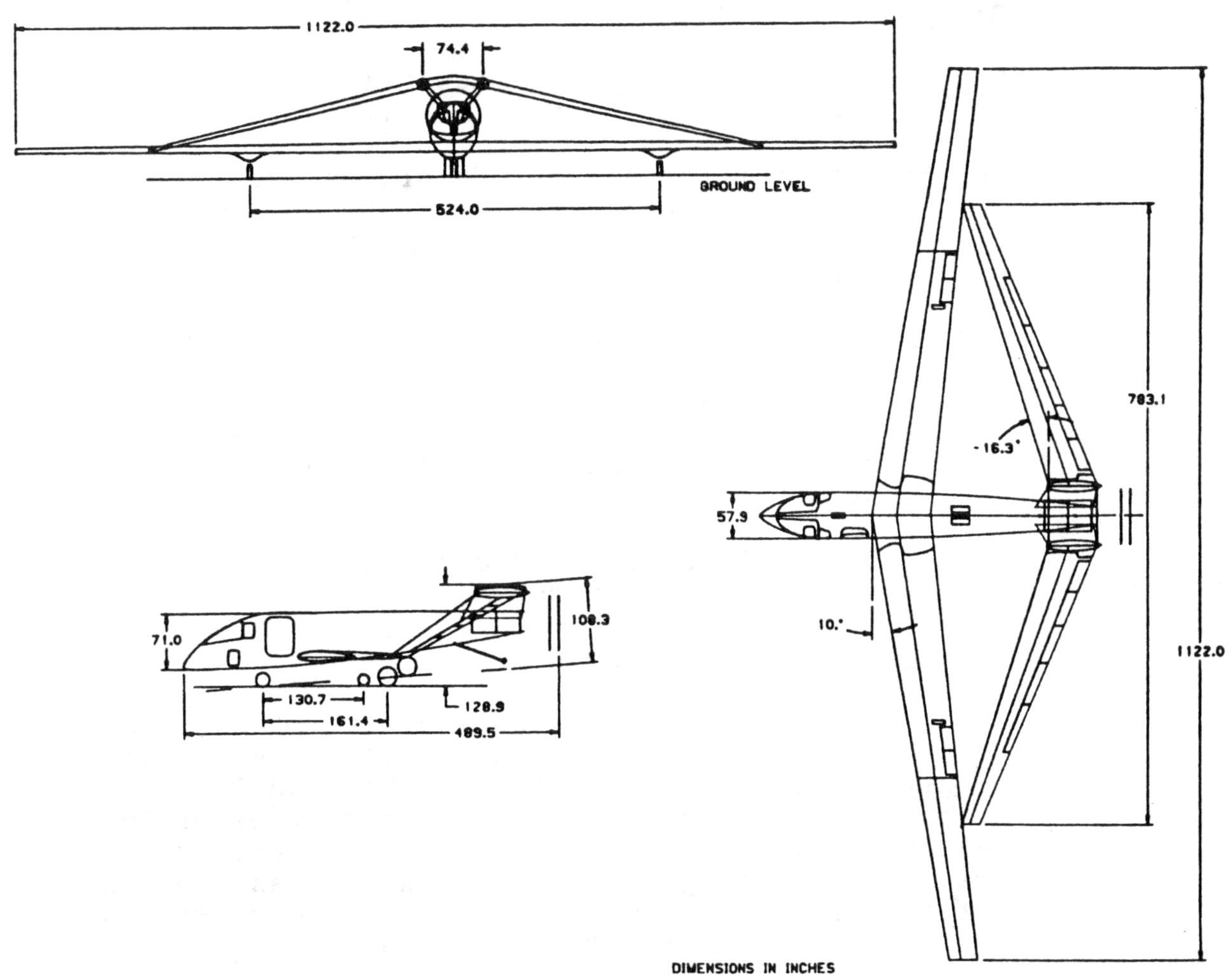

3.7 SPIN CHARACTERISTICS

3.7.1 Applicable Regulations

Civil: FAR 23.221, see Appendix A.

Military: Mil-F-8785C, Par.3.4.2.2, see Appendix B

3.7.2 Relationship to Preliminary Design

See Chapter 5 in Part III!

3.7.3 Mathematical Model for Analyzing Spin Characteristics

There is no suitable mathematical model for Class II design analysis purposes. A method for predicting aerodynamic forces and moments on a spinning airplane is given in Reference 16.

3.7.4 Step-by-Step Procedure for Analyzing Spin Characteristics

Step 1: Read the applicable regulations, see Table 1.3 and Section 3.7.1.

Step 2: From the regulations determine the flight conditions and airplane configurations for which satisfactory spin characteristics must be shown.

Step 3: Read the sections on aircraft spin and corresponding design guidelines in Stinton, Reference 17, pages 464 - 490. Check the design of the airplane in terms of the 'Stinton' approach and make design adjustments where required.

Step 4: Document the results obtained as well as any design changes made.

3.8 AEROELASTIC CONSIDERATIONS

All stability derivatives used in determining dynamic stability characteristics in this chapter are subject to aeroelastic effects. The method of Section 2.9 can be applied to all stability and control derivatives of Ch.3. Highly elastic airplanes, such as very large transport airplanes, are also subject to acceleration/mass induced aeroelastic effects. Acceleration/mass effects are discussed in detail in Chapter 8 of Reference 12.

4. RIDE AND COMFORT CHARACTERISTICS

The purpose of this chapter is to provide methods and guidelines for the analysis and selection of those design aspects which influence the ride and comfort characteristics of airplanes. These characteristics are important for the following reasons:

1. If ride and comfort are not acceptable to passengers, they are unlikely to return for another flight. This hurts the commercial viability of an airplane!

2. If ride and comfort are not acceptable to crewmembers, they may not be able to carry out their duties thus negatively affecting safety and/or mission effectiveness!

The following aspects of ride and comfort can be important, depending on such factors as time exposure and the requirement to perform duties:

1. Airplane response to atmospheric turbulence:

   High levels of vertical and lateral accelerations are uncomfortable to passengers and may make it difficult (sometimes impossible) for crew members to carry out their duties.

   Additional factors to be considered here are:

   a) distance to the center of gravity
   b) flexible (elastic) behavior of the structure

2. Cabin interior noise and temperature

3. Cabin (or cockpit) interior dimensions

4. Seat dimensions and seat comfort

References 18 through 23 should be consulted for detailed information (and further references) on the importance of these factors to ride and comfort.

<u>Neither</u> military <u>nor</u> civil regulations contain specific numerical design guidelines for the above factors. The design guidelines given in this chapter cover only turbulence induced accelerations as experienced by the crew and by the passengers. These design guidelines,

augmented with the use of 'common sense' and the use of 'standard' design practice in the other areas should suffice during the preliminary design evaluation of a new airplane.

The material in this chapter is organized as follows:

4.1 Relationship to preliminary design
4.2 Mathematical model for analyzing ride characteristics
4.3 Step-by-step procedure for analyzing ride characteristics

4.1 RELATIONSHIP TO PRELIMINARY DESIGN

Selection of wing loading (W/S), wing planform (A, Λ_{le}, λ), fuselage and cockpit interior dimensions and seating arrangement all affect the ride and comfort of passengers and crew members. Having said that, it is sobering to reflect on the following statements:

1. The airplane sizing process described in Part I results in a choice of wing-loading without even considering ride characteristics!

2. The decisions made in P.D. Sequence I, Steps 4 and 6 (Part II) came about without specific reference to comfort and ride!

As a result of the ride analysis and ride criteria presented in Section 4.2, the designer may wish to modify some of these early design decisions. <u>However</u>, the effect of such design changes on performance and/or on stability and control must be assessed!

For some airplane missions, flight through moderate to severe turbulence may be necessary. Examples are:

1. Low altitude attack missions
2. Pipeline spotting missions

In such cases, designing the basic airplane and its wing for reasonable ride quality levels at the crew station, turns out to be not feasible. In such cases it may become necessary to employ a so-called 'ride-control system'. The B-1 bomber has such a ride control system. A schematic of this type of system is shown in Figure 4.1.

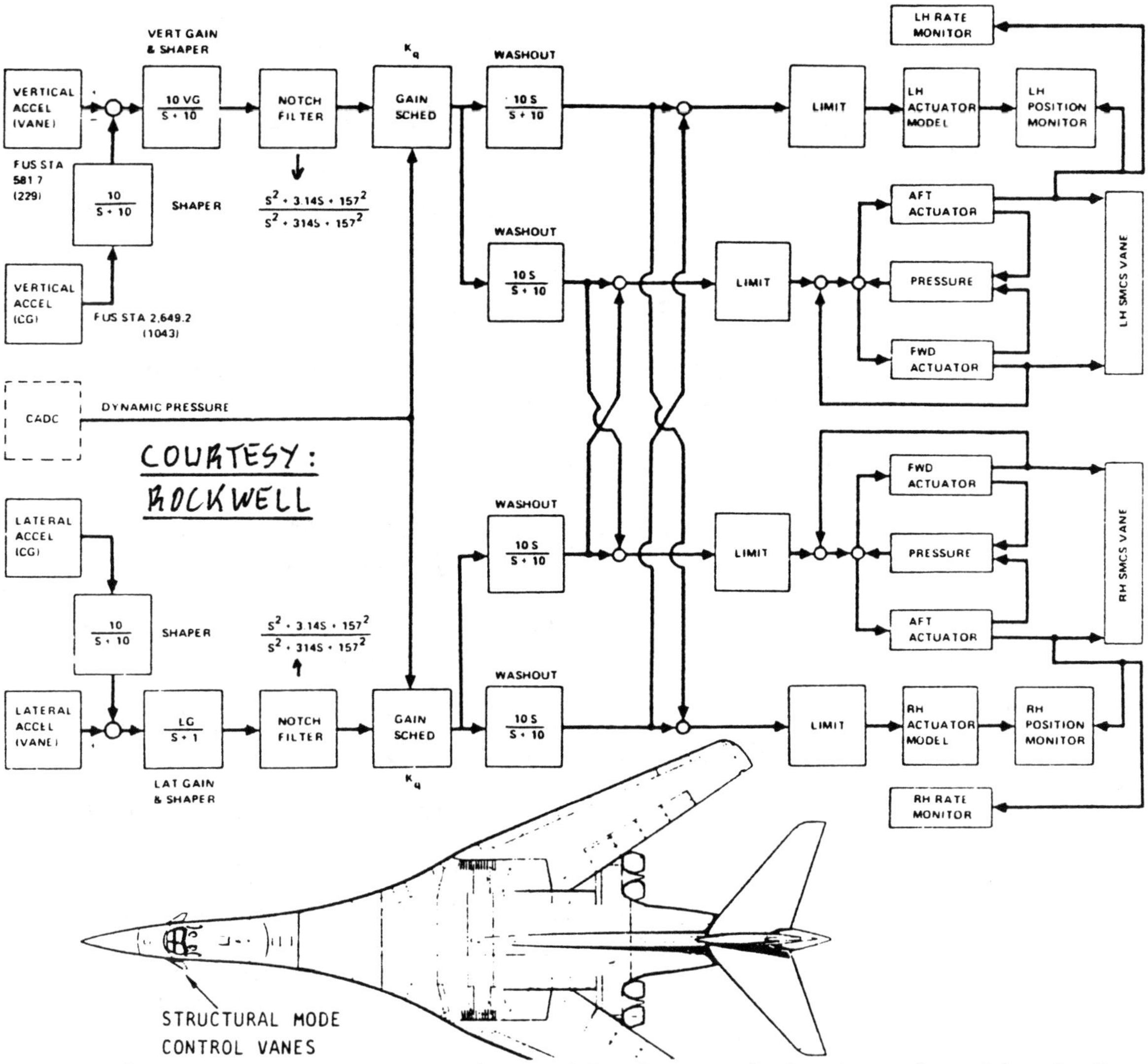

VERTICAL ACCEL (VANE)
VERT GAIN & SHAPER
10 VG / S + 10
NOTCH FILTER
K_q
GAIN SCHED
WASHOUT
10 S / S + 10
LIMIT
LH ACTUATOR MODEL
LH POSITION MONITOR
LH RATE MONITOR
FUS STA 581.7 (229)
10 / S + 10
SHAPER
$\frac{S^2 + 3.14S + 157^2}{S^2 + 314S + 157^2}$
VERTICAL ACCEL (CG)
FUS STA 2,649.2 (1043)
AFT ACTUATOR
PRESSURE
FWD ACTUATOR
LH SMCS VANE
CADC
DYNAMIC PRESSURE
COURTESY: ROCKWELL
LATERAL ACCEL (CG)
LATERAL ACCEL (VANE)
LG / S + 1
LAT GAIN & SHAPER
RH SMCS VANE
RH ACTUATOR MODEL
RH POSITION MONITOR
RH RATE MONITOR
STRUCTURAL MODE CONTROL VANES

Figure 4.1 Example of a Ride Control System for the B-1

100
80
60
40
20
0
PASSENGERS SATISFIED, PERCENT
FROM: REF.19
1
2
3
4
5
6
7
VERY COMFORTABLE
NEUTRAL
VERY UNCOMFORTABLE
RIDE COMFORT INDEX, C_{ride}

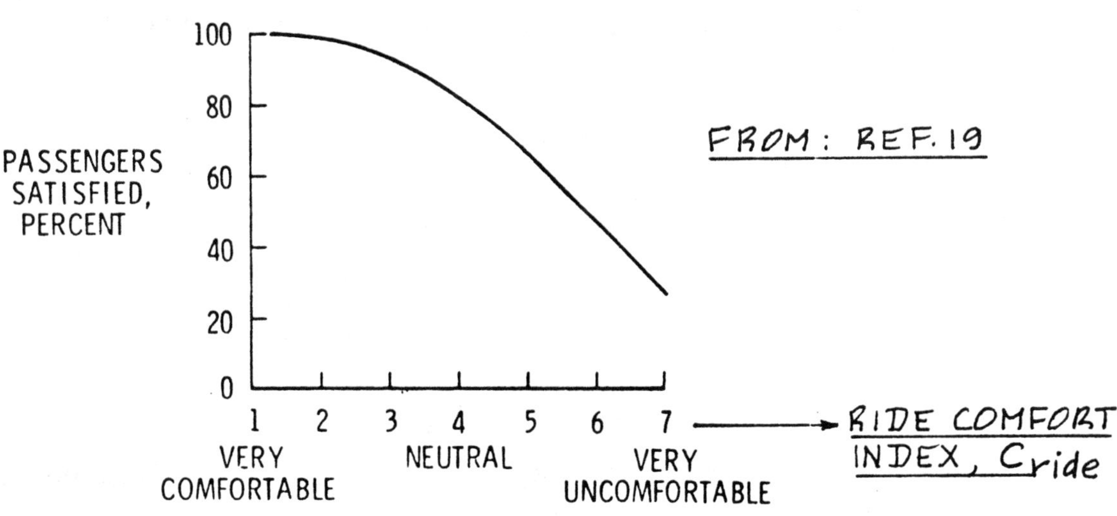

Figure 4.2 Effect of Ride Comfort Rating on Percentage of Passengers Satisfied with the Ride

4.2 MATHEMATICAL MODEL FOR ANALYZING RIDE AND COMFORT CHARACTERISTICS

Two ingredients are required for analyzing the ride characteristics of a new design:

1. A ride characteristic rating scale (metric)

2. A formula which relates vehicle design parameters to that metric.

Two models will be presented:

4.2.1 A model for the prediction of ride comfort from a passenger viewpoint (civil and military)

4.2.2 A model for the prediction of ride comfort from a crew station viewpoint (civil or military)

4.2.1 A Model for the Prediction of Ride Comfort from a Passenger Viewpoint (Civil or Military)

The following model was distilled from Reference 18.

The relative ride-comfort will be measured in terms of a ride comfort index, C_{ride} which is related to passenger satisfaction in Figure 4.2. In this section, only the effect of vertical and lateral accelerations on this ride comfort index will be accounted for.

The effect of airplane vertical and lateral accelerations (in response to atmospheric turbulence) on the ride comfort index, C_{ride} may be estimated from:

$$C_{ride} = 2 + 18.9a_{vert} + 12.1a_{lat} \qquad (4.1a)$$

which applies for $a_{vert} > 1.6a_{lat}$, and:

$$C_{ride} = 2 + 1.62a_{vert} + 38.9a_{lat} \qquad (4.1b)$$

which applies for $a_{vert} < 1.6a_{lat}$

where: the accelerations a_{vert} and a_{lat} are measured in

relative 'g'-level ('g'/fps of vertical or lateral rms gust). They are measured at the center of gravity of the airplane and can be found from:

$$a_{vert} = (0.5\rho U_1)(C_{L_\alpha})(\sigma_w)/(W/S) \quad (4.2)$$

and:

$$a_{lat} = (0.5\rho U_1)(C_{y_\beta})(\sigma_v)/(W/S) \quad (4.3)$$

where: the derivatives C_{L_α} and C_{y_β} are for the entire airplane (in 1/rad). Part VI contains methods for their estimation. For elastic airplanes, the method of Section 3.8 should be used.

σ_w and σ_v are the rms of gust (or turbulence) velocities induced by the atmosphere. Their values depend on altitude, terrain and probability of occurrence. Figure 4.3 can be used to determine these gust values.

4.2.2 A Model for the Prediction of Ride Comfort from a Crew Station Viewpoint (Civil or Military)

In preliminary design it is acceptable to use the following criterion for the acceptability of turbulence response at the crew station:

$$\bar{A} < 0.005 \quad (4.4)$$

where: $\bar{A}$ is the 'rms g-level' per fps gust input at the crew station. This gust (or turbulence) response may be computed from:

$$\bar{A} = (0.5\rho U_1 C_{L_\alpha})K_1 K_2/(W/S) \quad (4.5)$$

with: $K_1 = 0.66 + (0.39/\bar{c})l_{crew}$ (4.6)

where: $\bar{c}$ is the wing m.g.c. in ft

l_{crew} is the distance from the crew station to the leading edge of the wing m.g.c., in ft

C_{L_α} is the airplane liftcurve slope in 1/rad. Aeroelastic effects on

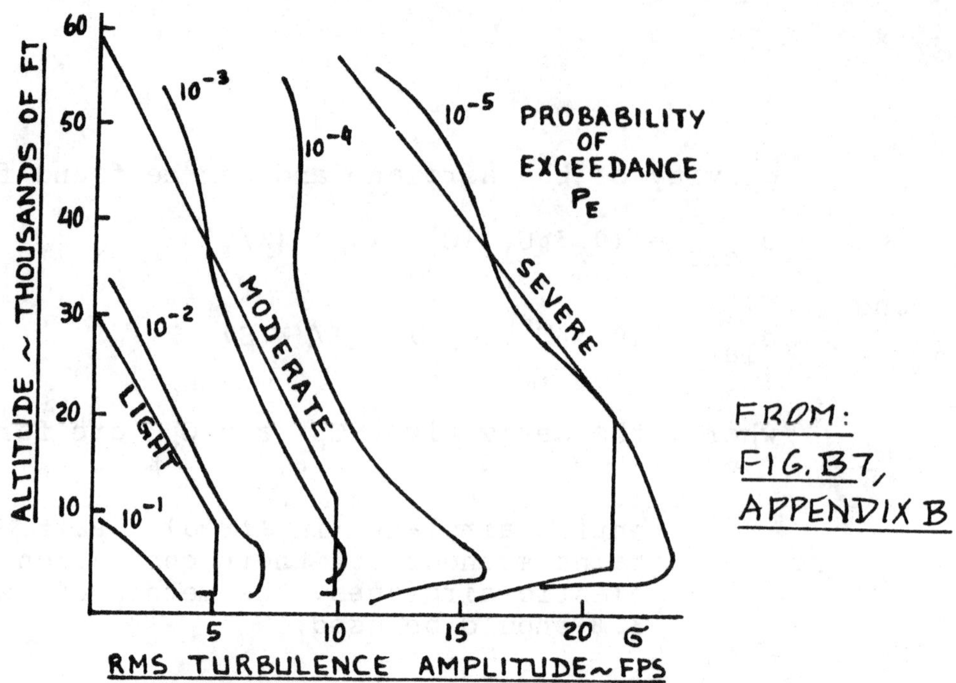

Figure 4.3 Root Mean Square (RMS) Gust or Turbulence Amplitudes as Related to Altitude and Probability of Exceedance

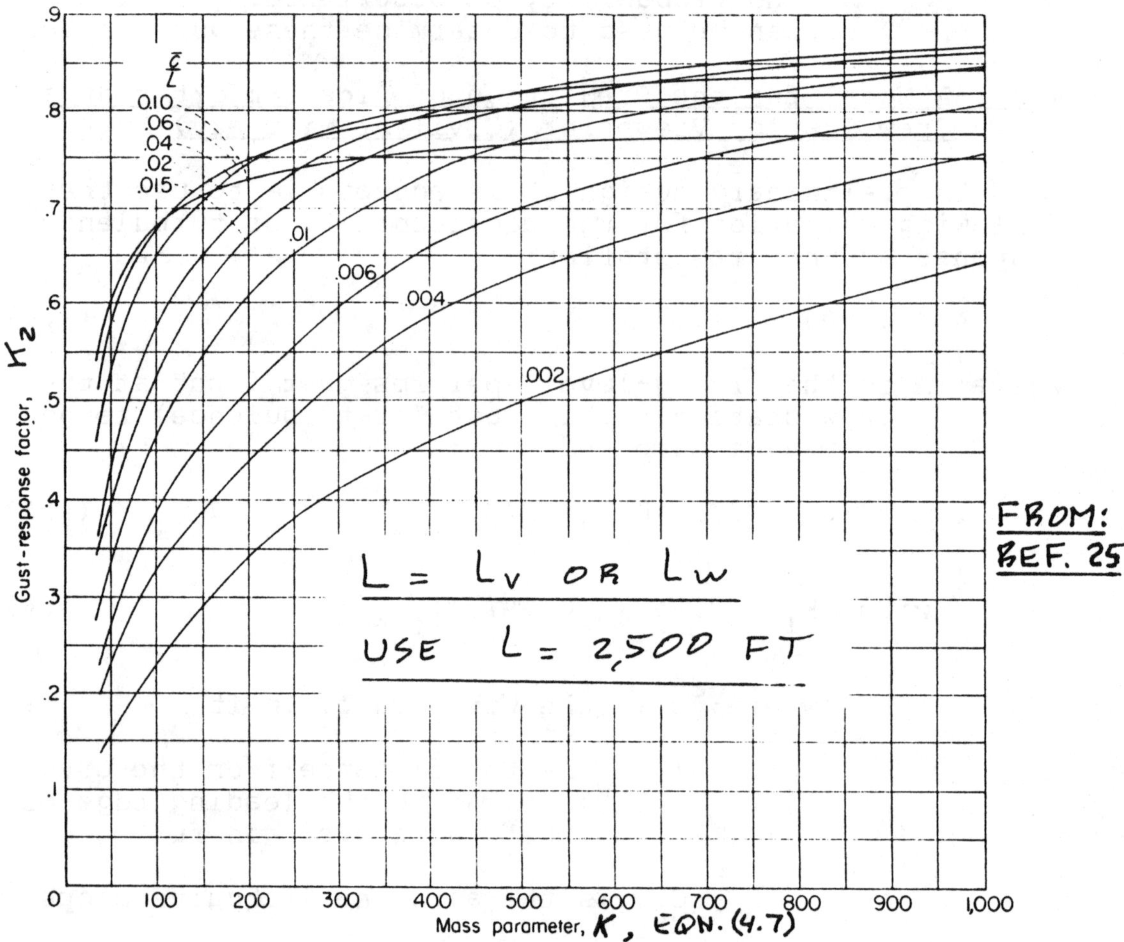

Figure 4.4 Effect of Gust Length and Mass Parameter on Gust Response Factor

this derivative may have to be accounted for: see Section 3.8.

K_2, the gust response factor, is found from: Figure 4.4.

Notes: 1.) In Figure 4.4, $L_{v\ or\ w}$ is the so-called gust length. In preliminary design it is acceptable to use: $L_{v\ or\ w} = 2,500$ ft

2. Also in Figure 4.4:

$$K = 4W/(32.2\pi\rho S\bar{c} \tag{4.7}$$

To give the reader a 'feel' for the meaning of ride criterion (4.4), consider the following. Table 4.1 lists a subjective crew rating of how rms vertical accelerations are perceived by pilots.

If an airplane with an $\bar{A}$ value of 0.005 at sealevel, encounters a rms vertical gust at sealevel of 10 fps (P = 0.001), the crew would feel a 0.05 rms 'g' level.

<u>Table 4.1 Subjective Ratings of Vertical Acceleration</u>

Pilot's Description of Turbulence		RMS Vertical Acceleration in 'g'
Negligible	(Data from:	0.05
Slight	Ref.20)	0.10
Moderate		0.10 - 0.15
Moderately Heavy		0.20 - 0.30
Severe		0.30 - 0.60
Extreme		0.60

4.3 STEP-BY-STEP PROCEDURE FOR ANALYZING RIDE AND COMFORT CHARACTERISTICS

<u>Step 1:</u> For those flight conditions and configurations for which ride qualities are a concern, list:

Weight, Mach Number (and Speed), altitude and configuration (flaps, power, loading, etc.).

<u>Step 2:</u> For the flight conditions of Step 1, determine:

a) the derivatives C_{y_β} and C_{L_α}

Note: include the effect of aeroelasticity

when necessary!

b) the atmospheric density

c) the wing loading, W/S

d) the gust (turbulence) rms values from Figure 4.3. In preliminary design a probability level of 0.01 or 0.001 is usually appropriate.

Step 3: Using Eqns.(4.2) and (4.3) compute the relative accelerations and using Eqn.(4.1) determine the comfort index. Use Figure 4.1 to determine the percentage of satisfaction with the ride.

This percentage of satisfaction should be about 80. If it is less, a design change should be considered.

From Eqns.(4.1)-(4.3) it is evident that the wing loading, W/S and the vertical tail size and shape are the only available design parameters. The real problem is, that these parameters are probably already 'fixed' on the basis of previous design considerations. If that is the case, a ride control system should be considered. For the design of such systems, References 26 and 27 are suggested. Figure 4.1 shows an example of such a system.

Step 4: Determine the additional parameters needed to

estimate $\bar{A}$ in Equation (4.4), then compute $\bar{A}$.

If $\bar{A}$ does not meet criterion (4.4) a design change is in order. Most likely, the only practical alternative is a ride control system, such as shown in Figure 4.1. For synthesis methods of such systems, see References 26 and 27.

Step 5: Document the results obtained, including any design changes made.

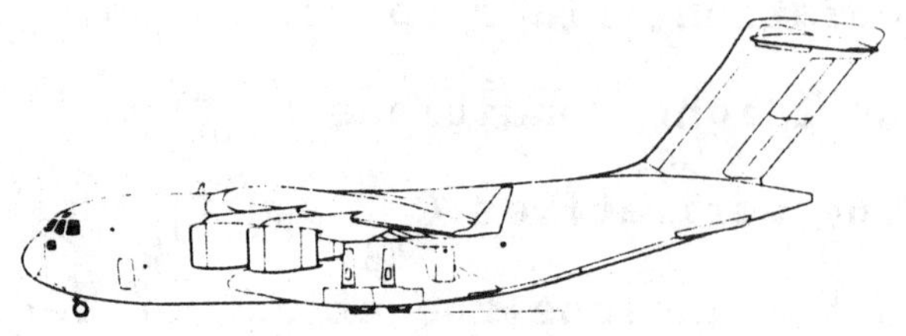

5. PERFORMANCE

The purpose of this chapter is to present Class II methods for predicting the performance characteristics of airplanes. These methods are compatible with Step 28 in Preliminary Design Sequence II as outlined in Chapter 2 of Part II.

The performance characteristics of airplanes must meet the following requirements:

1) Mission performance requirements

2) Airworthiness performance requirements (performance regulations)

The mission performance requirements are normally dictated by the customer, civil or military. The airworthiness performance requirements (referred to in this text as the REGULATIONS) are set by government agencies such as the FAA (civil) or one of the armed forces: USAF, USNavy, USMC or USArmy (military).

To provide the reader with insight into where a given performance characteristic fits into the airplane preliminary design process, the material in each section is organized to provide the following information:

1) identification of the applicable airworthiness regulation(s)

2) relationship to the performance sizing process of Part I of this series of books

3) presentation of a model for analyzing the performance

4) a step-by-step procedure for determining whether or not an airplane meets the mission and airworthiness performance requirements

An important assumption made in this chapter is that the airplane can be considered to be a so-called point-mass model. For the point-mass model to be valid, the stability and control characteristics of the airplane (as discussed in Chapters 3 and 4) must satisfy the corresponding regulations. In addition, the airplane is assumed to be in complete moment equilibrium: any drag polars used in this chapter MUST be the TRIMMED DRAG POLARS!

The material in this chapter is organized in the following manner:

5.1 Stall
5.2 Takeoff
5.3 Climb
5.4 Cruise, range and payload-range
5.5 Endurance and loiter
5.6 Dive
5.7 Maneuvering
5.8 Descent and glide
5.9 Landing
5.10 Mission profile analysis
5.11 Productivity
5.12 Presentation of airplane performance data

COURTESY: CANADAIR

5.1 STALL

5.1.1 Applicable Regulations

Civil: FAR 23.45, 23.49, FAR 25.101 and 25.103, see Appendix A.

Military: MIL-C-005011B, Par.3.4.2.3 or AS-5263, Par.3.5.2.3, see Appendix B.

5.1.2 Relationship to Preliminary Design

See Part I, Section 3.1 and Chapter 7, Part II.

5.1.3 Mathematical Model for Analyzing Stall

Figure 5.1 depicts the forces acting on the airplane in a 1-g stall in steady, level, symmetrical flight. The following equations of motion apply:

$$T\sin(\alpha + \phi_T) + L = W \qquad (5.1)$$

$$T\cos(\alpha + \phi_T) = D \qquad (5.2)$$

At the stall, the airplane is flying at:

$C_L = C_{L_{max}}$ and $\alpha = \alpha_{C_{L_{max}}}$. Therefore, the stall speed follows from:

$$V_s = [2\{W - T\sin(\alpha_{C_{L_{max}}} + \phi_T)\}/\{\rho C_{L_{max}} S\}]^{1/2} \qquad (5.3)$$

where: W is the weight at which the stall speed is to be determined

T is the thrust setting used in the stall maneuver. This will normally be equal to zero (power-off stall). Since thrust does depend on speed, an iterative solution to Eqn.(5.3) is required if T is not zero.

Note: If the thrust is derived from a propeller instead of from a jet engine, it may be computed from:

$$T = (550\eta_p SHP)/V_s \qquad (5.4)$$

where: η_p is the propeller efficiency

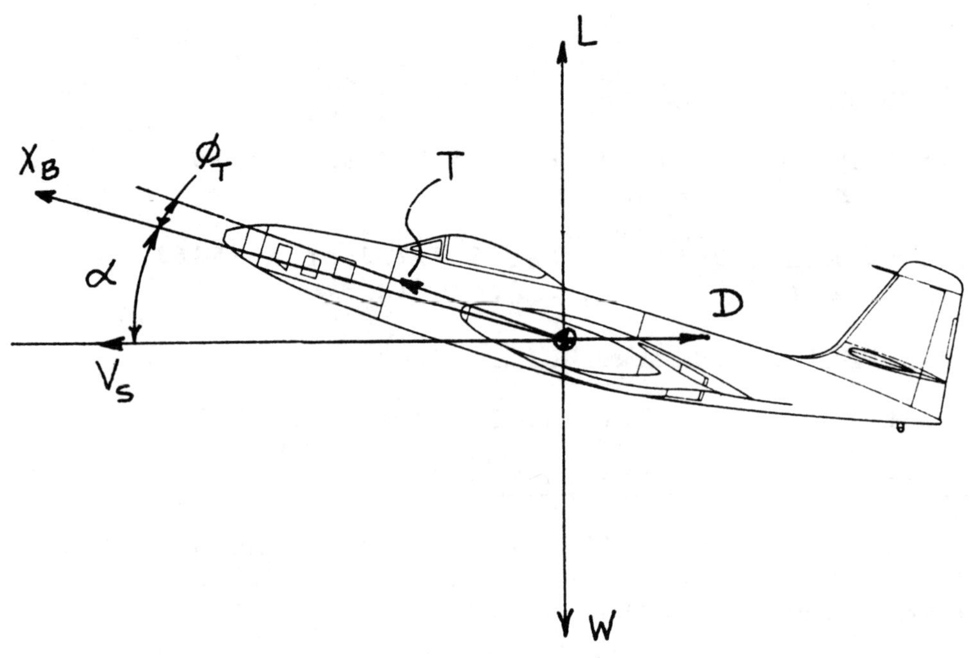

Figure 5.1 Forces Acting on an Airplane in a 1-g Stall
In Steady, Level symmetrical Flight

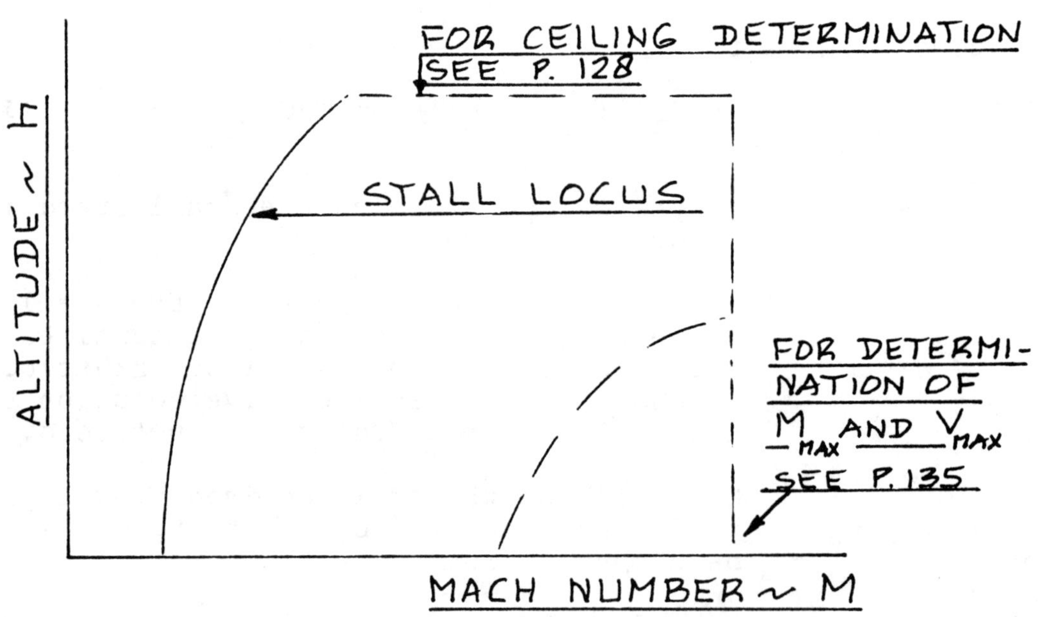

Figure 5.2 Example Flight Envelope

SHP is the shaft horsepower delivered by the engine(s)

V_s is the stall speed as found from Equation (5.3). Note that an iterative solution of Eqn.(5.3) is required if SHP is not zero,

$\alpha_{C_{L_{max}}}$ is the angle of attack at the stall

ϕ_T is the thrustline inclination, see Fig.5.1

Therefore, Eqn.(5.3) applies to vectorable thrust airplanes. For most airplanes it is acceptable to assume $\phi_T = 0$.

ρ is the air density corresponding to the altitude at which the stall is to be done

$C_{L_{max}}$ is the trimmed maximum lift coefficient of the airplane. As explained in Ch.2 of this text as well as in Section 8.3 of Part VI, its value depends strongly on center of gravity location AND on controllability and pitch-up behavior.

NOTE WELL: For high speed airplanes the maximum lift coefficient is also dependent on Mach number. This dependency is discussed in Chapter 9 of Part VI.

The dependency of maximum lift coefficient on Mach number is very important in defining the stall boundary of the airplane flight envelope. This is discussed further in Section 5.11.

S is the (reference) wing area

If T = 0 and $\phi_T = 0$, Equation (5.3) reduces to its classical form:

$$V_s = \{(2W)/(\rho C_{L_{max}} S)\}^{1/2} \tag{5.5}$$

IMPORTANT COMMENT: The 1-g stall speed as determined from this method is somewhat conservative in view of the manner in which the regulations define the stall speed as determined by certification flight tests. The conservatism usually amounts to about 6 percent. For a more discussion of this, see Reference 11, pages 482-486.

5.1.4 Step-by-Step Procedure for Analyzing Stall

The following step-by-step procedure is suggested to calculate the airplane stall speed.

Step 1: Determine which regulations apply to the design: see Table 1.3 and Sub-section 2.1.1. READ the regulations!

Step 2: Tabulate the flight conditions, configurations, loading conditions and c.g. locations for which the stall speed of the airplane must be determined. This information comes from the regulations AND from the mission performance requirements. The reader should consult the list of items 1-9 on page 7!

Step 3: For the flight conditions and configurations defined in Step 2, determine the value(s) of the maximum lift coefficient. Be sure to account for the effects of Mach number and c.g. location on $C_{L_{max}}$!

Step 4: For the conditions of Step 2 find the values of all other terms in Equation 5.3.

Step 5: Compute the stall speed(s) from Eqn.(5.3), and record in kts, fps and in Mach number.

Step 6: Check the stall speed(s) of Step 5 against the regulatory requirements and against the mission performance requirements. If a discrepancy is found, determine what (if any) redesign action needs to be taken.

Discrepancies occur usually as a result of not being able to generate the required magnitude of $C_{L_{max}}$ (TRIMMED!!). This in turn can be remedied usually by a change in wing and/or flap design!

Step 7: Plot the variation of Mach number at the stall with altitude. This constitutes the left side of the airplane operational flight envelope. Figure 5.2 shows an example.

Step 8: Document the results obtained, including any design changes made.

5.2 TAKE-OFF

5.2.1 Applicable Regulations

Civil: FAR 23.45, 23.51, FAR 25.101, and 25.107, see Appendix A.

Military: MIL-C-005011B, par. 3.4.2.4 and 3.4.5 or AS-5263, par. 3.5.2.4, 3.5.2.5 and 3.5.5, see Appendix B.

5.2.2 Relationship to Preliminary Design

See Part I, Section 3.2.

5.2.3 Mathematical Model for Analyzing Takeoff Performance

The definition of take-off distance and the associated reference speeds depends on which regulation is used to certify the airplane: FAR 23, FAR 25 or Military.

Figure 5.3 shows the differences in the definitions for takeoff distances and the associated reference speeds.

The following method for computing the takeoff distance, s_{TO} is due to Torenbeek (Reference 26). The takeoff distance, s_{TO} equals the takeoff field length, s_{TOFL} when the landing distance, s_L or s_{FL} (See Section 5.9) is less than or equal to s_{TO}.

$$s_{TO} = f_{TO}h_{TO}[(1/\gamma_{LOF}) + \frac{(V_3/V_{s_{TO}})^2 (W/S)_{TO}[\{(\bar{T}/W)_{TO} - \mu'\}^{-1} + 1.414]}{(h_{TO}\rho g C_{L_{max_{TO}}})(1 + 1.414\gamma_{LOF})}] \quad (5.6)$$

where: f_{TO} depends on the obstacle height: see Table 5.1.

h_{TO} is the obstacle height, see Table 5.1.

$(V_3/V_{s_{TO}})$ is the ratio of the speed at the obstacle height, V_3 to the stall speed in

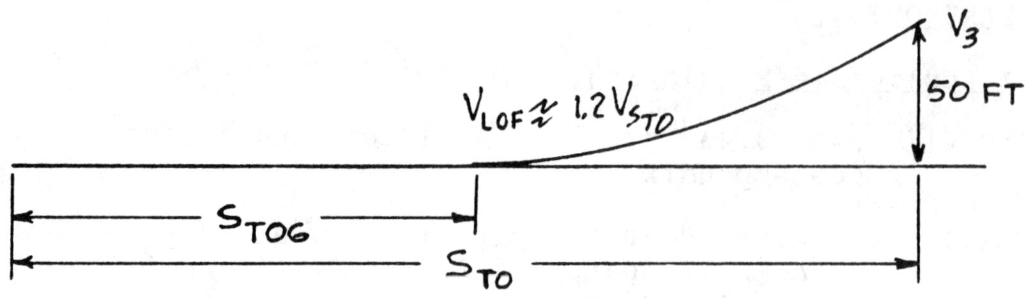

Definition of FAR 23 Take-off Distance

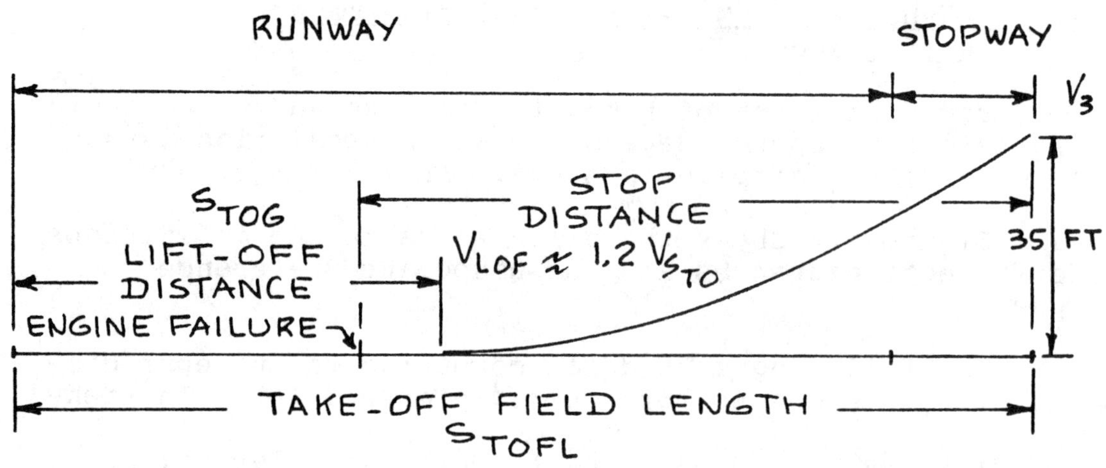

Definition of FAR 25 Take-off Distance

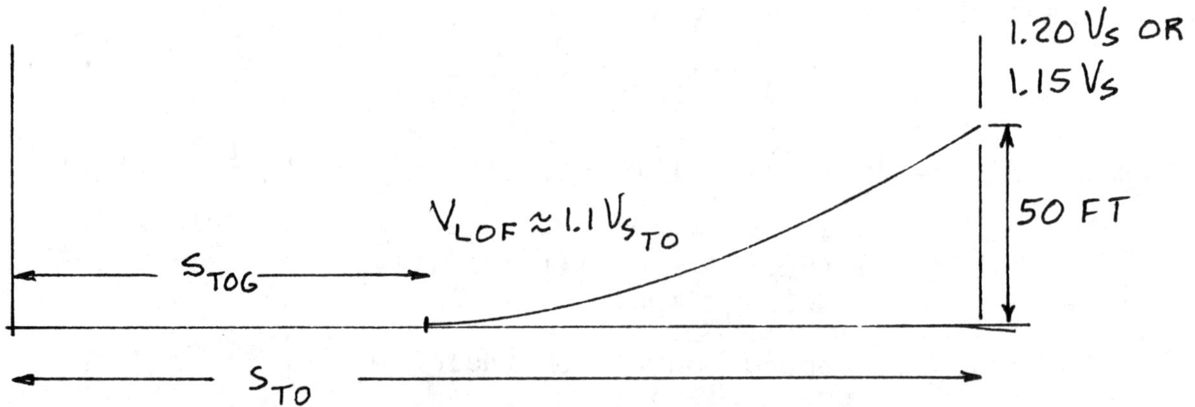

Definition of Military Takeoff Distance

Figure 5.3 Definition of Takeoff Distances According to the Regulations

the takeoff configuration, $V_{s_{TO}}$. This ratio is defined in Table 5.1.

Table 5.1 Parameter Values for Equation (5.6)

Regulation	$V_3/V_{s_{TO}}$	f_{TO}	h_{TO}
FAR 23	1.3	1.0	50 ft
FAR 25	1.25 to 1.3 (no requirement)	1.15	35 ft
AS-5263	1.2	1.0	50
MIL-C-005011B	1.15	1.0	50 ft

$(W/S)_{TO}$ is the takeoff wing loading

$(\bar{T}/W)_{TO}$ is the mean thrust-to-weight ratio taken at a speed of $0.707V_{LOF}$. The value of T may be computed from:

For Jet Driven Airplanes:

$$\bar{T} = 0.75T_{TO}(5 + \lambda)/(4 + \lambda) \qquad (5.7)$$

where: T_{TO} is the maximum static thrust max at takeoff

λ is the engine bypass ratio

For Propeller Driven Airplanes:

$$\bar{T} = 5.75P_{TO}\{(\sigma ND_p^2)/P_{TO}\}^{1/3} \qquad (5.8)$$

where: P_{TO} is the maximum shaft horsepower at takeoff (static), all engines operating

$(P_{TO}/ND_p^2$ is the propeller diskloading at takeoff (static). Its Class I determined value (Step 5.6 in Chapter 5 of Part II) may be checked for acceptability by referring to Figure 5.4.

NOTE:
FACTOR 5.75 IN EQN. (5.8) APPLIES TO VARIABLE PITCH PROPELLERS ONLY! FOR FIXED PITCH USE 4.60.

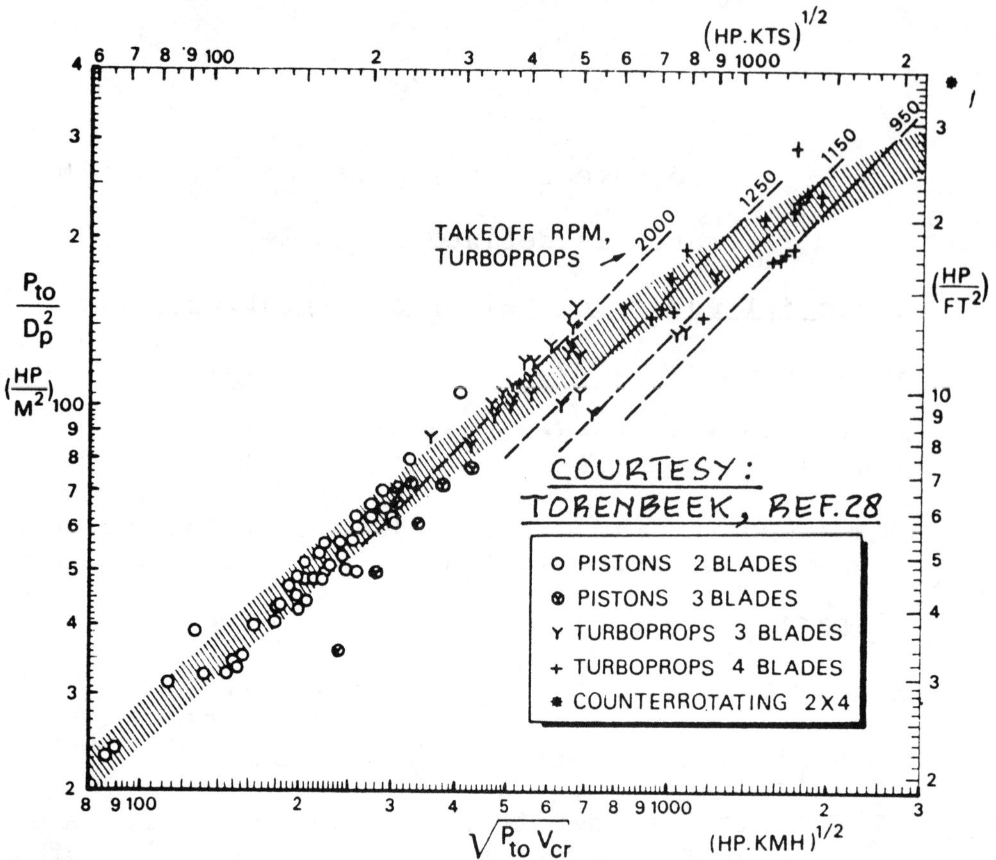

Figure 5.4 Method for Selecting Propeller Disk Loading During Preliminary Design

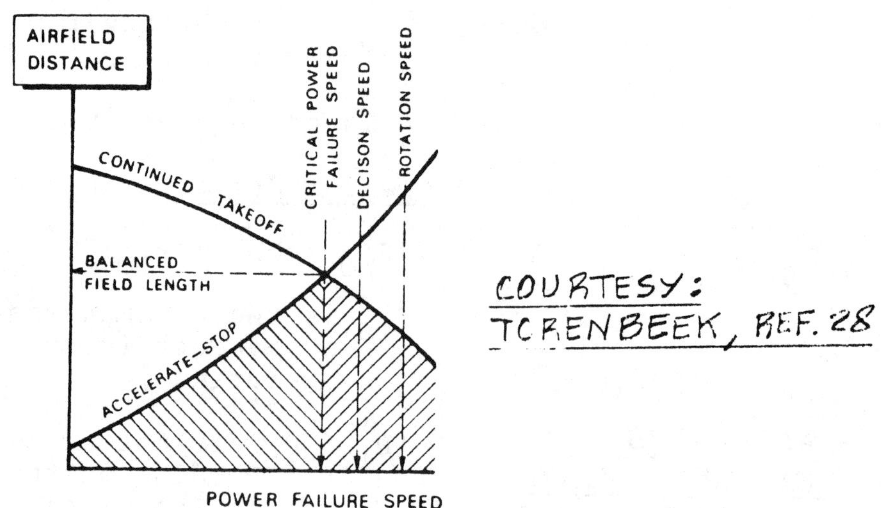

Figure 5.5 Sketch of the Meaning of Balanced Field Length

N is the number of engines

$$\mu' = \mu_g + 0.72(C_{D_o}/C_{L_{max_{TO}}}) \quad (5.9)$$

where: μ_g is the friction coefficient as determined from page 40

C_{D_o} is the zero-lift drag coefficient in in the takeoff configuration

$C_{L_{max_{TO}}}$ is the maximum lift coefficient in the takeoff configuration. It is determined from Part VI, Section 8.3. Ground effect must be accounted for.

$$\gamma_{LOF} = \{(T - D)/W\}_{LOF} \quad (5.10)$$

but this may be approximated by:

$$\gamma_{LOF} = 0.9(\bar{T}/W)_{TO} - 0.3/(A^{1/2}) \quad (5.11)$$

In the design of commercial transports and certain military transports the concept of balanced fieldlength, (BFL) is often used. In the case of military airplanes, BFL is normally called the Critical Field Length.

The definition of balanced fieldlength is illustrated in Figure 5.5. Torenbeek (Reference 28) shows that:

$$BFL = [\{655/(\sigma)^{1/2})\} + \quad (5.12)$$

$$+ \{0.863/(1 + 2.3(\gamma_2 - \gamma_{2_{min}}))\} *$$

$$* \{(W/S)_{TO}/(0.694\rho g C_{L_{max_{TO}}}) + h_{TO}\}\{1/((\bar{T}/W_{TO}) - \mu') + 2.7\}$$

$$\text{where: } \gamma_2 = (T/W)_{TO_{OEI}} - \{(C_L/C_D)_{TO_{OEI}}\}^{-1} \quad (5.13)$$

which is called the second-segment climb gradient with one engine inoperative,

with: $(T/W)_{TO_{OEI}}$ is the thrust-to-weight ratio in the takeoff configuration, but with one engine inoperative and at $1.2V_{s_{TO}}$.

$\{(C_L/C_D)_{TO_{OEI}}\}^{-1}$ is the lift-to-drag ratio in the takeoff configuration, with one engine inoperative (this does cause extra drag!!) and at $1.2V_{s_{TO}}$

γ_{2min} = 0.024 for N=2

0.027 for N=3

0.030 for N=4

All other parameters were previously defined.

In several instances a takeoff specification will call merely for a groundrun during takeoff to be less than some specified value. In such cases the following equation for the groundrun only is useful:

$$s_{TOG} = \{(V_{LOF})^2/2g\}/\{(\bar{T}/W)_{TO} - \mu'\} \tag{5.14}$$

where: $V_{LOF} = 1.2V_{s_{TO}}$ for commercial airplanes, and

$1.1V_{s_{TO}}$ for military airplanes

all other parameters have been previously defined.

<u>Important Note:</u>

Airplanes which are also carrier based must be compatible with the performance restrictions inherent in each catapult system. A suitable mathematical model for determining airplane compatibility with USNavy catapult systems is given in Sub-sub-section 3.2.5.2, page 103, in Part I.

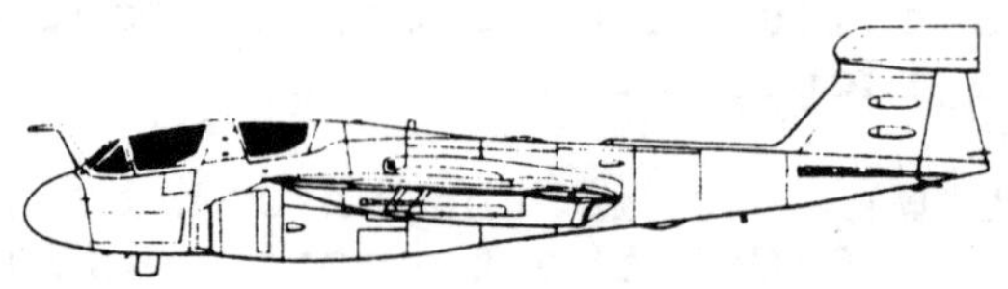

5.2.4 Step-by-Step Procedure for Analyzing Takeoff Performance

The following step-by-step procedure is suggested for determining the takeoff distance of a new airplane:

Step 1: Determine which regulation applies to the design and read that regulation. See Table 1.3 and Sub-section 2.1.1.

Determine the takeoff distance requirements from the mission specification.

Step 2: Determine whether Eqn.(5.6), Eqn.(5.12) or Eqn.(5.14) govern the takeoff distance calculation and prepare the required input data.

If the airplane has a catapulting requirement, such as carrier based airplanes, the reader should use the method of Sub-sub-section 3.2.5.2 of page 103 in Part I to determine the compatibility of the airplane with catapult performance capability.

Step 3: Compute the takeoff distance with either Eqn. (5.6), (5.12) or (5.14). Compare the result with the mission fieldlength requirements. If there is more than a 5 percent discrepancy, a design adjustment to the airplane is in order.

Note: The parameters which affect the takeoff distance most strongly are:

1. The takeoff thrust-to-weight ratio $(T/W)_{TO}$
2. The takeoff wing loading, $(W/S)_{TO}$
3. The takeoff maximum lift coefficient, $C_{L_{max_{TO}}}$

Remember: there is little value in significantly exceeding a mission requirement AND:

not meeting a mission requirement may lead to rejection of the design

Step 4: Document the results obtained, including any design changes made.

5.3 CLIMB

5.3.1 Applicable Regulations

Civil: FAR 23.45, 23.65, 23.67, and 23.77, see Appendix A.

FAR 25.101, 25.111, 25.115, 25.117, 25.119, 25.121 and 25.123, see Appendix A.

Military: MIL-C-005011B, Par.3.4.2.4 and 3.4.2.5 or AS-5263, Par.3.5.2.4.1 and 3.5.2.6, see Appendix B.

5.3.2 Relationship to Preliminary Design

See Part I, Chapter 3, Section 3.4. In addition, see Part II, Chapter 2, Step 14 and Step 27.

5.3.3 Mathematical Model for Analyzing Climb Performance

Figure 5.6 depicts the forces which act on an airplane in an accelerated, symmetrical flight condition. The corresponding equations of motion are:

$$T\cos(\alpha + \phi_T) - C_D\bar{q}S - W\sin\gamma = (W/g)\dot{U} \qquad (5.15)$$

$$T\sin(\alpha + \phi_T) + C_L\bar{q}S - W\cos\gamma = (W/g)U\dot{\gamma} \qquad (5.16)$$

The reader is reminded of the fact, that these equations assume that moment equilibrium exists. This implies, that the drag polar, which defines the relation between C_L and C_D is the 'trimmed' drag polar. See Part VI, Section 4.10 for a discussion of trim drag.

Equations (5.15) and (5.16) are used to determine the rate of climb and the climb gradient of which an airplane is capable in a range of flight conditions.

In preliminary design, the effect of acceleration normal to the flight path as expressed by the $\dot{\gamma}$-term will be neglected. Furthermore, other than for fighters, the climb angle, γ is usually smaller than about 15 degrees so that $\cos\gamma=1.0$ and $\sin\gamma=\gamma$ can be used.

The rate-of-climb, RC (for any flight path angle) is

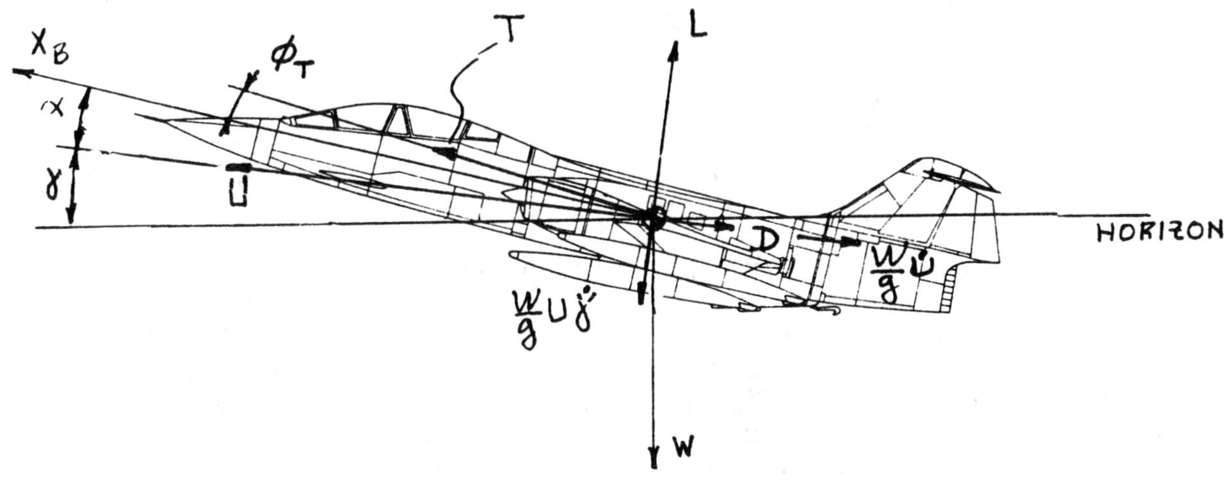

Figure 5.6 Forces Acting on an Airplane in Accelerated, Symmetrical Flight

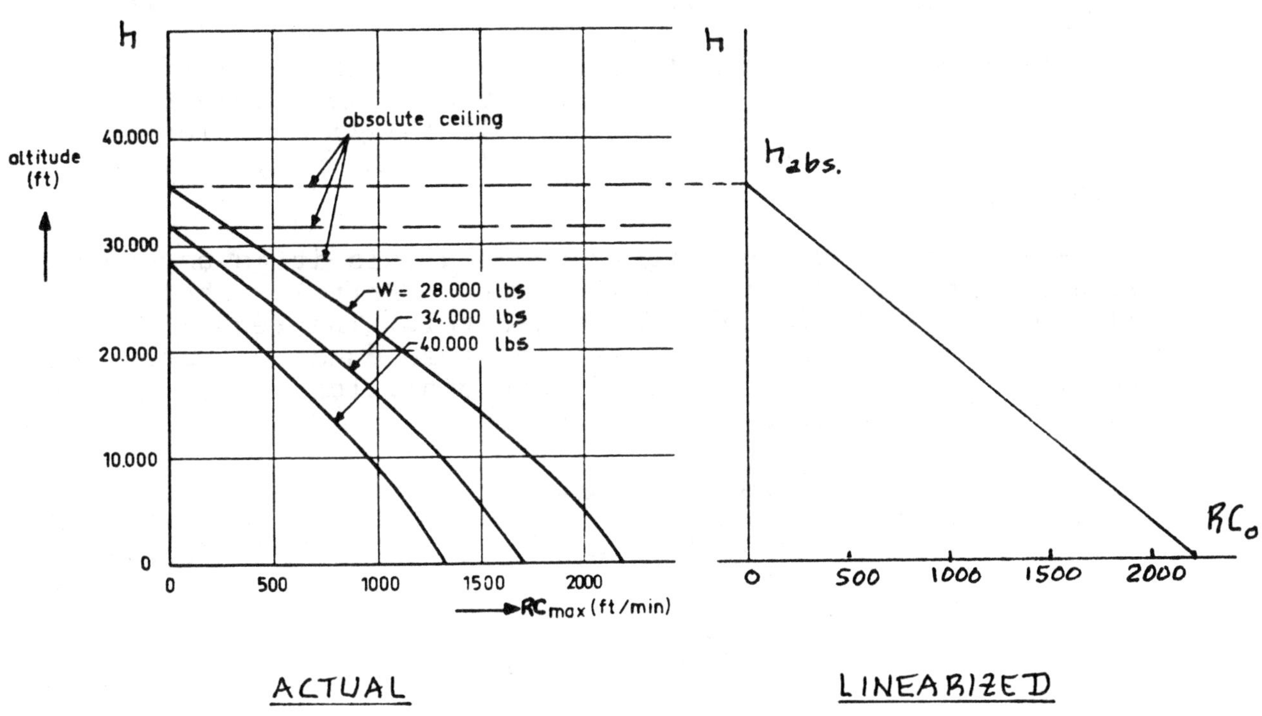

Figure 5.7 Variations of Rate-of-Climb with Altitude

defined as:

$$RC = dh/dt = U\sin\gamma \qquad (5.17)$$

With the help of Eqns.(5.16) - (5.17) it is shown in Reference 11, page 384, that:

$$RC = \{(T - D)U/W\}/\{1 + (U/g)dU/dh\} \qquad (5.18)$$

The term (U/g)dU/dh is called the acceleration factor. It has a significant effect on fighter performance. It also has a significant effect on climb performance at high altitude. Since most regulations which deal with climb performance apply close to the ground, it is usually acceptable to consider only climb at constant true airspeed, in which case the acceleration factor is zero.

Therefore, for steady, symmetrical flight the rate-of-climb is:

$$RC = (T - D)U_1/W \qquad (5.19)$$

From this, the climb gradient, CGR follows as:

$$CGR = RC/U_1 = (T - D)/W \qquad (5.20)$$

The regulations specify either a minimum required rate-of-climb, RC or a minimum required climb gradient, CGR. The reader should read the applicable regulations to determine which values for CR and/or CGR apply to a given airplane.

For Class II climb performance analysis it is acceptable to use the equations of Chapter 3, Part I. These equations will be stated here in general. The reader must realize that the parameters in these equations are different for each particular flight condition and for each particular airplane configuration!

<u>1. For propeller-driven airplanes:</u>

$$RC\ (fpm) = 33{,}000[\eta_p/(W/P) + - \{(W/S)^{1/2}/19(C_L^{\,3/2}/C_D)\sigma^{1/2}\}] \qquad (5.21)$$

$$CGR = - (L/D)^{-1} + + \{(C_L)^{1/2}18.97\eta_p\sigma^{1/2}\}/\{(W/P)(W/S)^{1/2}\} \qquad (5.22)$$

2. For jet-driven airplanes:

$$RC\ (fpm) = 60U_1\{(T/W) - (L/D)^{-1}\} \qquad (5.23)$$

$$CGR = (T/W) - (L/D)^{-1} \qquad (5.24)$$

Many airplane mission specifications require mission specific climb capabilities such as:

1. Minimum climb rate at some altitude (such as sea level)

2. Minimum time-to-climb to some altitude

3. Ceiling

4. Specific excess power

1. Minimum climb rate at some altitude

The climb rate at any altitude can be estimated with Equations (5.21) and (5.23).

2. Minimum time-to-climb to some altitude

The time to climb to any altitude can be estimated from:

$$t_{cl} = \int_0^h (1/RC)dh \qquad (5.25)$$

This equation can be solved by integration over several increments of altitude. Increments of 5,000 ft provide sufficient accuracy in preliminary design. The average value of the rate-of-climb, RC in Eqn.(5.25) at some altitude increment can be estimated from Eqn.(5.21) or (5.23). Figure 5.7 shows typical variations of rate-of-climb with altitude.

If an estimate is available for the absolute ceiling of an airplane (see next item 3.), AND if the RC varies approximately linearly with altitude, then it is possible to find the time-to-climb to any altitude between sealevel and the absolute ceiling from:

$$t_{cl} = (h_{abs}/RC_o)\ln\ (1 - h/h_{abs})^{-1} \qquad (5.26)$$

where: RC_o is the maximum rate-of-climb at sealevel, found from either Equation (5.21) or (5.23). Figure 5.7 also shows the linearized variation of rate-of-climb with altitude.

3. Ceiling

Equation (5.21) or (5.23) can be used to find that altitude for which the rate of climb corresponds to one of the ceiling definitions of Table 5.2. The ceiling is the upper side of the flight envelope: see Figure 5.2.

4. Specific excess power

The specific excess power of an airplane is computed from:

$$P_s = (T - D)U/W \tag{5.27}$$

Note that this equation is similar to Eqn.(5.18).

More accurate and specialized mathematical models for the computation of climb performance are presented in Reference 11. They will not be repeated here.

To help the reader find specific models for the computation of climb performance, the following guide is presented:

1. For Propeller Driven Airplanes:

   See Reference 11, Section 9.2, pages 384-395.

2. For Jet Powered Airplanes:

   See Reference 11, Section 9.3, pages 395-400.

3. For Fighters (Steep Climbs):

   See Reference 11, Section 9.4, pages 400-401.

4. For Ceilings and Time-to-Climb:

   See Reference 11, pages 405-407

5. For Specific Excess Power:

   See Reference 11, pages 510-516.

Table 5.2 Definition of Airplane Ceilings

Ceiling Type	Minimum Required Climb Rate
Absolute ceiling	0 fpm
Service ceiling	
Commercial/Piston-propeller	100 fpm
Commercial/jet	500 fpm
Military at maximum power	100 fpm
Combat ceiling	
Military/Subsonic/maximum power	500 fpm at M<1
Military/Supersonic/maximum power	1,000 fpm at M>1
Cruise ceiling	
Military/Subsonic/max.cont. power	300 fpm at M<1
Military/Supersonic/max.cont. power	1,000 fpm at M>1

Table 5.3 Summary of Regulatory Climb Requirements for FAR 25 Transports

PHASE OF FLIGHT		AIRPLANE CONFIGURATION FLAPS	U.C.	ENGINES		FLIGHT SPEED	MINIMUM, CLIMB GRADIENT, % N=1	N=2	N=3
LIFTOFF	1ST SEGMENT	TAKE OFF	↓	ONE ENGINE OUT	TAKE OFF	LIFT-OFF	0	.3	.5
TAKEOFF FLIGHT PATH	2ND SEGMENT	TAKE OFF	↑	ONE ENGINE OUT	TAKE OFF	V_2	2.4	2.7	3.0
TAKEOFF FLIGHT PATH	FINAL TAKEOFF	EN ROUTE	↑	ONE ENGINE OUT	MAX. CONT.	$\geq 1{,}25V_s$	1.2	1.5	1.7
APPROACH CLIMB		APPR.	↑	ONE ENGINE OUT	TAKEOFF	$\leq 1{,}5V_s$	2.1	2.4	2.7
LANDING CLIMB		LAND.	↓	ALL ENGINES TAKEOFF		$\leq 1{,}3V_s$	3.2	3.2	3.2

COURTESY: TORENBEEK, REF. 28

V_s = Stalling speed

V_2 = Takeoff safety speed ($\geq 1.2V_s$)

* Summary only

5.3.4 Step-by-Step Procedure for Determining Climb Performance

Step 1: Determine which regulations apply to the design and read that regulation.

Tabulate the regulatory climb requirements in a manner similar to that shown in Table 5.3.

Determine the climb performance requirements stated in the airplane mission requirements.

Tabulate all mission climb requirements in a manner similar to Table 5.3.

Note from Table 5.3 that the prescribed configuration of the airplane is carefully listed! This has significant consequences for the drag polars!

Step 2: Using the guidelines of Sub-section 5.3.3 determine which methods and/or equations apply to the analysis of the climb requirements of Step 1.

Prepare the necessary input data for all flight conditions and airplane configurations for which climb performance must be assessed.

Step 3: Carry out the climb performance calculations and compare the results against the regulations and/or the mission climb requirements. Note any discrepancies.

Step 4: Analyze what changes are required to eliminate the discrepancies in climb performance noted in Step 3.

Typical changes which may be contemplated are:

a) Increase or decrease in thrust or power

b) Change in aerodynamic design to lower the drag

Note that major changes in these areas may have repercussions for most other aspects of the design and may therefore require an iteration!

Step 5: Document the results, including any design changes made.

5.4 CRUISE, RANGE AND PAYLOAD-RANGE

5.4.1 Applicable Regulations

Civil: There are no airworthiness regulations which deal specifically with cruise performance. Fuel reserve regulations are specified in FAR 91. Most commercial operations are conducted with fuel reserve rules which are more conservative than those of FAR 91.

Military: MIL-C-005011C (USAF) and AS-5263 (USN and USMC), give definitions, see Appendix B.

5.4.2 Relationship to Preliminary Design

See Part I, Chapter 2. In addition, see Part II, Chapter 2, Step 14, Step 27 and Step 28.

5.4.3 Mathematical Model for Analyzing Cruise and Range Performance

Figure 5.8 depicts the forces which act on an airplane in a horizontal, steady, symmetrical, 1-g cruise flight condition. The equations of motion are:

$$T\cos(\alpha + \phi_T) - C_D\bar{q}S = 0 \tag{5.28}$$

$$T\sin(\alpha + \phi_T) + C_L\bar{q}S = W \tag{5.29}$$

The reader is reminded of the fact, that these equations assume that moment equilibrium exists. This implies, that the airplane drag polar, which defines the relationship between C_L and C_D is the 'trimmed' drag polar. Part VI, Section 4.10 presents a method for computing trim drag.

There also exists a unique relationship between the angle of attack, α and the lift coefficient, C_L. A method for determining C_L versus α is given in Part VI, Chapter 8.

The quantity T in Equations (5.28) and (5.29) is the so-called <u>installed thrust.</u> Methods for determining the installed thrust capability of an airplane are presented in Part VI, Chapter 6.

For most conventional airplanes, the angle $(\alpha + \phi_T)$

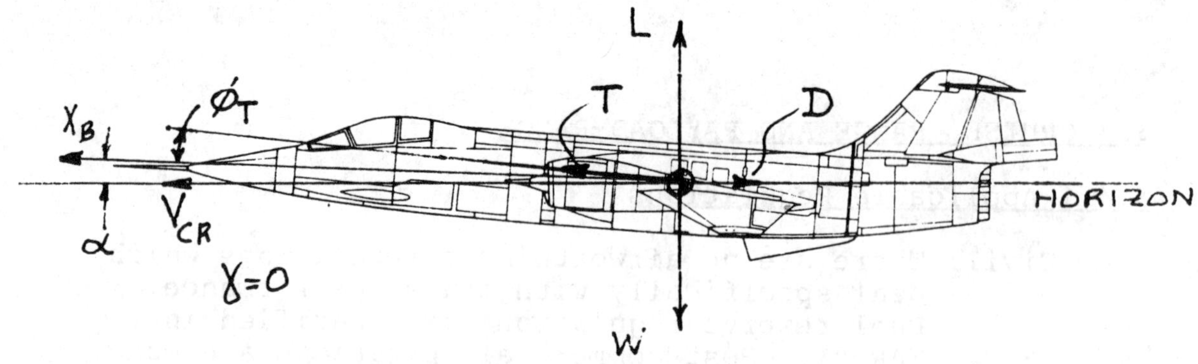

Figure 5.8 Forces Acting on an Airplane in Level, Steady, Symmetrical Flight

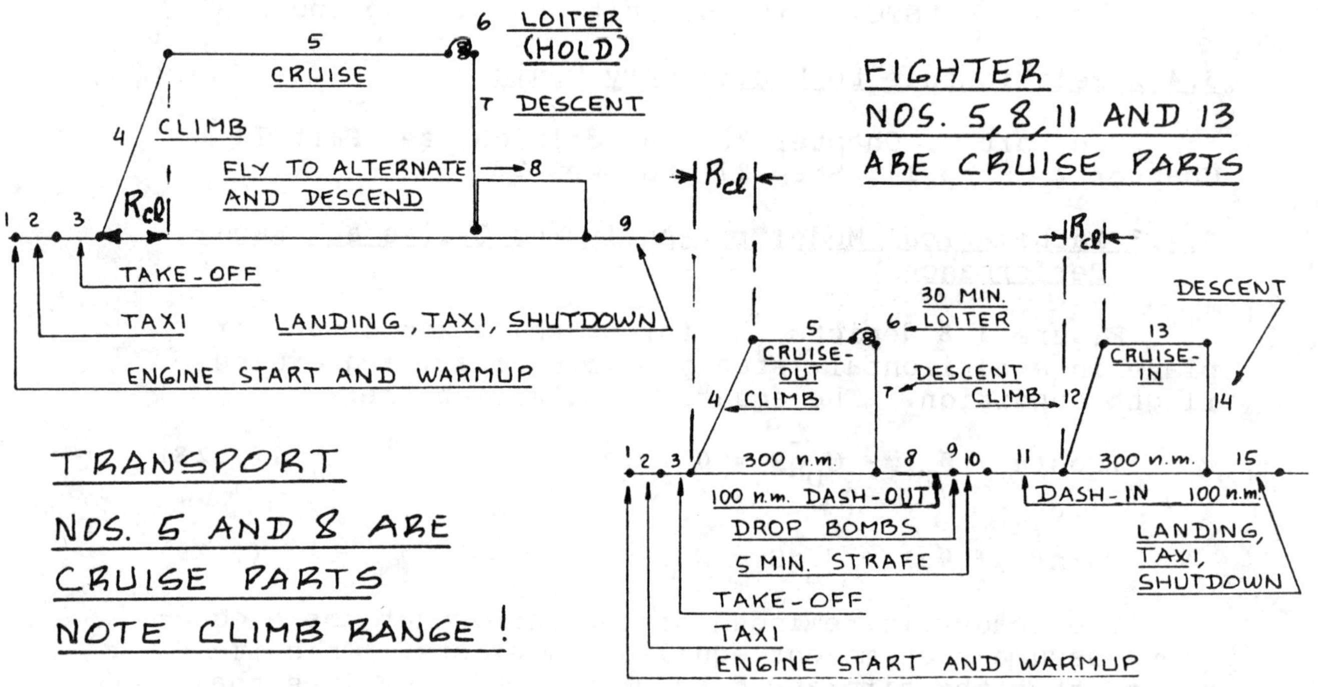

Figure 5.9 Example Mission Profiles for a Transport and for a Fighter

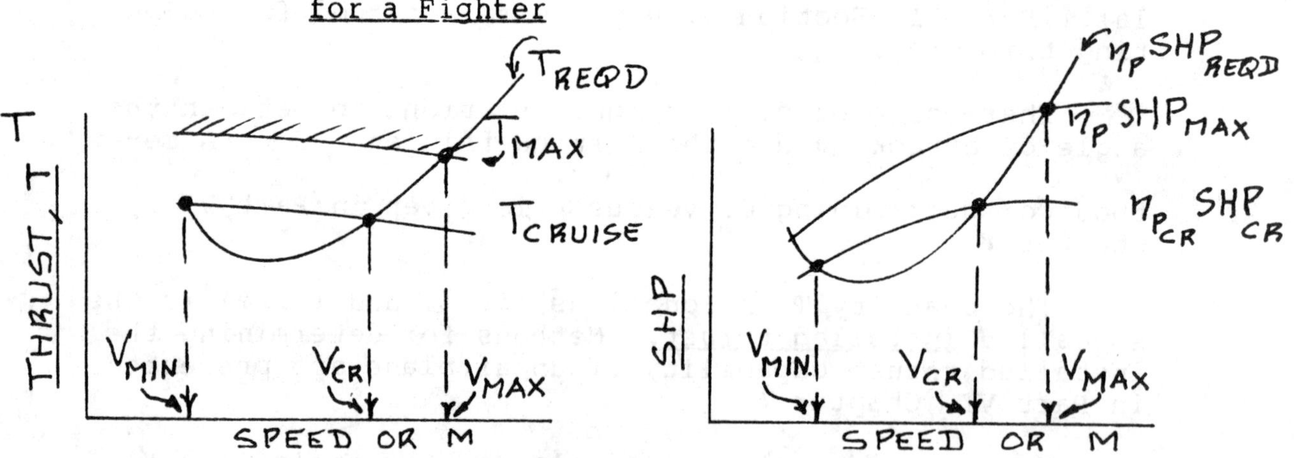

Figure 5.10 Determination of Cruise Speed and Maximum Level Flight Speed

is so small that it can be neglected. In that case, the cruise lift coefficient follows from:

$$C_{L_{cr(uise)}} = W/\bar{q}S \tag{5.30}$$

The required cruise thrust-to-weight ratio then is:

$$(T/W)_{cr} = 1/(L/D)_{cr} \tag{5.31}$$

If $(\alpha + \phi_T)$ is not negligibly small, Eqn.(5.30) is used to find a first approximation for the cruise lift coefficient. This value of C_L is then used to find C_D from the trimmed drag polar and also to find α from the C_L versus α curve. Since the thrust inclination angle, ϕ_T is assumed to be known, Eqn.(5.28) can now be used to find the required installed thrust. This thrust value <u>must be less than the maximum installed thrust available</u> in that flight condition! This thrust value is then substituted into Eqn.(5.29) and a new value for C_L is determined, etc., etc. until the process converges. Convergence may be assumed to have been reached when the lift-to-drag ratio is within 1 percent. This determines the cruise lift-to-drag ratio, $(L/D)_{cr}$.

<u>IMPORTANT NOTE:</u> The reader will find that in nearly all cruise flight conditions:

$$(L/D)_{cr} < (L/D)_{max} \tag{5.32}$$

In a 'cruise matched' airplane, the cruise lift-to-drag ratio is roughly 90 percent of the maximum lift-to-drag ratio.

Most airplane missions specify cruise requirements in the following manner:

1. Cruise speed and cruise altitude
2. Range and payload (Requirement for a specific Range-Payload Diagram)
3. Fuel reserves at the end of the design mission as a fraction of fuel used up to that point or in terms of a so-called reserve mission.

4. Maximum cruise speed, altitude and payload (some of which may be external)

5. Payload expended, as in military airplanes which expend ammunition and release weapons and stores.

It is always useful to translate airplane mission requirements into a mission profile. Figure 5.9 shows examples for a civil and for a military airplane.

For Class II analysis of cruise range performance it is acceptable to use the following Breguet equations, PROVIDED the procedure of Step 5 in Sub-section 5.4.4 is used:

For Propeller Driven Airplanes:

For constant altitude cruise:

$$R = f_{mp}(\eta_p/c_p)(L/D)\ln(W_{initial}/W_{end}) \tag{5.33}$$

Note that: when f_{mp} = 326, R is in nautical miles!

when f_{mp} = 375, R is in statue miles!

For constant speed cruise:

$$R = f_{mp}(\eta_p/c_p)(L/D)\ln(W_{initial}/W_{end}) \tag{5.34}$$

Note that this equation is identical to Eqn.(5.33)! This works only if the assumption is made that the airplane cruises roughly at the same values of η_p, c_p and L/D, regardless of the type of cruise. That assumption is usually valid.

For Jet Driven Airplanes:

For constant altitude cruise:

$$R = (f_{mj}/c_j)(\rho S)^{-1/2}\{(C_L)^{1/2}/C_D\}\{(W_{initial})^{1/2} - (W_{end})^{1/2}\} \tag{5.35}$$

Note that: when f_{mj} = 1.677, R is in nautical miles!

when f_{mj} = 1.929, R is in statute miles!

For constant speed cruise:

$$R = (V/c_j)(L/D)\ln(W_{initial}/W_{end}) \qquad (5.36)$$

Note that if V is expressed in sm/hr, R is in sm, but, if V is expressed in nm/hr, R is in nm!

In many missions (see Figure 5.9!) range credit may be taken for the climb and/or for the descent part of a mission. If that is the case, the following equations may be used to determine these range increments:

$$R_{cl} = V_{cl}t_{cl} \qquad (5.37)$$

where: V_{cl} is the speed at which the climb is conducted. For high performance airplanes, 250 kts is a good guess!

$$t_{cl} = h_{cl}/RC_{ave} \qquad (5.38)$$

with: RC_{ave} being determined by one of the climb equations in Section 5.3.

For descent range, Equations (5.37) and (5.38) must be changed to reflect the appropriate descent terms.

The construction of the payload-range diagram for airplanes is discussed in Sub-section 5.4.4.

If part of a mission profile requires a given cruise speed or a given maximum speed, this can be determined graphically from Figure 5.10. At a given thrust (or power) setting the corresponding speed is found from the intersection of the thrust (or power) available and the thrust (or power) required curves. Maximum speed corresponds to the right hand side of the flight envelope as shown in Figure 5.2.

More detailed methods for determining cruise range and cruise speed are presented in Ref.11, Chapter 11. These will not be repeated here. To help the reader find specific models for the computation of range performance, the following guide is presented:

For Propeller Driven Airplanes:

See Reference 11, Section 11.1, pages 454-464.

For Jet Driven Airplanes:

See Reference 11, Section 11.2, pages 464-478.

5.4.4 Step-by-Step Procedure for Analyzing Cruise and Range Performance

Step 1: From the mission requirements of the airplane determine the cruise and range requirements for the airplane. This is most readily done with the help of a mission profile which can be constructed from the airplane mission specification.

Figure 5.9 shows examples of mission profiles for a transport and for a fighter, with the cruise portions indicated.

Tabulate all cruise altitude, cruise speed, range and payload requirements. Also note the configuration the airplane is supposed to be in! For military airplanes, external stores and weapons can have a major effect on the drag polar!

NOTE: Certain military airplanes are required to fly several cruise segments under different speed and altitude conditions!

Step 2: For all flight conditions and configurations defined in Step 1, determine the airplane trimmed drag polars. This can be done with the method of Section 4.10 in Part VI.

Step 3: Using installed engine data, obtain the numerical values for the engine efficiency parameters: c_j (for jets) and/or c_p and η_p (for props).

These parameters depend on speed and altitude which are normally prescribed in the mission requirements.

Chapter 6 in Part VI contains methods for computing installed thrust and/or power characteristics, including efficiencies and s.f.c.'s.

Step 4: Determine the range capability of the airplane in each of the range portions of the mission profile. This is done as follows:

Decide whether the range is to be at constant altitude or at constant speed. Identify which of the Breguet equations (5.33)-(5.36) apply.

For airplanes with short ranges (about 500 nm) it is reasonable to assume that all parameters in the Breguet range equations are constant during the intended cruise operation. For airplanes with medium to long ranges this is not acceptable. For such airplanes it is suggested to break the cruise part of the mission into segments of approximately 500 nm each. The parameters in the Breguet range equations can be assumed constant but different for each cruise segment!

Now proceed as follows:

For the first range segment, estimate the average cruise lift coefficient from:

$$C_{L_{cr_1}} = (W_{begin} - 0.5W_{fuel_1})/\bar{q}_1 S \tag{5.39}$$

where for propeller driven airplanes:

$$W_{fuel_1} = (R_1/V_{cr_1})\{(c_p/\eta_p)P_{reqd}\}_1 \tag{5.40}$$

and where for jet driven airplanes:

$$W_{fuel_1} = (R_1/V_{cr_1})\{c_j W/(L/D)\}_1 \tag{5.41}$$

Note: the subscript '1' here means that the particular quantity applies to cruise segment 1.

The average value of cruise lift coefficient (in Eqn.(5.39)) is entered into the trimmed drag polar to determine the corresponding value of the drag coefficient. This information in turn is used to compute the values of (L/D) and/or of $\{(C_L)^{1/2}/C_D\}$ which are needed in the Breguet range Eqns.(5.33)-(5.36).

This procedure is repeated as many times as needed until the required total range is met or until the fuel available is exhausted.

Step 5: Note any discrepancies between the computed range and the required range. Decide what design changes (if any) must be made.

Possible design changes which can be contemplated at this stage are:

1. Improve L/D by lowering wetted area or increasing the wing loading and/or the aspect ratio.

2. Switch to engines with lower fuel consumption.

3. Switch to a more efficient propeller.

4. Try to design a more efficient structure so that the fuel-to-weight ratio can be improved.

5. Carry more or less fuel, as required.

Any of these design changes may have repercussions for other areas of the design. Design iterations may have to be performed.

<u>Step 6:</u> Prepare a payload range diagram.

This step normally applies only to transport type airplanes. Figure (5.11) shows an example of a payload-range diagram. The important points A, B, C and D are indicated. These points can be determined in the following manner:

Point A: At this point the airplane weight is equal to the sum of the operating weight empty, (W_{OE}) and the maximum payload weight, W_{PL}. There is no fuel on board and thus the range is zero.

Point B: At this point the range is that for maximum payload. This is sometimes called the harmonic range of the airplane. The weight of the airplane at takeoff is equal to the sum of the operating weight empty, W_{OE}, the maximum payload weight, W_{PL} and that fuel weight which causes the airplane to be at its maximum allowable takeoff weight.

The range corresponding to point B is computed with the procedure of Step 4.

Point C: Between points B and C, payload has to be traded for fuel. This can be done until the maximum volumetric capacity (in terms of fuel) of the airplane has been reached. That is the case at point C. The takeoff weight of the airplane is still at its maximum allowable value.

The range corresponding to point C is computed

with the procedure of Step 4. Make sure that the payload weight is computed correctly!

Note: fuel volume limits are normally reached first due to wing fuel volume limitations. In many airplanes additional fuel can be stored in 'safe' parts of the fuselage, in horizontal and /or vertical tails and sometimes in external containers.

Point D: Beyond point C, the only way to get more range out of the airplane is to unload payload weight. At point D, the takeoff weight of the airplane is the sum of its operating weight empty, W_{OE}

and its maximum fuel capability (on basis of volumetric capacity). The range corresponding to point D is called the ferry range.

The range corresponding to point D is computed with the procedure of Step 4. Make sure that NO payload is included and that the takeoff weight is no more than the maximum allowable weight. If there is no fuel volume limit, then the maximum allowable takeoff weight is the limit.

Step 7: Document all the results, including any design changes made.

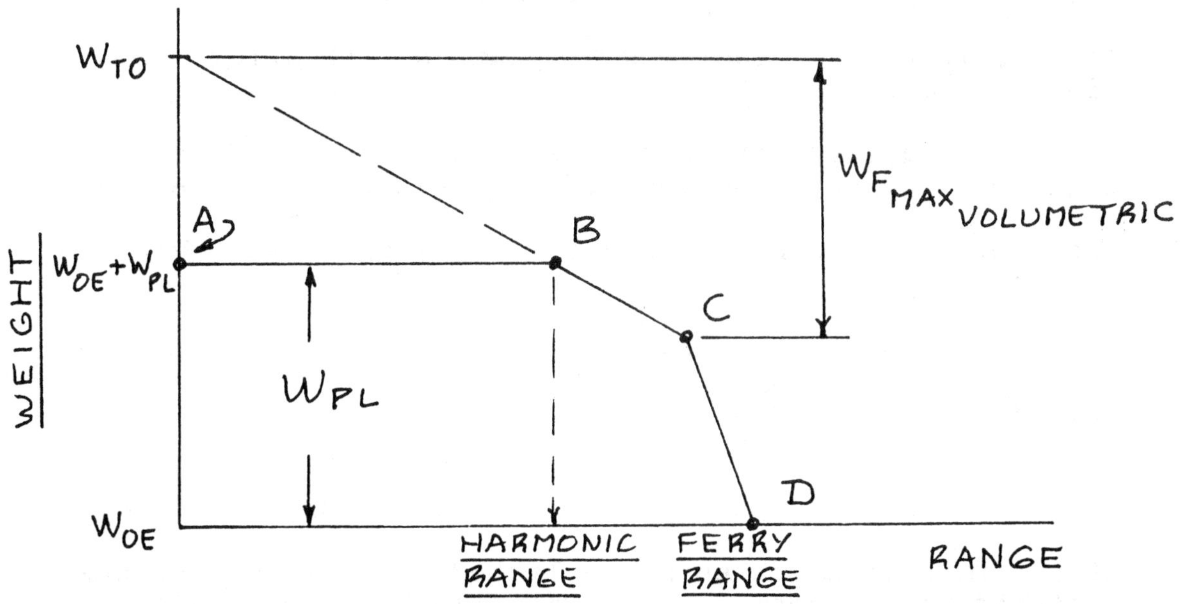

Figure 5.11 Example of a Payload-Range Diagram

5.5 ENDURANCE AND LOITER

5.5.1 Applicable Regulations

Civil: There are no airworthiness regulations which deal specifically with endurance and loiter. Fuel reserve regulations are specified in FAR 91. Most commercial operations are conducted with fuel reserve rules which are more conservative than those of FAR 91.

Military: MIL-C-005011C (USAF) and AS-5263 (USN and USMC), give definitions, see Appendix B.

5.5.2 Relationship to Preliminary Design

See Part I, Chapter 2. In addition, see Part II, Chapter 2, Step 14, Step 27 and Step 28.

5.5.3 Mathematical Model for Analyzing Endurance and Loiter

Figure 5.8 depicts the forces which act on an airplane in a horizontal, steady, symmetrical, 1-g loiter flight condition. The equations of motion are the same as those for range in Sub-section 5.4.3: Eqns.(5.28) and (5.29).

The reader is reminded of the fact, that these equations assume that moment equilibrium exists. This implies, that the airplane drag polar, which defines the relationship between C_L and C_D is the 'trimmed' drag polar. Part VI, Section 4.10 presents a method for computing trim drag.

There also exists a unique relationship between the angle of attack, α and the lift coefficient, C_L. A method for determining C_L versus α is given in Part VI, Chapter 8.

The quantity T in Equations (5.28) and (5.29) is the so-called <u>installed thrust.</u> Methods for determining the installed thrust capability of an airplane are presented in Part VI, Chapter 6.

For most conventional airplanes, the angle $(\alpha + \phi_T)$ is so small that it can be neglected. This, despite the fact that endurance or loitering flights are normally carried out at fairly low speeds and thus at relatively high angles of attack. The lift coefficient for endurance or loiter can be computed from:

$$C_{L_{ltr}} = W/\bar{q}S \tag{5.42}$$

where: W is that weight value appropriate to the endurance/loiter flight condition being analyzed.

The required loiter thrust-to-weight ratio then is:

$$(T/W)_{ltr} = 1/(L/D)_{ltr} \tag{5.43}$$

If $(\alpha + \phi_T)$ is not negligibly small, Eqn.(5.42) is used to find a first approximation for the loiter lift coefficient. This value of C_L is then used to find C_D from the trimmed drag polar and also to find α from the C_L versus α curve. Since the thrust inclination angle, ϕ_T is assumed to be known, Eqn.(5.28) can now be used to find the required installed thrust. This thrust value <u>must be less than the maximum installed thrust available</u> in that flight condition! This thrust value is then substituted into Eqn.(5.29) and a new value for C_L is determined, etc., etc. until the process converges. Convergence may be assumed to have been reached when the lift-to-drag ratio is within 1 percent. This determines the loiter lift-to-drag ratio, $(L/D)_{ltr}$.

<u>IMPORTANT NOTE:</u> The reader will find that in nearly all loiter flight conditions:

$$(L/D)_{ltr} \approx (L/D)_{max} \tag{5.44}$$

Most airplane missions specify loiter or endurance requirements in the following manner:

1. Loiter speed and loiter altitude.

   In high altitude observation airplanes it is essential that the loiter speed be at least equal to that of prevailing winds at loiter altitude.

   In civil airplanes there normally is a requirement to 'hold' at the end of a cruise mission. This is in fact a requirement to loiter. The loiter speed must be compatible with air traffic control requirements.

In military airplanes there often is a requirement to loiter over a given location to wait for attack or engagement instructions.

2. Payload to be carried while loitering.

It is always useful to translate airplane mission requirements and into a mission profile. Figure 5.9 shows examples for a civil and for a military airplane.

For Class II analysis of loiter/endurance performance it is acceptable to use the following Breguet equations PROVIDED the procedure of Step 4 in Sub-section 5.5.4 is used:

For Propeller Driven Airplanes:

For constant altitude endurance/loiter:

$$E = 778(\eta_p/c_p)(\rho S)^{1/2}\{(C_L)^{3/2}/C_D\}* *\{(W_{end})^{-1/2} - (W_{initial})^{-1/2}\} \quad (5.45)$$

Note that E is in hours!

For constant speed endurance/loiter:

$$E = 928(\eta_p/c_p)(1/V)(L/D)\ln(W_{initial}/W_{end}) \quad (5.46)$$

Note that E is in hours and V is in kts!

For Jet Driven Airplanes:

For constant altitude endurance/loiter:

$$E = (1/c_j)(L/D)\ln(W_{initial}/W_{end}) \quad (5.47)$$

Note that E is in hours!

For constant speed endurance/loiter:

$$E = (1/c_j)(L/D)\ln(W_{initial}/W_{end} \quad (5.48)$$

Note that this equation is identical to Eqn.(5.47)!

If part of a mission profile requires a given loiter speed, this can be determined graphically from Figure 5.10. At a given thrust (or power) setting the corresponding speed is found from the intersection of the thrust (or power) available and the thrust (or power) required curves. Note that loiter usually represents the low speed intersection while cruise was represented by the high speed intersection.

More detailed methods for determining endurance/loiter performance are presented in Ref.11, Chapter 11. These will not be repeated here. To help the reader find specific models for the computation of range performance, the following guide is presented:

For Propeller Driven Airplanes:

See Reference 11, Section 11.1, pages 454-464.

For Jet Driven Airplanes:

See Reference 11, Section 11.2, pages 464-478.

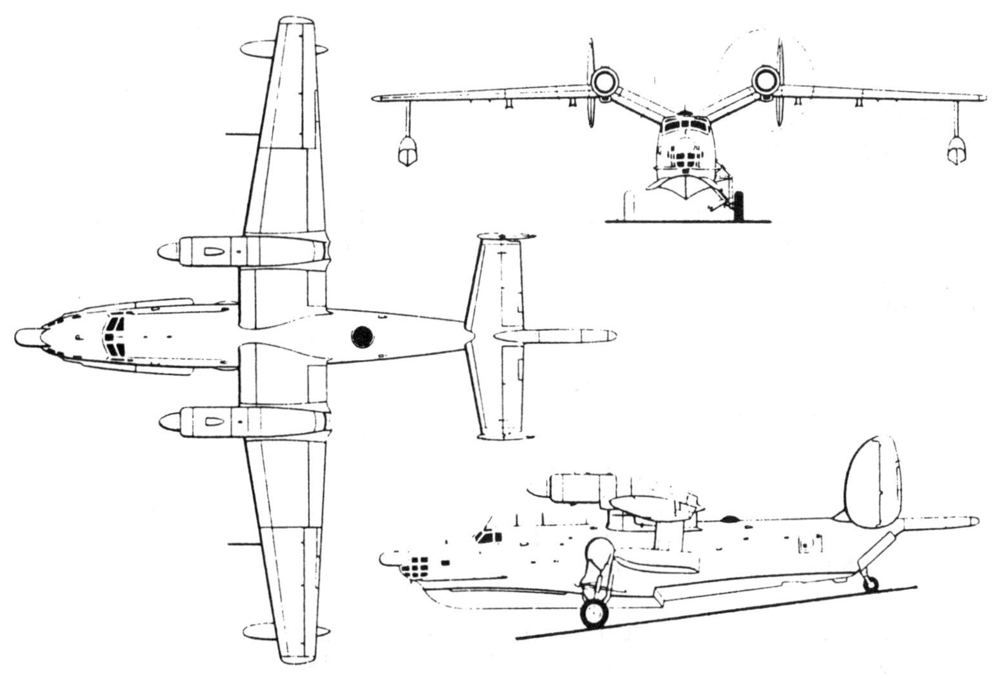

5.5.4 Step-by-Step Procedure for Analyzing Endurance and Loiter

Step 1: From the mission requirements of the airplane determine the endurance and/or loiter requirements. This is most readily done with the help of a mission profile which can be constructed from the airplane mission specification.

Figure 5.9 shows examples of mission profiles for a transport and for a fighter. In Figure 5.9 the loiter requirements are items 6.

Tabulate all endurance/loiter altitude, speed and payload requirements. Also note the configuration the airplane is supposed to be in! For military airplanes, external stores and weapons can have a major effect on the drag polar!

Step 2: For all flight conditions and configurations defined in Step 1, determine the airplane trimmed drag polars. This may be done with the method of Section 4.10 in Part VI.

Step 3: Using installed engine data, obtain the numerical values for the engine efficiency parameters: c_j (for jets) and/or c_p and η_p (for props).

These parameters depend on speed and altitude which are normally prescribed in the mission specification.

Methods for determining installed engine characteristics are given in Chapter 6 of Part VI.

Step 4: Determine the endurance and/or loiter capability of the airplane for each of the endurance or loiter portions of the mission profile. This is done as follows:

Decide whether the endurance and/or loiter is to be performed at constant altitude or at constant speed. Identify which of the Breguet equations (5.45)-(5.48) apply.

For airplanes with short endurance or loiter segments (approximately 0.5 hours) it is reasonable to assume that all parameters in the Breguet equations are constant during the intended operation. For airplanes with longer endurance or loiter requirements this is not acceptable. For such airplanes it is suggested to break the endurance or loiter part of the mission into segments of approximately 0.5 hours each. The parameters in the Breguet endurance/loiter equations can be assumed constant but different for each segment!

Now proceed as follows:

For the first endurance/loiter segment, estimate the average loiter lift coefficient from:

$$C_{L_{ltr_1}} = (W_{begin} - 0.5W_{fuel_1})/\bar{q}_1 S \quad (5.49)$$

where for propeller driven airplanes:

$$W_{fuel_1} = E_1\{(c_p/\eta_p)P_{reqd}\}_1 \quad (5.50)$$

and where for jet airplanes:

$$W_{fuel_1} = E_1\{c_j W/(L/D)\}_1 \quad (5.51)$$

Note: the subscript '1' here means that the particular quantity applies to endurance/loiter segment 1.

The average value of endurance/loiter lift coefficient (in Eqn.(5.49)) is entered into the trimmed drag polar to determine the corresponding value of the drag coefficient. This information in turn is used to compute the values of (L/D) or

$\{(C_L)^{3/2}/C_D\}$ or $\{(C_L)^{1/2}/C_D\}$ which are needed in

the Breguet endurance/loiter Eqns.(5.45)-(5.48).

This procedure is repeated as many times as needed until the required total endurance/loiter time is met or until the fuel is exhausted.

Step 5: Note any discrepancies between the computed endurance/loiter times and those required by the mission specification. Decide what design changes (if any) must be made.

Possible design changes are discussed in Step 5 in Sub-section 5.4.4.

Step 6: Document all the results, including any design changes made.

5.6 DIVE

5.6.1 Applicable Regulations

Civil: There are no airworthiness regulations which deal specifically with dives from a performance viewpoint. The following FAR's define the required load factors at the dive speed for civil airplanes:

FAR 23.333, 23.335, 25.333 and 25.335, see Appendix A and also Part V, pages 31-38.

Military: There are no performance related requirements placed on the dive speed. For load factor definitions, see Part V, pages 38 and 39.

5.6.2 Relationship to Preliminary Design

See Part II, Chapter 2, Step 20.

5.6.3 Mathematical Model for Analyzing Dives

Figure 5.12 depicts the forces which act on an airplane in a straight line dive. The equations of motion for a straight line dive at constant speed are:

$$T\cos(\alpha + \phi_T) - C_D\bar{q}S - W\sin\gamma = 0 \tag{5.52}$$

$$T\sin(\alpha + \phi_T) + C_L\bar{q}S - W\cos\gamma = 0 \tag{5.53}$$

These equations represent a 'snapshot' taken at constant altitude. The flight path (here: dive) angle, γ is negative in these equations and is negative as shown in Figure 5.12.

In these equations, which assume that moment equilibrium exists, the airplane drag coefficient comes from a 'trimmed' drag polar. Part VI, Section 4.10 presents a method for computing trim drag.

The stability and control characteristics of the airplane in dives (high speed) were already discussed in Chapter 4: Sections 2.1, 2.8 and 2.9.

There also exists a unique relationship between the angle of attack, α and the lift coefficient, C_L. A method for determining C_L versus α is given in Part VI, Chapter 8.

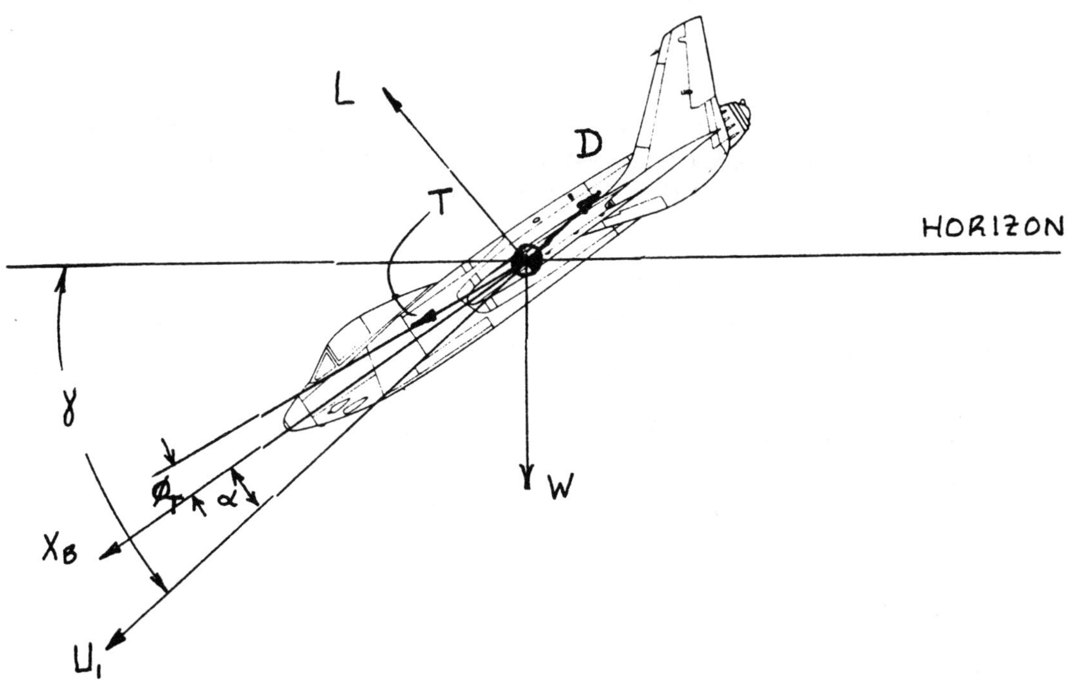

Regular Dive

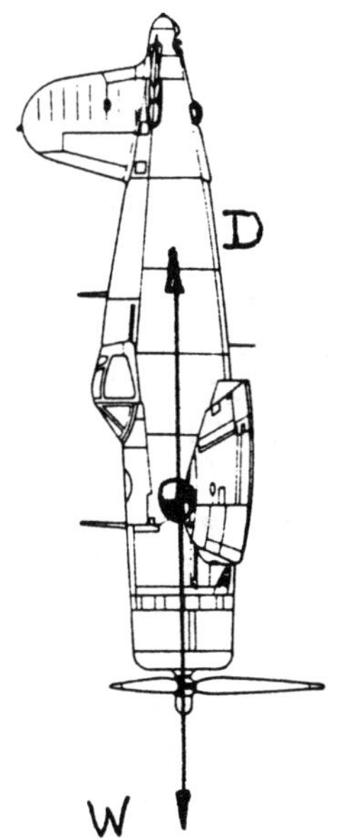

Vertical Dive

Figure 5.12 Forces Acting on an Airplane in a Dive

The quantity T in Equations (5.52) and (5.53) is the so-called installed thrust. Methods for determining the installed thrust capability of an airplane are presented in Part VI, Chapter 6.

The following quantities in Eqns.(5.52) and (5.53) are to be considered as variables: speed or dynamic pressure, $\bar{q}$, angle of attack, α and flight path angle, γ. The thrust (or power) setting, T, the weight, W and the thrust inclination angle ϕ_T are assumed to be known. Obviously one of the variables will have to be preselected!

Usually a dive is considered at some known dive angle or at some known speed.

1. Dive for known speed.

In this case, the dynamic pressure, $\bar{q}$ is known. The solution process goes as follows:

Assume a value for angle of attack, α. This is used to find C_D and C_L. Equation (5.52) is then used to solve for the flight path angle, γ. Next, Equation (5.53) is used to solve for α. This value of α is compared with the first one and an iteration is performed until there is agreement to within 0.1 degrees.

2. Dive for known dive angle.

In this case, the flight path angle, γ is known. The solution process goes as follows:

Assume a value for angle of attack, α. This is used to find C_D and C_L. Equation (5.52) is then used to solve for the dynamic pressure, $\bar{q}$. Next, Equation (5.53) is used to solve for α. This value of α is compared with the first one and an iteration is performed until there is agreement to within 0.1 degrees.

NOTE: in certain applications a speed brake may be employed. The effect of speedbrakes on the drag polar is discussed in Section 4.12 in Part VI.

In extreme cases an airplane may be required to dive vertically. The equilibrium dive speed in such a case is called the 'terminal dive speed'.

Figure 5.12 also shows the forces which act on the airplane in that case. Since no lift is required in a vertical dive, the drag coefficient is equal to the zero-lift drag coefficient, C_{D_o} and the equation of motion is:

$$T - W = C_{D_o}\bar{q}S \tag{5.54}$$

Since T and C_{D_o} both depend on speed, this equation must be solved also with an iteration. Assume a terminal Mach number at some altitude. Find C_{D_o} and the installed thrust (for whatever thrust setting has been assumed) and see if the equation is satisfied. If not, iterate until the terminal dive speed is within 0.5 percent.

5.6.4 Step-by-Step Procedure for Analyzing Dives

Step 1: Determine the flight conditions and airplane configurations for which dives must be performed. This information is normally contained in the mission specification.

Step 2: For the flight conditions and configurations defined in Step 1, determine the trimmed drag polars of the airplane. Also determine the installed thrust (or power) characteristics.

Trimmed drag polars are determined with the method of Chapter 4, Part VI. Installed thrust (or power) characteristics are determined with the method of Chapter 6, Part VI.

Step 3: Use the iteration process defined in Sub-section 5.6.3 to determine the dive performance of the airplane. Compare the results with the requirements and decide whether or not design adjustments are in order.

Step 4: Document the results, including any design changes made.

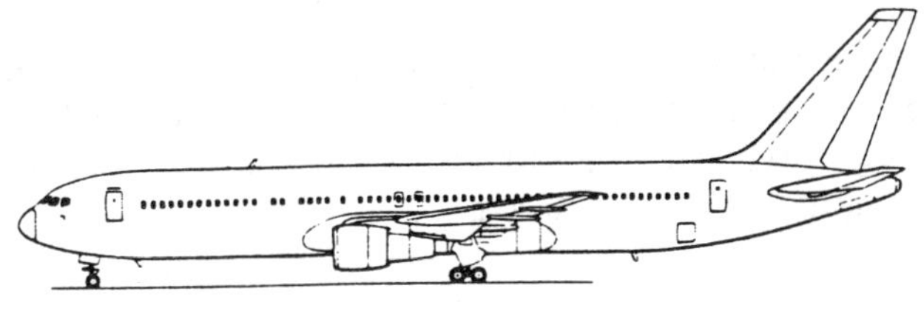

5.7 MANEUVERING

5.7.1 Applicable Regulations

Civil: There are no airworthiness regulations which deal specifically with maneuvering performance. The load factors which an airplane must be able to withstand from a structural viewpoint are covered in:

FAR 23.333, 23.335, 23.337, 25.333, 25.335 and 25.337.

Military: MIL-F-8785C, Pars. 3.1.7 and 3.2.3.5-6.

5.7.2 Relationship to Preliminary Design

See Part I, Section 3.5 and Step 27, Part II.

5.7.3 Mathematical Model for Analyzing Maneuvering Flight

The following maneuvers will be considered:

1. Instantaneous maneuvers: pull-up (push-over) and level turns
2. Sustained maneuvers: pull-up (push-over) and level turns.

Figures 5.13 and 5.14 show the forces which act on an airplane in pull-ups and in level turns.

The equations of motion for the situation of Figure 5.13, which represents a steady, symmetrical pullup are:

$$T\cos(\alpha + \phi_T) - C_D\bar{q}S - W\sin\gamma = 0 \quad (5.55)$$

$$T\sin(\alpha + \phi_T) + C_L\bar{q}S - (W/g)U_1Q_1 - W\cos\gamma = 0 \quad (5.56)$$

Note that at the bottom of the pullup: $\gamma = 0$.

These equations represent a 'snapshot' taken at constant altitude. The flight path (here: dive) angle, γ is negative in these equations and as shown in Figure 5.13.

In these equations, which assume that moment equilibrium exists, the airplane drag coefficient comes from a 'trimmed' drag polar. Part VI, Section 4.10 presents a method for computing trim drag.

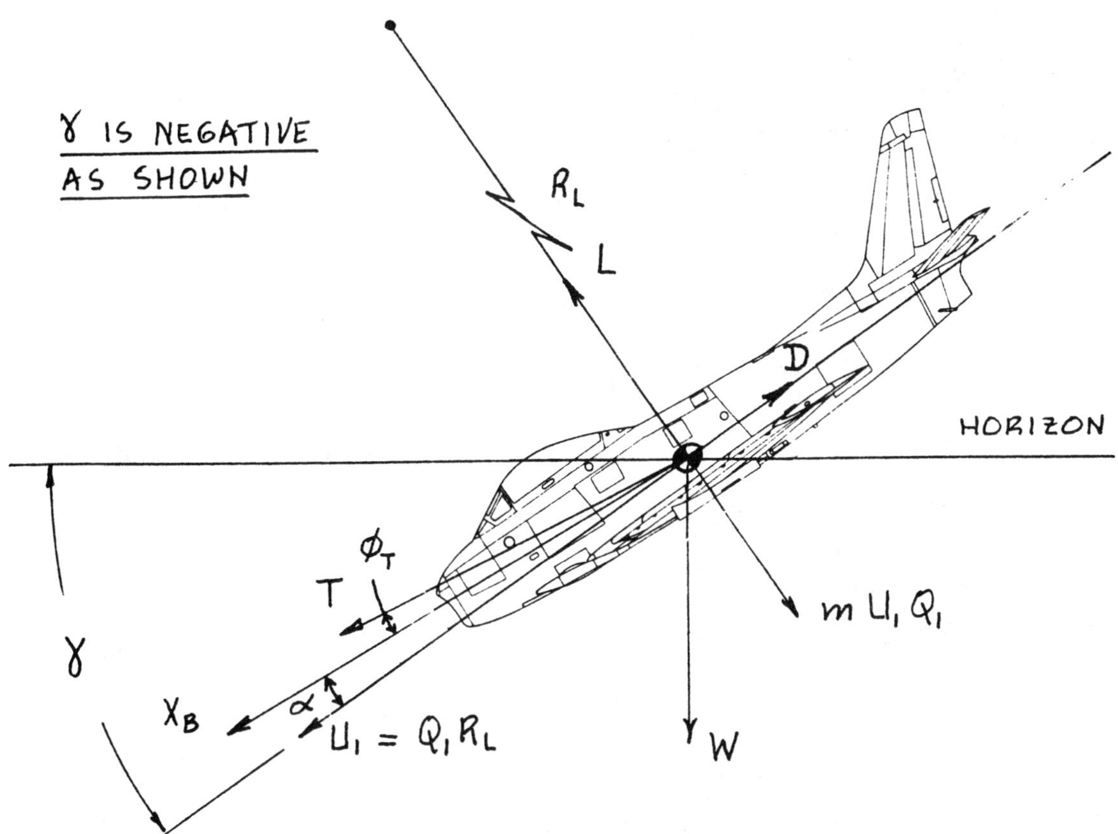

Figure 5.13 Forces Acting on an Airplane in a Pullup

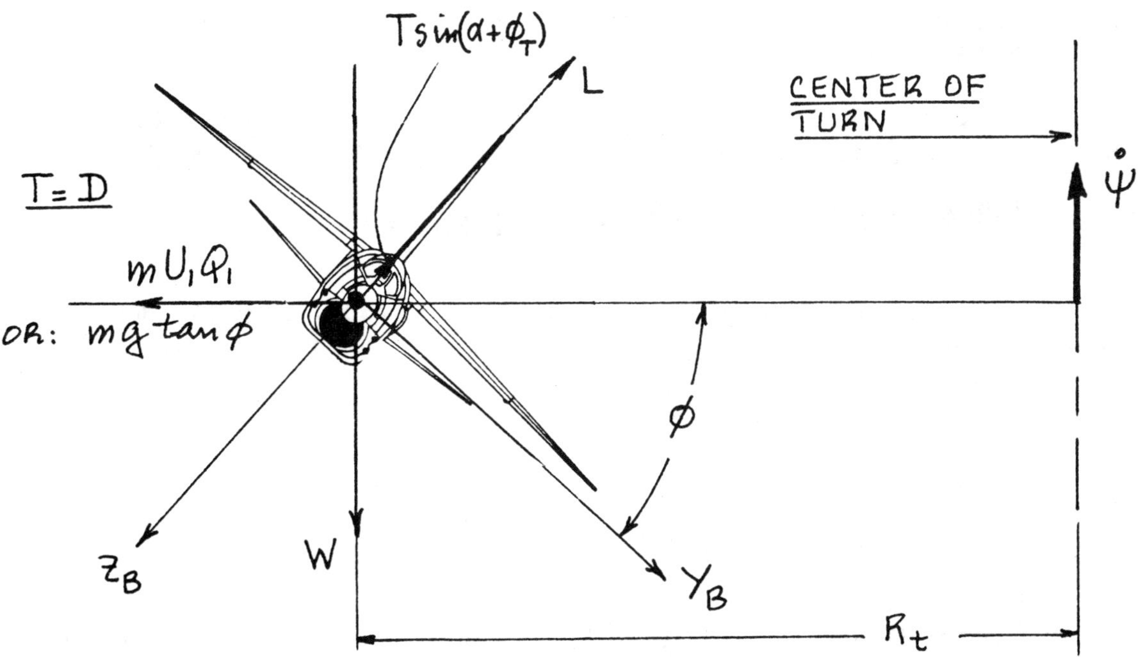

Figure 5.14 Forces Acting on an Airplane in a Level Turn

The stability and control characteristics of the airplane in dives (high speed) were already discussed in Chapter 4: Sections 2.1, 2.8 and 2.9.

There also exists a unique relationship between the angle of attack, α and the lift coefficient, C_L. A method for determining C_L versus α is given in Part VI, Chapter 8. The lift coefficient in this case is also dependent on pitchrate, Q_1 through the stability derivative: C_{L_q}. The reader is referred to Chapter 5 of Reference 12 for a discussion of this effect.

The pitchrate, Q_1 in a pullup is:

$$Q_1 = (g/U_1)(n - 1) \tag{5.57}$$

where: n is the load factor in the maneuver.

The quantity T in Equations (5.55) and (5.56) is the so-called <u>installed thrust.</u> Methods for determining the installed thrust capability of an airplane are presented in Part VI, Chapter 6.

The equations of motion for the situation depicted in Figure 5.14 (steady level turn) are:

$$T\cos(\alpha + \phi_T) - C_D\bar{q}S = 0 \tag{5.58}$$

$$T\sin(\alpha+\phi_t)+C_L\bar{q}S - W\cos\phi - (W/g)U_1Q_1\sin\phi = 0 \tag{5.59}$$

All comments made for Equations (5.55) and (5.56) apply also to these equations. The pitchrate, Q_1 in a level turn is:

$$Q_1 = (g/U_1)(n - 1/n) \tag{5.60}$$

The <u>turnrate</u> in a level turn is:

$$\dot{\psi}_1 = (g\tan\phi)/U_1 = (g/U_1)(n^2 - 1)^{1/2} \tag{5.61}$$

The <u>turn radius</u> in a level turn is:

$$R_t = \{(U_1)^2/g\}/\tan\phi = \{(U_1)^2/g\}/(n^2 - 1)^{1/2} \quad (5.62)$$

As a help to the reader, Figure 5.15 has been included. It allows rapid determination of turnrate and turn radius.

In the case of acrobatic airplanes and certain military airplanes the mission specification may contain specific numerical requirements for 'pulling g's or for specific turnrates and /or turn radii.

To meet these requirements on an <u>instantaneous</u> basis, all that is required is to show that the maximum trimmed lift capability of the airplane in a given flight condition and airplane configuration is not exceeded:

$$C_{L_{maneuver}} < C_{L_{max}} \text{ or } C_{L_{buffet}} \quad (5.63)$$

To meet these requirements on a <u>sustained</u> basis, condition (5.63) must still be satisfied. However, in addition, the following condition must be satisfied:

$$T_{reqd} < T_{max} \text{ or } P_{reqd} < P_{max} \quad (5.64)$$

At this stage in the preliminary design process it suffices to verify the sustained capability by showing that:

<u>for jet airplanes:</u>

$$T_{reqd} = \{C_{D_o} + (C_{L_{man}})^2/\pi Ae\}\bar{q}S < T_{max} \quad (5.65)$$

<u>for propeller driven airplanes:</u>

$$P_{reqd} = \{C_{D_o} + (C_{L_{man}})^2/\pi Ae\}\bar{q}SU_1/550 < P_{max} \quad (5.66)$$

The lift coefficient in Equations (5.65) and (5.66) is to be found from:

$$C_{L_{man}} = nC_{L_1} \quad (5.67)$$

where: n is the loadfactor in the maneuver and

$$C_{L_1} = W/\bar{q}S \quad (5.68)$$

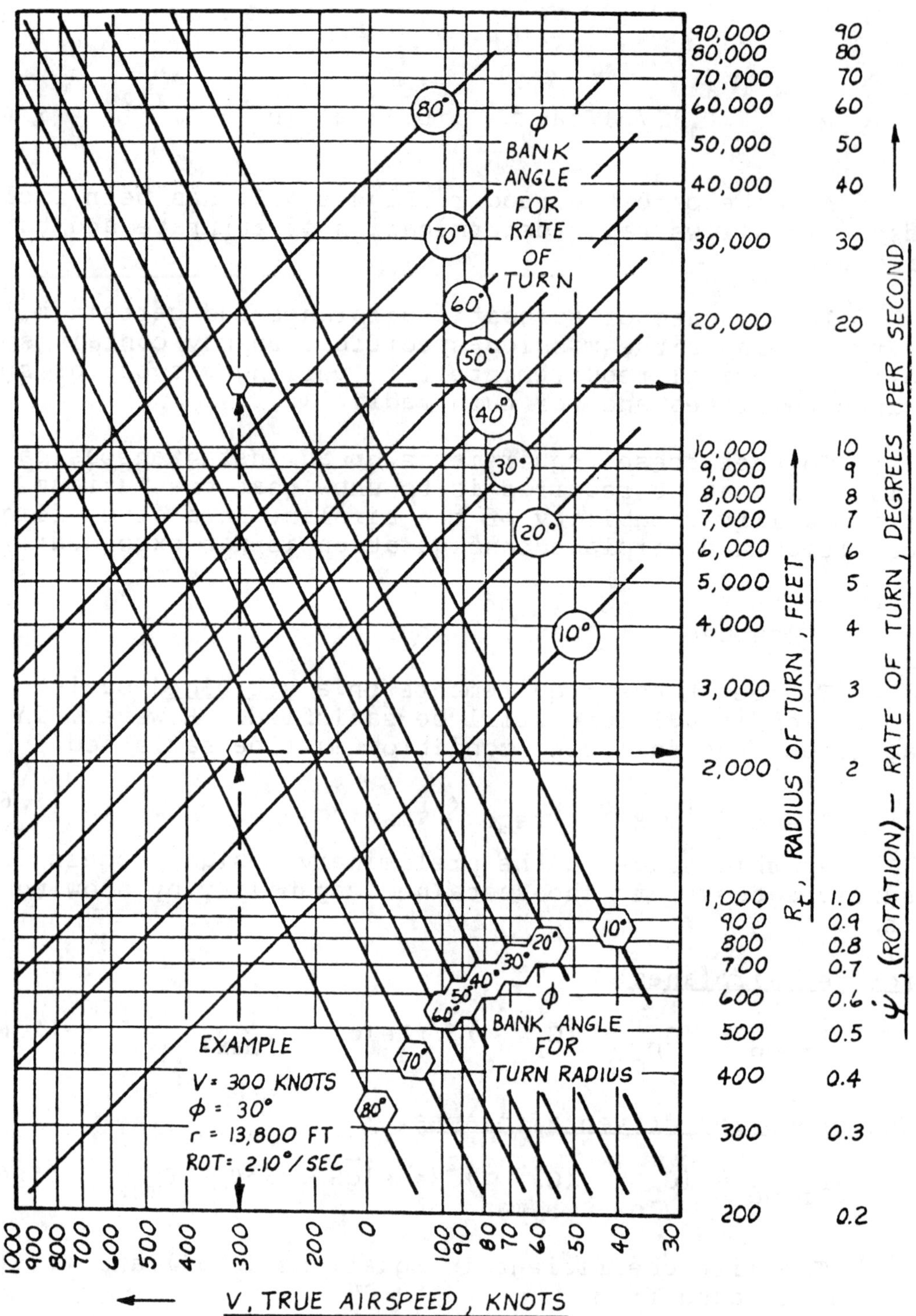

Figure 5.15 Generalized Turning Performance in a Level Turn

Taken from: Hurt, H.H.Jr., Aerodynamics for Pilots, ATC Manual 51-3, 1963.

IMPORTANT NOTE:

Whenever sufficient thrust (or power) IS NOT available to keep the speed constant in a pullup or turn, the speed will begin to bleed off. The rate at which this occurs is called the 'Bleed Rate'. See Appendix B for further information on bleed rate. Modern fighters may have to be designed to have certain minimum bleed rate values in certain combat situations. The equations of motion which govern the airplane behavior in such cases is too complex for Class II methods. Reference 12 in Chapter 2, page 43 shows a development of the general equations of motion. The bleed rate can be determined from these equations by integration.

An approximation for the bleed rate is given in Sub-section 5.7.4.

The reader is encouraged to read Reference 29 for some interesting views on fighter agility.

5.7.4 Step-by-Step Procedure for Analyzing Maneuvering Flight

Step 1: From the mission specification of the airplane determine the required maneuvering capabilities.

Typically these are stated in terms of:

1. Instantaneous g's
2. Sustained g's
3. Turn radius
4. Turnrate
5. Bleedrate

Tabulate the flight conditions and airplane configurations for which maneuvering requirements must be met.

Step 2: Match each maneuvering requirement with the appropriate equation in Sub-section 5.7.3 and determine the required input information.

This input information generally will consist of:

1. Trimmed drag polars for the appropriate Mach number and configuration.

2. Installed thrust (or power) data for the ap-

propriate Mach number and throttle setting.

3. Maximum trimmed lift capability and buffet boundary data.

NOTE: In sub-section 5.7.3 no equation was given for bleed rate. As a first and rough approximation it is suggested to use:

$$\text{Bleed rate} = \dot{u} = C_D\bar{q}S - T\cos(\alpha + \phi_T) \tag{5.69}$$

where: $$C_D = C_{D_o} + (C_{L_{man}})^2/\pi Ae \tag{5.70}$$

with: $C_{L_{man}}$ given by Eqn.(5.67).

Step 3: With the data and equations from Steps 1 and 2 determine whether the airplane meets the maneuvering requirements.

If discrepancies are evident, identify the reason(s). Typical reasons for not meeting maneuvering requirements are:

1. Deficiency in maximum lift capability: this requires adjustments in wing design

2. Deficiencies in thrust (or power) capability: this requires adjustments in powerplant choice or powerplant installation design.

Decide on any design adjustments required and see whether the design needs to be iterated.

Note: For fighter airplanes the maneuvering and specific excess power (specific energy) capabilities are often plotted as a function of speed and altitude. Figures 5.16 and 5.17 represent typical examples.

Step 4: Document the results, including any design changes made.

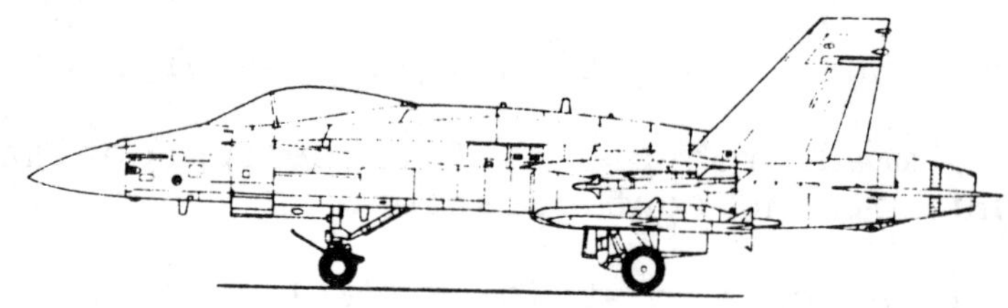

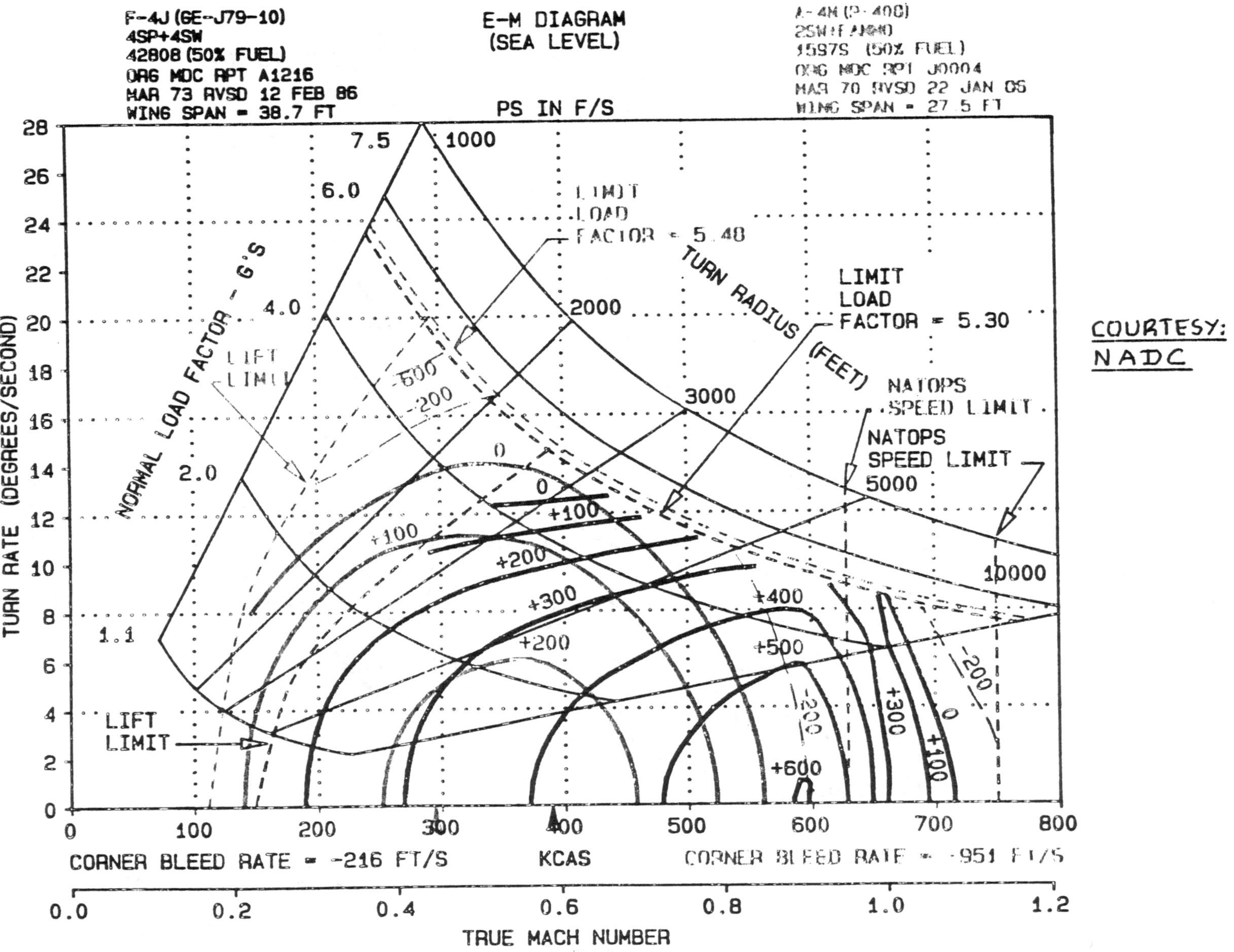

Figure 5.16 Maneuvering Performance: F-4J Versus A-4M

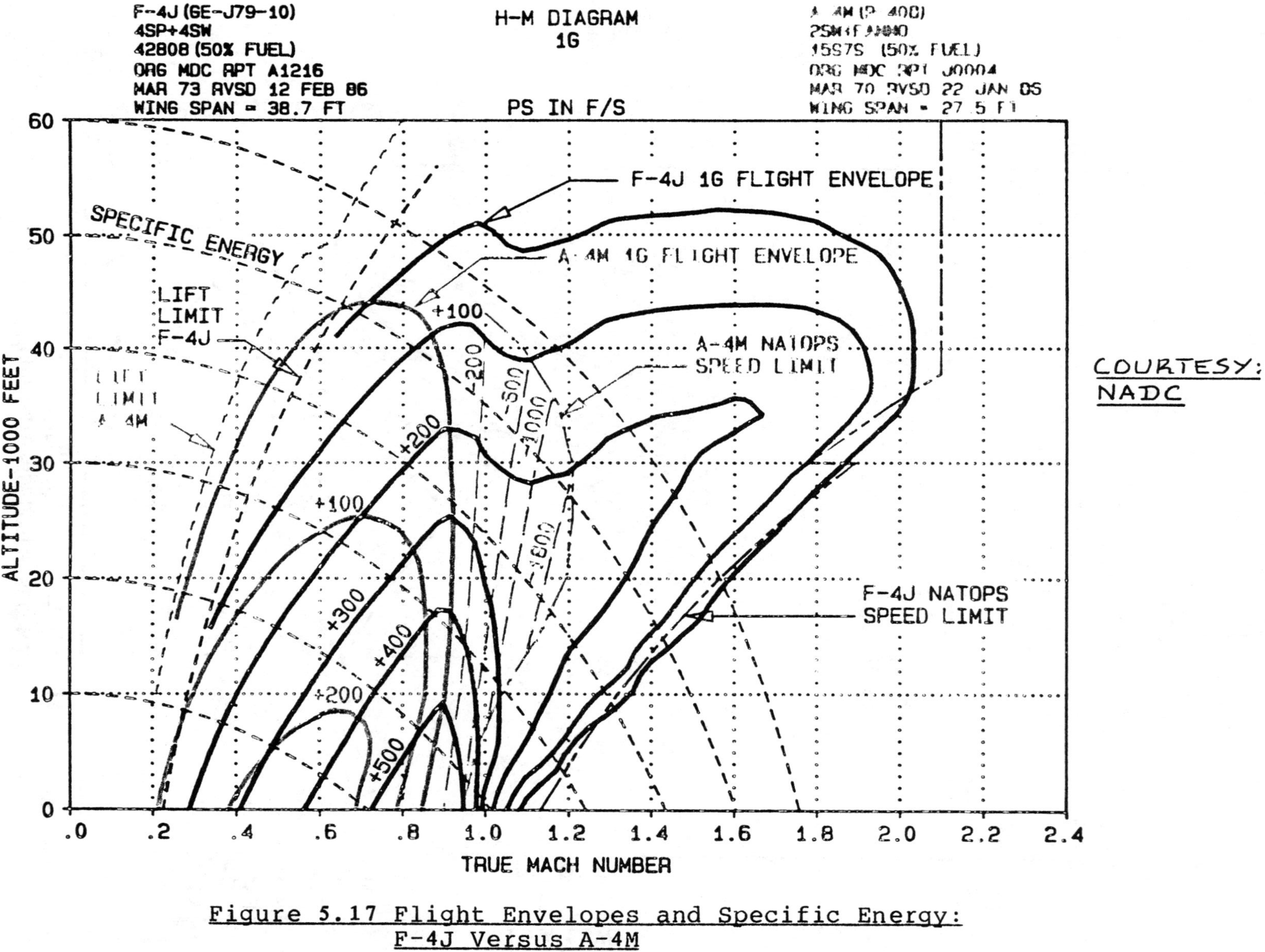

Figure 5.17 Flight Envelopes and Specific Energy: F-4J Versus A-4M

5.8 DESCENT AND GLIDE

5.8.1 Applicable Regulations

Civil: There are no regulations which deal with descents and glides from a performance viewpoint. The descent flight phase normally terminates in an approach to landing. During that phase the climb regulations are in effect: see Section 5.3.

Military: The only regulation in force is that which disallows range credit for descents by subsonic airplanes. For supersonic airplanes descent range credit may be taken in certain instances. See: MIL-C-005011B, par.3.5.3.4. The USNavy AS-5263 does not allow range credit for descent at all. See Appendix B.

5.8.2 Relationship to Preliminary Design

This performance item was not included in the airplane sizing process, except to account for fuel used: see Part I, Section 2.4.

5.8.3 Mathematical Model for Analyzing Descent and Glide

Descents and glides are closely related to climbs and dives. The differences are subtle. In a descent the flight path angle is normally shallow and thrust (or power) is reduced. In a glide the flight path angle is still shallow (the Space Shuttle is an exception!) but the thrust (or power) is at flight idle, zero or absent (such as in gliders!).

Figure 5.18 depicts the forces which act on an airplane in a descent, Figure 5.19 for a glide.

For a (partial) power descent, the equations of motion are:

$$T\cos(\alpha + \phi_T) - C_D\bar{q}S - W\sin\gamma = 0 \tag{5.71}$$

$$T\sin(\alpha + \phi_T) + C_L\bar{q}S - W\cos\gamma = 0 \tag{5.72}$$

These equations are identical to Eqns.(5.52) and (5.53), with the flight path angle, γ being NEGATIVE again. Solutions to these equations are discussed in Subsection 5.6.3 on pages 146-148.

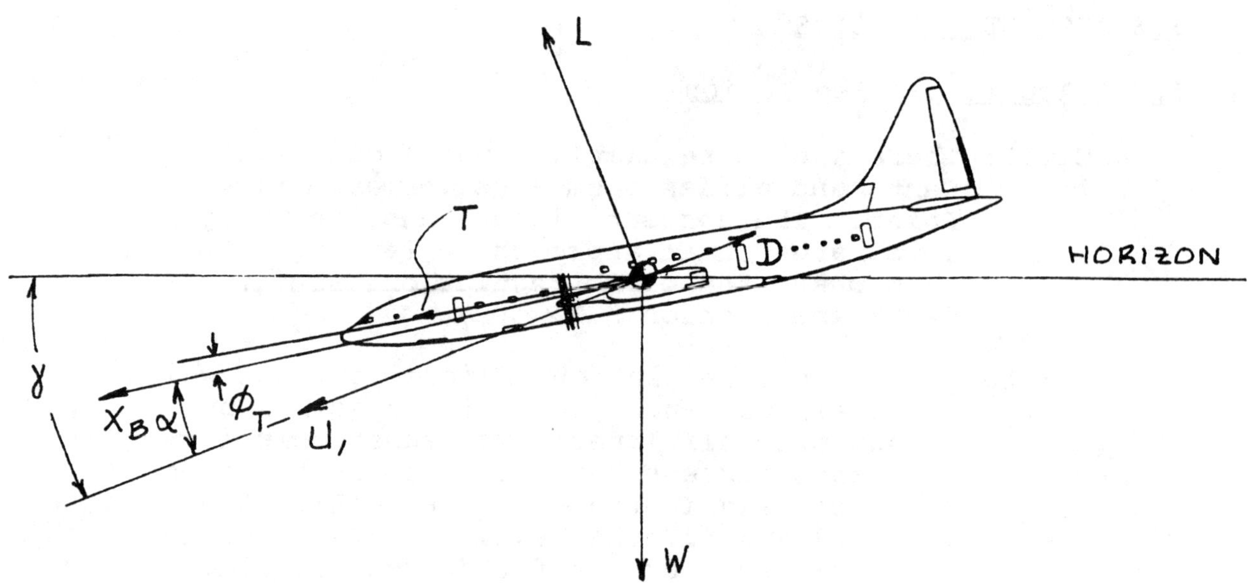

Figure 5.18 Forces Acting on an Airplane in a Descent

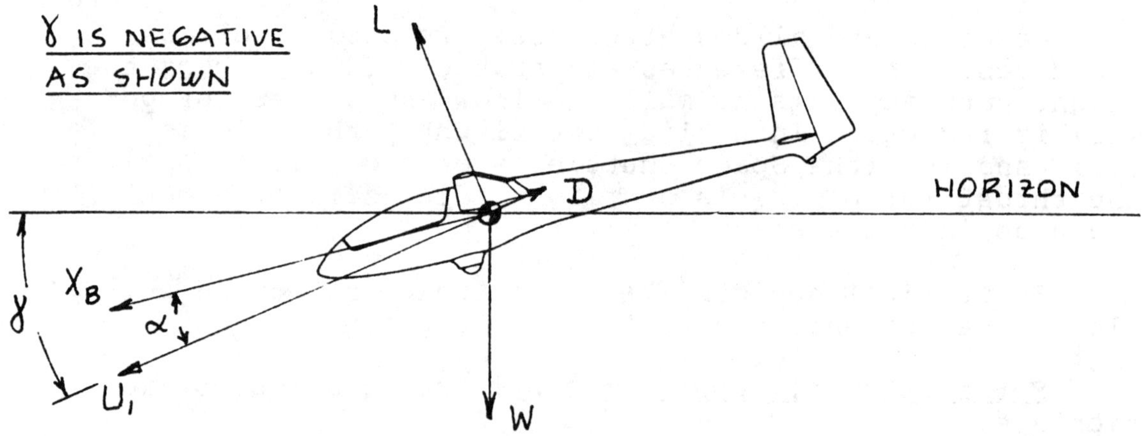

Figure 5.19 Forces Acting on an Airplane in a Glide

Once the flight path angle is known, the rate of descent, RD is found from:

$$RD = -U_1 \sin\gamma, \text{ with } \gamma \text{ being negative} \tag{5.73}$$

For a glide (power off), the equations of motion are:

$$C_D\bar{q}S + W\sin\gamma = 0 \tag{5.74}$$

$$C_L\bar{q}S - W\cos\gamma = 0 \tag{5.75}$$

In this case the flight path angle, γ follows from:

$$\tan\gamma = -(C_D/C_L) = -1/(C_L/C_D) \tag{5.76}$$

The rate of descent follows from:

$$RD = \left\{(W/S)(2/\rho)\left(C_D^2/C_L^3\right)(\cos\gamma)^3\right\}^{1/2} \tag{5.77}$$

If the glide is conducted at constant lift-to-drag ratio, the glide range is:

$$R_{GL} = -h/\tan\gamma \tag{5.78}$$

Similarly, the time-in-the-air follows from:

$$t_{GL} = h/RD \tag{5.79}$$

5.8.4 Step-by-Step Procedure for Analyzing Descent and Glide

Step 1: Determine the descent and/or glide requirements for the airplane from the mission specification.

Note: Except for gliders, most airplane specifications do not contain requirements for descents and/or glides.

Step 2: Determine which of equations (5.71)-(5.79) apply to and obtain the required input information.

Step 3: Compute the descent and/or glide flight path angle, speed, rate-of-descent, range and time-in-the-air. Compare these data with the requirements (if any). Determine what (if any) design adjustments must be made.

If the deficiency is in glide range or time-in-the-air, the problem is usually too much drag.

Step 4: Document the results of all calculations, including any design adjustments made.

5.9 LANDING

5.9.1 Applicable Regulations

Civil: FAR 23.75 and FAR 25.125, see Appendix A.

Military: MIL-C-005011B, par. 3.4.2.11, 3.4.2.12 and 3.4.7 and:
AS-5263, par. 3.5.2.12-13, and 3.5.7, see Appendix B.

5.9.2 Relationship to Preliminary Design

See Part I, Section 3.3.

5.9.3 Mathematical Model for Analyzing Landing Performance

The definition of landing distance and the associated reference speeds depends on which regulation is used to certify the airplane: FAR 23, FAR 25 or Military.

Figure 5.20 shows the differences in the definitions for landing distances and the associated reference speeds.

The following method for computing the landing distance, s_L and the landing fieldlength, s_{FL} is due to Torenbeek (Reference 28):

For FAR 25:

$$s_{FL} = s_L/0.6 \tag{5.80}$$

For FAR 23 and for Military:

$$s_L = s_{AIR} + s_{LG} \tag{5.81}$$

where: s_{AIR} is the distance from the obstacle height, h_L to the point of touchdown:

$$s_{AIR} = (1/\bar{\gamma})\{(V_A{}^2 - V_{TD}{}^2)/2g + h_L\} \tag{5.82}$$

with: $\bar{\gamma} = \{(D - T)/W\}_{ave}$, (5.83)

for which an average value of 0.10 is often used. This quantity actually ranges from about 0.05 (transports) at the obstacle, to a value of C_D/C_L in ground effect at touch-

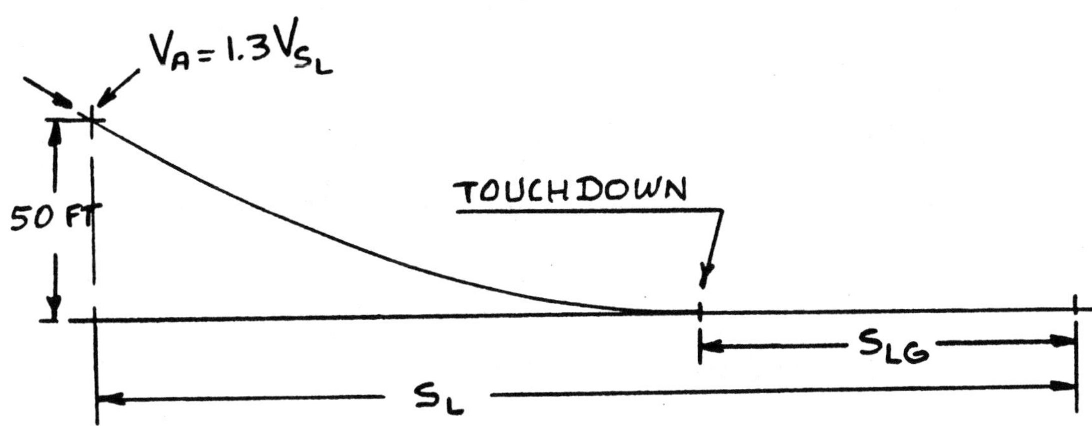

Definition of FAR 23 Landing Distance

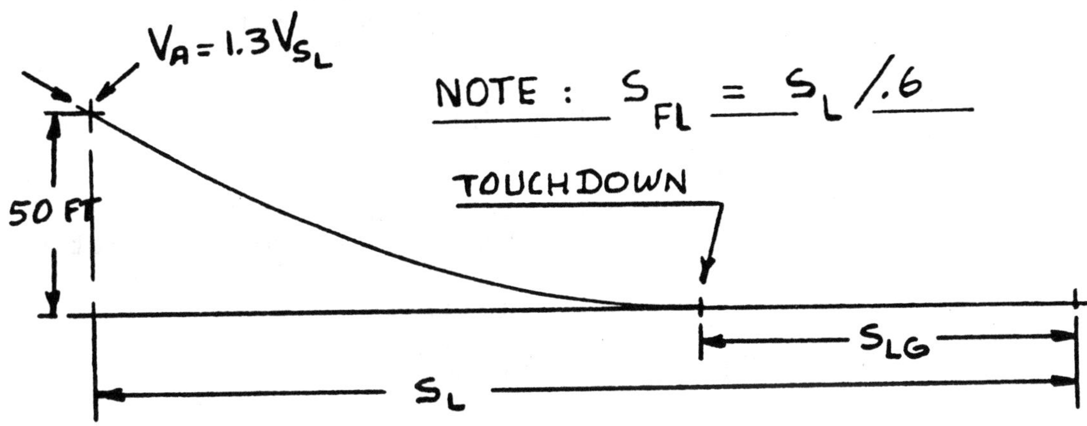

Definition of FAR 25 landing Distance

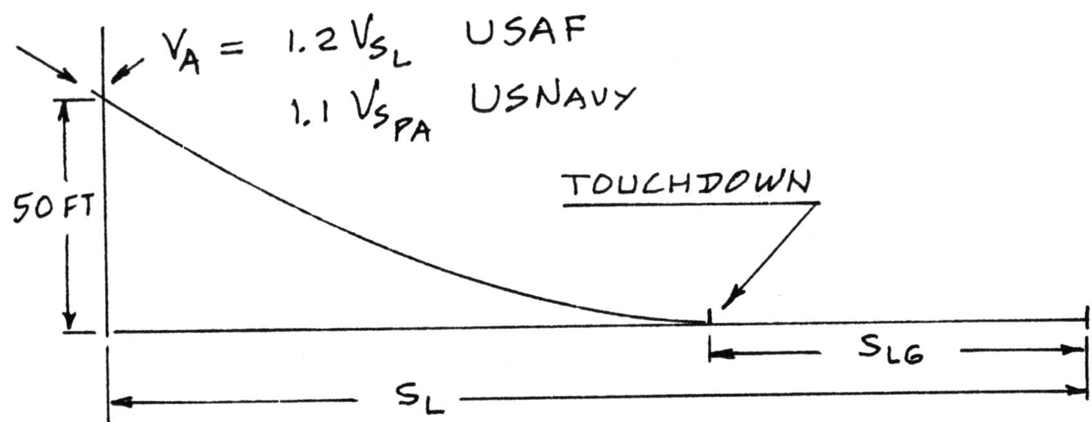

Definition of Military Landing Distance

Figure 5.20 Definition of Landing Distances According to the Regulations

down which assumes that T=0 at touchdown.

V_A is the approach speed at the obstacle:

<u>FAR 23 and 25:</u> $V_A = 1.3V_{s_L}$ (5.84)

<u>MIL-C-005011B:</u> $V_A = 1.2V_{s_L}$ (5.85)

<u>AS-5263:</u> $V_A = 1.1V_{s_{PA}}$ (5.86)

but with thrust required for level flight at 1.15V_s

$$V_{TD} = V_A[1 - \{(\bar{\gamma})^2/\Delta n\}]^{1/2} \quad (5.87)$$

with: Δn = 0.10 as a reasonable average: this quantity depends on pilot technique and on airplane handling qualities!

h_L = 50 feet in all regulations

s_{LG} is the landing ground run to zero speed on the runway:

$$s_{LG} = \{(V_{TD})^2\}/2\bar{a} \quad (5.88)$$

with: $\bar{a}$, the average deceleration for the groundrun. In preliminary design it is acceptable to use:

<u>For light airplanes</u> with simple brake systems:

$\bar{a}/g$ = 0.30 to 0.35

<u>For turboprops</u> without use of reversible propellers:

$\bar{a}/g$ = 0.35 to 0.45

For <u>turbojets</u> and <u>turbofans</u> with groundspoilers, antiskid devices and speed brakes (but no reverse thrust):

$\bar{a}/g = 0.40$ to 0.50

For the latter, including nosewheel braking:

$\bar{a}/g = 0.50$ to 0.60

Important Note:

Airplanes which are carrier based must be compatible with the performance restrictions inherent in each arresting system. A suitable mathematical model for determining compatibility with USNavy arresting gear systems is given in Sub-sub-section 3.3.5.2, page 115, Part I.

5.9.4 Step-by-Step Procedure for Analyzing Landing Performance

The following step-by-step procedure is suggested for determining the landing distance(s) of an airplane:

Step 1: Determine which regulation applies to the design and read that regulation. See Table 1.3 and Sub-section 2.1.1.

Determine the landing distance requirements from the mission specification.

Step 2: Determine whether Eqn.(5.80) or Eqn.(5.81) govern the landing distance calculation and prepare the necessary input data.

IMPORTANT NOTES:

1. Military airplanes may have to land with a variety of stores on board. Their effect on weight and on the drag polar must be accounted for.

2. The weight at landing is the so-called landing weight, W_L. The regulations require the designer to identify what that landing weight is in relationship to the takeoff weight, W_{TO}.

   Table 3.3, page 107 of Part I provides typical ranges of landing-weight-to-takeoff-weight ratios.

Step 3: Compute the landing distance(s) with the appropriate equation of Step 2 and compare the results with the requirements of Step 1. If there is a discrepancy of more than 5 percent, design changes are warranted.

Step 4: Decide what (if any) design changes are warrented. Typical design changes which can be contemplated are:

1. Lower wing loading, W/S

2. Higher maximum landing lift coefficient, $C_{L_{max_L}}$. This can be achieved with a change in wing flap design. The effect on weight, complexity and lateral control space must be accounted for!

Step 5: Document the results obtained, including any design changes made.

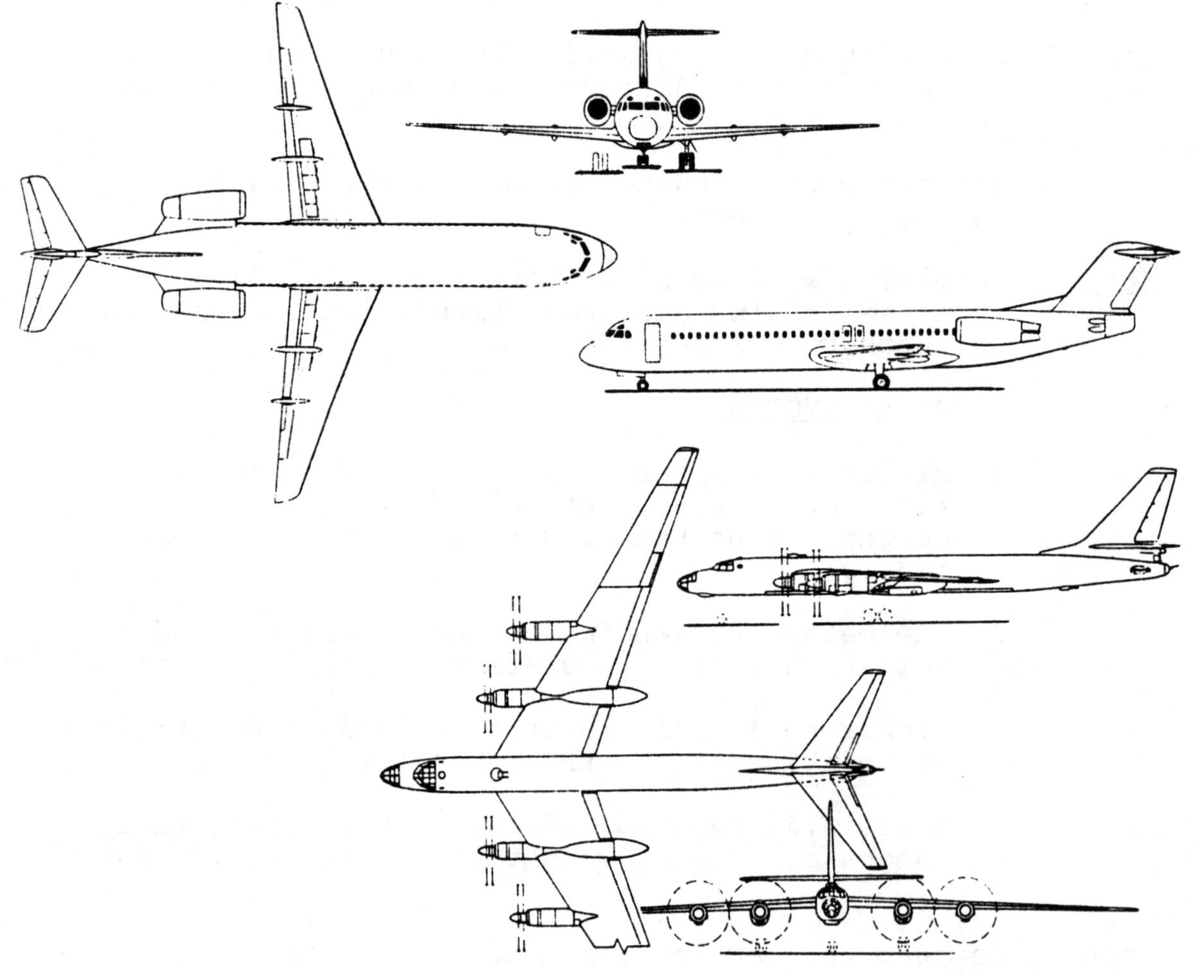

5.10 MISSION PROFILE ANALYSIS

Particularly in the case of military airplanes, but also for civil airplanes it is useful to prepare mission profiles for all intended missions of the airplane.

Two examples mission profiles are given in Fig.5.21. These mission profiles were used in the early sizing process as outlined in Chapter 2 of Part I. The initial mission performance verification was done as part of P.D. Sequence I, see Step 14, page 16, Part II.

These mission profiles are used again in the final mission performance verification process as outlined in Sections 5.1-5.9 of this chapter. This corresponds to Step 24 in P.D. Sequence II, see page 20, Part II.

For military airplanes various military missions have been given 'standardized' mission profiles. Detailed examples of these may be found in Appendix B.

It will be seen that these mission profiles consist of mission segments which are typically labelled as:

Takeoff,	Climb,	Cruise,	Loiter,
Descent,	Landing,	Combat,	etc.

The methods of Sections 5.1 - 5.9 can be used to perform almost any mission profile analysis.

A typical mission profile analysis will produce the following results:

1. Verification of stall speed requirements: see Section 5.1 for the method.

2. Verification of takeoff fieldlength requirements: see Section 5.2 for the method.

3. Verification of climb requirements: see Section 5.3 for the method.

4. Verification of cruise, range and payload-range requirements: see Section 5.4 for the method.

5. Verification of endurance/loiter requirements: see Section 5.5 for the method.

6. Verification of dive requirements: see Section 5.6 for the method.

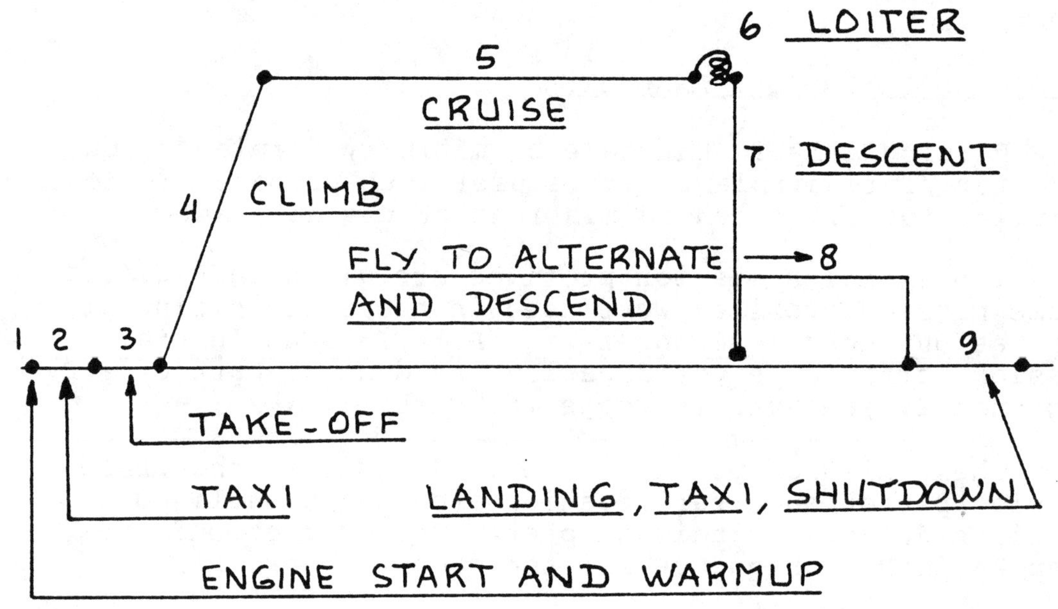

Transport

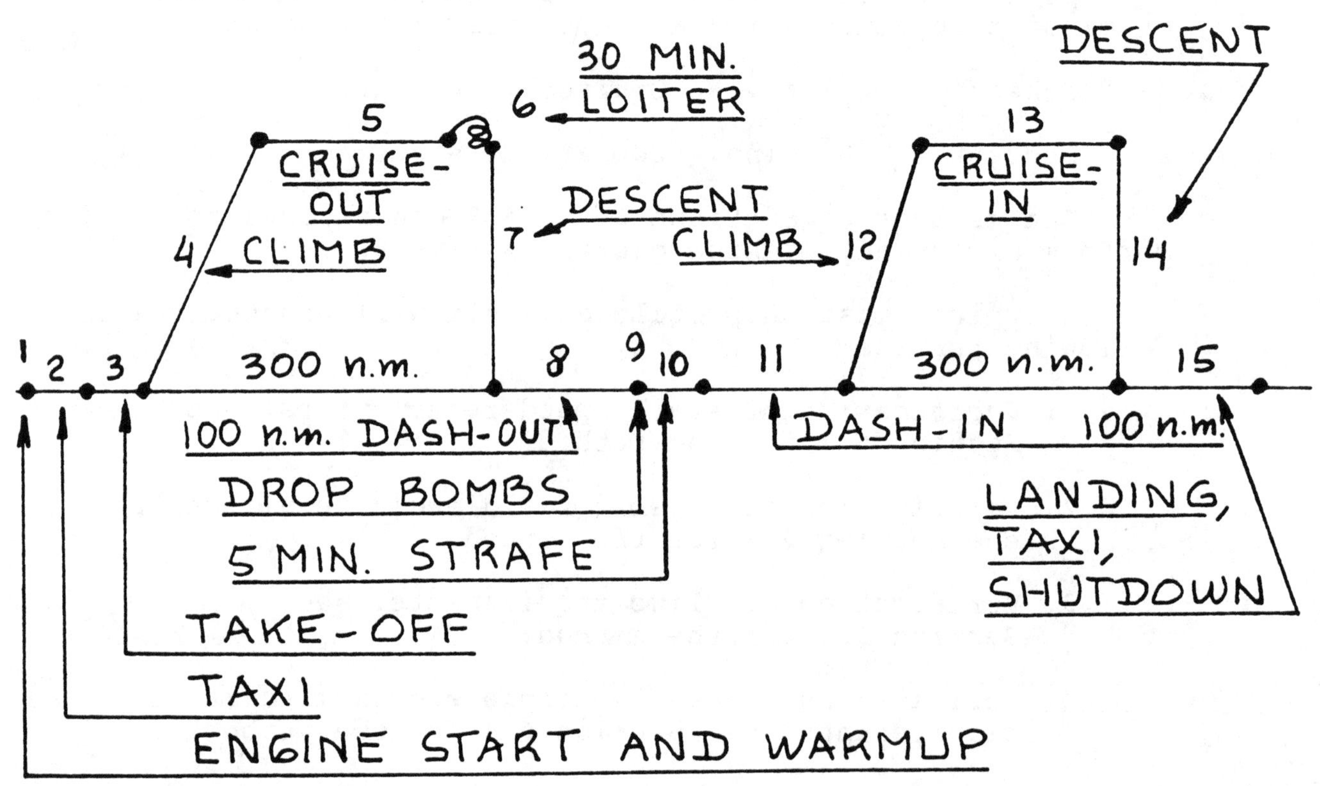

Fighter

Figure 5.21 Example Mission Profiles

7. Verification of maneuvering requirements: see Section 5.7 for the method.

8. Verification of descent and glide requirements: see Section 5.8 for the method.

9. Verification of landing fieldlength requirements: see Section 5.9 for the method.

10. Verification of fuel used during each segment of the intended mission profile:

    For each mission profile segment, i the fuel used can be estimated from:

$$(W_{F_{used}})_i = (\dot{W}_F)_i t_i \tag{5.89}$$

    where: $(\dot{W}_F)_i$ is the average fuel flow rate in pounds per second for segment i.

    t_i is the time to complete segment i.

    Notes: 1. for climb, cruise, loiter, and descent mission phases values for t_i are easily

    obtained. For other mission phases these times have to be based on the operational environment. For example, taxi-fuel will be more for Chicago O'Hare than for Kansas City International.

    2. for military airplanes the method used to compute 'fuel'used' in specific mission segments is outlined in Appendix B!

    3. lacking data on the operational environment of a civil airplane, use the military method of Appendix B.

11. Preparation of a payload-range diagram: see Section 5.4 for the methodology.

12. Mission performance critique: this consists of a list of performance shortcomings AND performance excesses PLUS a list of suggested 'fixes'

The effect of performance demands during each individual mission profile segment on the takeoff weight of an airplane is easily evaluated with the so-called 'Breguet-Partials' method of Section 2.7 in Part I.

5.11 PRODUCTIVITY

When the technical aspects of the design of a new airplane have been decided on and the configuration is frozen, the important question is:

IS THE PRODUCTIVITY OF THE AIRPLANE SUFFICIENTLY HIGH TO WARRANT ITS FULL SCALE DEVELOPMENT?

To give an answer to this question, two tasks must be performed:

1. An analysis of the COST of the airplane.

   This corresponds to Step 36, page 23 of Part II. Methods for cost analysis are given in Part VIII.

2. A set of productivity evaluation criteria must be agreed upon so that the new design can be judged in a fair and understood manner.

   A number of possible evaluation criteria are given in this section.

The methods of Parts I through VII are aimed at designing an airplane to a set of stated mission requirements, while meeting all applicable airworthiness regulations. Along the way a large number of 'arbitrary' design decisions are made. The impact of these design decisions on the productivity of the airplane are not always clear. One example of such an 'arbitrary' decision was the selection of the overall configuration: Step 3 in Preliminary Design Sequence I, page 11, Part II.

That such an important decision as the selection of the overall configuration is labelled as 'arbitrary' may surprise the reader, but it should not. Refer to Figure 1.1, page 5 of Part II and to Note 1 at the bottom of page 3 of Part II!!!

In many instances, the red-white-and-blue team approach will have been used and as a result several airplane designs have evolved, all of which meet the mission and airworthiness requirements. Which is 'best'?

Again, it will be necessary to establish a set of evaluation criteria before this question can be answered.

Typical evaluation criteria which are used to judge the productivity of airplane designs are:

1. Performance Related Criteria such as:

1.1 Takeoff weight (mostly because of a historical relationship between acquisition cost and weight)

All else being the same, a low takeoff weight is judged to be 'good'.

1.2 Volume of the payload-range diagram. Examples of payload-range diagrams with different 'volumes' are given in Figures 5.22 and 5.23.

All else being the same, a large payload-range volume is judged to be 'good'.

1.3 Specific range, nm/lbs of fuel: U_1/c_jT_{reqd}

or U_1/c_pP_{reqd}.

All else being the same, a large specific range is judged to be 'good'.

1.4 Seat-miles per pound of fuel:

U_1N_{seats}/c_jT_{reqd} or U_1N_{seats}/c_pP_{reqd}

All else being the same a high value of seat-miles per pound of fuel is judged to be 'good'.

1.5 Available sortie rate: high sortie rates are judged 'good'.

2. Cost Related Criteria such as:

2.1 Acquisition Cost (Also referred to as cost of ownership.

All else being the same this cost must be small for the airplane to be judged 'good'.

2.2 Profit potential: Payload available MINUS payload to break-even of operating costs.

All else being the same, the larger the profit potential, the 'better' the airplane.

2.3 (Speed times payload)/(Acquisition Cost), used in judging general aviation airplanes.

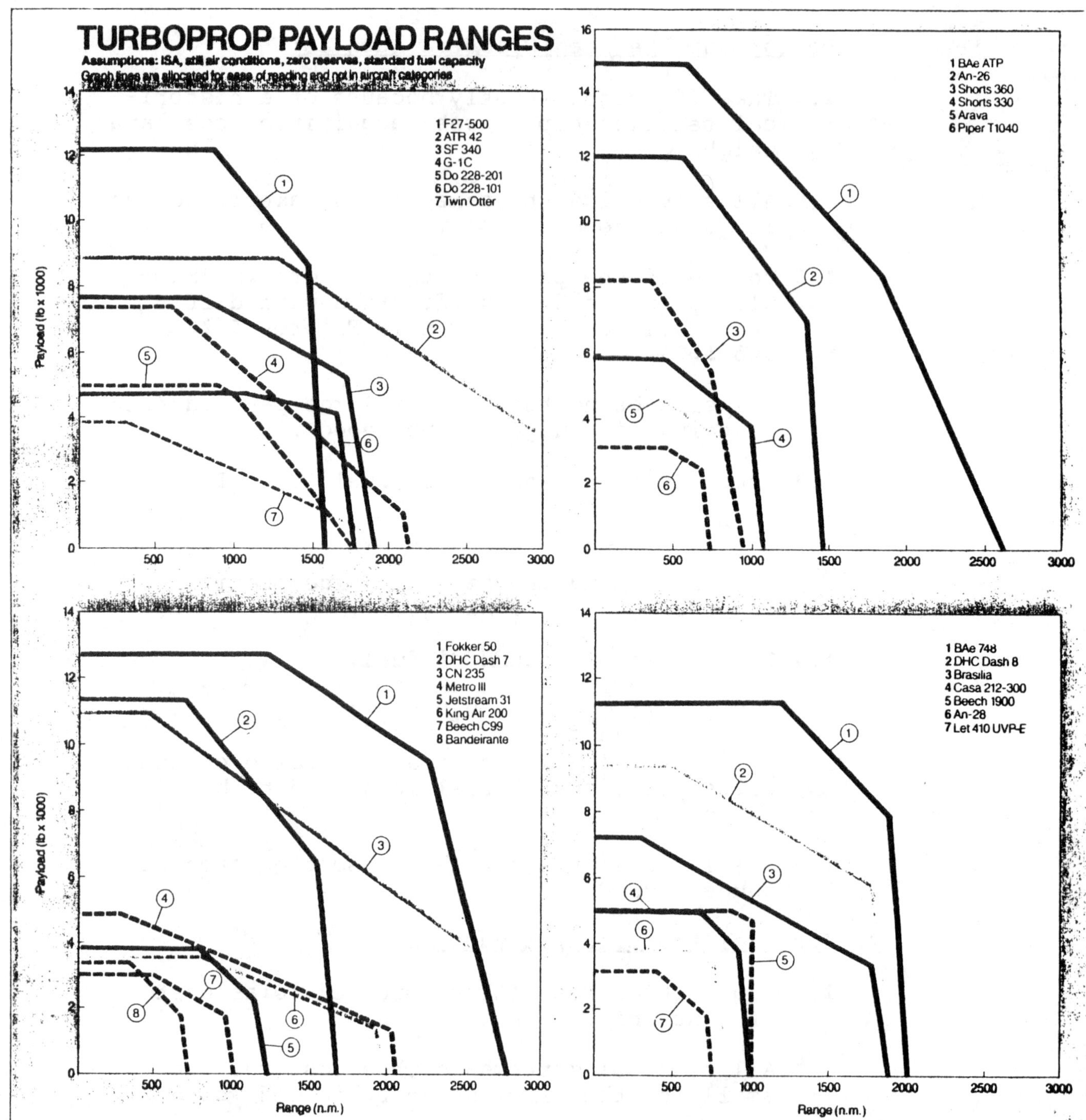

FROM: FLIGHT INTERNATIONAL*, MAY 10 1986
*BRITISH AEROSPACE WEEKLY

Figure 5.22 Payload-Range Diagrams for Turboprops

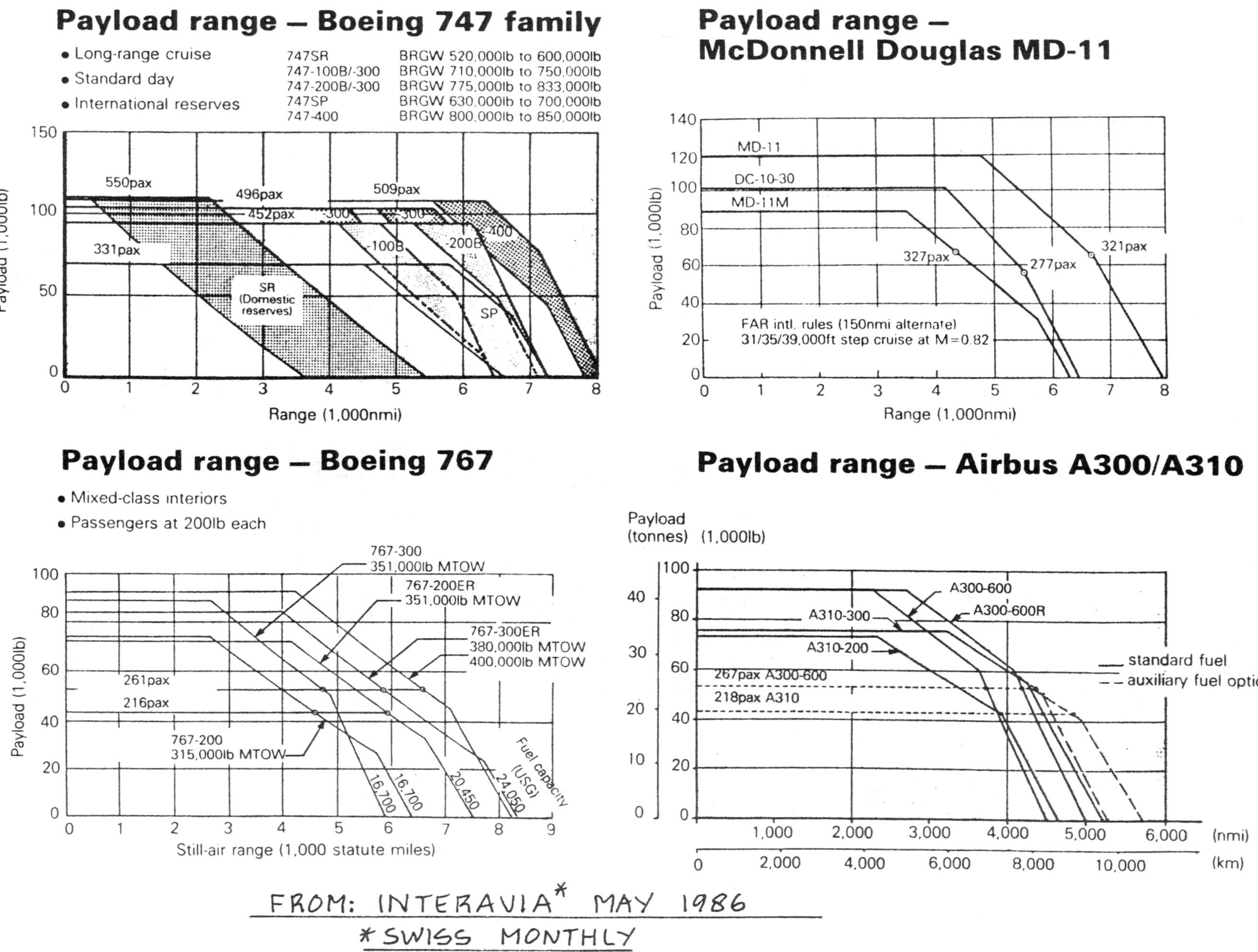

Figure 5.23 Payload-Range Diagrams for Jet Transports

All else being the same, when this parameter is larger, the airplane is judged to be better.

2.4 Direct Operating Cost (DOC).

All else being the same, low DOC is judged to be 'good'.

2.5 Return on Investment (ROI).

All else being the same, high ROI is judged to be 'good'.

2.6 Life Cycle Cost (LCC).

All else being the same, low LCC is judged to be 'good'.

2.7 Maintenance manhours required per flight hour or per sortie.

This quantity should be low for the airplane to be judged 'good'.

The 'performance' related criteria, 1.1-1.6 can be evaluated with the methods of Sections 5.1-5.10.

The 'cost' related criteria, 2.1-2.7 require a method to relate airplane design parameters to cost.

Part VIII specifically addresses the problem of estimating airplane cost. Once cost relationships are established it is possible to iterate certain influential (to cost) design parameters with as goal to 'minimize' certain costs. Reference 30 deals specifically with these design optimization problems.

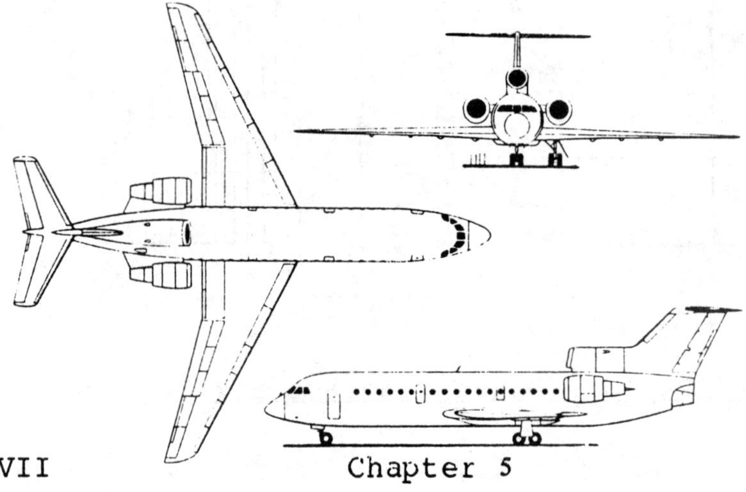

5.12 PRESENTATION OF AIRPLANE PERFORMANCE DATA

Once a new airplane design is 'finished' it is advisable to present the performance capabilities of the airplane in a generally understandable format AND to include the basic aerodynamic and installed thrust (or power) data on which all performance is based.

Since this type of documentation is not regulated by the FAA, there are no guidelines for the preparation of such data for civil airplanes. Each airplane manufacturer has evolved his own method of doing so.

For military airplanes the situation is different. The USAF, but in particular the USNAVY has standardized the required documentation of aerodynamic, thrust and performance data in the following manner:

For Aerodynamic and Thrust data: See Appendix B1.2, pages 265-271.

For Performance data: See Appendix B1.2, pages 272-279.

The author suggests that, when lacking a given format for the documentation of aerodynamic, thrust and performance data, this USNAVY method be used.

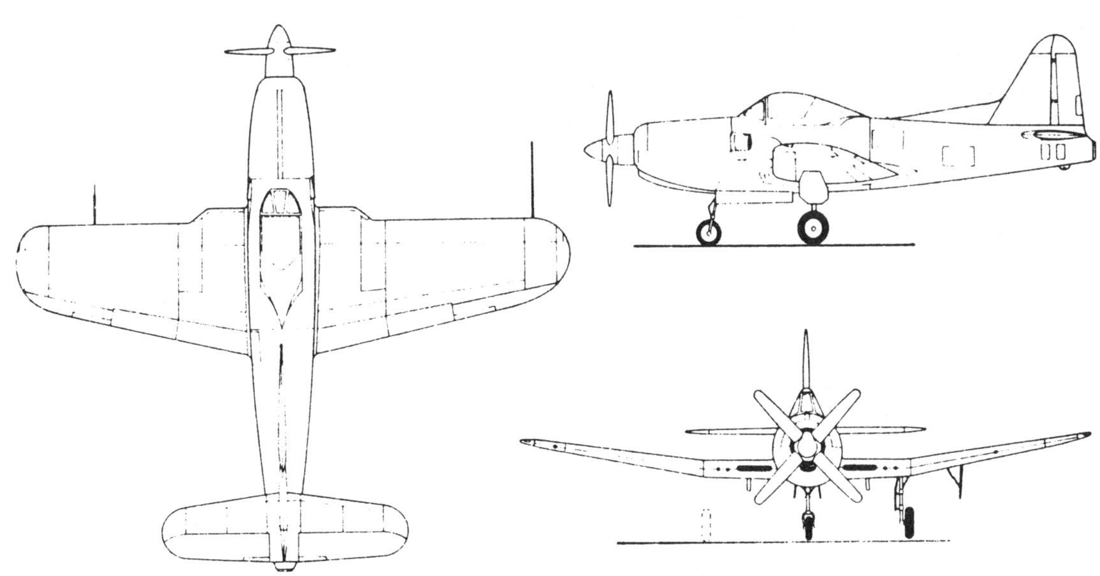

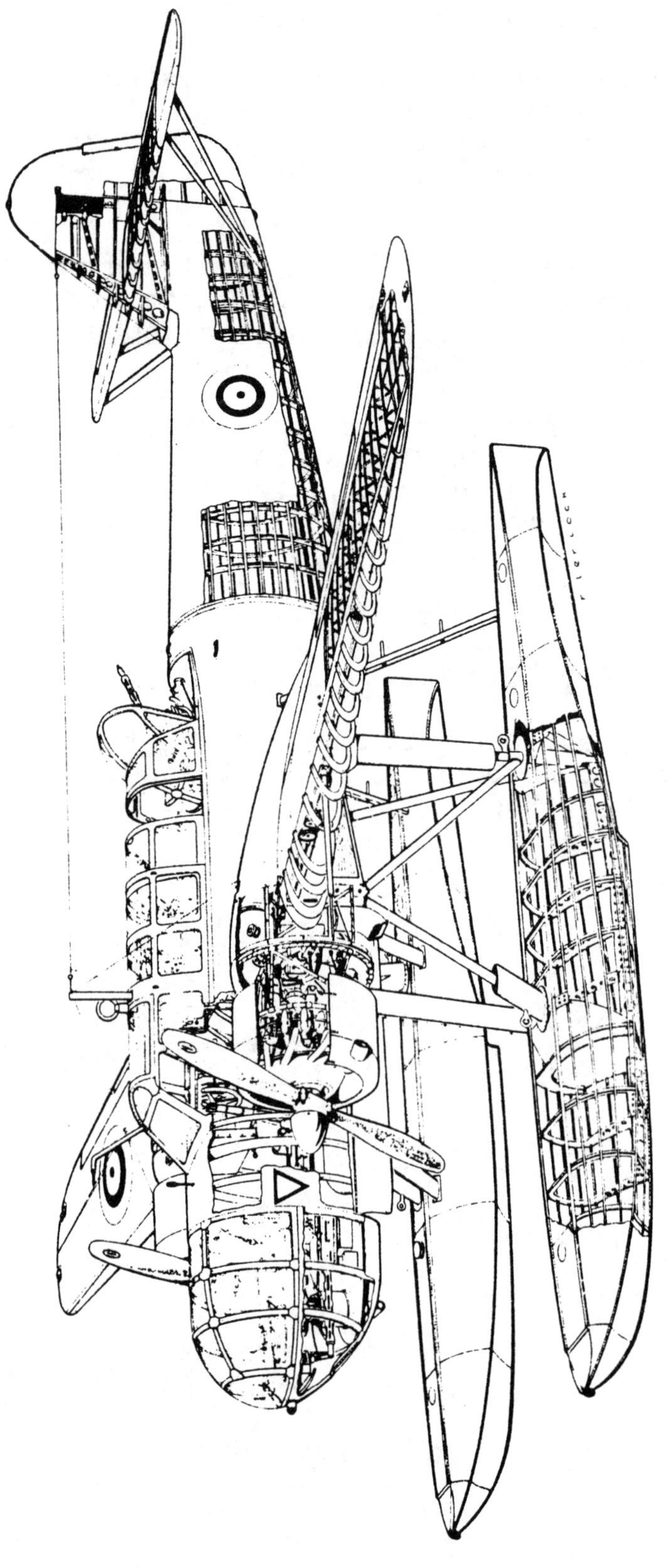

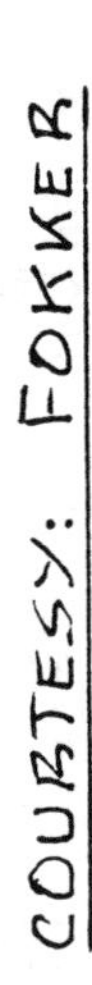

COURTESY: FOKKER

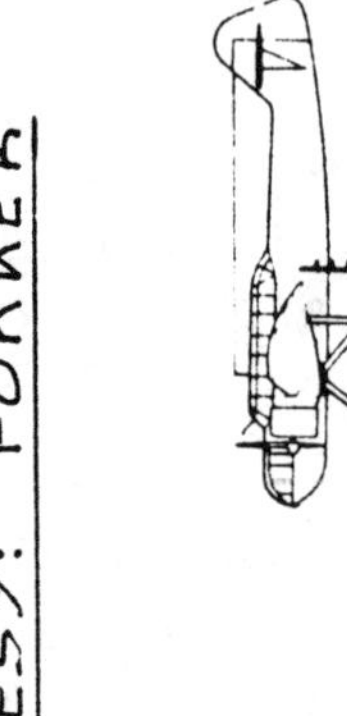

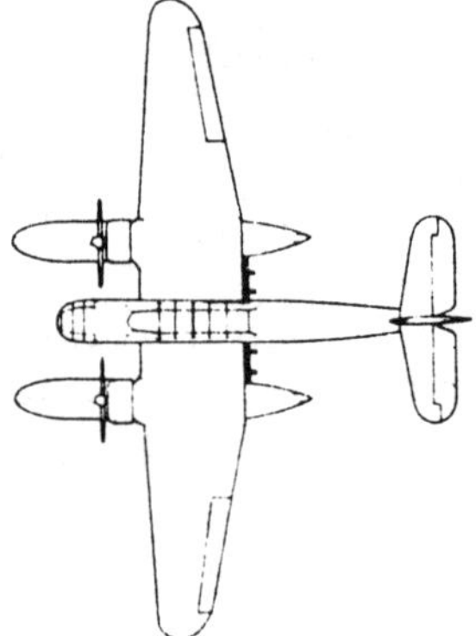

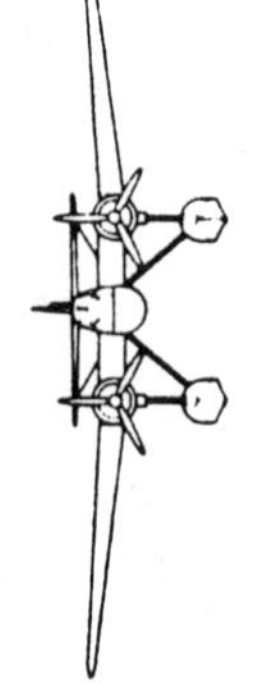

FOKKER T. VIII-W

6. REFERENCES

1. Roskam, J., Airplane Design: Part I, Preliminary Sizing of Airplanes.

2. Roskam, J., Airplane Design: Part II, Preliminary Configuration Design and Integration of the Propulsion System.

3. Roskam, J., Airplane Design: Part III, Layout Design of Cockpit, Fuselage, Wing and Empennage: Cutaways and Inboard Profiles.

4. Roskam, J., Airplane Design: Part IV, Layout Design of Landing Gear and Systems.

5. Roskam, J., Airplane Design: Part V, Component Weight Estimation.

6. Roskam, J., Airplane Design: Part VI, Preliminary Calculation of Aerodynamic, Thrust and Power Characteristics.

7. Roskam, J., Airplane Design: Part VIII, Airplane Cost Estimation and Optimization: Design, Development Manufacturing and Operating.

Note: These books are all published by: Roskam Aviation and Engineering Corporation, Rt4, Box 274, Ottawa, Kansas, 66067, Tel. 913-2421624.

8. Anon., Code of Federal Regulations, Aeronautics and Space, Parts 1- 59, January 1987, Superintendent of Documents, U.S. Government Printing Office, Washington, D.C., 20402.

9. Anon., MIL-F-8785C, Military Specification, Flying Qualities of Piloted Airplanes, November, 1980.

10a. Anon., MIL-C-005011B(USAF), Military Specification, Charts: Standard Aircraft Characteristics and Performance, Piloted Aircraft (Fixed Wing), June, 1977.

10b. Anon., AS-5263(USNavy), Guidelines for the Preparation of Standard Aircraft Characteristic Charts and Performance Data, Piloted Aircraft (Fixed Wing), October 1986.

11. Lan, C.E. and Roskam, J., Airplane Aerodynamics and

Performance, Roskam Aviation and Engineering Corp., Route 4, Box 274, Ottawa, Kansas, 66067, 1980.

12. Roskam, J., Airplane Flight Dynamics and Automatic Flight Control Systems, Roskam Aviation and Engineering Corp., Route 4, Box 274, Ottawa, Kansas, 1981.

13. Taylor, J.W.R., Jane's All The World's Aircraft, Jane's Publishing Company, London, England. (This book is reprinted annually)

14. Abbott, I.H. and Von Doenhoff, E., Theory of Wing Sections, Dover Publications, N.Y., 1959.

15. DeYoung, J., Theoretical Symmetric Span Loading Due To Flap Deflection For Wings of Arbitrary Planform At Subsonic Speeds, NACA TR 1071, 1952.

16. Pamadi, B.N. and Taylor, L.W., Jr., Semi-empirical Method for Prediction of Aerodynamic Forces and Moments on a Steadily Spinning Light Airplane, NASA TM 4009, December 1987.

17. Stinton, D., The Design of the Aeroplane, Granada, London, England, 1983.

18. Conner, D.W. and Jacobsen, I.D., Passenger Ride Comfort Technology for Transport Aircraft Situations, NASA TM X-73953, October 1976.

19. Conner, D.W., Passenger Comfort Technology for System Decision Making, NASA TM 81875, August 1980.

20. Notess, B., A Triangle, Flexible Airplanes, Gusts and Crew, Cornell Aero Lab., Inc., Memorandum No.343, May 1963.

21. Rex, H.R. and Magdaleno, R.E., Biomechanical Models for Vibration Feedthrough to Hands and Head for a Semisupine Pilot, Aviation, Space and Environmental Medicine, January 1978.

22. Dempsey, T.K., and Leatherwood, J.D., Discomfort Criteria for Single-Axis Vibration, NASA TP 1422, May 1979.

23. Rupf, J.A., Noise Effects on Passenger Communications in Light Aircraft, SAE Paper 770446, April 1977.

24. Roskam, J., Forward Swept Wings and Commuter Airplanes, Proceedings of the International Conference on

Forward Swept Wing Aircraft, University of Bristol, England, March 1982.

25. Press, H., Meadows, M.T. and Hadlock, I., A Reevaluation of Data on Atmospheric Turbulence and Airplane Gust Loads for Application in Spectral Calculations, NACA TR 1272, 1956.

26. Hammond, T.A., Amin, S.P. and Downing, D.R., Ride Quality Systems for Commuter Aircraft, SAE Paper 830744, April 1983.

27. Oehman, W.I., Optimum Design Considerations of a Gust Alleviator for Aircraft, NASA TN D-8152, March 1976.

28. Torenbeek, E., Synthesis of Subsonic Airplane Design, Delft University Press, Martinus Nijhoff Publishers, Kluwer Boston, Inc., Hingham, MA, 02043, 1982.

29. McAtee, T.P., Agility in Demand, Aerospace America, May, 1988.

30. Johnson, V.S., Life Cycle Cost in the Conceptual Design of Subsonic Commercial Aircraft, Ph.D. Dissertation, University of Kansas, May 1989.

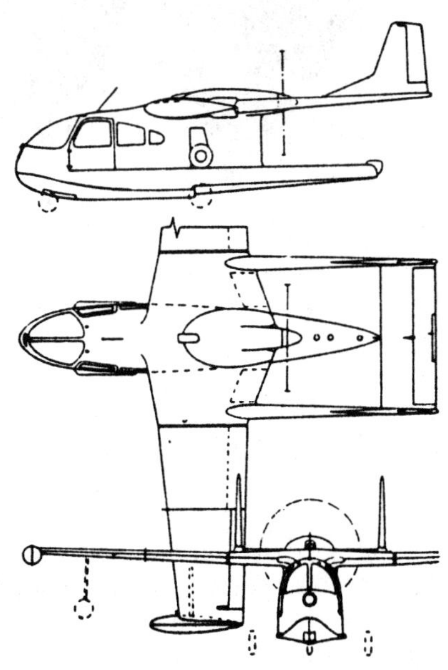

COURTESY: SAAB

7. INDEX

APPENDIX A: CIVIL AIRWORTHINESS REGULATIONS FOR AIRPLANE PERFORMANCE, STABILITY AND CONTROL

Before a civil airplane can be sold to the public, to corporations or to airlines a type certificate must have been issued. This type certificate ensures that the airplane has been designed and built in accordance with federally enforced minimum airworthiness standards. These minimum airworthiness standards are incorporated in the Federal Aviation Regulations (FAR's) of Reference 8. These regulations have a major impact on the design of airplanes. For that reason it is essential that airplane designers are aware of content and meaning of these regulations.

To obtain a type certificate for a new airplane design the procedures laid down in FAR 21 (Reference 8) must be followed.

The purpose of this appendix is to present copies of those federal aviation regulations which pertain to the minimum required performance, stability and control characteristics of airplanes. In the regulations, the minimum required performance characteristics are listed under the heading: <u>'performance'</u>. The minimum required stability and control characteristics are listed under the heading: <u>'flight characteristics'</u>.

Complete versions of the federal aviation regulations may be found in Reference 8. This appendix is organized as follows:

A1. Definitions and Abbreviations

In this Section a summary is given of those definitions which are needed for proper interpretation of those FAR 23 and 25 Parts which deal with performance and with flight characteristics.

PART 1—DEFINITIONS AND ABBREVIATIONS

Sec.
1.1 General definitions.
1.2 Abbreviations and symbols.
1.3 Rules of construction.

AUTHORITY: 49 U.S.C. 1347, 1348, 1354(a), 1357(d)(2), 1372, 1421 through 1430, 1432, 1442, 1443, 1472, 1510, 1522, 1652(e), 1655(c), 1657(f), 49 U.S.C. 106(g) (Revised Pub. L. 97-449, January 12, 1983).

§ 1.1 General definitions.

As used in Subchapters A through K of this chapter, unless the context requires otherwise:

"Aerodynamic coefficients" means non-dimensional coefficients for aerodynamic forces and moments.

"Aircraft" means a device that is used or intended to be used for flight in the air.

"Aircraft engine" means an engine that is used or intended to be used for propelling aircraft. It includes turbo-superchargers, appurtenances, and accessories necessary for its functioning, but does not include propellers.

"Airframe" means the fuselage, booms, nacelles, cowlings, fairings, airfoil surfaces (including rotors but excluding propellers and rotating airfoils of engines), and landing gear of an aircraft and their accessories and controls.

"Airplane" means an engine-driven fixed-wing aircraft heavier than air, that is supported in flight by the dynamic reaction of the air against its wings.

"Brake horsepower" means the power delivered at the propeller shaft (main drive or main output) of an aircraft engine.

"Calibrated airspeed" means the indicated airspeed of an aircraft, corrected for position and instrument error. Calibrated airspeed is equal to true airspeed in standard atmosphere at sea level.

"Category":

(1) As used with respect to the certification, ratings, privileges, and limitations of airmen, means a broad classification of aircraft. Examples include: airplane; rotorcraft; glider; and lighter-than-air; and

(2) As used with respect to the certification of aircraft, means a grouping of aircraft based upon intended use or operating limitations. Examples include: transport, normal, utility, acrobatic, limited, restricted, and provisional.

"Category A," with respect to transport category rotorcraft, means multiengine rotorcraft designed with engine and system isolation features specified in Part 29 and utilizing scheduled takeoff and landing operations under a critical engine failure concept which assures adequate designated surface area and adequate performance capability for continued safe flight in the event of engine failure.

"Category B," with respect to transport category rotorcraft, means single-engine or multiengine rotorcraft which do not fully meet all Category A standards. Category B rotorcraft have no guaranteed stay-up ability in the event of engine failure and unscheduled landing is assumed.

"Category II operations", with respect to the operation of aircraft, means a straight-in ILS approach to the runway of an airport under a Category II ILS instrument approach procedure issued by the Administrator or other appropriate authority.

"Category III operations," with respect to the operation of aircraft, means an ILS approach to, and landing on, the runway of an airport using a Category III ILS instrument approach procedure issued by the Administrator or other appropriate authority.

"Clearway" means:

(1) For turbine engine powered airplanes certificated after August 29, 1959, an area beyond the runway, not less than 500 feet wide, centrally located about the extended centerline of the runway, and under the control of the airport authorities. The clearway is expressed in terms of a clearway plane, extending from the end of the runway with an upward slope not exceeding 1.25 percent, above which no object nor any terrain protrudes. However, threshold lights may protrude above the plane if their height above the end of the runway is 26 inches or

less and if they are located to each side of the runway.

(2) For turbine engine powered airplanes certificated after September 30, 1958, but before August 30, 1959, an area beyond the takeoff runway extending no less than 300 feet on either side of the extended centerline of the runway, at an elevation no higher than the elevation of the end of the runway, clear of all fixed obstacles, and under the control of the airport authorities.

"Climbout speed," with respect to rotorcraft, means a referenced airspeed which results in a flight path clear of the height-velocity envelope during initial climbout.

"Critical altitude" means the maximum altitude at which, in standard atmosphere, it is possible to maintain, at a specified rotational speed, a specified power or a specified manifold pressure. Unless otherwise stated, the critical altitude is the maximum altitude at which it is possible to maintain, at the maximum continuous rotational speed, one of the following:

(1) The maximum continuous power, in the case of engines for which this power rating is the same at sea level and at the rated altitude.

(2) The maximum continuous rated manifold pressure, in the case of engines, the maximum continuous power of which is governed by a constant manifold pressure.

"Critical engine" means the engine whose failure would most adversely affect the performance or handling qualities of an aircraft.

"Decision height," with respect to the operation of aircraft, means the height at which a decision must be made, during an ILS or PAR instrument approach, to either continue the approach or to execute a missed approach.

"Equivalent airspeed" means the calibrated airspeed of an aircraft corrected for adiabatic compressible flow for the particular altitude. Equivalent airspeed is equal to calibrated airspeed in standard atmosphere at sea level.

"Flap extended speed" means the highest speed permissible with wing flaps in a prescribed extended position.

"Flightcrew member" means a pilot, flight engineer, or flight navigator assigned to duty in an aircraft during flight time.

"Flight level" means a level of constant atmospheric pressure related to a reference datum of 29.92 inches of mercury. Each is stated in three digits that represent hundreds of feet. For example, flight level 250 represents a barometric altimeter indication of 25,000 feet; flight level 255, an indication of 25,500 feet.

"Flight time" means the time from the moment the aircraft first moves under its own power for the purpose of flight until the moment it comes to rest at the next point of landing. ("Block-to-block" time.)

"Flight visibility" means the average forward horizontal distance, from the cockpit of an aircraft in flight, at which prominent unlighted objects may be seen and identified by day and prominent lighted objects may be seen and identified by night.

"Glider" means a heavier-than-air aircraft, that is supported in flight by the dynamic reaction of the air against its lifting surfaces and whose free flight does not depend principally on an engine.

"Ground visibility" means prevailing horizontal visibility near the earth's surface as reported by the United States National Weather Service or an accredited observer.

"Idle thrust" means the jet thrust obtained with the engine power control level set at the stop for the least thrust position at which it can be placed.

"IFR conditions" means weather conditions below the minimum for flight under visual flight rules.

"Indicated airspeed" means the speed of an aircraft as shown on its pitot static airspeed indicator calibrated to reflect standard atmosphere adiabatic compressible flow at sea level uncorrected for airspeed system errors.

"Landing gear extended speed" means the maximum speed at which an aircraft can be safely flown with the landing gear extended.

"Landing gear operating speed" means the maximum speed at which the landing gear can be safely extended or retracted.

"Large aircraft" means aircraft of more than 12,500 pounds, maximum certificated takeoff weight.

"Load factor" means the ratio of a specified load to the total weight of the aircraft. The specified load is expressed in terms of any of the following: aerodynamic forces, inertia forces, or ground or water reactions.

"Mach number" means the ratio of true airspeed to the speed of sound.

"Manifold pressure" means absolute pressure as measured at the appropriate point in the induction system and usually expressed in inches of mercury.

"Minimum descent altitude" means the lowest altitude, expressed in feet above mean sea level, to which descent is authorized on final approach or during circle-to-land maneuvering in execution of a standard instrument approach procedure, where no electronic glide slope is provided.

"Pitch setting" means the propeller blade setting as determined by the blade angle measured in a manner, and at a radius, specified by the instruction manual for the propeller.

"Propeller" means a device for propelling an aircraft that has blades on an engine-driven shaft and that, when rotated, produces by its action on the air, a thrust approximately perpendicular to its plane of rotation. It includes control components normally supplied by its manufacturer, but does not include main and auxiliary rotors or rotating airfoils of engines.

"Rated maximum continuous augmented thrust", with respect to turbojet engine type certification, means the approved jet thrust that is developed statically or in flight, in standard atmosphere at a specified altitude, with fluid injection or with the burning of fuel in a separate combustion chamber, within the engine operating limitations established under Part 33 of this chapter, and approved for unrestricted periods of use.

"Rated maximum continuous power," with respect to reciprocating, turbopropeller, and turboshaft engines, means the approved brake horsepower that is developed statically or in flight, in standard atmosphere at a specified altitude, within the engine operating limitations established under Part 33, and approved for unrestricted periods of use.

"Rated maximum continuous thrust", with respect to turbojet engine type certification, means the approved jet thrust that is developed statically or in flight, in standard atmosphere at a specified altitude, without fluid injection and without the burning of fuel in a separate combustion chamber, within the engine operating limitations established under Part 33 of this chapter, and approved for unrestricted periods of use.

"Rated takeoff augmented thrust", with respect to turbojet engine type certification, means the approved jet thrust that is developed statically under standard sea level conditions, with fluid injection or with the burning of fuel in a separate combustion chamber, within the engine operating limitations established under Part 33 of this chapter, and limited in use to periods of not over 5 minutes for takeoff operation.

"Rated takeoff power", with respect to reciprocating, turbopropeller, and turboshaft engine type certification, means the approved brake horsepower that is developed statically under standard sea level conditions, within the engine operating limitations established under Part 33, and limited in use to periods of not over 5 minutes for takeoff operation.

"Rated takeoff thrust", with respect to turbojet engine type certification, means the approved jet thrust that is developed statically under standard sea level conditions, without fluid injection and without the burning of fuel in a separate combustion chamber, within the engine operating limitations established under Part 33 of this chapter, and limited in use to periods of not over 5 minutes for takeoff operation.

Rated "30-minute power", with respect to helicopter turbine engines, means the maximum brake horsepower, developed under static conditions at specified altitudes and atmospheric temperatures, under the maximum conditions of rotor shaft rotational speed and gas temperature, and limited in use to periods of not over 30 minutes as shown on the engine data sheet.

Rated "2½ minute power", with respect to helicopter turbine engines, means the brake horsepower, developed statically in standard atmosphere at sea level, or at a specified altitude, for one-engine-out operation of multiengine helicopters for 2½ minutes at rotor shaft rotation speed and gas temperature established for this rating.

"Rating" means a statement that, as a part of a certificate, sets forth special conditions, privileges, or limitations.

"Small aircraft" means aircraft of 12,500 pounds or less, maximum certificated takeoff weight.

"Standard atmosphere" means the atmosphere defined in U.S. Standard Atmosphere, 1962 (Geopotential altitude tables).

"Stopway" means an area beyond the takeoff runway, no less wide than the runway and centered upon the extended centerline of the runway, able to support the airplane during an aborted takeoff, without causing structural damage to the airplane, and designated by the airport authorities for use in decelerating the airplane during an aborted takeoff.

"Takeoff power":

(1) With respect to reciprocating engines, means the brake horsepower that is developed under standard sea level conditions, and under the maximum conditions of crankshaft rota-

tional speed and engine manifold pressure approved for the normal takeoff, and limited in continuous use to the period of time shown in the approved engine specification; and

(2) With respect to turbine engines, means the brake horsepower that is developed under static conditions at a specified altitude and atmospheric temperature, and under the maximum conditions of rotor shaft rotational speed and gas temperature approved for the normal takeoff, and limited in continuous use to the period of time shown in the approved engine specification.

"Takeoff safety speed" means a referenced airspeed obtained after lift-off at which the required one-engine-inoperative climb performance can be achieved.

"Takeoff thrust", with respect to turbine engines, means the jet thrust that is developed under static conditions at a specific altitude and atmospheric temperature under the maximum conditions of rotorshaft rotational speed and gas temperature approved for the normal takeoff, and limited in continuous use to the period of time shown in the approved engine specification.

"Time in service", with respect to maintenance time records, means the time from the moment an aircraft leaves the surface of the earth until it touches it at the next point of landing.

"True airspeed" means the airspeed of an aircraft relative to undisturbed air. True airspeed is equal to equivalent airspeed multiplied by $(\rho 0/\rho)^{1/2}$.

§ 1.2 Abbreviations and symbols.

In Subchapters A through K of this chapter:

"AGL" means above ground level.

"ALS" means approach light system.

"ASR" means airport surveillance radar.

"ATC" means air traffic control.

"CAS" means calibrated airspeed.

"CAT II" means Category II.

"CONSOL or CONSOLAN" means a kind of low or medium frequency long range navigational aid.

"DH" means decision height.

"DME" means distance measuring equipment compatible with TACAN.

"EAS" means equivalent airspeed.

"FAA" means Federal Aviation Administration.

"FM" means fan marker.

"GS" means glide slope.

"HIRL" means high-intensity runway light system.

"IAS" means indicated airspeed.

"ICAO" means International Civil Aviation Organization.

"IFR" means instrument flight rules.

"ILS" means instrument landing system.

"IM" means ILS inner marker.

"INT" means intersection.

"LDA" means localizer-type directional aid.

"LFR" means low-frequency radio range.

"LMM" means compass locator at middle marker.

"LOC" means ILS localizer.

"LOM" means compass locator at outer marker.

"*M*" means mach number.

"MAA" means maximum authorized IFR altitude.

"MALS" means medium intensity approach light system.

"MALSR" means medium intensity approach light system with runway alignment indicator lights.

"MCA" means minimum crossing altitude.

"MDA" means minimum descent altitude.

"MEA" means minimum en route IFR altitude.

"MM" means ILS middle marker.

"MOCA" means minimum obstruction clearance altitude.

"MRA" means minimum reception altitude.

"MSL" means mean sea level.

"NDB(ADF)" means nondirectional beacon (automatic direction finder).

"NOPT" means no procedure turn required.

"OM" means ILS outer marker.

"PAR" means precision approach radar.

"RAIL" means runway alignment indicator light system.

"RBN" means radio beacon.

"RCLM" means runway centerline marking.

"RCLS" means runway centerline light system.

"REIL" means runway end identification lights.

"RR" means low or medium frequency radio range station.

"RVR" means runway visual range as measured in the touchdown zone area.

"SALS" means short approach light system.

"SSALS" means simplified short approach light system.

"SSALSR" means simplified short approach light system with runway alignment indicator lights.

"TACAN" means ultra-high frequency tactical air navigational aid.

"TAS" means true airspeed.

"TDZL" means touchdown zone lights.

"TVOR" means very high frequency terminal omnirange station.

V_A means design maneuvering speed.

V_B means design speed for maximum gust intensity.

V_C means design cruising speed.

V_D means design diving speed.

V_{DF}/M_{DF} means demonstrated flight diving speed.

V_F means design flap speed.

V_{FC}/M_{FC} means maximum speed for stability characteristics.

V_{FE} means maximum flap extended speed.

V_H means maximum speed in level flight with maximum continuous power.

V_{LE} means maximum landing gear extended speed.

V_{LO} means maximum landing gear operating speed.

V_{LOF} means lift-off speed.

V_{MC} means minimum control speed with the critical engine inoperative.

V_{MO}/M_{MO} means maximum operating limit speed.

V_{MU} means minimum unstick speed.

V_{NE} means never-exceed speed.

V_{NO} means maximum structural cruising speed.

V_R means rotation speed.

V_S means the stalling speed or the minimum steady flight speed at which the airplane is controllable.

V_{S0} means the stalling speed or the minimum steady flight speed in the landing configuration.

V_{S1} means the stalling speed or the minimum steady flight speed obtained in a specific configuration.

V_{TOSS} means takeoff safety speed for Category A rotorcraft.

V_X means speed for best angle of climb.

V_Y means speed for best rate of climb.

V_1 means takeoff decision speed (formerly denoted as critical engine failure speed).

V_2 means takeoff safety speed.

V_2 min means minimum takeoff safety speed.

"VFR" means visual flight rules.

"VHF" means very high frequency.

"VOR" means very high frequency omnirange station.

"VORTAC" means collocated VOR and TACAN.

[Doc. No. 1150, 27 FR 4590, May 15, 1962]

EDITORIAL NOTE: For FEDERAL REGISTER citations affecting § 1.2, see the List of CFR Sections Affected appearing in the Finding Aids, section of this volume.

§ 1.3 Rules of construction.

(a) In Subchapters A through K of this chapter, unless the context requires otherwise:

(1) Words importing the singular include the plural;

(2) Words importing the plural include the singular; and

(3) Words importing the masculine gender include the feminine.

(b) In Subchapters A through K of this chapter, the word:

(1) "Shall" is used in an imperative sense;

(2) "May" is used in a permissive sense to state authority or permission to do the act prescribed, and the words "no person may * * *" or "a person may not * * *" mean that no person is required, authorized, or permitted to do the act prescribed; and

(3) "Includes" means "includes but is not limited to".

[Doc. No. 1150, 27 FR 4590, May 15, 1962, as amended by Amdt. 1-10, 31 FR 5055, Mar. 29, 1966]

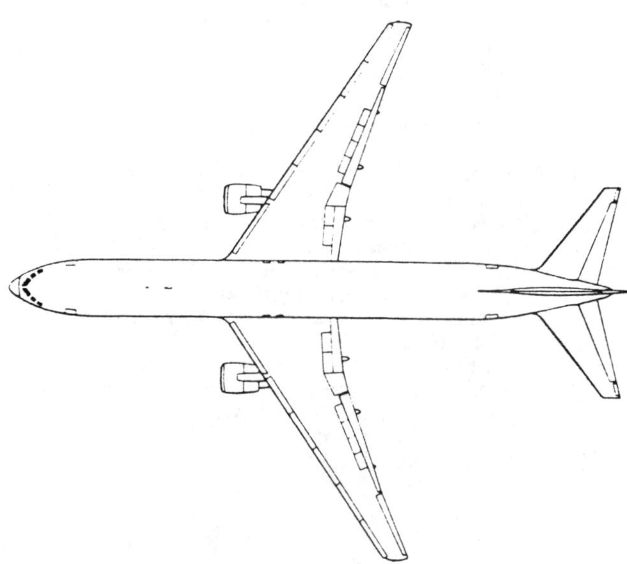

A2. Federal Aviation Regulation: FAR 23 with 1987 Amendments

In this Section a summary is given of that part of FAR 23 which deals with performance and with flight characteristics.

Subpart A—General

§ 23.1 Applicability.

(a) This part prescribes airworthiness standards for the issue of type certificates, and changes to those certificates, for small airplanes in the normal, utility, and acrobatic categories that have a passenger seating configuration, excluding pilot seats, of nine seats or less.

(b) Each person who applies under Part 21 for such a certificate or change must show compliance with the applicable requirements of this part.

[Doc. No. 4080, 29 FR 17955, Dec. 18, 1964, as amended by Amdt. 23-10, 36 FR 2864, Feb. 11, 1971]

§ 23.2 Special retroactive requirements.

Notwithstanding §§ 21.17 and 21.101 of this chapter and irrespective of the type certification basis, each normal, utility, and acrobatic category airplane having a passenger seating configuration, excluding pilot seats, of nine or less, manufactured one year after December 12, 1985, or any such foreign manufactured airplane for entry into the U.S., must meet the requirements of § 23.785 (g) and (h). For the purpose of this paragraph, the date of manufacture is:

(a) The date the inspection acceptance records, or equivalent, reflect that the airplane is complete and meets the FAA Approved Type Design Data; or

(b) In the case of a foreign manufactured airplane, the date the foreign civil airworthiness authority certifies the airplane is complete and issues an original standard airworthiness certificate, or the equivalent in that country.

[Doc. No. 23-32, 50 FR 46877, Nov. 13, 1985]

§ 23.3 Airplane categories.

(a) The normal category is limited to airplanes intended for nonacrobatic operation. Nonacrobatic operation includes—

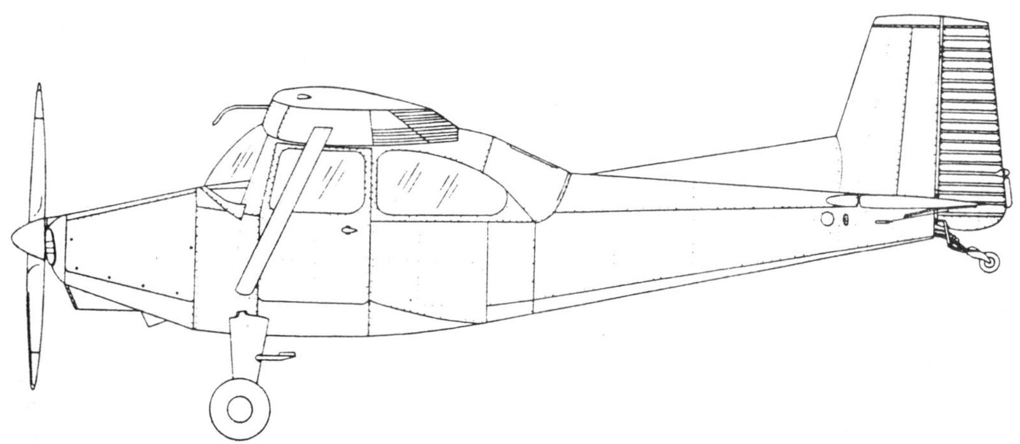

(1) Any maneuver incident to normal flying;

(2) Stalls (except whip stalls); and

(3) Lazy eights, chandelles, and steep turns, in which the angle of bank is not more than 60 degrees.

(b) The utility category is limited to airplanes intended for limited acrobatic operation. Airplanes certificated in the utility category may be used in any of the operations covered under paragraph (a) of this section and in limited acrobatic operations. Limited acrobatic operation includes—

(1) Spins (if approved for the particular type of airplane); and

(2) Lazy eights, chandelles, and steep turns, in which the angle of bank is more than 60 degrees.

(c) The acrobatic category is limited to airplanes intended for use without restrictions other than those shown to be necessary as a result of required flight tests.

(d) Small airplanes may be certificated in more than one category if the requirements of each requested category are met.

[Doc. No. 4080, 29 FR 17955, Dec. 18, 1964, as amended by Amdt. 23-4, 32 FR 5934, Apr. 14, 1967]

Subpart B—Flight

General

§ 23.21 Proof of compliance.

(a) Each requirement of this subpart must be met at each appropriate combination of weight and center of gravity within the range of loading conditions for which certification is requested. This must be shown—

(1) By tests upon an airplane of the type for which certification is requested, or by calculations based on, and equal in accuracy to, the results of testing; and

(2) By systematic investigation of each probable combination of weight and center of gravity, if compliance cannot be reasonably inferred from combinations investigated.

(b) The following general tolerances are allowed during flight testing. However, greater tolerances may be allowed in particular tests:

Item	Tolerance
Weight	+5%, -10%.
Critical items affected by weight	+5%, -1%.
C.G	±7% total travel.

§ 23.23 Load distribution limits.

Ranges of weight and centers of gravity within which the airplane may be safely operated must be established and must include the range for lateral centers of gravity if possible loading conditions can result in significant variation of their positions. If low fuel adversely affects balance or stability, the airplane must be tested under conditions simulating those that would exist when the amount of usable fuel does not exceed one gallon for each 12 maximum continuous horsepower of the engine or engines.

[Doc. No. 4080, 29 FR 17955, Dec. 18, 1964, as amended by Amdt. 23-17, 41 FR 55463, Dec. 20, 1976]

§ 23.25 Weight limits.

(a) *Maximum weight.* The maximum weight is the highest weight at which compliance with each applicable requirement of this part (other than those complied with at the design landing weight) is shown. The maximum weight must be established so that it is—

(1) Not more than—

(i) The highest weight selected by the applicant;

(ii) The design maximum weight, which is the highest weight at which compliance with each applicable structural loading condition of this part (other than those complied with at the design landing weight) is shown; or

(iii) The highest weight at which compliance with each applicable flight requirement is shown, except for airplanes equipped with standby power rocket engines, in which case it is the highest weight established in accordance with Appendix E of this part; or

(2) Assuming a weight of 170 pounds for each occupant of each seat for normal category airplanes and 190 pounds (unless otherwise placarded) for utility and acrobatic category airplanes, not less than the weight with—

(i) Each seat occupied, oil at full tank capacity, and at least enough fuel for one-half hour of operation at rated maximum continuous power; or

(ii) The required minimum crew, and fuel and oil to full tank capacity.

(b) *Minimum weight.* The minimum weight (the lowest weight at which compliance with each applicable requirement of this part is shown) must be established so that it is not more than the sum of—

(1) The empty weight determined under § 23.29;

(2) The weight of the required minimum crew (assuming a weight of 170 pounds for each crewmember); and

(3) The weight of—

(i) For turbojet powered airplanes, 5 percent of the total fuel capacity of that particular fuel tank arrangement under investigation, and

(ii) For other airplanes, the fuel necessary for one-half hour of operation at maximum continuous power.

[Doc. No. 4080, 29 FR 17955, Dec. 18, 1964, as amended by Amdt. 23-7, 34 FR 13086, Aug. 13, 1969; Amdt. 23-21, 43 FR 2317, Jan. 16, 1978]

§ 23.29 Empty weight and corresponding center of gravity.

(a) The empty weight and corresponding center of gravity must be determined by weighing the airplane with—

(1) Fixed ballast;

(2) Unusable fuel determined under § 23.959; and

(3) Full operating fluids, including—

(i) Oil;

(ii) Hydraulic fluid; and

(iii) Other fluids required for normal operation of airplane systems, except potable water, lavatory precharge water, and water intended for injection in the engines.

(b) The condition of the airplane at the time of determining empty weight must be one that is well defined and can be easily repeated.

[Doc. No. 4080, 29 FR 17955, Dec. 18, 1964; 30 FR 258, Jan. 9, 1965, as amended by Amdt. 23-21, 43 FR 2317, Jan. 16, 1978]

§ 23.31 Removable ballast.

Removable ballast may be used in showing compliance with the flight requirements of this subpart, if—

(a) The place for carrying ballast is properly designed and installed, and is marked under § 23.1557; and

(b) Instructions are included in the airplane flight manual, approved manual material, or markings and placards, for the proper placement of the removable ballast under each loading condition for which removable ballast is necessary.

[Doc. No. 4080, 29 FR 17955, Dec. 18, 1964; 30 FR 258, Jan. 9, 1965, as amended by Amdt. 23-13, 37 FR 20023, Sept. 23, 1972]

§ 23.33 Propeller speed and pitch limits.

(a) *General.* The propeller speed and pitch must be limited to values that will assure safe operation under normal operating conditions.

(b) *Propellers not controllable in flight.* For each propeller whose pitch cannot be controlled in flight—

(1) During takeoff and initial climb at V_Y, the propeller must limit the engine r.p.m., at full throttle or at maximum allowable takeoff manifold pressure, to a speed not greater than the maximum allowable takeoff r.p.m.; and

(2) During a closed throttle glide at the placarded "never-exceed speed", the propeller may not cause an engine speed above 110 percent of maximum continuous speed.

(c) *Controllable pitch propellers without constant speed controls.* Each propeller that can be controlled in flight, but that does not have constant speed controls, must have a means to limit the pitch range so that—

(1) The lowest possible pitch allows compliance with paragraph (b)(1) of this section; and

(2) The highest possible pitch allows compliance with paragraph (b)(2) of this section.

(d) *Controllable pitch propellers with constant speed controls.* Each controllable pitch propeller with constant speed controls must have—

(1) With the governor in operation, a means at the governor to limit the maximum engine speed to the maximum allowable takeoff r.p.m.; and

(2) With the governor inoperative, a means to limit the maximum engine speed to 103 percent of the maximum allowable takeoff r.p.m. with the pro-

peller blades at the lowest possible pitch and with takeoff manifold pressure, the airplane stationary, and no wind.

PERFORMANCE

§ 23.45 General.

(a) Unless otherwise prescribed, the performance requirements of this subpart must be met for still air and a standard atmosphere.

(b) The performance must correspond to the propulsive thrust available under the particular ambient atmospheric conditions, the particular flight condition, and the relative humidity specified in paragraph (d) or (e) of this section, as appropriate.

(c) The available propulsive thrust must correspond to engine power or thrust, not exceeding the approved power or thrust, less—

(1) Installation losses; and

(2) The power or equivalent thrust absorbed by the accessories and services appropriate to the particular ambient atmospheric conditions and the particular flight condition.

(d) For reciprocating engine-powered airplanes, the performance, as affected by engine power, must be based on a relative humidity of 80 percent in a standard atmosphere.

(e) For turbine engine-powered airplanes, the performance, as affected by engine power or thrust, must be based on a relative humidity of—

(1) 80 percent, at and below standard temperature; and

(2) 34 percent, at and above standard temperature plus 50 degrees F.

Between these two temperatures, the relative humidity must vary linearly.

[Amdt. 23-21, 43 FR 2317, Jan. 16, 1978]

§ 23.49 Stalling speed.

(a) V_{s0} is the stalling speed, if obtainable, or the minimum steady speed, in knots (CAS), at which the airplane is controllable, with the—

(1) Applicable power or thrust condition set forth in paragraph (e) of this section;

(2) Propellers in the takeoff position;

(3) Landing gear extended;

(4) Wing flaps in the landing position;

(5) Cowl flaps closed;

(6) Center of gravity in the most unfavorable position within the allowable landing range; and

(7) Weight used when V_{S0} is being used as a factor to determine compliance with a required performance standard.

(b) V_{S0} at maximum weight may not exceed 61 knots for—

(1) Single-engine airplanes; and

(2) Multiengine airplanes of 6,000 pounds or less maximum weight that cannot meet the minimum rate of climb specified in § 23.67(b) with the critical engine inoperative.

(c) V_{S1} is the calibrated stalling speed, if obtainable, or the minimum steady speed, in knots, at which the airplane is controllable, with the—

(1) Applicable power or thrust condition set forth in paragraph (e) of this section;

(2) Propellers in the takeoff position;

(3) Airplane in the condition existing in the test in which V_{S1} is being used; and

(4) Weight used when V_{S1} is being used as a factor to determine compliance with a required performance standard.

(d) V_{S0} and V_{S1} must be determined by flight tests, using the procedure specified in § 23.201.

(e) The following power or thrust conditions must be used to meet the requirements of this section:

(1) For reciprocating engine-powered airplanes, engines idling, throttles closed or at not more than the power necessary for zero thrust at a speed not more than 110 percent of the stalling speed.

(2) For turbine engine-powered airplanes, the propulsive thrust may not be greater than zero at the stalling speed, or, if the resultant thrust has no appreciable effect on the stalling speed, with engines idling and throttles closed.

[Doc. No. 4080, 29 FR 17955, Dec. 18, 1964, as amended by Amdt. 23-7, 34 FR 13086, Aug. 13, 1969; Amdt. 23-21, 43 FR 2317, Jan. 16, 1978]

§ 23.51 Takeoff.

(a) For each airplane (except a skiplane for which landplane takeoff data has been determined under this paragraph and furnished in the Airplane Flight Manual) the distance required to takeoff and climb over a 50-foot obstacle must be determined with—

(1) The engines operating within approved operating limitations; and

(2) The cowl flaps in the normal takeoff position.

(b) For multiengine airplanes, the lift-off speed, V_{LOF}, may not be less than V_{MC} determined in accordance with § 23.149.

(c) Upon reaching a height of 50 feet above the takeoff surface level, the airplane must have reached a speed of not less than the following:

(1) For multiengine airplanes, the higher of—

(i) 1.1 V_{MC}; or

(ii) 1.3 V_{S_1}, or any lesser speed, not less than Vx plus 4 knots, that is shown to be safe under all conditions, including turbulence and complete engine failure.

(2) For single engine airplanes—

(i) 1.3 V_{S_1}; or

(ii) Any lesser speed, not less than Vx plus 4 knots, that is shown to be safe under all conditions, including turbulence and complete engine failure.

(d) The starting point for measuring seaplane and amphibian takeoff distance may be the point at which a speed of not more than three knots is reached.

(e) Takeoffs made to determine the data required by this section may not require exceptional piloting skill or exceptionally favorable conditions.

[Amdt. 23-21, 43 FR 2317, Jan. 16, 1978]

§ 23.65 Climb: All engines operating.

(a) Each airplane must have a steady rate of climb at sea level of at least 300 feet per minute and a steady angle of climb of at least 1:12 for landplanes or 1:15 for seaplanes and amphibians with—

(1) Not more than maximum continuous power on each engine;

(2) The landing gear retracted;

(3) The wing flaps in the takeoff position; and

(4) The cowl flaps or other means for controlling the engine cooling air supply in the position used in the cooling tests required by §§ 23.1041 through 23.1047.

(b) Each airplane with engines for which the takeoff and maximum continuous power ratings are identical and that has fixed-pitch, two-position, or similar propellers, may use a lower propeller pitch setting than that allowed by § 23.33 to obtain rated engine r.p.m. at Vx, if—

(1) The airplane shows marginal performance (such as when it can meet the rate of climb requirements of paragraph (a) of this section but has difficulty in meeting the angle of climb requirements of paragraph (a) of this section or of § 23.77); and

(2) Acceptable engine cooling is shown at the lower speed associated with the best angle of climb.

(c) Each turbine engine-powered airplane must be able to maintain a steady gradient of climb of at least 4 percent at a pressure altitude of 5,000 feet and a temperature of 81 degrees F (standard temperature plus 40 degree F) with the airplane in the configuration prescribed in paragraph (a) of this section.

[Amdt. 23-21, 43 FR 2317, Jan. 16, 1978]

§ 23.67 Climb: one engine inoperative.

(a) Each reciprocating engine-powered multiengine airplane of more than 6,000 pounds maximum weight must be able to maintain a steady rate of climb of at least 0.027 $V_{S_0}^2$ (that is, the number of feet per minute is obtained by multiplying the square of the number of knots by 0.027 at an altitude of 5,000 feet with the—

(1) Critical engine inoperative, and its propeller in the minimum drag position;

(2) Remaining engines at not more than maximum continuous power;

(3) Landing gear retracted;

(4) Wing flaps in the most favorable position; and

(5) Cowl flaps in the position used in the cooling tests required by §§ 23.1041 through 23.1047.

(b) For reciprocating engine-powered multiengine airplanes of 6,000 pounds or less maximum weight, the following apply:

(1) Each airplane with a V_{S0} of more (than 61 knots must be able to maintain a steady rate of climb of at least 0.027 V_{S0}^2 (that is, the number of feet per minute is obtained by multiplying the square of the number of knots by 0.027), at an altitude of 5,000 feet with the—

(i) Critical engine inoperative and its propeller in the minimum drag position;

(ii) Remaining engines at not more than maximum continuous power;

(iii) Landing gear retracted;

(iv) Wing flaps in the most favorable position; and

(v) Cowl flaps in the position used in the cooling tests required by §§ 23.1041 through 23.1047.

(2) For each airplane with a stalling speed of 61 knots or less, the steady rate of climb at 5,000 feet must be determined with the—

(i) Critical engine inoperative and its propeller in the minimum drag position;

(ii) Remaining engines at not more than maximum continuous power;

(iii) Landing gear retracted;

(iv) Wing flaps in the most favorable position; and

(v) Cowl flaps in the position used in the cooling tests required by §§ 23.1041 through 23.1047.

(c) For turbine-powered multiengine airplanes the following apply:

(1) The steady gradient of climb must be determined at each weight, altitude, and ambient temperature within the operational limits established by the applicant, with the—

(i) Critical engine inoperative, and its propeller in the minimum drag position;

(ii) Remaining engines at not more than maximum continuous power or thrust;

(iii) Landing gear retracted;

(iv) Wing flaps in the most favorable position; and

(v) The means for controlling the engine cooling air supply in the position used in the engine cooling tests required by §§ 23.1041 through 23.1047.

(2) Each airplane must be able to maintain the following climb gradients with the airplane in the configuration prescribed in paragraph (c)(1) of this section:

(i) 1.2 percent (or, if greater, a gradient equivalent to a rate of climb of 0.027 Vs_o^2) at a pressure altitude of 5,000 feet and standard temperature (41 degrees F).

(ii) 0.6 percent (or, if greater, a gradient equivalent to a rate of climb of 0.014 Vs_o^2) at a pressure altitude of 5,000 feet and 81 degrees F (standard temperature plus 40 degrees F).

(3) The minimum climb gradient specified in paragraphs (c)(2) (i) and (ii) of this section must vary linearly between 41 degrees F and 81 degrees F and must change at the same rate up to the maximum operating termperature approved for the airplane.

(4) In paragraphs (c)(2) (i) and (ii) of this section, rate of climb is expressed in feet per minute and Vs_o is expressed in knots.

(d) For all multiengine airplanes, the speed for best rate of climb with one engine inoperative must be determined.

[Doc. No. 4080, 29 FR 17955, Dec. 18, 1964, as amended by Amdt. 23-7, 34 FR 13086, Aug. 13, 1969; Amdt. 23-21, 43 FR 2317, Jan. 16, 1978]

§ 23.75 Landing.

For airplanes (except skiplanes for which landplane landing data have been determined under this section and furnished in the Airplane Flight Manual), the horizontal distance necessary to land and come to a complete stop (or to a speed of approximately 3 knots for water landings of seaplanes and amphibians) from a point 50 feet above the landing surface must be determined as follows:

(a) A steady gliding approach with a calibrated airspeed of at least 1.3 Vs_1 must be maintained down to the 50-foot height.

(b) The landing may not require exceptional piloting skill or exceptionally favorable conditions.

(c) The landing must be made without excessive vertical acceleration or tendency to bounce, nose over, ground loop, porpoise, or water loop.

(d) It must be shown that a safe transition to the balked landing conditions of § 23.77 can be made from the conditions that exist at the 50-foot height.

(e) The pressures on the wheel braking system may not exceed those specified by the brake manufacturer.

(f) Means other than wheel brakes may be used if that means—

(1) Is safe and reliable;

(2) Is used so that consistent results can be expected in service; and

(3) Is such that exceptional skill is not required to control the airplane.

[Amdt. 23-21, 43 FR 2318, Jan. 16, 1978]

§ 23.77 Balked landing.

(a) For balked landings, each airplane must be able to maintain a steady angle of climb at sea level of at least 1:30 with—

(1) Takeoff power on each engine;

(2) The landing gear extended; and

(3) The wing flaps in the landing position, except that if the flaps may safely be retracted in two seconds or less without loss of altitude and without sudden changes of angle of attack or exceptional piloting skill, they may be retracted.

(b) Each turbine engine-powered airplane must be able to maintain a steady rate of climb of at least zero at a pressure altitude of 5,000 feet at 81 degrees F (standard temperature plus 40 degrees F), with the airplane in the configuration prescribed in paragraph (a) of this section.

[Amdt. 23-21, 43 FR 2318, Jan. 16, 1978]

FLIGHT CHARACTERISTICS

§ 23.141 General.

The airplane must meet the requirements of §§ 23.143 through 23.253 at the normally expected operating altitudes without exceptional piloting skill, alertness, or strength.

[Amdt. 23-17, 41 FR 55464, Dec. 20, 1976]

CONTROLLABILITY AND MANEUVERABILITY

§ 23.143 General.

(a) The airplane must be safely controllable and maneuverable during—

(1) Takeoff;

(2) Climb;

(3) Level flight;

(4) Dive; and

(5) Landing (power on and power off with the wing flaps extended and retracted).

(b) It must be possible to make a smooth transition from one flight condition to another (including turns and slips) without danger of exceeding the limit load factor, under any probable operating condition (including, for multiengine airplanes, those conditions normally encountered in the sudden failure of any engine).

(c) If marginal conditions exist with regard to required pilot strength, the "strength of pilots" limits must be shown by quantitative tests. In no case may the limits exceed those prescribed in the following table:

Values in pounds of force as applied to the control wheel or rudder pedals	Pitch	Roll	Yaw
(a) For temporary application:			
Stick	60	30	
Wheel (applied to rim)	75	60	
Rudder pedal			150
(b) For prolonged application	10	5	20

[Doc. No. 4080, 29 FR 17955, Dec. 18, 1964, as amended by Amdt. 23-14, 38 FR 31819, Nov. 19, 1973; Amdt. 23-17, 41 FR 55464, Dec. 20, 1976]

§ 23.145 Longitudinal control.

(a) It must be possible, at speeds below the trim speed, to pitch the nose downward so that the rate of increase in airspeed allows prompt acceleration to the trim speed with—

(1) Maximum continuous power on each engine and the airplane trimmed at V_X;

(2) Power off and the airplane trimmed at a speed determined in accordance with § 23.161(c)(3) or (4) as appropriate or at the minimum trim speed, whichever is higher; and

(3) Wing flaps and landing gear (i) retracted, and (ii) extended.

(b) With the landing gear extended no change in trim or exertion of more control force than can be readily applied with one hand for a short period of time may be required for the following maneuvers:

(1) With power off, flaps retracted, and the airplane trimmed at $1.4V_{S1}$ or the minimum trim speed, whichever is higher, extend the flaps as rapidly as possible and allow the airspeed to transition from $1.4V_{S1}$ to $1.4V_{S0}$, or if appropriate from the minimum trim speed to a speed equal to V_{S0} increased by the same percentage that the minimum trim speed at the initial condition was greater than V_{S1}.

(2) With power off, flaps extended, and the airplane trimmed at $1.4V_{S0}$ or the minimum trim speed, whichever is higher, retract the flaps as rapidly as possible and allow the airspeed to transition from $1.4V_{S0}$ to $1.4V_{S1}$, or if appropriate, from the minimum trim speed to a speed equal to $1.4V_{S1}$ increased by the same percentage that the minimum trim speed at the initial condition was greater than V_{S0}.

(3) Repeat paragraph (b)(2) of this section except with maximum continuous power.

(4) With power off, flaps retracted, and the airplane trimmed at a speed determined in accordance with § 23.161 (c)(3) or (4), as appropriate or at the minimum trim speed, whichever is higher, apply takeoff power rapidly while maintaining the same airspeed.

(5) Repeat subparagraph (4) of this paragraph, except with the flaps extended.

(6) With power off, flaps extended, and the airplane trimmed at a speed determined in accordance with § 23.161 (c)(3) or (4), as appropriate or at the minimum trim speed, whichever is higher, obtain and maintain airspeeds between 1.1 V_{S1} and either 1.7 V_{S1} or V_F, whichever is lower.

(c) It must be possible to maintain approximately level flight when flap retraction from any position is made during steady horizontal flight at 1.1 V_{S1} with simultaneous application of not more than maximum continuous power.

(d) It must be possible, with a pilot control force of not more than 10 pounds, to maintain a speed of not more than the speed determined in accordance with § 23.161(c)(4), during a power-off glide with landing gear and wing flaps extended.

(e) By using normal flight and power controls, except as otherwise noted in paragraphs (e)(1) and (e)(2), it must be possible in the following airplanes to establish a zero rate of descent at an attitude suitable for a controlled landing without exceeding the operational and structural limitations of the airplane:

(1) For single engine and multiengine airplanes, without the use of the primary longitudinal control system.

(2) For multiengine airplanes—

(i) Without the use of the primary directional control; and

(ii) If a single failure of any one connecting or transmitting link would affect both the longitudinal and directional primary control system, without the primary longitudinal and directional control system.

[Doc. No. 4080, 29 FR 17955, Dec. 18, 1964, as amended by Amdt. 23-7, 34 FR 13086, Aug. 13, 1969; Amdt. 23-14, 38 FR 31819, Nov. 19, 1973; Amdt. 23-17, 41 FR 55464, Dec. 20, 1976]

§ 23.147 Directional and lateral control.

(a) For each multiengine airplane, it must be possible to make turns with 15 degrees of bank both towards and away from an inoperative engine, from a steady climb at 1.4 V_{S1} or V_Y with—

(1) One engine inoperative and its propeller in the minimum drag position;

(2) The remaining engines at not more than maximum continuous power;

(3) The rearmost allowable center of gravity;

(4) The landing gear (i) retracted, and (ii) extended;

(5) The flaps in the most favorable climb position; and

(6) Maximum weight.

(b) For each multiengine airplane, it must be possible, while holding the wings level within five degrees, to make sudden changes in heading safely in both directions. This must be shown at 1.4 V_{S1} or V_Y with heading changes up to 15 degrees (except that the heading change at which the rudder force corresponds to the limits specified in § 23.143 need not be exceeded), with the—

(1) Critical engine inoperative and its propeller in the minimum drag position;

(2) Remaining engines at maximum continuous power;

(3) Landing gear (i) retracted, and (ii) extended;

(4) Flaps in the most favorable climb position; and

(5) Center of gravity at its rearmost allowable position.

§ 23.149 Minimum control speed.

(a) VMC is the calibrated airspeed, at which, when the critical engine is suddenly made inoperative, it is possible to recover control of the airplane with that engine still inoperative and maintain straight flight either with zero yaw or, at the option of the applicant, with an angle of bank of not more than five degrees. The method used to simulate critical engine failure must represent the most critical mode of powerplant failure with respect to controllability expected in service.

(b) For reciprocating engine-powered airplanes, VMC may not exceed 1.2 V_{S_1} (where V_{S_1} is determined at the maximum takeoff weight with—

(1) Takeoff or maximum available power on the engines;

(2) The most unfavorable center of gravity;

(3) The airplane trimmed for takeoff;

(4) The maximum sea level takeoff weight (or any lesser weight necessary to show VMC);

(5) Flaps in the takeoff position;

(6) Landing gear retracted;

(7) Cowl flaps in the normal takeoff position;

(8) The propeller of the inoperative engine—

(i) Windmilling;

(ii) In the most probable position for the specific design of the propeller control; or

(iii) Feathered, if the airplane has an automatic feathering device; and

(9) The airplane airborne and the ground effect negligible.

(c) For turbine engine-powered airplanes, VMC may not exceed 1.2 V_{S_1} (where V_{S_1} is determined at the maximum takeoff weight) with—

(1) Maximum available takeoff power or thrust on the engines;

(2) The most unfavorable center of gravity;

(3) The airplane trimmed for takeoff;

(4) The maximum sea level takeoff weight for any lesser weight necessary to show VMC);

(5) The airplane in the most critical takeoff configuration except with the landing gear retracted; and

(6) The airplane airborne and the ground effect negligible.

(d) At VMC, the rudder pedal force required to maintain control may not exceed 150 pounds, and it may not be necessary to reduce power or thrust of the operative engines. During recovery, the airplane may not assume any dangerous attitude and it must be possible to prevent a heading change of more than 20 degrees.

[Amdt. 23-21, 43 FR 2318, Jan. 16, 1978]

§ 23.151 Acrobatic maneuvers.

Each acrobatic and utility category airplane must be able to perform safely the acrobatic maneuvers for which certification is requested. Safe entry speeds for these maneuvers must be determined.

§ 23.153 Control during landings.

For an airplane that has a maximum weight of more than 6,000 pounds, it must be possible, while in the landing configuration, to safely complete a landing without encountering forces in excess of those prescribed in § 23.143(c) following an approach to land:

(a) At a speed 5 knots less than the speed used in complying with § 23.75 and with the airplane in trim or as nearly as possible in trim;

(b) With neither the trimming control being moved throughout the maneuver nor the power being increased during the landing flare; and

(c) With the thrust settings used in demonstrating compliance with § 23.75.

[Amdt. 23-14, 38 FR 31819, Nov. 19, 1973]

§ 23.155 Elevator control force in maneuvers.

(a) The elevator control force needed to achieve the positive limit maneuvering load factor may not be less than:

(1) For wheel controls, W/100 (where W is the maximum weight) or 20 pounds, whichever is greater, except that it need not be greater than 50 pounds; or

(2) For stick controls, W/140 (where W is the maximum weight) or 15 pounds, whichever is greater, except that it need not be greater than 35 pounds.

(b) The requirement of paragraph (a) of this section must be met with wing flaps and landing gear retracted under each of the following conditions:

(1) At 75 percent of maximum continuous power for reciprocating engines, or the maximum power or thrust selected by the applicant as an operating limitation for use during cruise for reciprocating or turbine engines.

(2) In a turn, after the airplane is trimmed with wings level at the minimum speed at which the required normal acceleration can be achieved without stalling, and at the maximum level flight trim speed except that the speed may not exceed V_{NE} or V_{MO}/M_{MO}, whichever is appropriate.

(c) Compliance with the requirements of this section may be demonstrated by measuring the normal acceleration that is achieved with the limiting stick force or by establishing the stick force per g gradient and extrapolating to the appropriate limit.

[Amdt. 23-14, 38 FR 31819, Nov. 19, 1973; 38 FR 32784, Nov. 28, 1973]

§ 23.157 Rate of roll.

(a) *Takeoff.* It must be possible, using a favorable combination of controls, to roll the airplane from a steady 30-degree banked turn through an angle of 60 degrees, so as to reverse the direction of the turn within:

(1) For an airplane of 6,000 pounds or less maximum weight, 5 seconds from initiation of roll; and

(2) For an airplane of over 6,000 pounds maximum weight,

$$(W+500)/1{,}300$$

seconds, where W is the weight in pounds.

(b) The requirement of paragraph (a) must be met when rolling the airplane in either direction in the following condition:

(1) Flaps in the takeoff position;

(2) Landing gear retracted;

(3) For a single engine airplane, at maximum takeoff power or thrust; and for a multiengine airplane, with the critical engine inoperative, the propeller in the minimum drag position, and the other engines at maximum continuous power or thrust; and

(4) The airplane trimmed at $1.2V_{S_1}$, or as nearly as possible in trim for straight flight.

(c) *Approach.* It must be possible, using a favorable combination of controls, to roll the airplane from a steady 30-degree banked turn through an angle of 60 degrees, so as to reverse the direction of the turn within:

(1) For an airplane of 6,000 pounds or less maximum weight, 4 seconds from initiation of roll; and

(2) For an airplane of over 6,000 pounds maximum weight,

$$(W+2{,}800)/2{,}200$$

seconds, where W is the weight in pounds.

(d) The requirement of paragraph (c) must be met when rolling the airplane in either direction in the following conditions:

(1) Flaps extended;

(2) Landing gear extended;

(3) All engines operating at idle power or thrust and with all engines operating at the power or thrust for level flight; and

(4) The airplane trimmed at the speed that is used in determining compliance with § 23.75.

[Amdt. 23-14, 38 FR 31819, Nov. 19, 1973]

Trim

§ 23.161 Trim.

(a) *General.* Each airplane must meet the trim requirements of this section after being trimmed, and without further pressure upon, or movement of, the primary controls or their corresponding trim controls by the pilot or the automatic pilot.

(b) *Lateral and directional trim.* The airplane must maintain lateral and directional trim in level flight at 0.9 V_H or V_C, whichever is lower, with the landing gear and wing flaps retracted.

(c) *Longitudinal trim.* The airplane must maintain longitudinal trim under each of the following conditions:

(1) A climb with maximum continuous power at a speed between Vx and 1.4 V_{S_1}, with—

(i) The landing gear and wing flaps retracted; and

(ii) The landing gear retracted and the wing flaps in the takeoff position.

(2) A power approach with a 3 degree angle of descent, the landing gear extended, and with—

(i) The wing flaps retracted and at a speed of 1.4 V_{S_1}; and

(ii) The applicable airspeed and flap position used in showing compliance with § 23.75.

(3) Level flight at any speed from 0.9 V_H to either Vx or 1.4 V_{S_1}, with the landing gear and wing flaps retracted.

(d) In addition, each multiengine airplane must maintain longitudinal and directional trim at a speed between V_Y and 1.4 V_{S1}, with—

(1) The critical engine inoperative;

(2) The remaining engines at maximum continuous power;

(3) The landing gear retracted;

(4) The wing flaps retracted; and

(5) An angle of bank of not more than five degrees.

[Doc. No. 4080, 29 FR 17955, Dec. 18, 1964, as amended by Amdt. 23-21, 43 FR 2318, Jan. 16, 1978]

Stability

§ 23.171 General.

The airplane must be longitudinally, directionally, and laterally stable under §§ 23.173 through 23.181. In addition, the airplane must show suitable stability and control "feel" (static stability) in any condition normally encountered in service, if flight tests show it is necessary for safe operation.

§ 23.173 Static longitudinal stability.

Under the conditions specified in § 23.175 and with the airplane trimmed as indicated, the characteristics of the elevator control forces and the friction within the control system must be as follows:

(a) A pull must be required to obtain and maintain speeds below the specified trim speed and a push required to obtain and maintain speeds above the specified trim speed. This must be shown at any speed that can be obtained, except that speeds requiring a control force in excess of 40 pounds or speeds above the maximum allowable speed or below the minimum speed for steady unstalled flight, need not be considered.

(b) The airspeed must return to within plus or minus 10 percent of the original trim speed when the control force is slowly released at any speed within the speed range specified in paragraph (a) of this section.

(c) The stick force must vary with speed so that any substantial speed change results in a stick force clearly perceptible to the pilot.

[Doc. No. 4080, 29 FR 17955, Dec. 18, 1964, as amended by Amdt. 23-14, 38 FR 31820 Nov. 19, 1973]

§ 23.175 Demonstration of static longitudinal stability.

Static longitudinal stability must be shown as follows:

(a) *Climb.* The stick force curve must have a stable slope, at speeds between 85 and 115 percent of the trim speed, with—

(1) Flaps in the climb position;

(2) Landing gear retracted;

(3) 75 percent of maximum continuous power for reciprocating engines or the maximum power or thrust selected by the applicant as an operating limitation for use during a climb for turbine engines; and

(4) The airplane trimmed for V_Y, except that the speed need not be less than 1.4 V_{S1}.

(b) *Cruise—Landing gear retracted (or fixed gear).* (1) For the cruise conditions specified in paragraphs (b) (2) and (3) of this section, the following apply:

(i) The speed need not be less than 1.3 V_{S1}.

(ii) For airplanes with V_{NE} established under § 23.1505(a), the speed need not be greater than V_{NE}.

(iii) For airplanes with V_{MO}/M_{MO} established under § 23.1505(c), the speed need not be greater than a speed midway between V_{MO}/M_{MO} and the lesser of V_D/M_D or the speed demonstrated under § 23.251, except that for altitudes where Mach number in the limiting factor, the speed need not exceed that corresponding to the Mach number at which effective speed warning occurs.

(2) *High speed cruise.* The stick force curve must have a stable slope at all speeds within a range that is the greater of 15 percent of the trim speed plus the resulting free return speed range, or 40 knots plus the resulting free return speed range, above and below the trim speed, with—

(i) Flaps retracted.

(ii) Seventy-five percent of maximum continuous power for reciprocating engines or, for turbine engines, the maximum cruising power or thrust selected by the applicant as an operating limitation, except that the power need not exceed that required at V_{NE} for airplanes with V_{NE} established under § 23.1505(a), or that required at V_{MO}/M_{MO} for airplanes with V_{MO}/M_{MO} established under § 23.1505(c).

(iii) The airplane trimmed for level flight.

(3) *Low speed cruise.* The stick force curve must have a stable slope under all the conditions prescribed in paragraph (b)(2) of this section, except that the power is that required for level flight at a speed midway between 1.3 V_{S1} and the trim speed obtained in the high speed cruise condition under paragraph (b)(2) of this section.

(c) *Landing gear extended (airplanes with retractable gear).* The stick force curve must have a stable slope at all speeds within a range from 15 percent of the trim speed plus the resulting free return speed range below the trim speed, to the trim speed (except that the speed range need not include speeds less than 1.4 V_{S1} nor speeds greater than V_{LE}, with—

(1) Landing gear extended;

(2) Flaps retracted;

(3) 75 percent of maximum continuous power for reciprocating engines, or for turbine engines, the maximum cruising power or thrust selected by the applicant as an operating limitation, except that the power need not exceed that required for level flight at V_{LE}; and

(4) The airplane trimmed for level flight.

(d) *Approach and landing.* The stick force curve must have a stable slope at speeds between 1.1 V_{S1} and 1.8 V_{S1} with—

(1) Wing flaps in the landing position;

(2) Landing gear extended;

(3) The airplane trimmed at a speed in compliance with § 23.161(c)(4).

(4) Both power off and enough power to maintain a 3° angle of descent.

[Amdt. 23-7, 34 FR 13087, Aug. 13, 1969, as amended by Amdt. 23-14, 38 FR 31820, Nov. 19, 1973; Amdt. 23-17, 41 FR 55464, Dec. 20, 1976]

§ 23.177 Static directional and lateral stability.

(a) *Three-control airplanes.* The stability requirements for three-control airplanes are as follows:

(1) The static directional stability, as shown by the tendency to recover from a skid with the rudder free, must be positive for any landing gear and flap position appropriate to the takeoff, climb, cruise, and approach configurations. This must be shown with symmetrical power up to maximum continuous power, and at speeds from 1.2 V_{S1} up to the maximum allowable speed for the condition being investigated. The angle of skid for these tests must be appropriate to the type of airplane. At larger angles of skid up to that at which full rudder is used or a control force limit in § 23.143 is reached, whichever occurs first, and at speeds from 1.2 V_{S1} to V_A, the rudder pedal force must not reverse.

(2) The static lateral stability, as shown by the tendency to raise the low wing in a slip, must be positive for any landing gear and flap positions. This must be shown with symmetrical power up to 75 percent of maximum continuous power at speeds above 1.2 V_{S1}, up to the maximum allowable speed for the configuration being investigated. The static lateral stability may not be negative at 1.2 V_{S1}. The angle of slip for these tests must be appropriate to the type of airplane, but in no case may the slip angle be less than that obtainable with 10 degrees of bank.

(3) In straight, steady slips at 1.2 V_{S1} for any landing gear and flap positions, and for any symmetrical power conditions up to 50 percent of maximum continuous power, the aileron and rudder control movements and forces must increase steadily (but not necessarily in constant proportion) as the angle of slip is increased up to the maximum appropriate to the type of airplane. At larger slip angles up to the angle at which the full rudder or aileron control is used or a control force limit contained in § 23.143 is obtained, the rudder pedal force may not reverse. Enough bank must accompany slipping to hold a constant heading. Rapid entry into, or recovery from, a maximum slip may not result in uncontrollable flight characteristics.

(b) *Two-control (or simplified control) airplanes.* The stability requirements for two-control airplanes are as follows:

(1) The directional stability of the airplane must be shown by showing that, in each configuration, it can be rapidly rolled from a 45 degree bank in one direction to a 45 degree bank in the opposite direction without showing dangerous skid characteristics.

(2) The lateral stability of the airplane must be shown by showing that it will not assume a dangerous attitude or speed when the controls are abandoned for two minutes. This must be done in moderately smooth air with the airplane trimmed for straight level flight at 0.9 V_H or V_C, whichever is lower, with flaps and landing gear retracted, and with a rearward center of gravity.

[Doc. No. 4080, 29 FR 17955, Dec. 18, 1964; 30 FR 258, Jan. 9, 1965, as amended by Amdt. 23-21, 43 FR 2318, Jan. 16, 1978]

§ 23.179 Instrumented stick force measurements.

Instrumented stick force measurements must be made unless—

(a) Changes in speed are clearly reflected by changes in stick forces; and

(b) The maximum forces obtained under §§ 23.173 and 23.175 are not excessive.

§ 23.181 Dynamic stability.

(a) Any short period oscillation not including combined lateral-directional oscillations occurring between the stalling speed and the maximum allowable speed appropriate to the configuration of the airplane must be heavily damped with the primary controls—

(1) Free; and

(2) In a fixed position.

(b) Any combined lateral-directional oscillations ("Dutch roll") occurring between the stalling speed and the maximum allowable speed appropriate to the configuration of the airplane must be damped to 1/10 amplitude in 7 cycles with the primary controls—

(1) Free; and

(2) In a fixed position.

[Amdt. 23-21, 43 FR 2318, Jan. 16, 1978]

STALLS

§ 23.201 Wings level stall.

(a) For an airplane with independently controlled roll and directional controls, it must be possible to produce and to correct roll by unreversed use of the rolling control and to produce and to correct yaw by unreversed use of the directional control, up to the time the airplane pitches.

(b) For an airplane with interconnected lateral and directional controls (2 controls) and for an airplane with only one of these controls, it must be possible to produce and correct roll by unreversed use of the rolling control without producing excessive yaw, up to the time the airplane pitches.

(c) The wing level stall characteristics of the airplane must be demonstrated in flight as follows: The airplane speed must be reduced with the elevator control until the speed is slightly above the stalling speed, then the elevator control must be pulled back so that the rate of speed reduction will not exceed one knot per second until a stall is produced, as shown by an uncontrollable downward pitching motion of the airplane, or until the control reaches the stop. Normal use of the elevator control for recovery is allowed after the pitching motion has unmistakably developed.

(d) Except where made inapplicable by the special features of a particular type of airplane, the following apply to the measurement of loss of altitude during a stall:

(1) The loss of altitude encountered in the stall (power on or power off) is the change in altitude (as observed on the sensitive altimeter testing installation) between the altitude at which the airplane pitches and the altitude at which horizontal flight is regained.

(2) If power or thrust is required during stall recovery the power or thrust used must be that which would be used under the normal operating procedures selected by the applicant for this maneuver. However, the power used to regain level flight may not be applied until flying control is regained.

(e) During the recovery part of the maneuver, it must be possible to prevent more than 15 degrees of roll or yaw by the normal use of controls.

(f) Compliance with the requirements of this section must be shown under the following conditions:

(1) *Wing flaps:* Full up, full down, and intermediate, if appropriate.

(2) *Landing gear:* Retracted and extended.

(3) *Cowl flaps:* Appropriate to configuration.

(4) *Power:* Power or thrust off, and 75 percent maximum continuous power or thrust.

(5) *Trim:* 1.5 V_{S_1} or at the minimum trim speed, whichever is higher.

(6) *Propeller:* Full increase rpm position for the power off condition.

[Amdt. 23-14, 38 FR 31820, Nov. 19, 1973]

§ 23.203 Turning flight and accelerated stalls.

Turning flight and accelerated stalls must be demonstrated in flight tests as follows:

(a) Establish and maintain a coordinated turn in a 30 degree bank. Reduce speed by steadily and progressively tightening the turn with the elevator until the airplane is stalled or until the elevator has reached its stop. The rate of speed reduction must be constant, and:

(1) For a turning flight stall, may not exceed one knot per second; and

(2) For an accelerated stall, be 3 to 5 knots per second with steadily increasing normal acceleration.

(b) When the stall has fully developed or the elevator has reached its stop, it must be possible to regain level flight without:

(1) Excessive loss of altitude;

(2) Undue pitchup;

(3) Uncontrollable tendency to spin;

(4) Exceeding 60 degree of roll in either direction from the established 30 degree bank; and

(5) For accelerated entry stalls, without exceeding the maximum permissible speed or the allowable limit load factor.

(c) Compliance with the requirements of this section must be shown with:

(1) *Wing flaps:* Retracted and fully extended for turning flight and accelerated entry stalls, and intermediate, if appropriate, for accelerated entry stalls;

(2) *Landing gear:* Retracted and extended;

(3) *Cowl flaps:* Appropriate to configuration;

(4) *Power:* 75 percent maximum continuous power; and

(5) *Trim:* 1.5 V_{S_1} or minimum trim speed, whichever is higher.

[Amdt. 23-14, 38 FR 31820, Nov. 19, 1973]

§ 23.205 Critical engine inoperative stalls.

(a) A multiengine airplane may not display any undue spinning tendency and must be safely recoverable without applying power to the inoperative engine when stalled. The operating engines may be throttled back during the recovery from stall.

(b) Compliance with paragraph (a) of the section must be shown with:

(1) *Wing flaps:* Retracted.

(2) *Landing gear:* Retracted.

(3) *Cowl flaps:* Appropriate to level flight critical engine inoperative.

(4) *Power:* Critical engine inoperative and the remaining engine(s) at 75 percent maximum continuous power or thrust or the power or thrust at which the use of maximum control travel just holds the wings laterally level in the approach to stall, whichever is lesser.

(5) *Propeller:* Normal inoperative position for the inoperative engine.

(6) *Trim:* Level flight, critical engine inoperative, except that for an air-

plane of 6,000 pounds or less maximum weight that has a stalling speed of 61 knots or less and cannot maintain level flight with the critical engine inoperative, the airplane must be trimmed for straight flight, critical engine inoperative, at a speed not greater than $1.5V_{S1}$.

[Amdt. 23-14, 38 FR 31820, Nov. 19, 1973]

§ 23.207 Stall warning.

(a) There must be a clear and distinctive stall warning, with the flaps and landing gear in any normal position, in straight and turning flight.

(b) The stall warning may be furnished either through the inherent aerodynamic qualities of the airplane or by a device that will give clearly distinguishable indications under expected conditions of flight. However, a visual stall warning device that requires the attention of the crew within the cockpit is not acceptable by itself.

(c) The stall warning must begin at a speed exceeding the stalling speed by a margin of not less than 5 knots, but not more than the greater of 10 knots or 15 percent of the stalling speed, and must continue until the stall occurs.

[Amdt. 23-7, 34 FR 13087, Aug. 13, 1969]

SPINNING

§ 23.221 Spinning.

(a) *Normal category.* A single-engine, normal category airplane must be able to recover from a one-turn spin or a 3-second spin, whichever takes longer, in not more than one additional turn, with the controls used in the manner normally used for recovery. In addition—

(1) For both the flaps-retracted and flaps-extended conditions, the applicable airspeed limit and positive limit maneuvering load factor may not be exceeded;

(2) There may be no excessive back pressure during the spin or recovery; and

(3) It must be impossible to obtain uncontrollable spins with any use of the controls.

For the flaps-extended condition, the flaps may be retracted during recovery.

(b) *Utility category.* A utility category airplane must meet the requirements of paragraph (a) of this section or the requirements of paragraph (c) of this section.

(c) *Acrobatic category.* An acrobatic category airplane must meet the following requirements:

(1) The airplane must recover from any point in a spin, in not more than one and one-half additional turns after normal recovery application of the controls. Prior to normal recovery application of the controls, the spin test must proceed for six turns or 3 seconds, whichever takes longer, with flaps retracted, and one turn or 3 seconds, whichever takes longer, with flaps extended. However, beyond 3 seconds, the spin may be discontinued when spiral characteristics appear with flaps retracted.

(2) For both the flaps-retracted and flaps-extended conditions, the applicable airspeed limit and positive limit maneuvering load factor may not be exceeded. For the flaps-extended condition, the flaps may be retracted during recovery, if a placard is installed prohibiting intentional spins with flaps extended.

(3) It must be impossible to obtain uncontrollable spins with any use of the controls.

(d) *Airplanes "characteristically incapable of spinning".* If it is desired to designate an airplane as "characteristically incapable of spinning", this characteristic must be shown with—

(1) A weight five percent more than the highest weight for which approval is requested;

(2) A center of gravity at least three percent aft of the rearmost position for which approval is requested;

(3) An available elevator up-travel four degrees in excess of that to which the elevator travel is to be limited for approval; and

(4) An available rudder travel seven degrees, in both directions, in excess of that to which the rudder travel is to be limited for approval.

[Doc. No. 4080, 29 FR 17955, Dec. 18, 1964, as amended by Amdt. 23-7, 34 FR 13087, Aug. 13, 1969]

Ground and Water Handling Characteristics

§ 23.231 Longitudinal stability and control.

(a) A landplane may have no uncontrollable tendency to nose over in any reasonably expected operating condition, including rebound during landing or takeoff. Wheel brakes must operate smoothly and may not induce any undue tendency to nose over.

(b) A seaplane or amphibian may not have dangerous or uncontrollable porpoising characteristics at any normal operating speed on the water.

§ 23.233 Directional stability and control.

(a) There may be no uncontrollable ground or water looping tendency in 90 degree cross winds, up to a wind velocity of 0.2 V_{SO}, at any speed at which the airplane may be expected to be operated on the ground or water.

(b) A landplane must be satisfactorily controllable, without exceptional piloting skill or alertness, in power-off landings at normal landing speed, without using brakes or engine power to maintain a straight path.

(c) The airplane must have adequate directional control during taxiing.

§ 23.235 Taxiing condition.

The shock-absorbing mechanism may not damage the structure of the airplane when the airplane is taxied on the roughest ground that may reasonably be expected in normal operation.

§ 23.239 Spray characteristics.

Spray may not dangerously obscure the vision of the pilots or damage the propellers or other parts of a seaplane or amphibian at any time during taxiing, takeoff, and landing.

Miscellaneous Flight Requirements

§ 23.251 Vibration and buffeting.

Each part of the airplane must be free from excessive vibration under any appropriate speed and power conditions up to at least the minimum value of V_D allowed in § 23.335. In addition, there may be no buffeting, in any normal flight condition, severe enough to interfere with the satisfactory control of the airplane, cause excessive fatigue to the crew, or result in structural damage. Stall warning buffeting within these limits is allowable.

§ 23.253 High speed characteristics.

If a maximum operating speed V_{MO}/M_{MO} is established under § 23.1505(c), the following speed increase and recovery characteristics must be met:

(a) Operating conditions and characteristics likely to cause inadvertent speed increases (including upsets in pitch and roll) must be simulated with the airplane trimmed at any likely cruise speed up to V_{MO}/M_{MO}. These conditions and characteristics include gust upsets, inadvertent control movements, low stick force gradient in relation to control friction, passenger movement, leveling off from climb, and descent from Mach to airspeed limit altitude.

(b) Allowing for pilot reaction time after effective inherent or artificial speed warning occurs, it must be shown that the airplane can be recovered to a normal attitude and its speed reduced to V_{MO}/M_{MO}, without—

(1) Exceptional piloting strength or skill;

(2) Exceeding V_D/M_D, the maximum speed shown under § 23.251, or the structural limitations; or

(3) Buffeting that would impair the pilot's ability to read the instruments or to control the airplane for recovery.

(c) There may be no control reversal about any axis at any speed up to the maximum speed shown under § 23.251. Any reversal of elevator control force or tendency of the airplane to pitch, roll, or yaw must be mild and readily controllable, using normal piloting techniques.

[Amdt. 23-7, 34 FR 13087, Aug. 13, 1969; as amended by Amdt. 23-26, 45 FR 60170, Sept. 11, 1980]

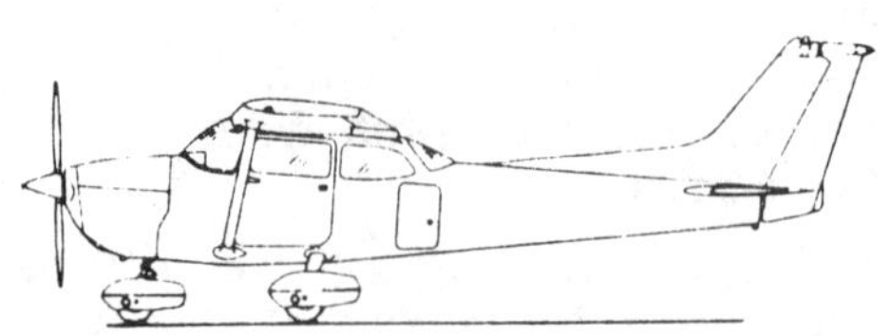

Adoption of the Amendments

Accordingly, Parts 21, 23, 36, 91, and 135 of the Federal Aviation Regulations (14 CFR Parts 21, 23, 36, 91, and 135) are amended, as follows:

1. By amending Part 23 by revising the title to read as follows:

PART 23—AIRWORTHINESS STANDARDS: NORMAL, UTILITY, ACROBATIC, AND COMMUTER CATEGORY AIRPLANES

2. The authority citation for Part 23 continues to read as follows:

Authority: 49 U.S.C. 1344, 1354(a), 1355, 1421, 1423, 1425, 1428, 1429, 1430, and 1502; and 49 U.S.C. 106(g) (Revised, Public L. 97-449, January 12, 1983).

3. By amending § 23.1 by revising paragraph (a) to read as follows:

§ 23.1 Applicability.

(a) This part prescribes airworthiness standards for the issue of type certificates, and changes to those certificates, for airplanes in the normal, utility, acrobatic, and commuter categories.

* * * * *

4. By amending § 23.3 by revising paragraphs (a) introductory text, (b) introductory text, and (c); by revising and redesignating paragraph (d) as (e), and by adding a new paragraph (d) to read as follows:

§ 23.3 Airplane categories.

(a) The normal category is limited to airplanes that have a seating configuration, excluding pilot seats, of nine or less, a maximum certificate takeoff weight of 12,500 pounds or less, and intended for nonacrobatic operation. Nonacrobatic operation includes:

* * * * *

(b) The utility category is limited to airplanes that have a seating configuration, excluding pilot seats, of nine or less, a maximum certificated takeoff weight of 12,500 pounds or less, and intended for limited acrobatic operation. Airplanes certificated in the utility category may be used in any of the operations covered under paragraph (a) of this section and in limited acrobatic operations. Limited acrobatic operation includes:

* * * * *

(c) The acrobatic category is limited to airplanes that have a seating configuration, excluding pilot seats, of nine or less, a maximum certificated takeoff weight of 12,500 pounds or less, and intended for use without restrictions, other than those shown to be necessary as a result of required flight tests.

(d) The communter category is limited to propeller-driven, multiengine airplanes that have a seating configuration excluding pilot seats, of 19 or less, and a maximum certificated takeoff weight of 19,000 pounds or less, intended for nonacrobatic operation as described in paragraph (a) of this section.

(e) Airplanes may be type certificated in more than one category of this part if the requirements of each requested category are met.

5. By amending § 23.25(a)(2) by inserting the words "and commuter" after the word "normal"; and by revising paragraph (a) introductory text to read as follows:

§ 23.25 Weight limits.

(a) *Maximum weight.* The maximum weight is the highest weight at which compliance with each applicable requirement of this Part (other than those complied with at the design landing weight) is shown. In addition, for commuter category airplanes, the applicant must establish a maximum zero fuel weight. The maximum weight must be established so that it is—

* * * * *

6. By amending § 23.45 by revising paragraph (a) and by adding a new paragraph (f) to read as follows:

§ 23.45 General.

(a) Unless otherwise prescribed, the performance requirements of this subpart must be met for still air; and

(1) Standard atmospheric conditions for normal, utility, and acrobatic category airplanes; or

(2) Ambient atmospheric conditions for commuter category airplanes.

* * * * *

(f) For commuter category airplanes, the following also apply:

(1) Unless otherwise prescribed, the applicant must select the takeoff, en route, approach, and landing configurations for the airplane;

(2) The airplane configuration may vary with weight, altitude, and temperature, to the extent they are compatible with the operating procedures required by paragraph (f)(3) of this section;

(3) Unless otherwise prescribed, in determining the critical-engine-inoperative takeoff performance, takeoff flight path, the accelerate-stop distance, takeoff distance, and landing distance, changes in the airplane's configuration, speed, power, and thrust must be made in accordance with procedures established by the applicant for operation in service;

(4) Procedures for the execution of missed approaches and balked landings associated with the conditions prescribed in §§ 23.67(e)(3) and 23.77(c) must be established; and

(5) The procedures established under paragraphs (f)(3) and (f)(4) of this section must—

(i) Be able to be consistently executed by a crew of average skill;

(ii) Use methods or devices that are safe and reliable; and

(iii) Include allowance for any reasonably expected time delays in the execution of the procedures.

7. By amending § 23.51 by removing paragraphs (b) and (c); by redesignating paragraphs (d) and (e) as (b) and (c) respectively; and by adding a new paragraph (d) to read as follows:

§ 23.51 Takeoff.

* * * * *

(d) For commuter category airplanes, takeoff performance and data as required by §§ 23.53 through 23.59 must be determined and included in the Airplane Flight Manual—

(1) For each weight, altitude, and ambient temperature within the operational limits selected by the applicant;

(2) For the selected configuration for takeoff;

(3) For the most unfavorable center of gravity position;

(4) With the operating engine within approved operating limitations;

(5) On a smooth, dry, hard surface runway; and

(6) Corrected for the following operational correction factors:

(i) Not more than 50 percent of nominal wind components along the takeoff path opposite to the direction of takeoff and not less than 150 percent of nominal wind components along the takeoff path in the direction of takeoff; and

(ii) Effective runway gradients.

8. By adding a new § 23.53 to read as follows:

§ 23.53 Takeoff speeds.

(a) For multiengine airplanes, the lift-off speed, V_{LOF}, may not be less than V_{MC} determined in accordance with § 23.149.

(b) Each normal, utility, and acrobatic category airplane, upon reaching a height of 50 feet above the takeoff surface level, must have reached a speed of not less than the following:

(1) For multiengine airplanes, the higher of—

(i) 1.1 V_{MC}; or

(ii) 1.3 V_{S1}, or any lesser speed, not less than V_X plus 4 knots, that is shown to be safe under all conditions, including turbulence and complete engine failure.

(2) For single engine airplanes—

(i) 1.3 V_{S1}; or

(ii) Any lesser speed, not less than V_X plus 4 knots, that is shown to be safer under all conditions, including turbulence and complete engine failure.

(c) For commuter category airplanes, the following apply:

(1) The takeoff decision speed, V_1, is the calibrated airspeed on the ground at which, as a result of engine failure or other reasons, the pilot is assumed to have made a decision to continue or discontinue the takeoff. The takeoff decision speed, V_1, must be selected by the applicant but may not be less than the greater of the following:

(i) 1.10 V_{S1};

(ii) 1.10 V_{MC} established in accordance with § 23.149;

(iii) A speed at which the airplane can be rotated for takeoff and shown to be adequate to safely continue the takeoff, using normal piloting skill, when the critical engine is suddenly made inoperative; or

(iv) V_{EF} plus the speed gained with the critcial engine inoperative during the time interval between the instant that the critical engine is failed and the instant at which the pilot recognizes and reacts to the engine failure as indicated by the pilot's application of the first retarding means during the accelerate-stop determination of § 23.55.

(2) The takeoff safety speed, V_2, in terms of calibrated airspeed, must be selected by the applicant so as to allow the gradient of climb required in § 23.67 but must not be less than V_1 or less than 1.2VV_{S1}.

(3) The critical engine failure speed, V_{EF}, is the calibrated airspeed at which the critical engine is assumed to fail. V_{EF} must be selected by the applicant but not less than V_{MC} determined in accordance with § 23.149.

(4) The rotation speed, V_R in terms of calibrated airspeed, must be selected by the applicant and may not be less than the greater of the following:

(i) V_1; or

(ii) The speed determined in accordance with § 23.57(c) that allows attaining the initial climb out speed, V_2, before reaching a height of 35 feet above the takeoff surface.

(5) For any given set of conditions, such as weight, altitude, configuration, and temperature, a single value of V_R must be used to show compliance with both the one-engine-inoperative takeoff and all-engines-operating takeoff requirements:

(i) One-engine-inoperative takeoff determined in accordance with § 23.57; and

(ii) All-engines-operating takeoff determined in accordance with § 23.59.

(6) The one-engine-inoperative takeoff distance, using a normal rotation rate at a speed of 5 knots less than V_R established in accordance with paragraphs (c)(4) and (5) of this section, must be shown not to exceed the corresponding one-engine-inoperative takeoff distance determined in accordance with §§ 23.57 and 23.59 using the established V_V. The take off distance determined in accordance with § 23.59 and the takeoff must be safely continued from the point at which the airplane is 35 feet above the takeoff surface at a speed not less than 5 knots less than the established V_2 speed.

(7) The applicant must show, with all engines operating, that marked increases in the scheduled takeoff distances determined in accordance with § 23.59 do not result from over-rotation of the airplane and out-of-trim conditions.

9. By adding a new § 23.55 to read as follows:

§ 23.55 Accelerate-stop distance.

For each commuter category airplane, the accelerate-stop distance must be determined as follows:

(a) The accelerate-stop distance is the sum of the distances necessary to—

(1) Accelerate the airplane from a standing start to V_1; and

(2) Come to a full stop from the point at which V_1 is reached assuming that in the case of engine failure, the pilot has decided to stop as indicated by application of the first retarding means at the speed V_1.

(b) Means other than wheel brakes may be used to determine the accelerate-stop distance if that means is available with the critical engine inoperative and if that means—

(1) Is safe and reliable;

(2) Is used so that consistent results can be expected under normal operating conditions; and

(3) Is such that exceptional skill is not required to control the airplane.

10. By adding a new § 23.57 to read as follows:

§ 23.57 Takeoff path.

For each commuter category airplane, the takeoff path is as follows:

(a) The takeoff path extends from a standing start to a point in the takeoff at which the airplane is 1,500 feet above the takeoff surface or at which the transition from the takeoff to the en route configuration is completed, whichever point is higher; and

(1) The takeoff path must be based on the procedures prescribed in § 23.45;

(2) The airplane must be accelerated on the ground to V_{EF} at which point the critical engine must be made inoperative and remain inoperative for the rest of the takeoff; and

(3) After reaching V_{EF}, the airplane must be accelerated to V_2.

(b) During the acceleration to speed V_2, the nose gear may be raised off the ground at a speed not less than V_R. However, landing gear retraction may not be initiated until the airplane is airborne.

(c) During the takeoff path determination, in accordance with paragraphs (a) and (b) of this section—

(1) The slope of the airborne part of the takeoff path must be positive at each point;

(2) The airplane must reach V_2 before it is 35 feet above the takeoff surface, and must continue at a speed as close as practical to, but not less than V_2, until it is 400 feet above the takeoff surface;

(3) At each point along the takeoff path, starting at the point at which the airplane reaches 400 feet above the takeoff surface, the available gradient of climb may not be less than—

(i) 1.2 percent for two-engine airplanes;

(ii) 1.5 percent for three-engine airplanes;

(iii) 1.7 percent for four-engine airplanes; and

(4) Except for gear retraction and automatic propeller feathering, the airplane configuration may not be changed, and no change in power or thrust that requires action by the pilot may be made, until the airplane is 400 feet above the takeoff surface.

(d) The takeoff path must be determined by a continuous demonstrated takeoff or by synthesis from segments. If the takeoff path is determined by the segmental method—

(1) The segments must be clearly defined and must be related to the distinct changes in the configuration, power or thrust, and speed;

(2) The weight of the airplane, the configuration, and the power or thrust must be constant throughout each segment and must correspond to the most critical condition prevailing in the segment;

(3) The flight path must be based on the airplane's performance without ground effect;

(4) The takeoff path data must be checked by continuous demonstrated takeoffs up to the point at which the airplane is out of ground effect and its speed is stabilized to ensure that the path is conservative relative to the continuous path; and

(5) The airplane is considered to be out of the ground effect when it reaches a height equal to its wing span.

11. By adding a new § 23.59 to read as follows:

§ 23.59 Takeoff distance and takeoff run.

For each commuter category airplane—

(a) Takeoff distance is the greater of—

(1) The horizontal distance along the takeoff path from the start of the takeoff to the point at which the airplane is 35 feet above the takeoff surface as determined under § 23.57; or

(2) With all engines operating, 115 percent of the horizontal distance along the takeoff path, with all engines operating, from the start of the takeoff to the point at which the airplane is 35 feet above the takeoff surface, as determined by a procedure consistent with § 23.57.

(b) If the takeoff distance includes a clearway, the takeoff run is the greater of—

(1) The horizontal distance along the takeoff path from the start of the takeoff to a point equidistant between the point at which V_{LOF} is reached and the point at which the airplane is 35 feet above the takeoff surface as determined under § 23.57; or

(2) With all engines operating, 115 percent of the horizontal distance along the takeoff path, with all engines operating, from the start of the takeoff to a point equidistant between the point at which V_{LOF} is reached and the point at which the airplane is 35 feet above the takeoff surface determined by a procedure consistent with § 23.57.

12. By adding a new § 23.61 to read as follows:

§ 23.61 Takeoff flight path.

For each commuter category airplane, the takeoff flight path must be determined as follows:

(a) The takeoff flight path begins 35 feet above the takeoff surface at the end of the takeoff distance determined in accordance with § 23.59.

(b) The net takeoff flight path data must be determined so that they represent the actual takeoff flight paths, as determined in accordance with § 23.57 and with paragraph (a) of this section, reduced at each point by a gradient of climb equal to—

(1) 0.8 percent for two-engine airplanes;

(2) 0.9 percent for three-engine airplanes; and

(3) 1.0 percent for four-engine airplanes.

(c) The prescribed reduction in climb gradient may be applied as an equivalent reduction in acceleration along that part of the takeoff flight path at which the airplane is accelerated in level flight.

13. By amending § 23.65 by adding a new paragraph (d) to read as follows:

§ 23.65 Climb: All engines operating.

* * * * *

(d) In addition for commuter category airplanes, performance data must be determined for variations in weight, altitude, and temperatures at the most critical center of gravity for which approval is requested.

14. By amending § 23.67 by inserting the words "normal, utility, and acrobatic category" before the word "reciprocating" in both paragraphs (a) and (b) and before the word "turbine" in paragraph (c); and by adding a new paragraph (e) to read as follows:

§ 23.67 Climb: One engine inoperative.

* * * * *

(e) For commuter category airplanes, the following apply:

(1) *Takeoff climb:* The maximum weight at which the airplane meets the minimum climb performance specified in paragraphs (i) and (ii) must be determined for each altitude and ambient temperature within the operating limitations established for the airplane, out of ground effect in free air, with the airplane in the takeoff configuration, with the most critical center of gravity, the critical engine inoperative, the remaining engines at the maximum takeoff power or thrust, and the propeller of the inoperative engine windmilling with the propeller controls in the normal position, except that, if an approved automatic propeller feathering system is installed, the propeller may be in the feathered position:

(i) *Takeoff, landing gear extended.* The minimum steady gradient of climb between the lift-off speed, V_{LOF}, and until the landing gear is retracted must be measurably positive for two-engine airplanes, not less than 0.3 percent for three-engine airplanes, or 0.5 percent for four-engine airplanes at all points along the flight path; and

(ii) *Takeoff, landing gear retracted.* The minimum steady gradient of climb must not be less than 2 percent for two-engine airplanes, 2.3 percent for three-engine airplanes, and 2.6 percent for four-engine airplanes at the speed V_2, until the airplane is 400 feet above the takeoff surface. For airplanes with fixed landing gear, this requirement must be met with the landing gear extended.

(2) *En route climb:* The maximum weight must be determined for each altitude and ambient temperature within the operational limits established for the airplane, at which the steady gradient of climb is not less than 1.2 percent for two-engine airplanes, 1.5 percent for three-engine airplanes, and 1.7 percent for four-engine airplanes at an altitude of 1,500 feet above the takeoff surface, with the airplane in the en route configuration, the critical engine inoperative, the remaining engine at the maximum continuous power or thrust, and the most unfavorable center of gravity.

(3) *Approach:* In the approach configuration corresponding to the normal all-engines-operating procedure in which V_{S_4} for this configuration does not exceed 110 percent of the V_{S_1} for the related landing configuration, the steady gradient of climb may not be less than 2.1 percent for two-engine airplanes, 2.4 percent for three-engine airplanes, and 2.7 percent for four-engine airplanes, with—

(i) The critical engine inoperative and the remaining engines at the available takeoff power or thrust;

(ii) The maximum landing weight; and

(iii) A climb speed established in connection with the normal landing procedures but not exceeding 1.5 V_{S_1}.

15. By amending § 23.75 by adding a new paragraph (g) to read as follows:

§ 23.75 Landing.

* * * * *

(g) In addition, for commuter category airplanes, the following apply:

(1) The landing distance must be determined for standard temperatures at each weight, altitude, and wind condition within the operational limits established by the applicant;

(2) A steady gliding approach, or a steady approach at a gradient of descent not greater than 5.2 percent (3°), at a calibrated airspeed not less than 1.3V_{S_1} must be maintained down to the 50-foot height; and

(3) The landing distance data must include correction factors for not more than 50 percent of the nominal wind components along the landing path opposite to the direction of landing and not less than 150 percent of the nominal wind components along the landing path in the direction of landing.

16. By amending § 23.77 by inserting the words "normal, utility, and acrobatic category" before the word "airplane"; and by adding an "s" to the word "airplane" in paragraph (a); by inserting the words "normal, utility, and acrobatic category" before the word "turbine"; by adding an "s" to the word "airplane" in the first part of the sentence in paragraph (b); and by adding a new paragraph (c) to read as follows:

§ 23.77 Balked landing.

* * * * *

(c) For each commuter category airplane, with all engines operating, the maximum weight must be determined with the airplane in the landing configuration for each altitude and ambient temperature within the operational limits established for the airplane, with the most unfavorable center of gravity and out-of-ground effect in free air, at which the steady gradient of climb will not be less than 3.3 percent with—

(1) The engines at the power or thrust that is available 8 seconds after initiation of movement of the power or thrust controls from the minimum flight-idle position to the takeoff position.

(2) A climb speed not greater than the approach speed established under § 23.75 and not less than the greater of 1.05 V_{MC} or 1.10V_{S_1}.

17. By amending § 23.161 by revising paragraphs (b), (c) introductory test, and (c)(3) to read as follows:

§ 23.161 Trim.

* * * * *

(b) *Lateral and directional trim.* The airplane must maintain lateral and directional trim in level flight with the landing gear and wing flaps retracted as follows:

(1) For normal, utility, and acrobatic category airplanes, at a speed of $0.9V_H$ or V_C, whichever is lower; and

(2) For commuter category airplanes, at a speed of V_H or V_{MO}/M_{MO}, whichever is lower.

(c) *Longitudinal trim.* The airplane must maintain longitudinal trim under each of the following conditions, except that it need not maintain trim at a speed greater than V_{MO}/M_{MO}:

* * * * *

(3) Level flight at any speed with the landing gear and wing flaps retracted as follows:

(i) For normal, utility, and acrobatic category airplanes, at any speed from $0.9V_H$ to either V_X or $1.4V_{S_1}$; and

(ii) For commuter category airplanes, at a speed of V_H or V_{MO}/M_{MO}, whichever is lower, to either V_X or $1.4V_{S_1}$.

* * * * *

18. By amending § 23.173 by revising paragraph (b) to read as follows:

§ 23.173 Static longitudinal stability.

* * * * *

(b) The airspeed must return to within the tolerances specified for applicable categories of airplanes when the control force is slowly released at any speed within the speed range specified in paragraph (a) of this section. The applicable tolerances are—

(1) The airspeed must return to within plus or minus 10 percent of the original trim airspeed; and

(2) For commuter category airplanes, the airspeed must return to within plus or minus 7.5 percent of the original trim airspeed for the cruising condition specified in § 23.175(b).

* * * * *

19. By amending § 23.175 by revising paragraph (b)(2) introductory text to read as follows:

§ 23.175 Demonstration of static longitudinal stability.

* * * * *

(b) *Cruise—Landing gear retracted (or fixed gear).*

* * * * *

(2) *High speed cruise.* The stick force curve must have a stable slope at all speeds within a range that is the greater of 15 percent of the trim speed plus the resulting free return speed range or 40 knots plus the resulting free return speed range for normal, utility, and acrobatic category airplanes, above and below the trim speed. For commuter category airplanes, the stick force curve must have a stable slope for a speed range of 50 knots from the trim speed, except that the speeds need not exceed V_{FC}/M_{FC} or be less than $1.4\ V_{S_1}$ and this speed range is considered to begin at the outer extremes of the friction band with a stick force not to exceed 50 pounds. In addition, for commuter category airplanes, V_{FC}/M_{FC} may not be less than a speed midway between V_{MO}/M_{MO} and V_{DF}/M_{DF}, except that, for altitudes where Mach number is the limiting factor, M_{FC} need not exceed the Mach number at which effective speed warning occurs. These requirements for all categories of airplane must be met with—

* * * * *

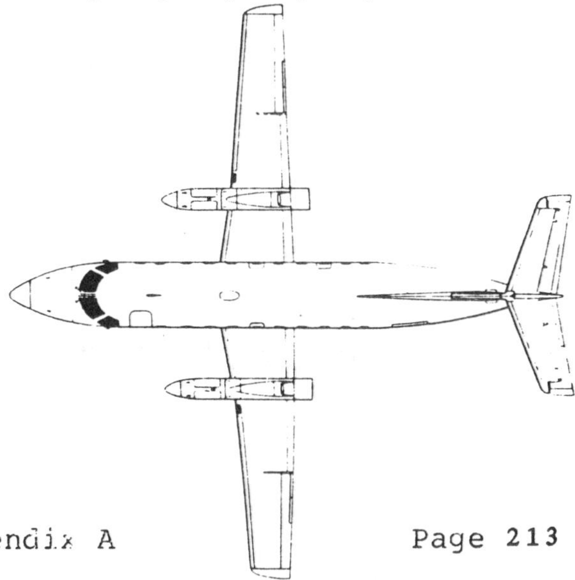

In this Section a summary is given of that part of FAR 25 which deals with performance and with flight characteristics.

Subpart A—General

§ 25.1 Applicability.

(a) This part prescribes airworthiness standards for the issue of type certificates, and changes to those certificates, for transport category airplanes.

(b) Each person who applies under Part 21 for such a certificate or change must show compliance with the applicable requirements in this part.

§ 25.2 Special retroactive requirements.

Notwithstanding §§ 21.17 and 21.101 of this chapter and irrespective of the date of application, each applicant for a type certificate and each applicant for a supplemental-type certificate (or an amendment to a type certificate) involving an increase in passenger seating capacity to a total greater than that for which the airplane has been type certificated, must show:

(a) After October 23, 1967, that the airplane concerned meets the requirements of §§ 25.783(g), 25.803(c) (2) through (9), 25.803(d), 25.807 (a), (c), and (d), 25.809 (f), and (h), 25.811 (a), (b), (d), (e), (f), and (g), 25.812(a)(1), (b), (c), (d), (e), (h), (i), (j), and (k) (1) and (2), 25.813 (a), (b), and (c), 25.815, 25.817, 25.853 (a) and (b), 25.855(a), 25.993(f), and 25.1359(c), in effect on October 24, 1967, or June 20, 1968, and

(b) After April 24, 1969, that the airplane concerned meets the requirements of §§ 25.721(d), 25.803(e), 25.811(c), 25.812 (a)(2), (f), (g), and (k)(3) in effect on October 24, 1967; and

(c) After April 23, 1969, that the airplane concerned meets the requirements of § 25.785(c) in effect either prior to or on that date; and

(d) After April 23, 1969, that the airplane concerned meets the requirements of §§ 25.803(b) and 25.803(c)(1) in effect on that date.

(Sec. 604, 72 Stat. 778; (49 U.S.C. 1424)

[Amdt. 25-15, 32 FR 13262, Sept. 20, 1967; 32 FR 13635, Sept. 29, 1967; Amdt. 25-17, 33 FR 9066, June 20, 1968; Amdt. 25-20, 34 FR 5544, Mar. 22, 1969]

Subpart B—Flight

General

§ 25.21 Proof of compliance.

(a) Each requirement of this subpart must be met at each appropriate combination of weight and center of gravity within the range of loading conditions for which certification is requested. This must be shown—

(1) By tests upon an airplane of the type for which certification is requested, or by calculations based on, and equal in accuracy to, the results of testing; and

(2) By systematic investigation of each probable combination of weight and center of gravity, if compliance cannot be reasonably inferred from combinations investigated.

(b) If there is less than a 2 knot difference in the forward and rearward c.g. stalling speeds, the flying qualities may be based upon the forward c.g. stalling speeds.

(c) The controllability, stability, trim, and stalling characteristics of the airplane must be shown for each altitude up to the maximum expected in operation.

(d) The following general tolerances from specified values are allowed during flight testing. However, greater tolerances may be allowed in particular tests. These tolerances are plus or minus variations unless otherwise noted in the particular test:

Item	Tolerance
Weight	+5%, −10%.
Critical items affected by weight.	+5%, −1%.
C.G.	7% total travel.
Airspeed	3 knots or 3%, whichever is higher.
Power	5%.
Wind (takeoff and landing tests).	As low as possible but not to exceed approximately 12% V_{S1} or 10.0 knots, whichever is lower, along the runway surface.

(e) If compliance with the flight characteristics requirements is dependent upon a stability augmentation system or upon any other automatic or power-operated system, compliance must be shown with §§ 25.671 and 25.672.

(f) In meeting the requirements of §§ 25.105(d), 25.125, 25.233, and 25.237, the wind velocity must be measured at a height of 10 meters above the surface, or corrected for the difference between the height at which the wind velocity is measured and the 10-meter height.

(Secs. 313(a), 601, 603, 604, and 605 of the Federal Aviation Act of 1958 (49 U.S.C. 1354(a), 1421, 1423, 1424, and 1425); and sec. 6(c) of the Dept. of Transportation Act (49 U.S.C. 1655(c)))

[Doc. No. 5066, 29 FR 18291, Dec. 24, 1964, as amended by Amdt. 25-23, 35 FR 5671, Apr. 8, 1970; Amdt. 25-42, 43 FR 2320, Jan. 16, 1978]

§ 25.23 Load distribution limits.

(a) Ranges of weights and centers of gravity within which the airplane may be safely operated must be established. If a weight and center of gravity combination is allowable only within certain load distribution limits (such as spanwise) that could be inadvertently exceeded, these limits and the corresponding weight and center of gravity combinations must be established.

(b) The load distribution limits may not exceed—

(1) The selected limits;

(2) The limits at which the structure is proven; or

(3) The limits at which compliance with each applicable flight requirement of this subpart is shown.

§ 25.25 Weight limits.

(a) *Maximum weights.* Maximum weights corresponding to the airplane operating conditions (such as ramp, ground or water taxi, takeoff, en route, and landing), environmental conditions (such as altitude and temperature), and loading conditions (such as zero fuel weight, center of gravity position and weight distribution) must be established so that they are not more than—

(1) The highest weight selected by the applicant for the particular conditions; or

(2) The highest weight at which compliance with each applicable structural loading and flight requirement is shown, except that for airplanes equipped with standby power rocket engines the maximum weight must not be more than the highest weight established in accordance with Appendix E of this part.

(b) *Minimum weight.* The minimum weight (the lowest weight at which compliance with each applicable requirement of this part is shown) must be established so that it is not less than—

(1) The lowest weight selected by the applicant;

(2) The design minimum weight (the lowest weight at which compliance with each structural loading condition of this part is shown); or

(3) The lowest weight at which compliance with each applicable flight requirement is shown.

[Doc. No. 5066, 29 FR 18291, Dec. 24, 1964, as amended by Amdt. 25-23, 35 FR 5671, Apr. 8, 1970]

§ 25.27 Center of gravity limits.

The extreme forward and the extreme aft center of gravity limitations must be established for each practicably separable operating condition. No such limit may lie beyond—

(a) The extremes selected by the applicant;

(b) The extremes within which the structure is proven; or

(c) The extremes within which compliance with each applicable flight requirement is shown.

§ 25.29 Empty weight and corresponding center of gravity.

(a) The empty weight and corresponding center of gravity must be determined by weighing the airplane with—

(1) Fixed ballast;

(2) Unusable fuel determined under § 25.959; and

(3) Full operating fluids, including—

(i) Oil;

(ii) Hydraulic fluid; and

(iii) Other fluids required for normal operation of airplane systems, except potable water, lavatory precharge water, and water intended for injection in the engines.

(b) The condition of the airplane at the time of determining empty weight must be one that is well defined and can be easily repeated.

(Secs. 313(a), 601, 603, 604, and 605 of the Federal Aviation Act of 1958 (49 U.S.C. 1354(a), 1421, 1423, 1424, and 1425); and sec. 6(c) of the Dept. of Transportation Act (49 U.S.C. 1655(c)))

[Doc. No. 5066, 29 FR 18291, Dec. 24, 1964, as amended by Amdt. 25-42, 43 FR 2320, Jan. 16, 1978]

§ 25.31 Removable ballast.

Removable ballast may be used on showing compliance with the flight requirements of this subpart.

§ 25.33 Propeller speed and pitch limits.

(a) The propeller speed and pitch must be limited to values that will ensure-

(1) Safe operation under normal operating conditions; and

(2) Compliance with the performance requirements of §§ 25.101 through 25.125.

(b) There must be a propeller speed limiting means at the governor. It must limit the maximum possible governed engine speed to a value not exceeding the maximum allowable r.p.m.

(c) The low pitch blade stop, or other means used to limit the low pitch position of the propeller blades, must be set so that the engine speed does not exceed 103 percent of the maximum allowable engine r.p.m. with—

(1) The propeller blades at the low pitch limit and governor inoperative; and

(2) Takeoff manifold pressure with the airplane stationary under standard atmospheric conditions.

[Doc. No. 5066, 29 FR 18291, Dec. 24, 1964, as amended by Amdt. 25-57, 49 FR 6848, Feb. 23, 1984]

PERFORMANCE

§ 25.101 General.

(a) Unless otherwise prescribed, airplanes must meet the applicable performance requirements of this subpart for ambient atmospheric conditions and still air.

(b) The performance, as affected by engine power or thrust, must be based on the following relative humidities;

(1) For turbine engine powered airplanes, a relative humidity of—

(i) 80 percent, at and below standard temperatures; and

(ii) 34 percent, at and above standard temperatures plus 50° F.

Between these two temperatures, the relative humidity must vary linearly.

(2) For reciprocating engine powered airplanes, a relative humidity of 80 percent in a standard atmosphere. Engine power corrections for vapor pressure must be made in accordance with the following table:

Altitude H (ft.)	Vapor pressure e (In. Hg.)	Specific humidity w (Lb. moisture per lb. dry air)	Density ratio $\rho/\sigma=0.0023769$
0	0.403	0.00849	0.99508
1,000	.354	.00773	.96672
2,000	.311	.00703	.93895
3,000	.272	.00638	.91178
4,000	.238	.00578	.88514
5,000	.207	.00523	.85910
6,000	.1805	.00472	.83361
7,000	.1566	.00425	.80870
8,000	.1356	.00382	.78434
9,000	.1172	.00343	.76053
10,000	.1010	.00307	.73722
15,000	.0463	.001710	.62868
20,000	.01978	.000896	.53263
25,000	.00778	.000436	.44806

(c) The performance must correspond to the propulsive thrust available under the particular ambient atmospheric conditions, the particular flight condition, and the relative humidity specified in paragraph (b) of this section. The available propulsive thrust must correspond to engine power or thrust, not exceeding the approved power or thrust less—

(1) Installation losses; and

(2) The power or equivalent thrust absorbed by the accessories and services appropriate to the particular ambient atmospheric conditions and the particular flight condition.

(d) Unless otherwise prescribed, the applicant must select the takeoff, en route, approach, and landing configurations for the airplane.

(e) The airplane configurations may vary with weight, altitude, and temperature, to the extent they are compatible with the operating procedures required by paragraph (f) of this section.

(f) Unless otherwise prescribed, in determining the accelerate-stop distances, takeoff flight paths, takeoff distances, and landing distances, changes in the airplane's configuration, speed, power, and thrust, must be made in accordance with procedures established by the applicant for operation in service.

(g) Procedures for the execution of balked landings and missed approaches associated with the conditions prescribed in §§ 25.119 and 25.121(d) must be established.

(h) The procedures established under paragraphs (f) and (g) of this section must—

(1) Be able to be consistently executed in service by crews of average skill;

(2) Use methods or devices that are safe and reliable; and

(3) Include allowance for any time delays, in the execution of the procedures, that may reasonably be expected in service.

[Doc. No. 5066, 29 FR 18291, Dec. 24, 1964, as amended by Amdt. 25-38, 41 FR 55466, Dec. 20, 1976]

§ 25.103 Stalling speed.

(a) V_S is the calibrated stalling speed, or the minimum steady flight speed, in knots, at which the airplane is controllable, with—

(1) Zero thrust at the stalling speed, or, if the resultant thrust has no appreciable effect on the stalling speed, with engines idling and throttles closed;

(2) Propeller pitch controls (if applicable) in the position necessary for compliance with paragraph (a)(1) of this section and the airplane in other respects (such as flaps and landing gear) in the condition existing in the test in which V_S is being used;

(3) The weight used when V_S is being used as a factor to determine compliance with a required performance standard; and

(4) The most unfavorable center of gravity allowable.

(b) The stalling speed V_S is the minimum speed obtained as follows:

(1) Trim the airplane for straight flight at any speed not less than 1.2 V_S or more than 1.4 V_S At a speed sufficiently above the stall speed to ensure steady conditions, apply the elevator control at a rate so that the airplane speed reduction does not exceed one knot per second.

(2) Meet the flight characteristics provisions of § 25.203.

§ 25.105 Takeoff.

(a) The takeoff speeds described in § 25.107, the accelerate-stop distance described in § 25.109, the takeoff path described in § 25.111, and the takeoff distance and takeoff run described in § 25.113, must be determined—

(1) At each weight, altitude, and ambient temperature within the operational limits selected by the applicant; and

(2) In the selected configuration for takeoff.

(b) No takeoff made to determine the data required by this section may require exceptional piloting skill or alertness.

(c) The takeoff data must be based on—

(1) A smooth, dry, hard-surfaced runway, in the case of land planes and amphibians;

(2) Smooth water, in the case of seaplanes and amphibians; and

(3) Smooth, dry snow, in the case of skiplanes.

(d) The takeoff data must include, within the established operational limits of the airplane, the following operational correction factors:

(1) Not more than 50 percent of nominal wind components along the takeoff path opposite to the direction of takeoff, and not less than 150 per-

cent of nominal wind components along the takeoff path in the direction of takeoff.

(2) Effective runway gradients.

§ 25.107 Takeoff speeds.

(a) V_1 must be established in relation to V_{EF} as follows:

(1) V_{EF} is the calibrated airspeed at which the critical engine is assumed to fail. V_{EF} must be selected by the applicant, but may not be less than V_{MCG} determined under § 25.149(e).

(2) V_1, in terms of calibrated airspeed, is the takeoff decision speed selected by the applicant; however, V_1 may not be less than V_{EF} plus the speed gained with the critical engine inoperative during the time interval between the instant at which the critical engine is failed, and the instant at which the pilot recognizes and reacts to the engine failure, as indicated by the pilot's application of the first retarding means during accelerate-stop tests.

(b) V_{2MIN}, in terms of calibrated airspeed, may not be less than—

(1) 1.2 V_S for—

(i) Two-engine and three-engine turbopropeller and reciprocating engine powered airplanes; and

(ii) Turbojet powered airplanes without provisions for obtaining a significant reduction in the one-engine-inoperative power-on stalling speed;

(2) 1.15 V_S for—

(i) Turbopropeller and reciprocating engine powered airplanes with more than three engines; and

(ii) Turbojet powered airplanes with provisions for obtaining a significant reduction in the one-engine-inoperative power-on stalling speed; and

(3) 1.10 times V_{MC} established under § 25.149.

(c) V_2, in terms of calibrated airspeed, must be selected by the applicant to provide at least the gradient of climb required by § 25.121(b) but may not be less than—

(1) V_{2MIN}, and

(2) V_R plus the speed increment attained (in accordance with § 25.111 (c)(2)) before reaching a height of 35 feet above the takeoff surface.

(d) V_{MU} is the calibrated airspeed at and above which the airplane can safely lift off the ground, and continue the takeoff. V_{MU} speeds must be selected by the applicant throughout the range of thrust-to-weight ratios to be certificated. These speeds may be established from free air data if these data are verified by ground takeoff tests.

(e) *VR*, in terms of calibrated airspeed, must be selected in accordance with the conditions of paragraphs (e) (1) through (4) of this section:

(1) V_R may not be less than—

(i) V_1;

(ii) 105 percent of V_{MC};

(iii) The speed (determined in accordance with § 25.111(c)(2)) that allows reaching V_2 before reaching a height of 35 feet above the takeoff surface; or

(iv) A speed that, if the airplane is rotated at its maximum practicable rate, will result in a V_{LOF} of not less than 110 percent of V_{MU} in the all-engines-operating condition and not less than 105 percent of V_{MU} determined at the thrust-to-weight ratio corresponding to the one-engine-inoperative condition.

(2) For any given set of conditions (such as weight, configuration, and temperature), a single value of V_R, obtained in accordance with this paragraph, must be used to show compliance with both the one-engine-inoperative and the all-engines-operating takeoff provisions.

(3) It must be shown that the one-engine-inoperative takeoff distance, using a rotation speed of 5 knots less than V_R established in accordance with paragraphs (e)(1) and (2) of this section, does not exceed the corresponding one-engine-inoperative takeoff distance using the established V_R. The takeoff distances must be determined in accordance with § 25.113(a)(1).

(4) Reasonably expected variations in service from the established takeoff procedures for the operation of the airplane (such as over-rotation of the airplane and out-of-trim conditions) may not result in unsafe flight characteristics or in marked increases in the scheduled takeoff distances established in accordance with § 25.113(a).

(f) V_{LOF} is the calibrated airspeed at which the airplane first becomes airborne.

(Secs. 313(a), 601, 603, 604, and 605 of the Federal Aviation Act of 1958 (49 U.S.C. 1354(a), 1421, 1423, 1424, and 1425); and sec. 6(c) of the Dept. of Transportation Act (49 U.S.C. 1655(c)))

[Doc. No. 5066, 29 FR 18291, Dec. 24, 1964, as amended by Amdt. 25-38, 41 FR 55466, Dec. 20, 1976; Amdt. 25-42, 43 FR 2320, Jan. 16, 1978]

§ 25.109 Accelerate-stop distance.

(a) The accelerate-stop distance is the greater of the following distances:

(1) The sum of the distances necessary to—

(i) Accelerate the airplane from a standing start to V_{EF} with all engines operating;

(ii) Accelerate the airplane from V_{EF} to V_1 and continue the acceleration for 2.0 seconds after V_1 is reached, assuming the critical engine fails at V_{EF}; and

(iii) Come to a full stop from the point reached at the end of the acceleration period prescribed in paragraph (a)(1)(ii) of this section, assuming that the pilot does not apply any means of retarding the airplane until that point is reached and that the critical engine is still inoperative.

(2) The sum of the distances necessary to—

(i) Accelerate the airplane from a standing start to V_1 and continue the acceleration for 2.0 seconds after V_1 is reached with all engines operating; and

(ii) Come to a full stop from the point reached at the end of the acceleration period prescribed in paragraph (a)(2)(i) of this section, assuming that the pilot does not apply any means of retarding the airplane until that point is reached and that all engines are still operating.

(b) Means other than wheel brakes may be used to determine the accelerate-stop distance if that means—

(1) Is safe and reliable;

(2) Is used so that consistent results can be expected under normal operating conditions; and

(3) Is such that exceptional skill is not required to control the airplane.

(c) The landing gear must remain extended throughout the accelerate-stop distance.

(d) If the accelerate-stop distance includes a stopway with surface characteristics substantially different from those of a smooth hard-surfaced runway, the takeoff data must include operational correction factors for the accelerate-stop distance. The correction factors must account for the particular surface characteristics of the stopway and the variations in these characteristics with seasonal weather conditions (such as temperature, rain, snow, and ice) within the established operational limits.

(Secs. 313(a), 601, 603, 604, and 605 of the Federal Aviation Act of 1958 (49 U.S.C. 1354(a), 1421, 1423, 1424, and 1425); and sec. 6(c) of the Dept. of Transportation Act (49 U.S.C. 1655(c)))

[Doc. No. 5066, 29 FR 18291, Dec. 24, 1964, as amended by Amdt. 25-42, 43 FR 2321, Jan. 16, 1978]

§ 25.111 Takeoff path.

(a) The takeoff path extends from a standing start to a point in the takeoff at which the airplane is 1,500 feet above the takeoff surface, or at which the transition from the takeoff to the en route configuration is completed and a speed is reached at which compliance with § 25.121(c) is shown, whichever point is higher. In addition—

(1) The takeoff path must be based on the procedures prescribed in § 25.101(c);

(2) The airplane must be accelerated on the ground to V_{EF}, at which point the critical engine must be made inoperative and remain inoperative for the rest of the takeoff; and

(3) After reaching V_{EF}, the airplane must be accelerated to V_2.

(b) During the acceleration to speed V_2, the nose gear may be raised off the ground at a speed not less than V_R. However, landing gear retraction may not be begun until the airplane is airborne.

(c) During the takeoff path determination in accordance with paragraphs (a) and (b) of this section—

(1) The slope of the airborne part of the takeoff path must be positive at each point;

(2) The airplane must reach V_2 before it is 35 feet above the takeoff surface and must continue at a speed as close as practical to, but not less than V_2, until it is 400 feet above the takeoff surface;

(3) At each point along the takeoff path, starting at the point at which the airplane reaches 400 feet above the takeoff surface, the available gradient of climb may not be less than—

(i) 1.2 percent for two-engine airplanes;

(ii) 1.5 percent for three-engine airplanes; and

(iii) 1.7 percent for four-engine airplanes; and

(4) Except for gear retraction and propeller feathering, the airplane configuration may not be changed, and no change in power or thrust that requires action by the pilot may be made, until the airplane is 400 feet above the takeoff surface.

(d) The takeoff path must be determined by a continuous demonstrated takeoff or by synthesis from segments. If the takeoff path is determined by the segmental method—

(1) The segments must be clearly defined and must be related to the distinct changes in the configuration, power or thrust, and speed;

(2) The weight of the airplane, the configuration, and the power or thrust must be constant throughout each segment and must correspond to the most critical condition prevailing in the segment;

(3) The flight path must be based on the airplane's performance without ground effect; and

(4) The takeoff path data must be checked by continuous demonstrated takeoffs up to the point at which the airplane is out of ground effect and its speed is stabilized, to ensure that the path is conservative relative to the continous path.

The airplane is considered to be out of the ground effect when it reaches a height equal to its wing span.

(e) For airplanes equipped with standby power rocket engines, the takeoff path may be determined in accordance with section II of Appendix E.

(Secs. 313(a), 601, 603, 604, and 605 of the Federal Aviation Act of 1958 (49 U.S.C. 1354(a), 1421, 1423, 1424, and 1425); and sec. 6(c) of the Dept. of Transportation Act (49 U.S.C. 1655(c)))

[Doc. No. 5066, 29 FR 18291, Dec. 24, 1964, as amended by Amdt. 25-6, 30 FR 8468, July 2, 1965; Amdt. 25-42, 43 FR 2321, Jan. 16, 1978; Amdt. 25-54, 45 FR 60172, Sept. 11, 1980]

§ 25.113 Takeoff distance and takeoff run.

(a) Takeoff distance is the greater of—

(1) The horizontal distance along the takeoff path from the start of the takeoff to the point at which the airplane is 35 feet above the takeoff surface, determined under § 25.111; or

(2) 115 percent of the horizontal distance along the takeoff path, with all engines operating, from the start of the takeoff to the point at which the airplane is 35 feet above the takeoff surface, as determined by a procedure consistent with § 25.111.

(b) If the takeoff distance includes a clearway, the takeoff run is the greater of—

(1) The horizontal distance along the takeoff path from the start of the takeoff to a point equidistant between the point at which V_{LOF} is reached and the point at which the airplane is 35 feet above the takeoff surface, as determined under § 25.111; or

(2) 115 percent of the horizontal distance along the takeoff path, with all engines operating, from the start of the takeoff to a point equidistant between the point at which V_{LOF} is reached and the point at which the airplane is 35 feet above the takeoff surface, determined by a procedure consistent with § 25.111.

[Doc. No. 5066, 29 FR 18291, Dec. 24, 1964, as amended by Amdt. 25-23, 35 FR 5671, Apr. 8, 1970]

§ 25.115 Takeoff flight path.

(a) The takeoff flight path begins 35 feet above the takeoff surface at the end of the takeoff distance determined in accordance with § 25.113(a).

(b) The net takeoff flight path data must be determined so that they represent the actual takeoff flight paths (determined in accordance with § 25.111 and with paragraph (a) of this section) reduced at each point by a gradient of climb equal to—

(1) 0.8 percent for two-engine airplanes;

(2) 0.9 percent for three-engine airplanes; and

(3) 1.0 percent for four-engine airplanes.

(c) The prescribed reduction in climb gradient may be applied as an equivalent reduction in acceleration along that part of the takeoff flight path at which the airplane is accelerated in level flight.

§ 25.117 Climb: general.

Compliance with the requirements of §§ 25.119 and 25.121 must be shown at each weight, altitude, and ambient temperature within the operational limits established for the airplane and with the most unfavorable center of gravity for each configuration.

§ 25.119 Landing climb: All-engine-operating.

In the landing configuration, the steady gradient of climb may not be less than 3.2 percent, with—

(a) The engines at the power or thrust that is available eight seconds after initiation of movement of the power or thrust controls from the minimum flight idle to the takeoff position; and

(b) A climb speed of not more than 1.3 V_S.

§ 25.121 Climb: One-engine-inoperative.

(a) *Takeoff; landing gear extended.* In the critical takeoff configuration existing along the flight path (between the points at which the airplane reaches V_{LOF} and at which the landing gear is fully retracted) and in the configuration used in § 25.111 but without ground effect, the steady gradient of climb must be positive for two-engine airplanes, and not less than 0.3 percent for three-engine airplanes or 0.5 percent for four-engine airplanes, at V_{LOF} and with—

(1) The critical engine inoperative and the remaining engines at the power or thrust available when retraction of the landing gear is begun in accordance with § 25.111 unless there is a more critical power operating condition existing later along the flight path but before the point at which the landing gear is fully retracted; and

(2) The weight equal to the weight existing when retraction of the landing gear is begun, determined under § 25.111.

(b) *Takeoff; landing gear retracted.* In the takeoff configuration existing at the point of the flight path at which the landing gear is fully retracted, and in the configuration used in § 25.111 but without ground effect, the steady gradient of climb may not be less than 2.4 percent for two-engine airplanes, 2.7 percent for three-engine airplanes, and 3.0 percent for four-engine airplanes, at V_2 and with—

(1) The critical engine inoperative, the remaining engines at the takeoff power or thrust available at the time the landing gear is fully retracted, determined under § 25.111, unless there is a more critical power operating condition existing later along the flight path but before the point where the airplane reaches a height of 400 feet above the takeoff surface; and

(2) The weight equal to the weight existing when the airplane's landing gear is fully retracted, determined under § 25.111.

(c) *Final takeoff.* In the en route configuration at the end of the takeoff path determined in accordance with § 25.111, the steady gradient of climb may not be less than 1.2 percent for two-engine airplanes, 1.5 percent for three-engine airplanes, and 1.7 percent for four-engine airplanes, at not less than 1.25 V_S and with—

(1) The critical engine inoperative and the remaining engines at the available maximum continuous power or thrust; and

(2) The weight equal to the weight existing at the end of the takeoff path, determined under § 25.111.

(d) *Approach.* In the approach configuration corresponding to the normal all-engines-operating procedure in which V_S for this configuration does not exceed 110 percent of the V_S for the related landing configuration, the steady gradient of climb may not be less than 2.1 percent for two-engine airplanes, 2.4 percent for three-engine airplanes, and 2.7 percent for four-engine airplanes, with—

(1) The critical engine inoperative, the remaining engines at the available takeoff power or thrust;

(2) The maximum landing weight; and

(3) A climb speed established in connection with normal landing procedures, but not exceeding 1.5 V_S.

§ 25.123 En route flight paths.

(a) For the en route configuration, the flight paths prescribed in paragraphs (b) and (c) of this section must be determined at each weight, altitude, and ambient temperature, within the operating limits established for the airplane. The variation of weight along the flight path, accounting for the progressive consumption of fuel and oil by the operating engines, may be included in the computation. The flight paths must be determined at any selected speed, with—

(1) The most unfavorable center of gravity;

(2) The critical engines inoperative;

(3) The remaining engines at the available maximum continuous power or thrust; and

(4) The means for controlling the engine-cooling air supply in the position that provides adequate cooling in the hot-day condition.

(b) The one-engine-inoperative net flight path data must represent the actual climb performance diminished by a gradient of climb of 1.1 percent for two-engine airplanes, 1.4 percent for three-engine airplanes, and 1.6 percent for four-engine airplanes.

(c) For three- or four-engine airplanes, the two-engine-inoperative net flight path data must represent the actual climb performance diminished by a gradient of climb of 0.3 percent for three-engine airplanes and 0.5 percent for four-engine airplanes.

§ 25.125 Landing.

(a) The horizontal distance necessary to land and to come to a complete stop (or to a speed of approximately 3 knots for water landings) from a point 50 feet above the landing surface must be determined (for standard temperatures, at each weight, altitude, and wind within the operational limits established by the applicant for the airplane) as follows:

(1) The airplane must be in the landing configuration.

(2) A steady gliding approach, with a calibrated airspeed of not less than 1.3 V_S, must be maintained down to the 50 foot height.

(3) Changes in configuration, power or thrust, and speed, must be made in accordance with the established procedures for service operation.

(4) The landing must be made without excessive vertical acceleration, tendency to bounce, nose over, ground loop, porpoise, or water loop.

(5) The landings may not require exceptional piloting skill or alertness.

(b) For landplanes and amphibians, the landing distance on land must be determined on a level, smooth, dry, hard-surfaced runway. In addition—

(1) The pressures on the wheel braking systems may not exceed those specified by the brake manufacturer;

(2) The brakes may not be used so as to cause excessive wear of brakes or tires; and

(3) Means other than wheel brakes may be used if that means—

(i) Is safe and reliable;

(ii) Is used so that consistent results can be expected in service; and

(iii) Is such that exceptional skill is not required to control the airplane.

(c) For seaplanes and amphibians, the landing distance on water must be determined on smooth water.

(d) For skiplanes, the landing distance on snow must be determined on smooth, dry, snow.

(e) The landing distance data must include correction factors for not more than 50 percent of the nominal wind components along the landing path opposite to the direction of landing, and not less than 150 percent of the nominal wind components along the landing path in the direction of landing.

(f) If any device is used that depends on the operation of any engine, and if the landing distance would be noticeably increased when a landing is made with that engine inoperative, the landing distance must be determined with that engine inoperative unless the use of compensating means will result in a landing distance not more than that with each engine operating.

CONTROLLABILITY AND MANEUVERABILITY

§ 25.143 General.

(a) The airplane must be safely controllable and maneuverable during—

(1) Takeoff;

(2) Climb;

(3) Level flight;

(4) Descent; and

(5) Landing.

(b) It must be possible to make a smooth transition from one flight condition to any other flight condition without exceptional piloting skill, alertness, or strength, and without danger of exceeding the airplane limit-load factor under any probable operating conditions, including—

(1) The sudden failure of the critical engine;

(2) For airplanes with three or more engines, the sudden failure of the second critical engine when the airplane is in the en route, approach, or landing configuration and is trimmed with the critical engine inoperative; and

(3) Configuration changes, including deployment or retraction of deceleration devices.

(c) If, during the testing required by paragraphs (a) and (b) of this section, marginal conditions exist with regard to required pilot strength, the "strength of pilots" limits may not exceed the limits prescribed in the following table:

Values in pound of force as applied to the control wheel or rudder pedals	Pitch	Roll	Yaw
For temporary application	75	60	150
For prolonged application	10	5	20

(d) In showing the temporary control force limitations of paragraph (c) of this section, approved operating procedures or conventional operating practices must be followed (including being as nearly trimmed as possible at the next preceding steady flight condition, except that, in the case of takeoff, the airplane must be trimmed in accordance with approved operating procedures).

(e) For the purpose of complying with the prolonged control force limitations of paragraph (c) of this section, the airplane must be as nearly trimmed as possible.

(Secs. 313(a), 601 603, 604, and 605 of the Federal Aviation Act of 1958 (49 U.S.C. 1354(a), 1421, 1423, 1424, and 1425); and sec. 6(c) of the Dept. of Transportation Act (49 U.S.C. 1655 (c)))

[Doc. No. 5066, 29 FR 18291, Dec. 24, 1964, as amended by Amdt. 25-42, 43 FR 2321, Jan. 16, 1978]

§ 25.145 Longitudinal control.

(a) It must be possible at any speed between the trim speed prescribed in § 25.49(c)(2)(i) and V_{S1} (for reciprocating engine powered airplanes), or at any speed between the trim speed prescribed in § 25.103(b)(1) and V_S (for turbine engine powered airplanes), to pitch the nose downward so that the acceleration to this selected trim speed is prompt with—

(1) The airplane trimmed at the trim speed prescribed in § 25.49(c)(2)(i) (for reciprocating engine powered airplanes), or in § 25.103(b)(1) (for turbine engine powered airplanes);

(2) The landing gear extended;

(3) The wing flaps (i) retracted and (ii) extended; and

(4) Power (i) off and (ii) at maximum continuous power on the engines.

(b) With the landing gear extended, no change in trim control, or exertion of more than 50 pounds control force (representative of the maximum temporary force that readily can be applied by one hand) may be required for the following maneuvers:

(1) With power off, flaps retracted, and the airplane trimmed at 1.4 V_{S1}, extend the flaps as rapidly as possible while maintaining the airspeed at approximately 40 percent above the stalling speed existing at each instant throughout the maneuver.

(2) Repeat paragraph (b)(1) except initially extend the flaps and then retract them as rapidly as possible.

(3) Repeat paragraph (b)(2) except with takeoff power.

(4) With power off, flaps retracted, and the airplane trimmed at 1.4 V_{S1}, apply takeoff power rapidly while maintaining the same airspeed.

(5) Repeat paragraph (b)(4) except with flaps extended.

(6) With power off, flaps extended, and the airplane trimmed at 1.4 V_{S1}, obtain and maintain airspeeds between 1.1 V_{S1}, and either 1.7 V_{S1}, or V_{FE}, whichever is lower.

(c) Is must be possible, without exceptional piloting skill, to prevent loss of altitude when complete retraction of the high lift devices from any position is begun during steady, straight, level flight at 1.1 V_{S1} for propeller powered airplanes, or 1.2 V_{S1} for turbojet powered airplanes, with—

(1) Simultaneous application of not more than takeoff power taking into account the critical engine operating conditions;

(2) The landing gear extended; and

(3) The critical combinations of landing weights and altitudes.

If gated high-lift device control positions are provided, retraction must be shown from any position from the maximum landing position to the first gated position, between gated positions, and from the last gated position to the full retraction position. In addition, the first gated control position from the landing position must correspond with the high-lift devices configuration used to establish the go-around procedure from the landing configuration. Each gated control position must require a separate and distinct motion of the control to pass through the gated position and must have features to prevent inadvertent movement of the control through the gated position.

[Doc. No. 5066, 29 FR 18291, Dec. 24, 1964, as amended by Amdt. 25-23, 35 FR 5671, Apr. 8, 1970]

§ 25.147 Directional and lateral control.

(a) *Directional control; general.* It must be possible, while holding the wings approximately level, to safely make reasonably sudden changes in heading in both directions. This must be shown at 1.4 V_{S1} for heading changes up to 15° (except that the heading change at which the rudder pedal force is 150 pounds need not be exceeded), and with—

(1) The critical engine inoperative and its propeller in the minimum drag position;

(2) The power required for level flight at 1.4 V_{S1}, but not more than maximum continuous power;

(3) The most unfavorable center of gravity;

(4) Landing gear retracted;

(5) Flaps in the approach position: and

(6) Maximum landing weight.

(b) *Directional control; airplanes with four or more engines.* Airplanes with four or more engines must meet the requirements of paragraph (a) of this section except that—

(1) The two critical engines must be inoperative with their propellers (if applicable) in the minimum drag position;

(2) The center of gravity must be in the most forward position; and

(3) The flaps must be in the most favorable climb position.

(c) *Lateral control; general.* It must be possible to make 20° banked turns, with and against the inoperative engine, from steady flight at a speed equal to 1.4 V_{S1}, with—

(1) The critical engine inoperative and its propeller (if applicable) in the minimum drag position;

(2) The remaining engines at maximum continuous power;

(3) The most unfavorable center of gravity;

(4) Landing gear (i) retracted and (ii) extended;

(5) Flaps in the most favorable climb position; and

(6) Maximum takeoff weight.

(d) *Lateral control; airplanes with four or more engines.* Airplanes with four or more engines must be able to make 20° banked turns, with and against the inoperative engines, from steady flight at a speed equal to 1.4 V_{S1}, with maximum continuous power, and with the airplane in the configuration prescribed by paragraph (b) of this section.

(e) *Lateral control; all engines operating.* With the engines operating, roll response must allow normal maneuvers (such as recovery from upsets produced by gusts and the initiation of evasive maneuvers). There must be enough excess lateral control in sideslips (up to sideslip angles that might be required in normal operation), to allow a limited amount of maneuvering and to correct for gusts. Lateral control must be enough at any speed up to V_{FC}/M_{FC} to provide a peak roll rate necessary for safety, without excessive control forces or travel.

(Secs. 313(a), 601, 603, 604, and 605 of the Federal Aviation Act of 1958 (49 U.S.C. 1354(a), 1421, 1423, 1424, and 1425); and sec. 6(c) of the Dept. of Transportation Act (49 U.S.C. 1655 (c)))

[Doc. No. 5066, 29 FR 18291, Dec. 24, 1964, as amended by Amdt. 25-42, 43 FR 2321, Jan. 16, 1978]

§ 25.149 Minimum control speed.

(a) In establishing the minimum control speeds required by this section, the method used to simulate critical engine failure must represent the most critical mode of powerplant failure with respect to controllability expected in service.

(b) V_{MC} is the calibrated airspeed, at which, when the critical engine is suddenly made inoperative, it is possible to recover control of the airplane with that engine still inoperative, and maintain straight flight either with zero yaw or, at the option of the applicant, with an angle of bank of not more than five degrees.

(c) V_{MC} may not exceed 1.2 V_S with—

(1) Maximum available takeoff power or thrust on the engines;

(2) The most unfavorable center of gravity;

(3) The airplane trimmed for takeoff;

(4) The maximum sea level takeoff weight (or any lesser weight necessary to show V_{MC});

(5) The airplane in the most critical takeoff configuration existing along the flight path after the airplane becomes airborne, except with the landing gear retracted;

(6) The airplane airborne and the ground effect negligible; and

(7) If applicable, the propeller of the inoperative engine—

(i) Windmilling;

(ii) In the most probable position for the specific design of the propeller control; or

(iii) Feathered, if the airplane has an automatic feathering device acceptable for showing compliance with the climb requirements of § 25.121.

(d) The rudder forces required to maintain control at V_{MC} may not exceed 150 pounds nor may it be necessary to reduce power or thrust of the operative engines. During recovery, the airplane may not assume any dangerous attitude or require exceptional piloting skill, alertness, or strength to prevent a heading change of more than 20 degrees.

(e) V_{MCG}, the minimum control speed on the ground, is the calibrated airspeed during the takeoff run, at which, when the critical engine is suddenly made inoperative, it is possible to recover control of the airplane with the use of primary aerodynamic controls alone (without the use of nosewheel steering) to enable the takeoff to be safely continued using normal piloting skill and rudder control forces not exceeding 150 pounds. In the determination of V_{MCG}, assuming that the path of the airplane accelerating with all engines operating is along the centerline of the runway, its path from the point at which the critical engine is made inoperative to the point at which recovery to a direction parallel to the centerline is completed may not deviate more than 30 feet laterally from the centerline at any point. V_{MCG} must be established with—

(1) The airplane in each takeoff configuration or, at the option of the applicant, in the most critical takeoff configuration;

(2) Maximum available takeoff power or thrust on the operating engines;

(3) The most unfavorable center of gravity;

(4) The airplane trimmed for takeoff; and

(5) The most unfavorable weight in the range of takeoff weights.

(f) V_{MCL}, the minimum control speed during landing approach with all engines operating, is the calibrated airspeed at which, when the critical engine is suddenly made inoperative, it is possible to recover control of the airplane with that engine still inoperative, and maintain straight flight either with zero yaw or, at the option of the applicant, with an angle of bank of not more than 5 degrees. V_{MCL} must be established with—

(1) The airplane in the most critical configuration for approach with all engines operating;

(2) The most unfavorable center of gravity;

(3) The airplane trimmed for approach with all engines operating;

(4) The maximum sea level landing weight (or any lesser weight necessary to show V_{MCL}); and

(5) Maximum available takeoff power or thrust on the operating engines.

(g) For airplanes with three or more engines, V_{MCL-2}, the minimum control speed during landing approach with one critical engine inoperative, is the calibrated airspeed at which, when a second critical engine is suddenly made inoperative, it is possible to recover control of the airplane with both engines still inoperative and maintain straight flight either with zero yaw or, at the option of the applicant, with an angle of bank of not more than 5 degrees. V_{MCL-2}, must be established with—

(1) The airplane in the most critical configuration for approach with the critical engine inoperative;

(2) The most unfavorable center of gravity;

(3) The airplane trimmed for approach with the critical engine inoperative;

(4) The maximum sea level landing weight (or any lesser weight necessary to show V_{MCL-2});

(5) The power or thrust on the operating engines required to maintain an approach path angle of 3 degrees when one critical engine is inoperative; and

(6) The power or thrust on the operating engines rapidly changed, immediately after the second critical engine is made inoperative, from the power or thrust prescribed in paragraph (g)(5) of this section to—

(i) Minimum available power or thrust; and

(ii) Maximum available takeoff power or thrust.

(h) The rudder control forces required to maintain control at V_{MCL} and V_{MCL-2} may not exceed 150 pounds, nor may it be necessary to reduce the power or thrust of the operating engines. In addition, the airplane may not assume any dangerous attitudes or require exceptional piloting skill, alertness, or strength to prevent a divergence in the approach flight path that would jeopardize continued safe approach when—

(1) The critical engine is suddenly made inoperative; and

(2) For the determination of V_{MCL-2}, the power or thrust on the operating engines is changed in accordance with paragraph (g)(6) of this section.

(Secs. 313(a), 601, 604, and 605 of the Federal Aviation Act of 1958 (49 U.S.C. 1354(a), 1421, 1423, 1424, and 1425); and sec. 6(c) of the Dept. of Transportation Act (49 U.S.C. 1655(c)))

[Doc. No. 5066, 29 FR 18291, Dec. 24, 1964, as amended by Amdt. 25-42, 43 FR 2321, Jan. 16, 1978]

Trim

§ 25.161 Trim.

(a) *General.* Each airplane must meet the trim requirements of this section after being trimmed, and without further pressure upon, or movement of, either the primary controls or their corresponding trim controls by the pilot or the automatic pilot.

(b) *Lateral and directional trim.* The airplane must maintain lateral and directional trim with the most adverse lateral displacement of the center of gravity within the relevant operating limitations, during normally expected conditions of operation (including operation at any speed from 1.4 V_{S_1} to V_{MO}/M_{MO}).

(c) *Longitudinal trim.* The airplane must maintain longitudinal trim during—

(1) A climb with maximum continuous power at a speed not more than 1.4 V_{S_1}, with the landing gear retracted, and the flaps (i) retracted and (ii) in the takeoff position;

(2) A glide with power off at a speed not more than 1.4 V_{S_1}, with the landing gear extended, the wing flaps (i) retracted and (ii) extended, the most unfavorable center of gravity position approved for landing with the maximum landing weight, and with the most unfavorable center of gravity position approved for landing regardless of weight; and

(3) Level flight at any speed from 1.4 V_{S1}, to V_{MO}/M_{MO}, with the landing gear and flaps retracted, and from 1.4 V_{S1} to V_{LE} with the landing gear extended.

(d) *Longitudinal, directional, and lateral trim.* The airplane must maintain longitudinal, directional, and lateral trim (and for the lateral trim, the angle of bank may not exceed five degrees) at 1.4 V_{S1} during climbing flight with—

(1) The critical engine inoperative;

(2) The remaining engines at maximum continuous power; and

(3) The landing gear and flaps retracted.

(e) *Airplanes with four or more engines.* Each airplane with four or more engines must maintain trim in rectilinear flight—

(1) At the climb speed, configuration, and power required by § 25.123(a) for the purpose of establishing the rate of climb;

(2) With the most unfavorable center of gravity position; and

(3) At the weight at which the two-engine-inoperative climb is equal to at least 0.013 $V_{S0}{}^2$ at an altitude of 5,000 feet.

[Doc. No. 5066, 29 FR 18291, Dec. 24, 1964, as amended by Amdt. 25-23, 35 FR 5671, Apr. 8, 1970; Amdt. 25-38, 41 FR 55466, Dec. 20, 1976]

STABILITY

§ 25.171 General.

The airplane must be longitudinally, directionally, and laterally stable in accordance with the provisions of §§ 25.173 through 25.177. In addition, suitable stability and control feel (static stability) is required in any condition normally encountered in service, if flight tests show it is necessary for safe operation.

[Doc. No. 5066, 29 FR 18291, Dec. 24, 1964, as amended by Amdt. 25-7, 30 FR 13117, Oct. 15, 1965]

§ 25.173 Static longitudinal stability.

Under the conditions specified in § 25.175, the characteristics of the elevator control forces (including friction) must be as follows:

(a) A pull must be required to obtain and maintain speeds below the specified trim speed, and a push must be required to obtain and maintain speeds above the specified trim speed. This must be shown at any speed that can be obtained except speeds higher than the landing gear or wing flap operating limit speeds or V_{FC}/M_{FC}, whichever is appropriate, or lower than the minimum speed for steady unstalled flight.

(b) The airspeed must return to within 10 percent of the original trim speed for the climb, approach, and landing conditions specified in § 25.175 (a), (c), and (d), and must return to within 7.5 percent of the original trim speed for the cruising condition specified in § 25.175(b), when the control force is slowly released from any speed within the range specified in paragraph (a) of this section.

(c) The average gradient of the stable slope of the stick force versus speed curve may not be less than 1 pound for each 6 knots.

(d) Within the free return speed range specified in paragraph (b) of this section, it is permissible for the airplane, without control forces, to stabilize on speeds above or below the desired trim speeds if exceptional attention on the part of the pilot is not required to return to and maintain the desired trim speed and altitude.

[Amdt. 25-7, 30 FR 13117, Oct. 15, 1965]

§ 25.175 Demonstration of static longitudinal stability.

Static longitudinal stability must be shown as follows:

(a) *Climb.* The stick force curve must have a stable slope at speeds between 85 and 115 percent of the speed at which the airplane—

(1) Is trimmed, with—

(i) Wing flaps retracted;

(ii) Landing gear retracted;

(iii) Maximum takeoff weight; and

(iv) 75 percent of maximum continuous power for reciprocating engines or the maximum power or thrust selected by the applicant as an operating limitation for use during climb for turbine engines; and

(2) Is trimmed at the speed for best rate-of-climb except that the speed need not be less than 1.4 V_{S1}.

(b) *Cruise.* Static longitudinal stability must be shown in the cruise condition as follows:

(1) With the landing gear retracted at high speed, the stick force curve must have a stable slope at all speeds within a range which is the greater of 15 percent of the trim speed plus the resulting free return speed range, or 50 knots plus the resulting free return speed range, above and below the trim speed (except that the speed range need not include speeds less than 1.4 V_{S1}, nor speeds greater than V_{FC}/M_{FC}. nor speeds that require a stick force of more than 50 pounds), with—

(i) The wing flaps retracted;

(ii) The center of gravity in the most adverse position (see § 25.27);

(iii) The most critical weight between the maximum takeoff and maximum landing weights;

(iv) 75 percent of maximum continuous power for reciprocating engines or for turbine engines, the maximum cruising power selected by the applicant as an operating limitation (see § 25.1521), except that the power need not exceed that required at V_{MO}/M_{MO}; and

(v) The airplane trimmed for level flight with the power required in paragraph (b)(1)(iv) of this section.

(2) With the landing gear retracted at low speed, the stick force curve must have a stable slope at all speeds within a range which is the greater of 15 percent of the trim speed plus the resulting free return speed range, or 50 knots plus the resulting free return speed range, above and below the trim speed (except that the speed range need not include speeds less than 1.4 V_{S1}, nor speeds greater than the minimum speed of the applicable speed range prescribed in paragraph (b)(1), nor speeds that require a stick force of more than 50 pounds), with—

(i) Wing flaps, center of gravity position, and weight as specified in paragraph (b)(1) of this section;

(ii) Power required for level flight at a speed equal to V_{MO} + 1.4 $V_{S1}/2$; and

(iii) The airplane trimmed for level flight with the power required in paragraph (b)(2)(ii) of this section.

(3) With the landing gear extended, the stick force curve must have a stable slope at all speeds within a range which is the greater of 15 percent of the trim speed plus the resulting free return speed range, or 50 knots plus the resulting free return speed range, above and below the trim speed (except that the speed range need not include speeds less than 1.4 V_{S1}, nor speeds greater than V_{LE}, nor speeds that require a stick force of more than 50 pounds), with—

(i) Wing flap, center of gravity position, and weight as specified in paragraph (b)(1) of this section;

(ii) 75 percent of maximum continuous power for reciprocating engines or, for turbine engines, the maximum cruising power selected by the applicant as an operating limitation, except that the power need not exceed that required for level flight at V_{LE}; and

(iii) The aircraft trimmed for level flight with the power required in paragraph (b)(3)(ii) of this section.

(c) *Approach.* The stick force curve must have a stable slope at speeds between 1.1 V_{S1} and 1.8 V_{S1}, with—

(1) Wing flaps in the approach position;

(2) Landing gear retracted;

(3) Maximum landing weight; and

(4) The airplane trimmed at 1.4 V_{S1} with enough power to maintain level flight at this speed.

(d) *Landing.* The stick force curve must have a stable slope, and the stick force may not exceed 80 pounds, at speeds between 1.1 V_{S0} and 1.3 V_{S0} with—

(1) Wing flaps in the landing position;

(2) Landing gear extended;

(3) Maximum landing weight;

(4) Power or thrust off on the engines; and

(5) The airplane trimmed at 1.4 V_{S0} with power or thrust off.

[Doc. No. 5066, 29 FR 18291, Dec. 24, 1964, as amended by Amdt. 25-7, 30 FR 13117, Oct. 15, 1965]

§ 25.177 Static directional and lateral stability.

(a) The static directional stability (as shown by the tendency to recover from a skid with the rudder free) must be positive for any landing gear and flap position and symmetrical power condition, at speeds from 1.2 V_{S1} up to V_{FE}, V_{LE}, or V_{FC}/M_{FC} (as appropriate).

(b) The static lateral stability (as shown by the tendency to raise the low wing in a sideslip with the aileron controls free and for any landing gear and flap position and symmetrical power condition) may not be negative at any airspeed (except speeds higher than V_{FE} or V_{LE}, when appropriate) in the following airspeed ranges:

(1) From 1.2 V_{S_1} to V_{MO}/M_{MO}.

(2) From V_{MO}/M_{MO} to V_{FC}/M_{FC} unless the Administrator finds that the divergence is—

(i) Gradual;

(ii) Easily recognizable by the pilot; and

(iii) Easily controllable by the pilot.

(c) In straight, steady, sideslips (unaccelerated forward slips) the aileron and rudder control movements and forces must be substantially proportional to the angle of sideslip, and the factor of proportionality must lie between limits found necessary for safe operation throughout the range of sideslip angles appropriate to the operation of the airplane. At greater angles, up to the angle at which full rudder control is used or a rudder pedal force of 180 pounds is obtained, the rudder pedal forces may not reverse and increased rudder deflection must produce increased angles of sideslip. Unless the airplane has a yaw indicator, there must be enough bank accompanying sideslipping to clearly indicate any departure from steady unyawed flight.

(Secs. 313(a), 601, 603, 604, and 605 of the Federal Aviation Act of 1958 (49 U.S.C. 1354(a), 1421, 1423, 1424, and 1425); and sec. 6(c) of the Dept. of Transportation Act (49 U.S.C. 1655(c)))

[Doc. No. 5066, 29 FR 18291. Dec. 24, 1964, as amended by Amdt. 25-42, 43 FR 2322, Jan. 16, 1978]

§ 25.181 Dynamic stability.

(a) Any short period oscillation, not including combined lateral-directional oscillations, occurring between stalling speed and maximum allowable speed appropriate to the configuration of the airplane must be heavily damped with the primary controls—

(1) Free; and

(2) In a fixed position.

(b) Any combined lateral-directional oscillations ("Dutch roll") occurring between stalling speed and maximum allowable speed appropriate to the configuration of the airplane must be positively damped with controls free, and must be controllable with normal use of the primary controls without requiring exceptional pilot skill.

(Secs. 313(a), 601, 603, 604, and 605 of the Federal Aviation Act of 1958 (49 U.S.C. 1354(a), 1421, 1423, 1424, and 1425); and sec. 6(c) of the Dept. of Transportation Act (49 U.S.C. 1655(c)))

[Amdt. 25-42, 43 FR 2322, Jan. 16, 1978]

STALLS

§ 25.201 Stall demonstration.

(a) Stalls must be shown in straight flight and in 30 degree banked turns with—

(1) Power off; and

(2) The power necessary to maintain level flight at 1.6 V_{S_1} (where V_{S_1} corresponds to the stalling speed with flaps in the approach position, the landing gear retracted, and maximum landing weight).

(b) In either condition required by paragraph (a) of this section, it must be possible to meet the applicable requirements of § 25.203 with—

(1) Flaps and landing gear in any likely combination of positions;

(2) Representative weights within the range for which certification is requested; and

(3) The most adverse center of gravity for recovery.

(c) The following procedure must be used to show compliance with § 25.203:

(1) With the airplane trimmed for straight flight at the speed prescribed in § 25.103(b)(1), reduce the speed with the elevator control until it is steady at slightly above stalling speed. Apply elevator control so that the speed reduction does not exceed one knot per second until (i) the airplane is stalled, or (ii) the control reaches the stop.

(2) As soon as the airplane is stalled, recover by normal recovery techniques.

(d) Occurrence of stall is defined as follows:

(1) The airplane may be considered stalled when, at an angle of attack measurably greater than that for maximum lift, the inherent flight characteristics give a clear and distinctive indication to the pilot that the airplane is stalled. Typical indications of a stall,

occurring either individually or in combination, are—

(i) A nose-down pitch that cannot be readily arrested;

(ii) A roll that cannot be readily arrested; or

(iii) If clear enough, a loss of control effectiveness, an abrupt change in control force or motion, or a distinctive shaking of the pilot's controls.

(2) For any configuration in which the airplane demonstrates an unmistakable inherent aerodynamic warning of a magnitude and severity that is a strong and effective deterrent to further speed reduction, the airplane may be considered stalled when it reaches the speed at which the effective deterrent is clearly manifested.

(Secs. 313(a), 601, 603, 604, and 605 of the Federal Aviation Act of 1958 (49 U.S.C. 1354(a), 1421, 1423, 1424, and 1425); and sec. 6(c) of the Dept. of Transportation Act (49 U.S.C. 1655(c)))

[Doc. No. 5066, 29 FR 18291, Dec. 24, 1964, as amended by Amdt. 25-38, 41 FR 55466, Dec. 20, 1976; Amdt. 25-42, 43 FR 2322, Jan. 16, 1978]

§ 25.203 Stall characteristics.

(a) It must be possible to produce and to correct roll and yaw by unreversed use of the aileron and rudder controls, up to the time the airplane is stalled. No abnormal nose-up pitching may occur. The longitudinal control force must be positive up to and throughout the stall. In addition, it must be possible to promptly prevent stalling and to recover from a stall by normal use of the controls.

(b) For level wing stalls, the roll occurring between the stall and the completion of the recovery may not exceed approximately 20 degrees.

(c) For turning flight stalls, the action of the airplane after the stall may not be so violent or extreme as to make it difficult, with normal piloting skill, to effect a prompt recovery and to regain control of the airplane.

§ 25.205 Stalls: Critical engine inoperative.

(a) It must be possible to safely recover from a stall with the critical engine inoperative—

(1) Without applying power to the inoperative engine;

(2) With flaps and landing gear retracted; and

(3) With the remaining engines at up to 75 percent of maximum continuous power, or up to the power at which the wings can be held level with the use of maximum control travel, whichever is less.

(b) The operating engines may be throttled back during stall recovery from stalls with the critical engine inoperative.

§ 25.207 Stall warning.

(a) Stall warning with sufficient margin to prevent inadvertent stalling with the flaps and landing gear in any normal position must be clear and distinctive to the pilot in straight and turning flight.

(b) The warning may be furnished either through the inherent aerodynamic qualities of the airplane or by a device that will give clearly distinguishable indications under expected conditions of flight. However, a visual stall warning device that requires the attention of the crew within the cockpit is not acceptable by itself. If a warning device is used, it must provide a warning in each of the airplane configuations prescribed in paragraph (a) of this section at the speed prescribed in paragraph (c) of this section.

(c) The stall warning must begin at a speed exceeding the stalling speed (i.e., the speed at which the airplane stalls or the minimum speed demonstrated, whichever is applicable under the provisions of § 25.201(d)) by seven percent or at any lesser margin if the stall warning has enough clarity, duration, distinctiveness, or similar properties.

(Secs. 313(a), 601, 603, 604, and 605 of the Federal Aviation Act of 1958 (49 U.S.C. 1354(a), 1421, 1423, 1424, and 1425); and sec. 6(c) of the Dept. of Transportation Act (49 U.S.C. 1655(c)))

[Doc. No. 5066, 29 FR 18291, Dec. 24, 1964, as amended by Amdt. 25-7, 30 FR 13118, Oct. 15, 1965; Amdt. 25-42, 43 FR 2322, Jan. 16, 1978]

Ground and Water Handling Characteristics

§ 25.231 Longitudinal stability and control.

(a) Landplanes may have no uncontrollable tendency to nose over in any reasonably expected operating condition or when rebound occurs during landing or takeoff. In addition—

(1) Wheel brakes must operate smoothly and may not cause any undue tendency to nose over; and

(2) If a tail-wheel landing gear is used, it must be possible, during the takeoff ground run on concrete, to maintain any altitude up to thrust line level, at 80 percent of V_{S1}.

(b) For seaplanes and amphibians, the most adverse water conditions safe for takeoff, taxiing, and landing, must be established.

§ 25.233 Directional stability and control.

(a) There may be no uncontrollable ground-looping tendency in 90° cross winds, up to a wind velocity of 20 knots or 0.2 V_{S0}, whichever is greater, except that the wind velocity need not exceed 25 knots. At any speed at which the airplane may be expected to be operated on the ground. This may be shown while establishing the 90° cross component of wind velocity required by § 25.237.

(b) Landplanes must be satisfactorily controllable, without exceptional piloting skill or alertness, in power-off landings at normal landing speed, without using brakes or engine power to maintain a straight path. This may be shown during power-off landings made in conjunction with other tests.

(c) The airplane must have adequate directional control during taxiing. This may be shown during taxiing prior to takeoffs made in conjunction with other tests.

(Secs. 313(a), 601, 603, 604, and 605 of the Federal Aviation Act of 1958 (49 U.S.C. 1354(a), 1421, 1423, 1424, and 1425); and sec. 6(c) of the Dept. of Transportation Act (49 U.S.C. 1655(c)))

[Doc. No. 5066, 29 FR 18291, Dec. 24, 1964, as amended by Amdt. 25-23, 35 FR 5671, Apr. 8, 1970; Amdt. 25-42, 43 FR 2322, Jan. 16, 1978]

§ 25.235 Taxiing condition.

The shock absorbing mechanism may not damage the structure of the airplane when the airplane is taxied on the roughest ground that may reasonably be expected in normal operation.

§ 25.237 Wind velocities.

(a) For landplanes and amphibians, a 90-degree cross component of wind velocity, demonstrated to be safe for takeoff and landing, must be established for dry runways and must be at least 20 knots or 0.2 V_{S0}, whichever is greater, except that it need not exceed 25 knots.

(b) For seaplanes and amphibians, the following applies:

(1) A 90-degree cross component of wind velocity, up to which takeoff and landing is safe under all water conditions that may reasonably be expected in normal operation, must be established and must be at least 20 knots or 0.2 V_{S0}, whichever is greater, except that it need not exceed 25 knots.

(2) A wind velocity, for which taxiing is safe in any direction under all water conditions that may reasonably be expected in normal operation, must be established and must be at least 20 knots or 0.2 V_{S0}, whichever is greater, except that it need not exceed 25 knots.

(Secs. 313(a), 601, 603, 604, and 605 of the Federal Aviation Act of 1958 (49 U.S.C. 1354(a), 1421, 1423, 1424, and 1425); and sec. 6(c) of the Dept. of Transportation Act (49 U.S.C. 1655(c)))

[Amdt. 25-42, 43 FR 2322, Jan. 16, 1978]

§ 25.239 Spray characteristics, control, and stability on water.

(a) For seaplanes and amphibians, during takeoff, taxiing, and landing, and in the conditions set forth in paragraph (b) of this section, there may be no—

(1) Spray characteristics that would impair the pilot's view, cause damage, or result in the taking in of an undue quantity of water;

(2) Dangerously uncontrollable porpoising, bounding, or swinging tendency; or

(3) Immersion of auxiliary floats or sponsons, wing tips, propeller blades,

or other parts not designed to withstand the resulting water loads.

(b) Compliance with the requirements of paragraph (a) of this section must be shown—

(1) In water conditions, from smooth to the most adverse condition established in accordance with § 25.231;

(2) In wind and cross-wind velocities, water currents, and associated waves and swells that may reasonably be expected in operation on water;

(3) At speeds that may reasonably be expected in operation on water;

(4) With sudden failure of the critical engine at any time while on water; and

(5) At each weight and center of gravity position, relevant to each operating condition, within the range of loading conditions for which certification is requested.

(c) In the water conditions of paragraph (b) of this section, and in the corresponding wind conditions, the seaplane or amphibian must be able to drift for five minutes with engines inoperative, aided, if necessary, by a sea anchor.

MISCELLANEOUS FLIGHT REQUIREMENTS

§ 25.251 Vibration and buffeting.

(a) The airplane must be designed to withstand any vibration and buffeting that might occur in any likely operating condition. This must be shown by calculations, resonance tests, or other tests found necessary by the Administrator.

(b) Each part of the airplane must be shown in flight to be free from excessive vibration, under any appropriate speed and power conditions up to at least the minimum value of V_D allowed in § 25.335. The maximum speeds shown must be used in establishing the operating limitations of the airplane in accordance with § 25.1505. In addition, it must be shown by analysis or tests, that the airplane is free from such vibration that would prevent safe flight under the conditions in § 25.629(d).

(c) Except as provided in paragraph (d) of this section, there may be no buffeting condition, in normal flight, including configuration changes during cruise, severe enough to interfere with the control of the airplane, to cause excessive fatigue to the crew, or to cause structural damage. Stall warning buffeting within these limits is allowable.

(d) There may be no perceptible buffeting condition in the cruise configuration in straight flight at any speed up to V_{MO}/M_{MO}, except that stall warning buffeting is allowable.

(e) With the airplane in the cruise configuration, the positive maneuvering load factors at which the onset of perceptible buffeting occurs must be determined for the ranges of airspeed or Mach Number, weight, and altitude for which the airplane is to be certificated. The envelopes of load factor, speed, altitude, and weight must provide a sufficient range of speeds and load factors for normal operations. Probable inadvertent excursions beyond the boundaries of the buffet onset envelopes may not result in unsafe conditions.

[Doc. No. 5066, 29 FR 18291, Dec. 24, 1964, as amended by Amdt. 25-23, 35 FR 5671, Apr. 8, 1970]

§ 25.253 High-speed characteristics.

(a) *Speed increase and recovery characteristics.* The following speed increase and recovery characteristics must be met:

(1) Operating conditions and characteristics likely to cause inadvertent speed increases (including upsets in pitch and roll) must be simulated with the airplane trimmed at any likely cruise speed up to V_{MO}/M_{MO}. These conditions and characteristics include gust upsets, inadvertent control movements, low stick force gradient in relation to control friction, passenger movement, leveling off from climb, and descent from Mach to airspeed limit altitudes.

(2) Allowing for pilot reaction time after effective inherent or artificial speed warning occurs, it must be shown that the airplane can be recovered to a normal attitude and its speed reduced to V_{MO}/M_{MO}, without-

(i) Exceptional piloting strength or skill;

(ii) Exceeding V_D/M_D, V_{DF}/M_{DF}, or the structural limitations; and

(iii) Buffeting that would impair the pilot's ability to read the instruments or control the airplane for recovery.

(3) There may be no control reversal about any axis at any speed up to V_{DF}/M_{DF}. Any reversal of elevator control force or tendency of the airplane to pitch, roll, or yaw must be mild and readily controllable, using normal piloting techniques.

(b) *Maximum speed for stability characteristics,* V_{FC}/M_{FC}. V_{FC}/M_{FC} is the maximum speed at which the requirements of §§ 25.147(e), 25.175(b)(1), 25.177, and 25.181 must be met with flaps and landing gear retracted. It may not be less than a speed midway between V_{MO}/M_{MO} and V_{DF}/M_{DF}, except that, for altitudes where Mach number is the limiting factor, M_{FC} need not exceed the Mach number at which effective speed warning occurs.

[Doc. No. 5066, 29 FR 18291, Dec. 24, 1964, as amended by Amdt. 25-23, 35 FR 5671, Apr. 8, 1970; Amdt. 25-54, 45 FR 60172, Sept. 11, 1980]

§ 25.255 Out-of-trim characteristics.

(a) From an initial condition with the airplane trimmed at cruise speeds up to V_{MO}/M_{MO}, the airplane must have satisfactory maneuvering stability and controllability with the degree of out-of-trim in both the airplane nose-up and nose-down directions, which results from the greater of—

(1) A three-second movement of the longitudinal trim system at its normal rate for the particular flight condition with no aerodynamic load (or an equivalent degree of trim for airplanes that do not have a power-operated trim system), except as limited by stops in the trim system, including those required by § 25.655(b) for adjustable stabilizers; or

(2) The maximum mistrim that can be sustained by the autopilot while maintaining level flight in the high speed cruising condition.

(b) In the out-of-trim condition specified in paragraph (a) of this section, when the normal acceleration is varied from +1 g to the positive and negative values specified in paragraph (c) of this section—

(1) The stick force vs. g curve must have a positive slope at any speed up to and including V_{FC}/M_{FC}; and

(2) At speeds between V_{FC}/M_{FC} and V_{DF}/M_{DF} the direction of the primary longitudinal control force may not reverse.

(c) Except as provided in paragraphs (d) and (e) of this section, compliance with the provisions of paragraph (a) of this section must be demonstrated in flight over the acceleration range—

(1) −1 g to +2.5 g; or

(2) 0 g to 2.0 g, and extrapolating by an acceptable method to −1 g and +2.5 g.

(d) If the procedure set forth in paragraph (c)(2) of this section is used to demonstrate compliance and marginal conditions exist during flight test with regard to reversal of primary longitudinal control force, flight tests must be accomplished from the normal acceleration at which a marginal condition is found to exist to the applicable limit specified in paragraph (b)(1) of this section.

(e) During flight tests required by paragraph (a) of this section, the limit maneuvering load factors prescribed in §§ 25.333(b) and 25.337, and the maneuvering load factors associated with probable inadvertent excursions beyond the boundaries of the buffet onset envelopes determined under § 25.251(e), need not be exceeded. In addition, the entry speeds for flight test demonstrations at normal acceleration values less than 1 g must be limited to the extent necessary to accomplish a recovery without exceeding V_{DF}/M_{DF}.

(f) In the out-of-trim condition specified in paragraph (a) of this section, it must be possible from an overspeed condition at V_{DF}/M_{DF} to produce at least 1.5 g for recovery by applying not more than 125 pounds of longitudinal control force using either the primary longitudinal control alone or the primary longitudinal control and the longitudinal trim system. If the longitudinal trim is used to assist in producing the required load factor, it must be shown at V_{DF}/M_{DF} that the longitudinal trim can be actuated in the airplane nose-up direction with the primary surface loaded to correspond to the least of the following airplane nose-up control forces:

(1) The maximum control forces expected in service as specified in §§ 25.301 and 25.397.

(2) The control force required to produce 1.5 g.

(3) The control force corresponding to buffeting or other phenomena of such intensity that it is a strong deterrent to further application of primary longitudinal control force.

(Secs. 313(a), 601, 603, 604, and 605 of the Federal Aviation Act of 1958 (49 U.S.C. 1354(a), 1421, 1423, 1424, and 1425); and sec. 6(c) of the Dept. of Transportation Act (49 U.S.C. 1655(c)))

[Amdt. No. 25-42, 43 FR 2322, Jan. 16, 1978]

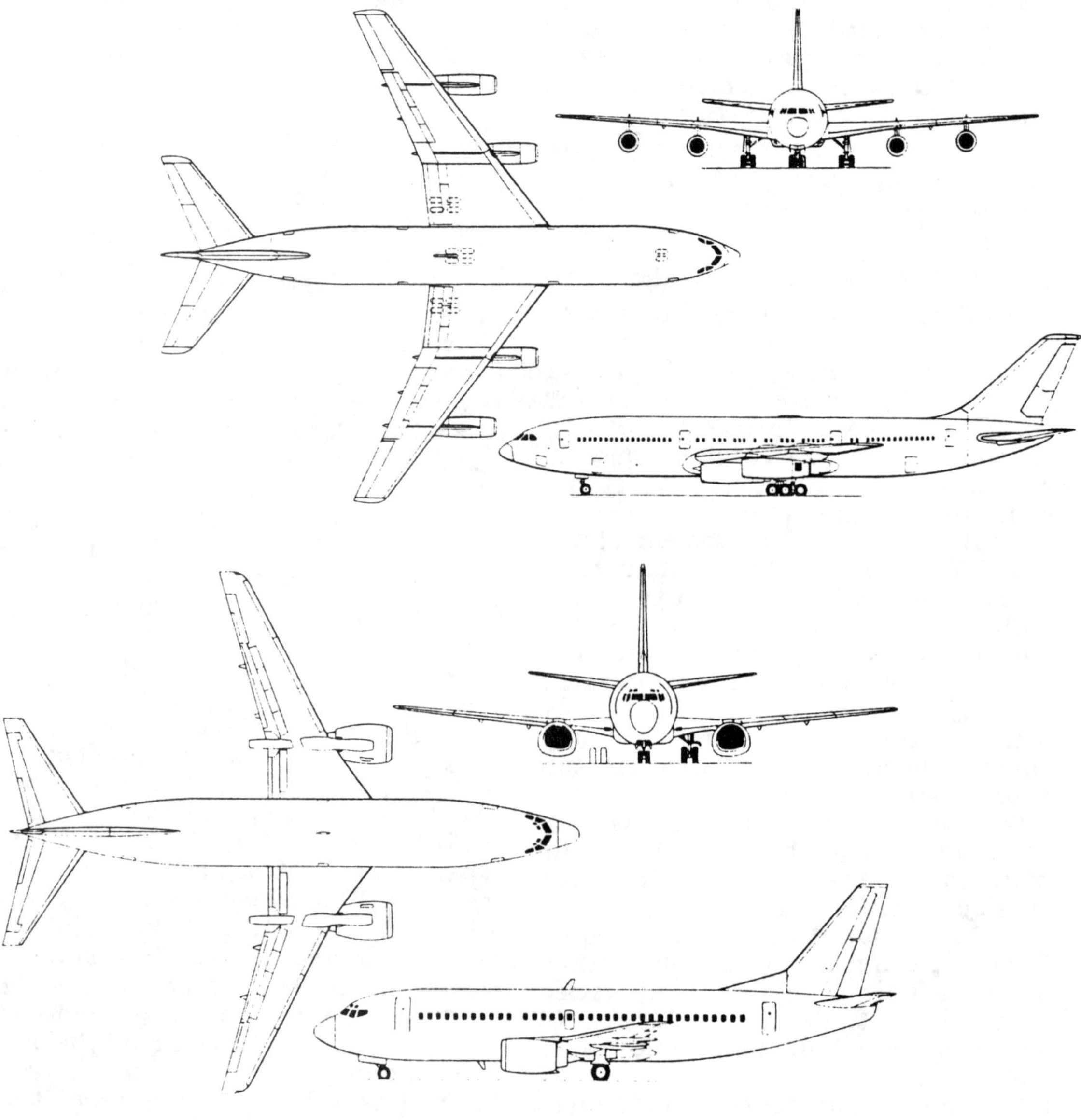

APPENDIX B: MILITARY AIRWORTHINESS REGULATIONS FOR AIRPLANE PERFORMANCE, STABILITY AND CONTROL

Before a military airplane is accepted for service in the US Air Force, the US Navy, the US Marine Corps or the US Army it must meet a number of safety and airworthiness standards which are spelled out in so-called Military Specifications. For purposes of airplane preliminary design, the following specifications are important:

B1. Airplane Performance

B1.1 MIL-C-005011B(USAF): Military Specification, Charts: Standard Aircraft Characteristics and Performance, Piloted Aircraft (Fixed Wing), June 1977.

B1.2 AS-5263(USNAVY): Naval Air Systems Command Specification, Guidelines for the Preparation of Standard Aircraft Characteristics Charts and Performance Data, Piloted Aircraft (Fixed Wing), October 1986.

B2. Airplane Stability, Control and Flying Qualities

B2.1 MIL-F-8785C: Military Specification, Flying Qualities of Piloted Airplanes, November 1980.

IMPORTANT NOTE: Only those parts of the specifications which are of importance to the preliminary designer are reproduced in this Appendix and organized as follows:

Note: a listing of contents by paragraph is given on pages 341-343

B1. Airplane Performance

B1.1 MIL-C-005011B(USAF): Military Specification, Charts: Standard Aircraft Characteristics and Performance, Piloted Aircraft (Fixed Wing), June 1977.

This limited coordination Military Specification has been prepared by the Air Force based upon currently available technical information, but it has not been approved for promulgation as a coordinated revision of Military Specification MIL-C-5011A. It is subject to modification. However, pending its promulgation as a coordinated Military Specification, it may be used in procurement.

1. SCOPE

1.1 Scope. This specification governs the definitions of requirements for, and methods of presenting characteristics and performances for military piloted airplanes. This specification while primarily oriented to conventional take-off and landing (CTOL) aircraft may be applied to STOL and VTOL airplanes if the design criteria established by requirements for specific designs are substituted for the CTOL criteria established herein.

1.2 Application. This specification is applicable to the preparation and presentation of characteristics and performance data. It is also applicable, when appropriate, as an outline of design requirements and mission rules for use in contractual documents and specifications.

1.3 Classification. Characteristics and performance data shall be presented on the following types of charts as required by the procuring agency, and utilizing format as provided. Unauthorized reproduction of such charts bearing the (by authority of the Secretary of the Air Force) statement is prohibited; however no restriction is placed upon use of the format.

1.3.1 Standard aircraft characteristics charts. The standard aircraft characteristics charts are intended to provide a concise, accurate compilation of physical characteristics and performance capabilities of a weapon system.

1.3.1.1 Arrangement. The standard aircraft characteristics chart is basically composed of 10 pages with provisions for supplemental pages as required by the procuring agency. Pages 1, 2, 3, 4, 6 and 9 are mandatory. Pages 5, 7 and 8 are optional as determined by the procuring agency. If certain pages are not required for a specific weapon system, and are omitted, the remaining pages shall be numbered consecutively.

1.3.1.1.1 **Basic. The arrangement** of the standard aircraft characteristics chart **shall be as follows:**

a. Page 1 -- Cover sheet which shall include a photograph or perspective drawing of the aircraft model in flight.

b. Page 2 -- Drawings showing descriptive details of the aircraft, such as: Three-view, fuel and oil tankage, armament, inboard profile, etc.

c. Page 3 -- Mission, description, and principal characteristics of the aircraft.

d. Page 4 -- Performance data for the aircraft in tabulated form.

e. Page 5 -- Supplemental tabulated performance data.

f. Page 6 -- Performance graphs.

g. Page 7 -- Supplemental performance graphs.

h. Page 8 -- External store loadings.

i. Page 9 -- Notes. Mission profiles, applicable allowances, and explanatory notes.

Specific requirements are detailed in 3.6.2.

1.3.1.1.2 **Supplemental pages. Aircraft characteristics and performance data not coming within the scope of the** standard aircraft characteristics charts shall **be presented on supplemental pages. Reasons for preparing** supplemental pages **may be as follows:**

a. Possible special loadings or conditions which may:

(1) Be used in restricted tactical operations

(2) Involve non-standard procedures and special operating techniques

(3) Show the maximum potential use of certain aircraft in special missions.

b. Special loadings that may involve equipment, which, for security reasons are only suitable for limited distribution.

c. Theater operations involving non-standard atmospheric conditions.

d. To show additional drawings, illustrations, and graphs. The supplemental page format should be the same as the standard aircraft characteristics chart but may consist of a special design suitable for binding along with the corresponding pages.

1.3.2 Characteristics summary. The characteristics summary is intended to present a summary of performance capabilities on the design mission and principal features in an abbreviated format. Data shown on the characteristics summary shall be in agreement with similar data shown on the standard aircraft characteristics chart. The standard format for the characteristics summary of each model, shall consist basically of a two-page, single-sheet, and shall be 8 by 10-1/2 inches in size after reproduction.

1.4 Categories. The foregoing charts shall be identified by categories to show the development status of the aircraft or data involved.

1.4.1 Development. Charts in this category provide information on new designs during the detail design development after the design becomes stabilized and only minor configuration changes are anticipated.

1.4.2 Service. Charts in this category provide information of aircraft during production and operational use.

1.5 Markings. Each of the foregoing chart types shall be marked as follows:

1.5.1 Designation. The military model designation shall be shown on the lower outer corner.

1.5.2 Category. The chart category as defined in 1.4 shall be shown on the upper outer corner.

1.5.3 Date. The date of publication will be inserted by the procuring agency on the lower inner corner.

1.5.4 Security. The security classification shall be marked as specified by the current DOD Security Regulations. For security purposes each block or graph shall be considered as a paragraph.

1.5.5 Reserved. The upper inner corner is reserved for the use of the procuring agency.

1.6 Submittal. Initial submittal of charts in the development category shall be accomplished after the design has stabilized as determined by the procuring agency. Charts in the service category shall be submitted after the system has been approved for production.

2. APPLICABLE DOCUMENTS

2.1 Issues of documents. The following documents, (effective on the date of invitation for request for proposal) form a part of this specification to the extend specified herein:

SPECIFICATIONS

MILITARY

MIL-G-5572	Gasoline, Aviation, Grades 80/87, 100/130, 115/145
MIL-T-5624	Turbine Fuel, Aviation, Grades JP-4 and JP-5
MIL-M-7700	Manuals, Flight
MIL-F-8785	Flying Qualities of Piloted Airplanes
MIL-A-008860	Airplane Strength and Rigidity, General Specification for
MIL-W-25140	Weight and Balance Control System (For Airplanes and Rotorcraft)
MIL-T-83133	Turbine Fuel, Aviation, Kerosene Type, Grade JP-8

STANDARDS

MILITARY

MIL-STD-210	Climatic Extremes for Military Equipment
MIL-STD-1374	Weight and Balance Data Reporting Forms for Aircraft (Including Rotorcraft)

MANUAL

AFM 60-16	General Flight Rules

(Copies of specifications, standards, drawings, and publications required by contractors in connection with specific procurement functions should be obtained from the procuring activity or as directed by the contracting officer.)

3. REQUIREMENTS

3.1 General. Unless otherwise specified by the procuring agency, preparation by contractors of charts (and revision thereto) for each model shall include the preparation of photographically reproducible copy in the required types and categories. Substantiating reports containing supporting characteristics and performance data are required.

3.1.1 Revisions. Revisions to the charts, shall be prepared and submitted by the contractor. Unless otherwise specified by the procuring agency, revisions are required whenever significant changes in vehicle configuration or data occur, as for:

a. A change in vehicle dimensions
b. An accumulation of changes resulting in a significant performance change. (See 3.1.1.1).

c. A change in propulsion system designation, augmentation, or rating.
d. The addition of external stores.
e. The availability of test data showing significant performance change. (See 3.1.1.1).
f. When specifically directed by the procuring agency.

3.1.1.1 Criteria. The following criteria will be used in forming a judgment as to whether a significant change in performance exists:

a. A change of 5 percent or more in drag.
b. A change of 5 percent or more in installed thrust.
c. A change of 5 percent or more in specific fuel consumption.
d. A change in weight which in itself results in a 5 percent or greater change in mission radius or range.
e. Any combination of two or more of the above resulting in a change of 5 percent or more in any performance parameter.

3.1.1.2 Number. Each chart shall cover only one aircraft model. The probable number of charts and revisions which are required throughout the life of the aircraft model will depend on the number of aircraft changes experienced.

3.2 Substantiating report. All data presented on the charts shall be substantiated by reports submitted with the charts. The reports may be legible rough draft copies of the contractor's work sheets. They shall be complete and shall present in detail the contractor's build up of aerodynamic and propulsive data and shall contain a listing of adequate references, authority, and justification for all data used. Contractors are free to use calculation methods of their own selection, but such methods shall be explained in detail so as to permit a ready understanding of aerodynamic, propulsive and weights bookkeeping methods. Calculations shall be presented in sufficient detail as to permit ready review and check of conclusions.

3.2.1 Basic aerodynamic data. Prior to proceeding with the initial performance calculations for the Standard Aircraft Characteristics charts mutual agreement shall be established between the contractor and the procuring agency relative to the aerodynamic and propulsive and weight data to be used for performance data. This agreement shall be accomplished through normal review and reporting procedures.

3.2.2 Report. The basic aerodynamic propulsive and weight data (see 3.2.1) shall, after review and acceptance by the procuring agency, form the basis for the detailed preparation of the substantiating data report. These data shall be expanded as necessary and used to prepare the detailed performance data required to substantiate the Standard Aircraft Characteristics.

3.2.3 Revisions. The substantiating data report shall be revised under the same criteria as the charts (see 3.1.1).

3.2.4 Text. The required data and the arrangement of the substantiating data report is contained in Appendix 1A.

3.3 Standards. Characteristics and performance data shall be based on engineering analysis which produce results consistent with flight test results.

3.3.1 Basis for data. All characteristics and performance data shall be based on the latest reliable aerodynamic, propulsion system, and weight information. The information given shall include the effects on weight and performance of all authorized contract and service changes, together with important changes assured of authorization but pending at the date of chart issue.

3.3.1.1 Changes in characteristics. Changes in aircraft characteristics which do not result in a significant performance change (see 3.1.1.1) do not require a revision by the contractor. However, the procuring agency shall be notified by correspondence so that proper notat on may be appended to the published chart.

3.3.1.2 Flight test. The latest flight test data approved by the procuring agency shall be used as a basis for performance.

3.3.2 Limitations. Performance data shall fall within all established limitations on the vehicle and its components.

3.3.3 Aircraft condition. Performance shall be presented in such a manner as to show clearly the applicable aerodynamic configuration, propulsion system, and loading information. Aircraft configurations shall include the installation of complete service equipment applicable to that particular aircraft model for the mission concerned. Flight performance shall be presented with guns, rotable enclosures, bomb bay doors, etc., in position of least drag, and external bombs or other armament in position for each loading condition, as noted.

3.3.4 Atmosphere. Performance shall be based on the latest approved standard atmospheric tables as specified by the procuring agency.

3.3.4.1 Standard day. Unless otherwise specified, performance shall be based on the standard atmosphere as tabulated and described in Appendix IC.

3.3.4.2 Non-standard day. Tropical and Hot day properties must conform to Appendix IC.

3.4 Definitions. The following definitions are used for the various data on the charts and shall be strictly adhered to.

3.4.1 Weights. Weights given on the charts shall comply with the following definitions derived from, and consistent with, MIL-STD-1374, MIL-W-25140 and T.O.AN 01-1B-50 (see 6.2).

3.4.1.1 Empty weight. The weight of the structure, propulsion system, equipment, etc., in the configuration defined in current system specification.

3.4.1.2 Basic weight. The empty weight adjusted for non-expendable operational items. (Weight empty plus unusable fuel and oil and all fixed armament and equipment for normal operation.)

3.4.1.3 Operating weight. Mission take-off weight less payload and usable fuel. (Basic weight plus usable oil, crew, crew baggage, steward equipment, emergency equipment, special mission fixed equipment, pylon and racks not in basic weight, and other nonexpendable items not in basic weight.)

3.4.1.4 Design weight. Weight at which specified structural design requirements are met or are required to be met.

3.4.1.5 Take-off weight. Take-off weight is the total weight of the aircraft with the fuel and payload (see 3.4.1.10) for the mission presented. The take-off weight normally shall be determined prior to start of engines except in specially approved cases when weight expended during taxi and take-off are excluded (see 3.4.1.5.1.b).

3.4.1.5.1 Maximum. Maximum take-off weight is the greatest weight for take-off established by Technical Orders, design requirements, or other specific recommendations of the procuring agency and is the least weight determined by the following criteria:

a. The weight of the vehicle fully loaded with fuel, oil, armament or cargo to the capacity for which space or tankage is normally provided. The bearing load for the floor and supporting structure shall not be exceeded.
b. The aircraft and its components (wings, landing gear, supporting structures for ordnance, cargo, etc.) shall be capable of sustaining the authorized load factor and shall not violate the minimum criteria of applicable specifications for taxi and ground handling. When ground handling criteria permits a higher weight than does the flight limit, those items expended during take-off, (water, ATO, etc.) may be added to the quoted maximum take-off weight for mission computations, and proper notation thereof will be carried in qualifying note on the performance charts.
c. Throughout the mission profile the center of gravity shall remain within design limits.
d. The maximum tow force, shall not be exceeded.

3.4.1.5.2 Typical design criteria. For design purposes consideration may be made of alternate definitions of maximum take-off weight such as: Specifying the critical field length and ground run associated with the operational concept of the design, including the effects of such items as runway surface (hard, sod, etc.), ambient runway temperature and pressure altitudes.

3.4.1.6 Maximum inflight weight. The maximum weight at which the aircraft is authorized to be airborne. This weight may be greater than maximum take-off weight if in-flight refueling is utilized.

3.4.1.7 Maximum ramp weight. Maximum in-flight weight unrefueled plus fuel, water, etc., used during engine start, taxi, and take-off, shall not exceed other limits such as those for taxiing, ground handling, wheel jacking, etc., as specified in MIL-A-008860.

3.4.1.8 Combat weight. Weight over the target for the mission presented with fuel and oil but without bombs, missiles, mines, cargo or droppable tanks unless otherwise noted.

3.4.1.8.1 Fuel load is determined as follows:

a. Bomber, Fighter Bomber, Missile Carrier (for ground attack) - Immediately after dropping the offensive ordnance, but prior to escape.

b. Fighter (interceptor, air superiority) - Immediately prior to combat.

c. Tanker - Immediately after completion of fuel transfer.

d. Reconnaissance - Immediately after arrival at target (after drop of photo flash bombs if carried).

e. Others (cargo-trainers) - Prior to start of return flight for resupply (radius mission) and prior to landing for range missions.

f. Ferry Mission (all vehicle types) - Reserve fuel only.

3.4.1.8.1.1 Typical design criteria. For design purposes, consideration of alternate definitions of combat fuel load such as: with 50 percent of combat fuel allowance consumed, with 100 percent of combat fuel allowance consumed, or any other criteria selected to optimize the aircraft design.

3.4.1.9 Landing weight

3.4.1.9.1 Maximum. Maximum landing weight is the greatest weight established for landing by structural criteria.

3.4.1.9.2 Mission. The weight at the end of the mission as determined by the mission ground rules. It shall include the fuel reserve as specified by the mission.

3.4.1.10 Payload. The load which justifies the mission. Payload includes cargo, personnel other than crew, bombs, chaff, missiles, reconnaissance cameras, electronic countermeasures pods, photo flash flares, fuel carried for transfer by tankers, and ammunition.

Special equipment required for the mission such as winterization, rescue equipment, except that carried for drop by (H) type vehicles (search-rescue), cargo handling, etc., shall not be included in payload.

3.4.1.11 Fuel. Standard fuel weight of fuel in pounds per U. S. gallon shall be as follows:

a. MIL-F-5572 (Gasoline in all grades) — 6.0 lbs/gal.
b. MIL-F-5624 (JP-4) Jet fuel — 6.5 lbs/gal.
c. MIL-F-5624C (JP-5) Jet fuel — 6.8 lbs/gal.
d. MIL-T-83133 (JP-8) Jet fuel — 6.7 lbs/gal.
e. If design requires special fuels of specified densities or BTU content, such shall be used and specified in the chart notes.

3.4.2 Speeds. All speeds shall be level flight true airspeeds in knots and mach number as applicable.

3.4.2.1 Maximum speed. The highest speed obtainable for configuration and weight in level flight. The altitude at which this speed occurs shall be stated. It shall be the lesser of the speeds determined by the intersection of the thrust (power) available and required curves or the speed limit imposed through structural or heating consideration.

3.4.2.2 Penetration speed. A specified speed ( ) at which the aircraft shall conduct the final run in to the target at a specified altitude. This speed shall be specified by design requirements.

3.4.2.2.1 Combat speed. Maximum speed at combat weight and combat altitude with maximum power.

3.4.2.3 Stall speed. The stall speed shall be computed on the basis of 1.0g flight with the maximum trimmed lift coefficient established by computation or wind tunnel testing. Upon availability of flight test results, stall speed shall be changed to the highest of the speeds for steady straight 1.0g flight at C_L max., the speed at which abrupt loss of control occurs about any of the pitch, roll or yaw axes, the speed at which intollerable buffet or structural vibration in encountered, or other minimum permissible speed as defined in MIL-F-8785.

3.4.2.3.1 Power-off. The stall speed without power.

3.4.2.4 Take-off speed

3.4.2.4.1 Take-off speed shall be the highest of the speeds specified below:

a. A speed corresponding to 110 percent of power off stall speed in the take-off configuration.
b. A speed determined by the lift coefficient, in ground effect, for the maximum angle of attack attainable with the main landing gear oleo in the static position with aircraft on ground.
c. Minimum speed at which the aircraft has a climb gradient potential of 1/2 percent (0.005), with maximum power, in the take-off configuration, out of ground effect. For multi-engine aircraft this potential shall be obtainable with the most critical engine inoperative. Where;

$$\text{gradient} = \frac{[\text{Vertical Height in climb (ft)}]}{[\text{Horizontal distance in climb (ft)}]} \qquad (1)$$

d. Air minimum control speed as specified in 3.4.2.8.2.
e. The speed which permits attaining obstacle climb-out speed, as defined in 3.4.2.5, at or before reaching 50 ft. height above the runway.

3.4.2.4.1.1 Typical design criteria. For design purposes, consideration may be made of alternate definitions of take-off speed such as: a higher or lower percentage of stall speed, a higher climb gradient potential or other criteria which optimizes the design.

3.4.2.5 Obstacle climb-out speed. The climb speed at the 50-foot obstacle shall not be less than the highest of the speeds specified below.

a. One hundred fifteen percent of power off, 1.0g, stall speed.
b. Air minimum control speed.
c. Speed at which the aircraft has a climb gradient of 2.5 percent (0.025) with gear up, flaps in take-off position, with maximum power, out-of-ground effect. For multi-engine aircraft this potential shall be obtainable with the most critical engine inoperative.
d. If gear retraction results in a transient drag increase over that for gear down, the speed at which the aircraft has a 1/2 percent (0.005) climb gradient potential with flaps in take-off setting, gear in transit, with maximum thrust out-of-ground effect. For multi-engine aircraft, the most critical engine shall be inoperative.

3.4.2.5.1 Typical design criteria. For design purposes, consideration may be made of alternative limitations to the obstacle climb-out speed such as: a higher or lower percentage of the stall speed, an increase in climb gradient potential or any criteria which is in keeping with the operational concept of the design.

3.4.2.6 Climb speed. The climb speed shall be the airspeed at which the maximum rate-of-climb is attained for the given configuration, weight, altitude, and power. Consideration shall be made for kinetic energy corrections in optimizing the climb speed schedule. When authorized in the applicable flight manual, a simplified, non-optimum speed schedule may be used.

3.4.2.7 Critical engine failure speed. The critical engine failure speed shall be the speed at which the most critical engine can fail and the same distance be required to either continue the take-off or abort. See 3.4.5.4.

3.4.2.8 Minimum engine-out control speed

3.4.2.8.1 Ground. The minimum control speed, ground, shall be the minimum speed during the take-off run where the engine, most critical to directional control, can fail and directional control can be maintained as defined in MIL-F-8785.

3.4.2.8.2 Air. The minimum control speed, air, shall be the minimum airborne speed with maximum thrust where the engine, most critical to control, can fail and directional control can be maintained.

3.4.2.9 Cruise speed

3.4.2.9.1 Maximum range cruise speed. The speed for maximum range operation shall be the speed at which maximum nautical miles per pound of fuel are attainable at the momentary weight and altitude.

3.4.2.9.2 Long range cruise speed. The higher of the two airspeeds which give nautical miles per pound of fuel equal to 99 percent of the maximum nautical miles per pound of fuel for momentary weight and altitude. This speed may be used to decrease mission time without severe penalty to range.

3.4.2.9.3 Maximum cruise speed. The highest speed that can be maintained with maximum continuous power at stated altitude, weight and configuration.

3.4.2.9.4 Average cruise speed. Total distance covered in cruise divided by the time for cruise (distance and time for climb, acceleration to combat speed, combat time, loiter time etc. are not included).

3.4.2.10 Maximum endurance (loiter) speed. The airspeed for maximum endurance shall correspond to the speed for minimum fuel flow attainable at momentary weight and altitude except as limited by acceptable flying qualities.

3.4.2.10.1 Combat loiter speed. The airspeed for maximum endurance shall correspond to the speed for minimum fuel flow attained at momentary weight and attitude except that the airspeed must be adequate to allow an instantaneous load factor of a specified value.

3.4.2.11 Approach speed. The approach speed down to the 50-foot obstacle shall be the higher of:

a. Air minimum control speed, gear down, flaps in approach configuration and lift augmentation operable.
b. A speed of 120 percent of 1.0g power-off stall speed, out-of-ground effect, gear down, flaps in approach configuration.

c. A speed at which the aircraft has a climb gradient potential of 2.5 percent (0.025) with gear retracted, flaps in approach configuration, and with maximum dry take-off power. For multi-engine aircraft the most critical engine shall be inoperative.

Note: If other than landing flap is selected for approach, it's characteristics shall be specified i.e., approach flap develops a stall -- percent higher than does landing flap.

3.4.2.11.1 Typical design criteria. For design purposes, consideration may be made of alternate definitions of approach speed such as: higher or lower percentage of stall speed, a higher climb gradient potential, alternate go-around power settings or any other criteria which might optimize the design.

3.4.2.12 Landing speed. The landing speed shall be the greater of:

a. A speed determined by the lift coefficient, in ground effect, for the maximum angle attainable with the main landing gear oleo in the static compressed position with aircraft on ground.
b. One hundred fifteen percent (115 percent) of 1.0g power-off stall speed in the landing configuration.

3.4.2.12.1 Typical design criteria. For design purposes, consideration may be given to alternate definitions of landing speed such as: geometry-limited with oleos in full or partial extended position, changes in percentage of stall speed and climb gradient potential or any other criteria which would optimize the design.

3.4.3 Ceiling

3.4.3.1 Service ceiling. The altitude at which the maximum rate of climb at subsonic speed is 100 ft/min at stated weight and engine power.

3.4.3.2 Combat ceiling

3.4.3.2.1 Subsonic. The altitude at which the max subsonic rate of climb is 500 ft/min at stated weight and power.

3.4.3.2.2 Supersonic. The highest altitude at which the vehicle can fly supersonically and have a climb potential of 1000 fpm at stated power and weight.

3.4.3.3 Cruise ceiling

3.4.3.3.1 Subsonic. The altitude at which the maximum rate-of-climb potential is 300 ft/min at maximum continuous engine rating at momentary weight.

3.4.3.3.2 Supersonic. The highest altitude at which the vehicle can fly supersonic at maximum continuous power with a climb potential of 1000 fpm at momentary weight.

3.4.4 Altitude

3.4.4.1 Cruise altitude. The altitude at which the cruise portion of the missions is computed. Depending on the mission ground rules, the cruise altitude may be assigned or it may be otherwise governed by limitations such as terrain clearance, mission length, ceilings, oxygen or other crew/aircraft restrictions. In no case shall cruise altitude exceed cruise ceiling.

3.4.4.2 Optimum cruise altitude. The altitude at which the aircraft attains the maximum nautical miles per pound of fuel for the momentary weight and configuration. If this altitude exceeds cruise ceiling the latter shall be used for cruise.

3.4.4.3 Combat altitude. The altitude at the target for the specific mission shown.

3.4.5 Take-off. Criteria for conventional take-off aircraft shall comply with the following: (for STOL aircraft the criteria shall be determined by design criteria.) (Vertical components of thrust may be used in take-off computation.)

3.4.5.1 Ground run distance (i.e. take-off distance). Take-off ground run distance shall be that normally obtainable in service operation at Sea Level with standard atmospheric conditions, zero wind, no runway slope on hard (concrete or asphalt) surfaced runways. The take-off speed criteria of 3.4.2.4 shall be used.

3.4.5.1.1 Typical design criteria. For design purposes, consideration may be made of alternate definitions of take-off ground run such as: non-standard atmospheric conditions, higher pressure altitudes, alternate runway surfaces (hard, sod etc.), head or tail-wind or other criteria in keeping with the operational concept of the design.

3.4.5.2 Distance to 50 ft. The distance to clear a 50-foot obstacle shall be the sum of take-off ground run distance of 3.4.5.1 plus the airborne distance needed to accelerate and climb to arrive at the 50-foot height at the speed specified in 3.4.2.5.

3.4.5.3 Take-off time. The take-off time shall be that normally obtainable in service operation at sea level under standard day atmospheric conditions with no wind. The time is measured from start of take-off (brake release) to start of enroute climb (attainment of climb speed).

3.4.5.4 Critical field length. Critical field length is the sum of the distance required to accelerate with all engines operative to critical engine failure speed (3.4.2.7) plus the distance to accelerate with the critical engine inoperative to take-off or to decelerate to a stop from critical engine failure speed in the same distance.

3.4.5.4.1 Data basis. The data basis for the computation of the stopping distance for the chart for critical field length shall be as follows:

a. At engine failure speed the aircraft continues to accelerate for 3 seconds pilot reaction time with remaining engines at maximum power and zero thrust on the inoperative engine.
b. At the end of the 3-second acceleration time, power on all engines is instantaneously reduced to idle, brakes applied, and deceleration devices deployed.
c. Sufficient time, after, b, above, shall be allowed for deployment of the deceleration device(s) or for reverse thrust to reach maximum before including its effect on deceleration.

3.4.5.5 Coefficient of friction. The coefficient μ, as used in this document is defined as the ratio of the total retardation force attributable to the braking system to the momentary gross weight of the aircraft. The following values will be used unless ground or flight test data are available.

3.4.5.5.1 Rolling μ. The rolling (unbraked) coefficient of friction for a dry, hard surface runway shall be assumed equal to 0.025.

3.4.5.5.2 Braking μ. The total braking coefficient of friction for a dry hard surface runway shall be assumed equal to 0.30.

3.4.5.5.3 Test data. Test μ values may be either the results of tests conducted on the specific aircraft or similar types, i.e. commercial aircraft.

3.4.5.5.4 Typical design criteria. For design purposes, consideration may be given to the effects of new and improved methods of increasing the total retardation force such as by anti-skid devices.

3.4.6 Climb. Climb after take-off may be divided into two segments as specified by the procuring agency: Initial climb-out and enroute climb.

3.4.6.1 Initial climb-out. Climb-out shall be at a speed which shall not be less than that limited by the criteria of 3.4.2.5. Gear retraction shall be initiated as soon as an adequate positive climb gradient (3.4.2.5c and d), using applicable power, has been established and maintained while accelerating to climb-out speed. Flaps shall be in the take-off position.

3.4.6.1.1 All engines operating. Initial climb-out with all engines operating shall be based on all engines operating from brake release to take-off. Acceleration to climb-out speed and climb-out shall be based on the thrust (power) available with all available engines.

3.4.6.1.2 One engine inoperative. Initial climb-out with one engine inoperative shall be based on all engines operating from brake release to critical engine failure speed and with the critical engine inoperative from critical engine failure speed to take-off. Acceleration to climb-out speed and climb-out shall be based upon the thrust (power) available with the remaining engines at take-off thrust and the drag of the inoperative engine. If means of reducing drag of the inoperative engine are a design feature, such drag reduction shall be utilized with a time allowance for activation.

3.4.6.2 Climb path angle. The climb flight path angle shall be expressed in terms of a gradient (vertical feet per 100 horizontal feet). This path shall be determined from the 50-foot height point and at the 50-foot height climb-out speed as determined in 3.4.2.5. Conditions shall be with gear up, flaps in take-off position, out of ground effect and with appropriate configuration, power and weight. For multi-engine aircraft the climb flight path with the critical engine inoperative shall be included.

3.4.6.3 Enroute climb. Enroute climb data shall be based on the appropriate configuration, power and weight. The aircraft shall have the landing gear and flaps retracted and have attained the airspeed for best climb for the applicable condition.

3.4.6.4 Time to climb. The time to climb to specified altitude(s) shall be expressed in minutes from start of enroute climb. Weight reduction as a result of fuel consumption shall be applied to the calculations.

3.4.6.5 Combat climb. Combat climb is the instantaneous maximum vertical speed capability in feet per minute at combat conditions, such as, weight, configuration, altitude, and power.

3.4.7 Landing distance. The following criteria are for conventional aircraft. (For STOL aircraft the criteria shall be as established by design requirements.) Landing distance includes: (a) landing ground roll and (b) distance over a 50 foot height. Distances shall be for the landing configuration and weight and shall be based on the landing speeds defined in 3.4.2.12. Unless otherwise specified, ground roll deceleration shall be based on operation at Sea Level, standard day, zero wind, no runway slope, idle power and a braking coefficient as defined in 3.4.5.5.2.

3.4.7.1 Typical design criteria. For design purposes, consideration may be given to alternate definitions of landing distance such as: reverse thrust, atmospheric conditions, runway slopes and winds of a non-standard nature, a rigid computer analysis of the air distance and other similar criteria selected to optimize the design of the airplane.

3.4.8 Power. The term (power) is used to mean brake horsepower or thrust as applicable with due consideration for installation effects and limitations. Engine and assisted takeoff ratings as defined in 3.6.2.1.5 c and 3.6.3.1.4 shall be those which appear in the approved engine model specification without regard to installation effects or limitations.

3.4.8.1 Maximum power. Maximum engine power output. This condition of operation may have an incremental duration time limit. This term is used for both augmented and non-augmented engines.

3.4.8.2 Intermediate power. Maximum engine power output without augmentation. This condition may be time limited. This term is used only for augmented engines.

3.4.8.3 Maximum continuous power. Maximum engine power output which may be used continuously, no time limit is imposed.

3.4.8.4 Cruise power. The power required to fly the aircraft at cruise speed for the configuration, altitude and weight designated.

3.4.8.5 Minimum augmented. Lowest power at which the engine will operate with augmentation at any point specified within the augmented operating envelope.

3.4.9 Fuel. Unless otherwise specified, fuel for gas turbine engines shall be JP-4. Weights shall be obtained from 3.4.1.11.

3.4.9.1 Fuel consumption corrections. Corrections or allowances to engine fuel flow shall be made for all propulsion system installation losses such as accessory drives, BLC bleed, environmental system bleed, nozzle losses, pressure recovery, etc.

3.4.10 Mission types. Representative operational missions for various types of aircraft are specified in table I. Typical maximum effort missions are shown in Appendix IB to this specification. These maximum effort missions specify the exact fuel allowances for take-off and climb, combat, and landing reserves and are included since they are often used to compare USAF aircraft and foreign aircraft performance capabilities on a common basis.

3.4.10.1 Design mission. The design mission is defined as the primary mission for which the aircraft was specifically procured. This mission will normally be defined in procurement documents such as the statement of work and will include the flight profile, allowances, fuel (clean or external tanks) and payload. Ground rules and allowances for the design mission are dictated by the specific operational requirements and will be used in describing the mission capabilities in the Standard Aircraft Characteristics charts. Some useful alternate design criteria are discussed in 3.5.3 and in other applicable parts of this specification.

3.4.10.2 Ferry mission (ferry range). The greatest distance attainable on a practical one-way mission with maximum authorized fuel and no payload.

3.4.10.3 Typical missions. Any missions, preferably from table I, which would present the additional capabilit es of the aircraft. Normally these will include at least one mission at the maximum take-off weight (3.4.1.5.1) with the ground rules corresponding to the design mission.

3.4.10.4 Inflight refueled mission. For aircraft capable of inflight refueling, a refueled mission is the distance (radius or range) attainable through receipt of replacement fuel during flight. A single refueling operation is required although multiple refueling operations may be added if considered to be feasible. Basic profiles from table I shall apply with special allowance from table II considered.

3.4.10.5 Combat range. Combat range is the distance (including distance covered in climb) attainable on a one-way flight carrying payload (bombs, cargo, personnel) the entire distance. Droppable fuel tanks are dropped when empty. Allowances for take-off, climb, cruise are taken from the design mission. Combat range for bomber, fighter, and attack aircraft should be computed without landing reserves. Landing reserves should be included for aircraft.

3.4.10.6 Combat radius. Combat radius is the distance [including distance covered in climb(s)] to the mid-point of a equal legged mission from base to target and return. Specific mission profile actions, allowances and reserves shall be as set forth in table I and in the mission being considered.

3.4.10.6.1 Typical design criteria. For design purposes, consideration may be given to the requirement for missions containing unequal legs (offset). Significant design impact could result from a mission where the aircraft is recovered at a remote base without the requirement of returning to home base.

3.5 Mission detailed requirements

3.5.1 General mission requirements. Unless otherwise specified, the following general ground rules shall apply:

3.5.1.1 Standard atmosphere. Data shall be presented for standard day atmosphere.

3.5.1.2 Wind. Data shall be for a no-wind condition.

3.5.1.3 Formation flight. Data shall be for a single aircraft only.

3.5.1.4 Ordnance expenditure. All ordnance shall be expended at the start of combat unless otherwise specified.

3.5.1.5 Off-Loading fuel. Fuel may be off-loaded to avoid exceeding the maximum allowable take-off weight.

3.5.1.6 External fuel tanks. External fuel tanks on combat aircraft, shall be dropped when empty or prior to combat unless such tanks are designed to be carried during combat. Unless otherwise restricted (Center of Gravity etc.), dropping of external tanks shall be sequenced to provide maximum range. Cargo and tanker aircraft shall not drop empty external tanks.

3.5.1.7 Pylons/Racks. In the computation of range/radius performance, pylons and racks shall be retained unless required to be dropped by design requirements

3.5.1.8 Reduced engine operation. When applicable, a minimum number of engines may be used to increase range if such operation would represent normal service usage. However, such action shall conform to 3.5.1.9.

3.5.1.9 Authorized operation. No operational technique, see 3.5.1.8, shall be utilized that is not included, or is not intended to be included as recommended procedure in the applicable flight manual.

3.5.1.10 Trainer aircraft. Thr trainer mission as defined by table I is applicable to basic and advanced trainer airplanes. Combat and tactical trainer airplanes fly the design mission for the appropriate parent-type airplane.

3.5.1.11 Variable geometry wing (VGW) aircraft. Normally VGW aircraft will have wings in unswept position for take-off and subsonic flight and swept for supersonic dash and chase profile segment unless footnoted otherwise.

3.5.2 Mission loading requirements. In order to facilitate and expedite the submittal of the charts, the contractor should contact the procuring agency to discuss the various mission loadings prior to submittal. In the absence of special instructions, the following shall apply.

3.5.2.1 Design mission loading. The fuel and payload loading for the design mission shall be the primary loading condition as defined in the system specification for the aircraft.

3.5.2.2 Typical missions loading. Loadings shall be selected from those included in the system specification or other approved loadings which depict a particular capability of the aircraft. At least one mission shall conform to the maximum gross weight specified in 3.4.1.5.1.

3.5.2.3 Ferry mission loading. Loading shall consist of the maximum authorized fuel and no payload.

3.5.2.4 Inflight refueled mission loading. One mission shall be for the same loading as the design mission. Other loadings may be selected from the typical missions.

3.5.2.5 Combat range mission loading. Identical to the loading of the associated combat radius mission.

3.5.3 Mission segments. Rationale for mission segments is presented below.

3.5.3.1 Take-off. Fuel allowances for ground operation including starting engines warm-up, taxi, take-off and acceleration to climb speed, are as defined in the requirements for the design mission.

3.5.3.1.1 Typical design criteria. For design purposes, consideration may be given to defining the take-off allowance to fully utilize the state-of-the-art. Some typical examples are:

a. Specify engine operation for specific time periods at specified powers. Such as, fuel used during 5 minutes of maximum continuous power operation at Sea Level on a standard day plus 1 minute of maximum power operation if afterburner is used during take-off.

b. Estimate fuel required to start the engine(s), run-up, taxi a specified distance at a specified power setting and to accelerate from brake release to climb speed at a specified power.

c. Estimate fuel for a specified time at a specified thrust/weight ratio to account for starting and taxi plus fuel for take-off and acceleration to climb speed computed from the following:

$$W_{f_{TO}} = \frac{V_c W_{TO}}{2g} \cdot \frac{(\dot{W}_o + \dot{W}_c)}{T-D}$$

When: $W_{f_{TO}}$ = Take-off and acceleration fuel, lbs

V_c = initial climb speed, ft/sec

W_{TO} = take-off weight, lbs

$\dot{W}_o$ = static fuel flow at take-off power, lbs/sec

$\dot{W}_c$ = fuel flow at initial climb speed at take-off power, lbs/sec

T-D = thrust minus drag at V_c, lbs

g = acceleration of gravity, S.L., ft/sec^2 (2)

Note: If power is to be varied between lift-off and climb speed this equation can be so modified.

d. Other specific criteria may be selected to more accurately portray the operational characteristics of the specific design.

3.5.3.2 Climb. Except for point intercept missions, all climbs shall be enroute with power and speed schedules optimized to maximize mission range. Point intercept missions shall be optimized to obtain minimum time to combat altitude.

3.5.3.2.1 Typical design criteria. For design purposes, consideration may be given to alternate climb schedules to more adequately portray the desired operational capability of the design. For example the following schedules could apply: minimum time, minimum fuel, maximum range, specified power or speed, accelerate during climb, etc.

3.5.3.3 Cruise. Unless specifically assigned, aircraft shall cruise at the speed and altitude for maximum or long range for the applicable configuration, power and weight. Except where the altitude is specified, the aircraft may utilize a cruise climb to optimize cruise distance. This altitude shall not exceed cruise ceiling.

3.5.3.3.1 Typical design criteria. For design purposes, consideration may be given to specifying a cruise technique selected to optimize the desired characteristics of the design. Techniques to be considered include: constant altitude cruise, constant speed cruise, cruise climb profile, step climb, cruise at specified power, cruise with reduced number of engines, cruise altitude in excess of cruise ceiling, fixed distance segment, headwinds or tail winds, non-standard temperatures, etc.

3.5.3.4 Combat. Combat shall be considered by setting aside a quantity of fuel based upon a specified measure of combat performance. For task-oriented fuel allowances, computation shall be based upon weight at start of combat period with benefit due to weight reduction cridited; change in speed due to weight reduction shall be ignored.

3.5.3.4.1 Escape and evasion. Escape and evasion shall be considered by setting aside a quantity of fuel based upon a specified measure of performance.

3.5.3.4.2 Typical design criteria. For design purposes, consideration may be given to various methods of accounting for the fuel to be used during combat or escape and evasion action. Some examples of methods are:

a. Fuel required for a specified time with a specified power at a specified speed and a specified altitude.

b. Fuel consumed in expending a specified quantity of energy. For example:

$$\text{Combat fuel} = \frac{E_s \dot{W}_f}{P_s}$$

When: E_s = Specific energy, ft

$\dot{W}_f$ = fuel flow at combat speed, power, and altitude, lbs/sec

P_s = excess energy or $\frac{(T-D)V_c}{W_{T_c}}$, ft/sec

V_c = combat true airspeed, ft/sec

W_{T_c} = combat weight, lbs

(T-D) = thrust minus drag, lbs (3)

c The quantity of fuel determined as the sum of the fuel required to accelerate from cruise speed to a specified speed, plus fuel required to make a specified number of sustainable turns at a specified speed or speeds. These operations shall be performed at a selected power(s) and altitude(s).

d. All or a portion of the armament may be expended.

e. Other specific criteria selected to more accurately portray the operational characteristics of the specific design.

3.5.3.4 Descent. For vehicles whose best cruise is subsonic, no time, fuel or distance shall be credited for descent. For supersonic cruise vehicles, credit shall be taken for descent and deceleration to a specified altitude and speed. Vehicles which conduct a supersonic run out from the target may, if the cruise altitude and speed are lower than the run out altitude and speed, account for distance in descent and deceleration to cruise.

3.5.3.5 Typical design criteria. For design purposes, consideration may be given to alternate definitions of descent. For example: Time, fuel and distance could be credited, descent could be a long range (airline) approach, use of power could vary from none to full, speeds could vary from near stall to redline, altitudes could be reduced in step increments, etc.

3.5.3.6 Landing reserve. Since the mission profiles of table I are generalized, no compliance with the alternate landing destination of AFM 60-16 is possible. Instead, a landing reserve is required which would be typical of operational use.

3.5.3.6.1 Typical design criteria. For design purposes, consideration may be given to defining the landing reserves to fully utilize the state-of-the-art. Some examples are:

a. The fuel required for a ground controlled approach; a wave-off, go-around and a second, successful landing. This could be approximated by using the equivalent of fuel consumed during a specified time at maximum endurance at Sea Level with all engines operating.

b. A specified percentage of initial fuel load.

c. Fuel consumed during a specified time of operation at a specified power at a specified altitude.

d. The greater of the fuel required for 10 percent of mission time or 20 minutes at maximum endurance speed at 10,000 feet (AFM 60-16).

e. Fuel required to fly to an alternate field (specify distance) plus a specified time at a specified speed at a specified altitude to account for landing.

f. Combinations of the above or other criteria selected to optimize the design.

3.5.4 Mission time. Time in air excluding the time before the start of initial climb and reserve unless otherwise specified and noted. For interceptors only: includes actual time required for take-off and acceleration to climb speed.

3.5.5 Cycle time. The time of flight from the start of initial climb (omitting take-off time) to the time when the engines are stopped after landing.

3.5.6 Block time. The total time of flight from engine start to engine stop after landing.

3.5.7 Intercept time. The time from engine start until initiation of combat at the intercept altitude. This time includes the period required for take-off and acceleration to climb speed.

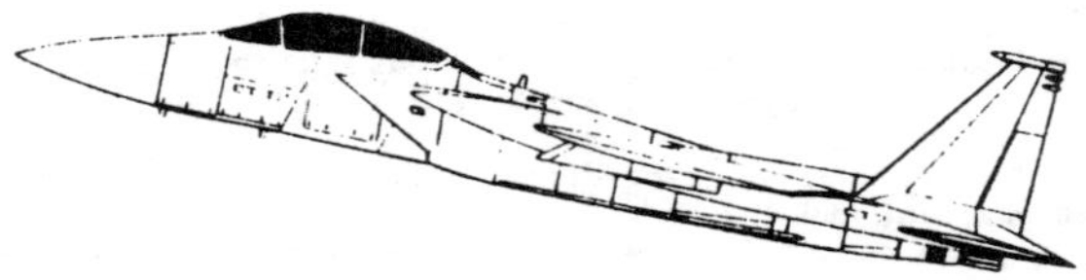

TABLE I

STANDARD MISSIONS

ATTACK
- * A-1 Hi-Hi-Hi
- A-2 Hi-Lo-Hi
- * A-3 Hi-Lo-Lo-Hi
- A-4 Lo-Lo-Lo-Hi
- * A-5 Lo-Lo-Lo-Lo
- * A-6 CAP

BOMBER
- * B-1 Hi-Hi-Hi-Hi
- B-2 Hi-Lo-Lo-Hi

CARGO
- C-1 Supply
- * C-2 Assault

FIGHTER
- * F-1 Air Superiority
- F-2 Point Intercept
- F-3 Area Intercept
- F-4 CAP
- F-5 Hi-Hi-Hi
- F-6 Hi-Lo-Hi
- F-7 Hi-Lo-Lo-Hi
- F-8 Lo-Lo-Lo-Hi
- F-9 Lo-Lo-Lo

TANKER
- T-1 Buddy Refuel
- * T-2 Rendezvous Refuel

GENERAL
- G-1 Airborne Warning and Control
- G-2 Rescue
- G-3 Forward Air Controller
- G-4 Trainer
- G-5 ASW Search
- * G-6 Ferry Mission

* MISSION PROFILES INCLUDED IN THIS TEXT. FOR OTHERS SEE MIL-C-005011B

NOTES
1. For segment details and rationale - see 3.5.3
2. For each segment, enter incremental values: (Time; hours; Fuel; pounds; Distance; n. miles)
3. For tanker missions with a specified receiver - See table III

TABLE I. STANDARD MISSIONS (Continued)

MISSION A-1

HI-HI-HI - ATTACK

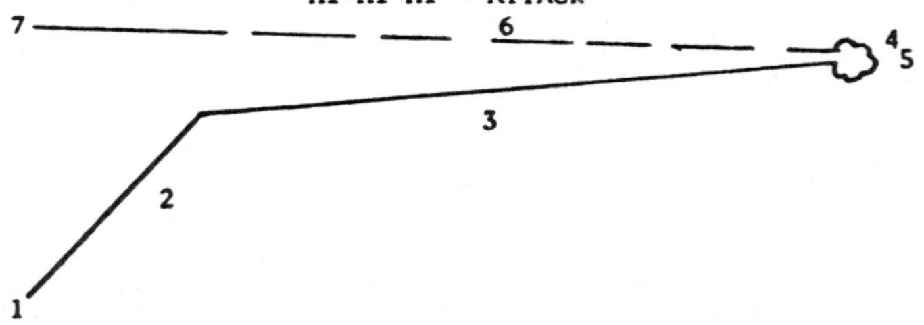

SEGMENT	ALLOWANCE
1. Take-off and accelerate to climb speed ( )	1. See 3.5.3.1
2. Climb on course to cruise altitude ( )	2. Speed and power for maximum range
3. Cruise to target ( )	3. Speed and altitude for maximum range
4. Drop Stores ( )	4. Weight reduction equal to store weight
5. Escape and evasion ( )	5. See 3.5.3.4.1
6. Cruise to base ( )	6. Same as 3
7. Arrive over base with reserve fuel ( )	7. See 3.5.3.6

TABLE I. STANDARD MISSIONS (Continued)

MISSION A-3

HI-LO-LO-HI - ATTACK

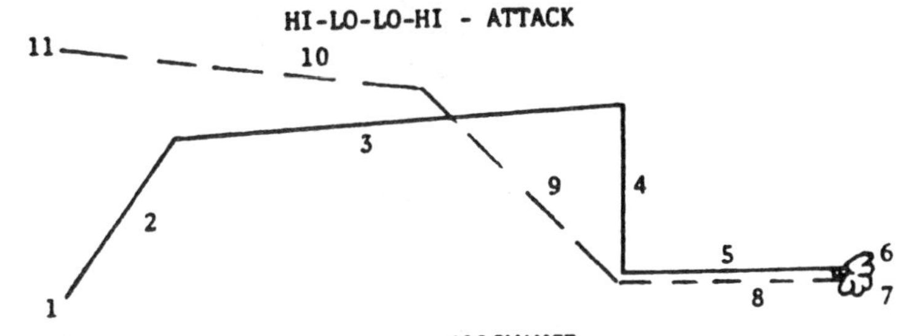

SEGMENT	ALLOWANCE
1. Take-off and accelerate to climb speed ( )	1. See 3.5.3.1
2. Climb on course to cruise altitude ( )	2. Speed and power for maximum range
3. Cruise to start of penetration ( )	3. Speed and altitude for maximum range
4. Descend to Sea Level	4. No time, fuel or distance credited except where specified
5. Run-in specified distance at Sea Level to target ( )	5. At penetration speed at Sea Level with power as required
6. Drop Stores ( )	6. Weight reduction equal to store weight
7. Attack target ( )	7. See 3.5.3.4
8. Run-out specified distance at Sea Level from target ( )	8. Same as 5
9. Climb on course to cruise	9. Same as 2
10. Cruise to base ( )	10. Same as 3
11. Arrive over base with reserve fuel ( )	11. See 3.5.3.6

TABLE I. STANDARD MISSIONS (Continued)

MISSION A-5

LO-LO-LO-LO - ATTACK

SEGMENT	ALLOWANCE
1. Take-off and accelerate to cruise speed ( )	1. See 3.5.3.1
2. Cruise at Sea Level to target ( )	2. Speed and power for maximum range
3. Drop stores ( )	3. Weight reduction equal to store weight
4. Attack target ( )	4. See 3.5.3.4
5. Cruise to base at Sea Level	5. Same as 2
6. Arrive over base with reserve fuel ( )	6. See 3.5.3.6

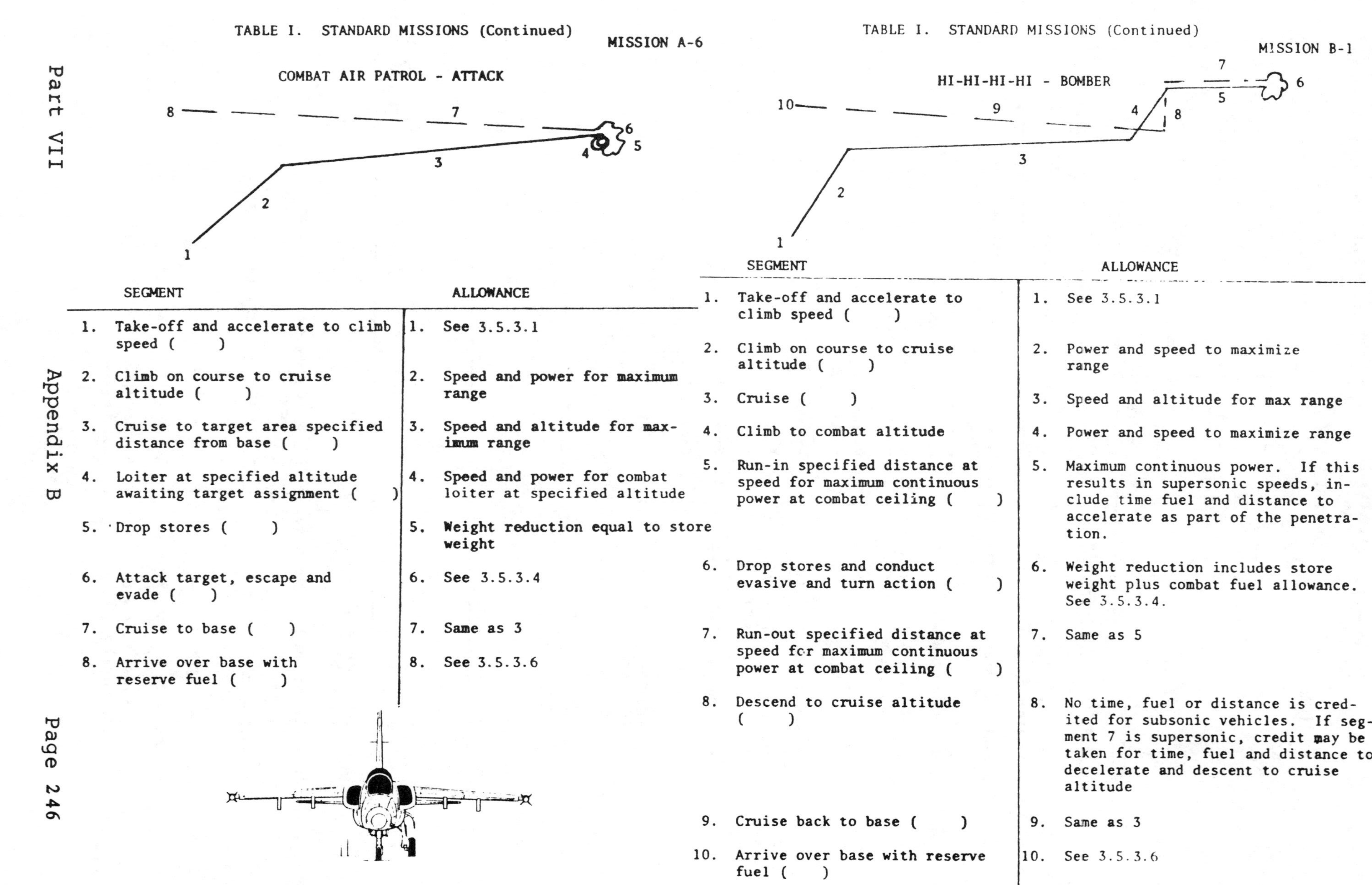

TABLE I. STANDARD MISSIONS (Continued)

MISSION A-6

COMBAT AIR PATROL - ATTACK

SEGMENT	ALLOWANCE
1. Take-off and accelerate to climb speed ( )	1. See 3.5.3.1
2. Climb on course to cruise altitude ( )	2. Speed and power for maximum range
3. Cruise to target area specified distance from base ( )	3. Speed and altitude for maximum range
4. Loiter at specified altitude awaiting target assignment ( )	4. Speed and power for combat loiter at specified altitude
5. Drop stores ( )	5. Weight reduction equal to store weight
6. Attack target, escape and evade ( )	6. See 3.5.3.4
7. Cruise to base ( )	7. Same as 3
8. Arrive over base with reserve fuel ( )	8. See 3.5.3.6

TABLE I. STANDARD MISSIONS (Continued)

MISSION B-1

HI-HI-HI-HI - BOMBER

SEGMENT	ALLOWANCE
1. Take-off and accelerate to climb speed ( )	1. See 3.5.3.1
2. Climb on course to cruise altitude ( )	2. Power and speed to maximize range
3. Cruise ( )	3. Speed and altitude for max range
4. Climb to combat altitude	4. Power and speed to maximize range
5. Run-in specified distance at speed for maximum continuous power at combat ceiling ( )	5. Maximum continuous power. If this results in supersonic speeds, include time fuel and distance to accelerate as part of the penetration.
6. Drop stores and conduct evasive and turn action ( )	6. Weight reduction includes store weight plus combat fuel allowance. See 3.5.3.4.
7. Run-out specified distance at speed for maximum continuous power at combat ceiling ( )	7. Same as 5
8. Descend to cruise altitude ( )	8. No time, fuel or distance is credited for subsonic vehicles. If segment 7 is supersonic, credit may be taken for time, fuel and distance to decelerate and descent to cruise altitude
9. Cruise back to base ( )	9. Same as 3
10. Arrive over base with reserve fuel ( )	10. See 3.5.3.6

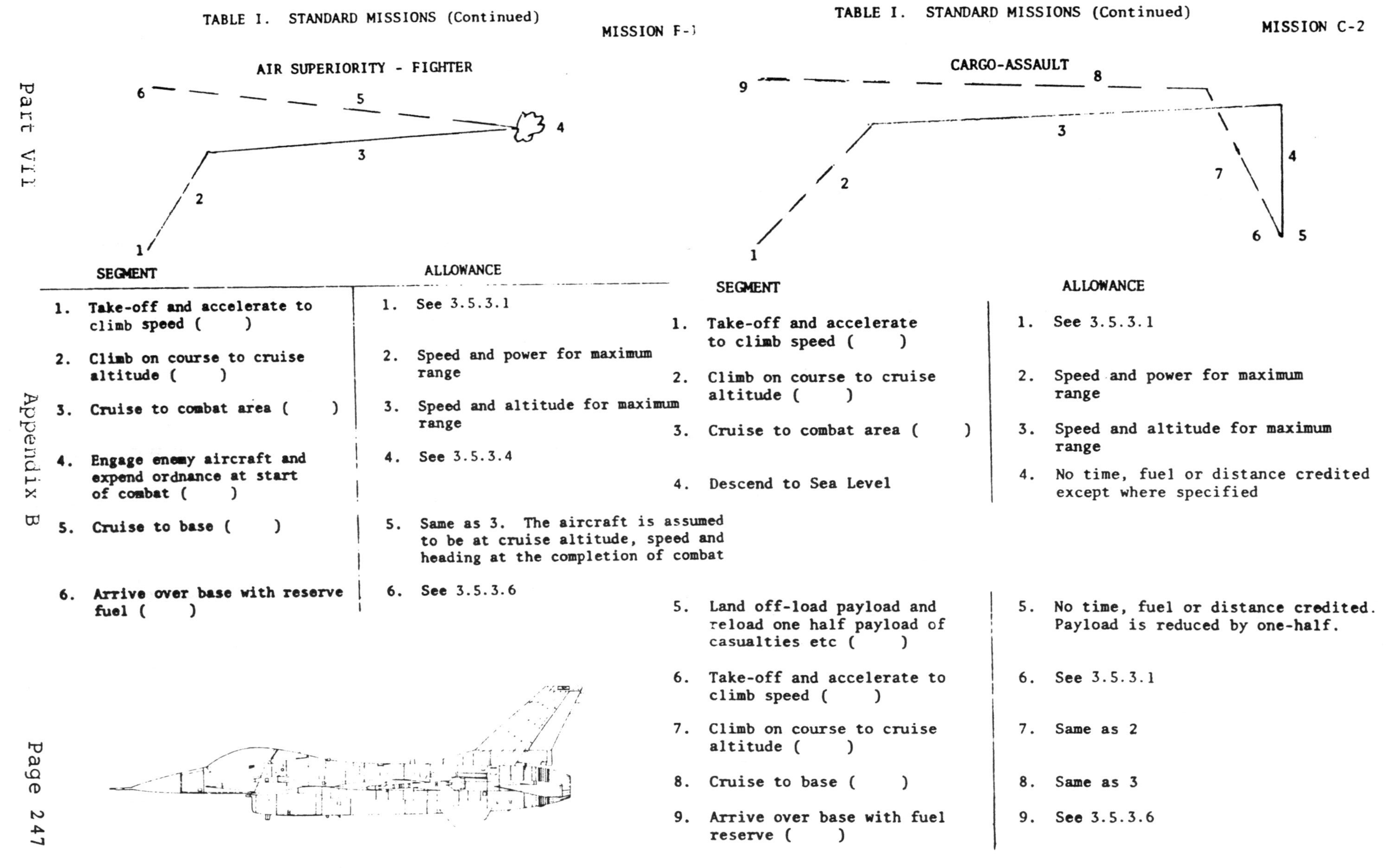

TABLE I. STANDARD MISSIONS (Continued)

MISSION F-1

AIR SUPERIORITY - FIGHTER

SEGMENT	ALLOWANCE
1. Take-off and accelerate to climb speed ( )	1. See 3.5.3.1
2. Climb on course to cruise altitude ( )	2. Speed and power for maximum range
3. Cruise to combat area ( )	3. Speed and altitude for maximum range
4. Engage enemy aircraft and expend ordnance at start of combat ( )	4. See 3.5.3.4
5. Cruise to base ( )	5. Same as 3. The aircraft is assumed to be at cruise altitude, speed and heading at the completion of combat
6. Arrive over base with reserve fuel ( )	6. See 3.5.3.6

TABLE I. STANDARD MISSIONS (Continued)

MISSION C-2

CARGO-ASSAULT

SEGMENT	ALLOWANCE
1. Take-off and accelerate to climb speed ( )	1. See 3.5.3.1
2. Climb on course to cruise altitude ( )	2. Speed and power for maximum range
3. Cruise to combat area ( )	3. Speed and altitude for maximum range
4. Descend to Sea Level	4. No time, fuel or distance credited except where specified
5. Land off-load payload and reload one half payload of casualties etc ( )	5. No time, fuel or distance credited. Payload is reduced by one-half.
6. Take-off and accelerate to climb speed ( )	6. See 3.5.3.1
7. Climb on course to cruise altitude ( )	7. Same as 2
8. Cruise to base ( )	8. Same as 3
9. Arrive over base with fuel reserve ( )	9. See 3.5.3.6

TABLE I. STANDARD MISSIONS (Continued)

MISSION T-2

TANKER - RENDEZVOUS

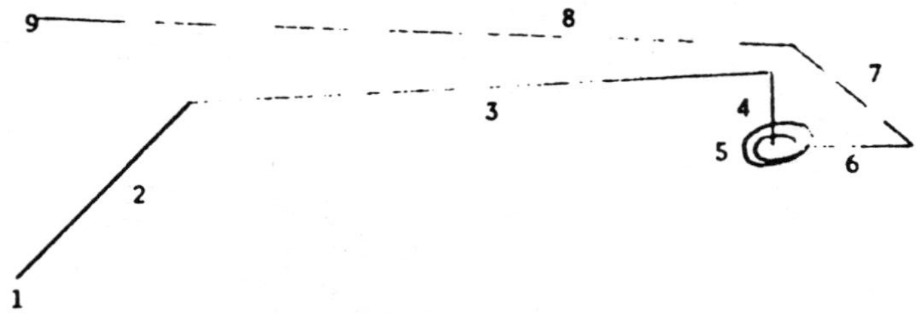

SEGMENT	ALLOWANCE
1. Take-off and accelerate to climb speed ( )	1. See 3.5.3.1
2. Climb on course to cruise altitude ( )	2. Speed and power for maximum range
3. Cruise to refuel point ( )	3. Speed and altitude for maximum range
4. Descend to specified altitude	4. No fuel, time or distance credited except where specified
5. Loiter 1 hour for rendezvous ( )	5. Fuel for 1 hour maximum endurance. No distance credited
6. Transfer fuel at speed for maximum continuous power ( )	6. Credit time, fuel and distance while transferring fuel at maximum rate. Segment performed at maximum continuous power
7. Climb on course to return cruise altitude ( )	7. Same as 2
8. Cruise to base	8. Same as 3
9. Arrive over base with reserve fuel ( )	9. See 3.5.3.6

Note: This mission is to present tanker capability without cons deration of a specific receiver.

TABLE I. STANDARD MISSIONS (Continued)

MISSION G-6

FERRY MISSION

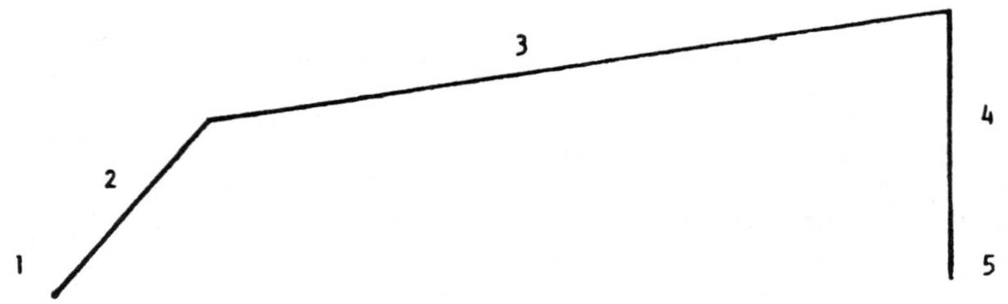

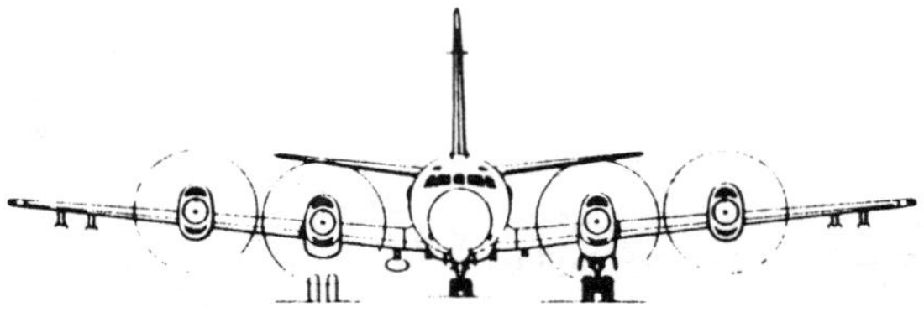

SEGMENT	ALLOWANCE
1. Take-off and accelerate to climb speed ( )	1. See 3.5.3.1
2. Climb on course to cruise altitude ( )	2. Speed and power for maximum range
3. Cruise to remote base	3. Speed and altitude for maximum range. Normally external fuel tanks shall be retained if carried.
4. Descent to sea level	4. No time, fuel or distance credited unless otherwise specified
5. Arrive over remote base with reserve fuel ( )	5. See 3.5.3.6

B1.2 AS-5263(USNAVY): Naval Air Systems Command Specification, Guidelines for the Preparation of Standard Aircraft Characteristics Charts and Performance Data, Piloted Aircraft (Fixed Wing), October 1986.

THIS SPECIFICATION HAS BEEN APPROVED BY THE
NAVAL AIR SYSTEMS COMMAND, DEPARTMENT OF THE NAVY

1. SCOPE.

1.1 SCOPE. This specification governs the definition of requirements for and methods of presenting characteristics and performance for Navy piloted fixed wing aircraft.

1.2 APPLICATION. For all piloted fixed wing aircraft proposed or contracted for subsequent to the effective date of this specification, characteristics and performance data shall be prepared and presented in accordance with the provisions of this specification and submitted to the Naval Air Systems Command for acceptance, unless specifically exempted by the Navy. Deviations from the provisions of this specification to portray more adequately the capability of certain aircraft are permissible, but shall in all cases be approved by the Naval Air Systems Command. Authorized deviations shall be fully explained through proper annotations on the data charts.

1.3 TYPES OF CHARTS. Characteristics and performance data shall be presented on the following types of charts as required by the Navy and utilizing formats as provided. Unauthorized reproduction of such charts is prohibited.

1.3.1 Standard Aircraft Characteristics Charts. The Standard Aircraft Characteristics (SAC) Charts are intended to provide Navy technical and staff personnel with a concise, accurate compilation of physical characteristics and performance capabilities of a weapon system. Standardization is required for convenience and to allow direct comparison with other weapon systems intended for a similar mission.

1.3.1.1 Arrangement. The Standard Aircraft Characteristics Chart is basically composed of ten pages with provisions for supplemental pages as required by the Naval Air Systems Command. If certain pages are not required for a specific weapon system, they shall be omitted and the remaining pages renumbered consecutively.

1.3.1.1.1 Basic. The normal arrangement of the Standard Aircraft Characteristics Chart shall be as follows (Refer to Sample SAC Chart in Appendix I):

a. Page 1. Cover sheet, which shall include a photograph or perspective drawing of the aircraft model in flight.

b. Page 2. A drawing showing a descriptive arrangement of the aircraft and a drawing showing the armament installations, the tankage installation, cargo space or interior arrangements as required by the Navy.

c. Page 3. Mission, description and principal characteristics of the aircraft.

d. Page 4. Performance data for the aircraft in tabulated form, with applicable notes.

e. Page 5. Auxiliary performance page, giving alternate loadings and the respective radii and associated performance, where applicable.

f. Page 6. Performance graphs. Speed, takeoff and landing distance, rates of climb, maneuverability, etc.

g. Page 7. Performance graphs. Trade-off curves as applicable.

h. Page 8. Carrier suitability graphs. Performance curves for catapulting, arresting, single engine climb, accelerations, approach speeds, and required Wind over Deck.

i. Page 9. External store loadings. Tabulated stores and stations on which they may be carried.

j. Page 10. Notes. Mission profiles, applicable allowances and explanatory notes.

1.3.1.1.2 Supplemental Pages. Aircraft characteristics and performance data not coming within the scope of the Standard Aircraft Characteristics Charts shall be presented on supplemental pages. Reasons for preparing supplemental pages may be as follows:

a. Possible special loadings or extreme overload conditions which may:

1. Be used in restricted tactical operations.
2. Involve non-standard procedures and special operating techniques.
3. Show the maximum potential use of certain aircraft in special missions.

b. Such loadings that may involve equipment which for security reasons are only suitable for limited distribution.

c. Theater operations involving non-standard atmospheric conditions.

d. To show inboard profiles, additional drawings, illustrations and graphs.

The supplemental page format should be the same as the Standard Aircraft Characteristics Chart or may consist of a special design suitable for binding along with the corresponding basic Standard Aircraft Characteristics Charts.

1.4 CATEGORIES. The foregoing charts shall be identified by categories to show the development status of the aircraft or data involved. All chart format shall be completed in full detail.

1.4.1 Proposal. Proposal data charts are intended to provide information during the evaluation of new designs, design studies and proposed modifications of existing designs and are primarily for limited distribution within the Navy.

1.4.2 Mock-Up. Mock-up charts are intended to provide information on new designs during the initial period from source selection to completion of mock-up. The initial mock-up chart need not include the effect of all design changes recommended by the Navy, but should contain under notes a complete list of major design changes.

1.4.3 Pre-Service. Pre-service charts are intended to provide information on new designs from the period of time from completion of mock-up to roll out of flight test article. Initial pre-service chart will normally be issued as soon after mock-up as the configuration and weight have stabilized to define the initial test article to be fabricated.

1.4.4 Service. Service data charts are intended to provide information on service models. Preparation of the initial issue of a chart on a service model shall normally be initiated not later than when the configuration and weight have stabilized following mock-up inspection. Thus, it may take the place of pre-service charts or may be delayed until after initial flight test if design changes are anticipated therefrom.

1.5 MARKINGS. Each of the foregoing chart types shall be marked as follows (Refer to Sample SAC Chart in Appendix I):

1.5.1 Designation. The military model designation or the contractor's model designation (in the case of charts in the proposal category) shall be shown on the lower outer corner.

1.5.2 Category. The chart category as defined in Paragraph 1.4 shall be shown on the upper outer corner.

1.5.3 Date. The date of publication will be inserted by the Navy on the lower inner corner.

1.5.4 Security. The security classification shall be specified by the Navy and shall be shown on center at top and bottom.

1.5.5 Chart Identification. The upper inner corner is to be used for chart identification. Identification number shall be obtained from the Navy prior to submission of the charts for approval.

2. APPLICABLE SPECIFICATIONS AND OTHER PUBLICATIONS.

The following publications (effective on the date of invitation for request for proposal) shall form a part of this specification to the extent specified herein:

2.1 SPECIFICATIONS AND PRIMARY PUBLICATIONS.

MILITARY

MIL-D-7822	DRAWINGS: FOR STANDARD AIRCRAFT CHARACTERISTICS AND PERFORMANCE CHARTS, PILOTED AIRCRAFT.
MIL-A-08860	AIRPLANE STRENGTH AND RIGIDITY; GENERAL SPECIFICATION FOR.
MIL-G-5572	FUEL; AVIATION GRADES 80/87, 100/130, 115/145 - 6.0 LBS/GAL.
MIL-T-5624	FUEL; AIRCRAFT TURBINE AND JET ENGINE, GRADES JP-4 - 6.5 LBS/GAL. AND JP-5 - 6.8 LBS/GAL.
MIL-T-83133	TURBINE FUEL, AVIATION, KEROSENE TYPE, GRADE JP-8 - 6.7 LBS/GAL.

MILITARY

MIL-F-8785C	FLYING QUALITIES OF PILOTED AIRPLANES.
MIL-M-85025(AS)	MANUALS, NATOPS FLIGHT; REQUIREMENTS FOR PREPARATION OF.
MIL-STD-210	CLIMATIC EXTREMES FOR MILITARY EQUIPMENT.
MIL-F-22203(AER)	PERFORMANCE DATA REPORT FOR STANDARD AIRCRAFT CHARACTERISTICS CHARTS FOR PILOTED AIRCRAFT.
MIL-STD-1374	WEIGHT AND BALANCE DATA REPORTING FORMS FOR AIRCRAFT (INCLUDING ROTORCRAFT).
MIL-W-25140	WEIGHT AND BALANCE CONTROL SYSTEM. (FOR AIRPLANES AND ROTORCRAFT).
OPNAVINST 3710.7	NATOPS GENERAL FLIGHT AND OPERATING INSTRUCTIONS.
NAVAIR 01-1B-40	NAVY TECHNICAL MANUAL OF WEIGHT AND BALANCE DATA.
NAVAIR 01-1B-50	NAVY TECHNICAL MANUAL, USN AIRCRAFT WEIGHT AND BALANCE CONTROL.
TECHNICAL ORDER 01-1B-40	AIR FORCE TECHNICAL MANUAL OF WEIGHT AND BALANCE DATA.

2.2 OTHER PUBLICATIONS. AS 2694. Engines, Aircraft, Turboshaft and Turboprop, General Specification for.

(Copies of specifications, standards and drawings required by contractors in connection with specific procurement functions should be obtained from the procuring agency or as directed by the contracting officer).

3. REQUIREMENTS.

3.1 GENERAL. Unless otherwise specified by the Navy, preparation by contractors of charts (and revision thereto) for each model shall include the preparation of photographically reproducible copy in the required types and categories, and, in addition, satisfactory reports containing supporting characteristics and performance data.

3.1.1 Revisions. Revisions to the charts shall be prepared and submitted by the contractor throughout the life of the contract unless specified otherwise by the Navy. Revisions are required whenever significant changes in vehicle configuration or data occur, as for example:

1. A change in vehicle dimensions.
2. An accumulation of weight changes resulting in a significant performance change (Paragraph 3.1.1.1).
3. A change in power plant designation, augmentation, or power plant rating.
4. The addition of external stores.
5. The availability of test data or new test data showing significant performance change (Paragraph 3.1.1.1).
6. When specifically directed by the Navy.

3.1.1.1 Criteria. The following criteria will be used in forming a judgement as to whether a significant change in performance exists:

1. A change of 5 percent or more in drag.
2. A change of 5 percent or more in installed thrust (power).
3. A change of 5 percent or more in specific fuel consumption.
4. A change in weight which in itself results in a 5 percent or greater change in mission radius or range.
5. Any combination of two or more of the above resulting in a change of 5 percent or more in mission radius or range.

3.1.1.2 Number. Each chart shall cover only one aircraft model. For the information of the contractor, the following guide is given regarding the probable number of charts and revisions thereto which are required throughout the life of the aircraft model. The exact number of revisions required will depend on the number of aircraft changes experienced.

CATEGORY OF CHART	REASON	BASIS FOR DATA
PROPOSAL	NEW DESIGN	ESTIMATED
MOCK-UP	CONTRACT FOR NEW AIRCRAFT	ESTIMATED
PRE-SERVICE	BETWEEN MOCK-UP AND FIRST FLIGHT	ESTIMATED
SERVICE	FLIGHT TEST	FLIGHT TEST
SERVICE (REVISION)	OPERATIONAL OR FLEET INTRODUCTION	FLIGHT TEST

3.2 STANDARD AIRCRAFT CHARACTERISTICS CHARTS.

3.2.1 Required Characteristic Data (Including Descriptive Detail). A sample Standard Aircraft Characteristics Chart is provided for reference in Appendix I.

3.2.1.1 Page 1. Cover Sheet. The cover sheet shall include a picture of the aircraft. In order of preference: A photograph of the aircraft in flight, a photograph of the aircraft on the ground, a photograph of a model, or an artist's conceptual drawing of the aircraft in flight. The photograph or drawing shall be of good contrast or permit satisfactory reproduction and should portray the distinguishing features of the aircraft. The photograph shall be glossy black and white and have dimensions not less than 5" x 8" and not greater than 7" x 11 1/2", not including the border. The aircraft model designation and the approved popular name shall be typeset using 24 point Futura Demibold or equivalent, centered below the title leaving a 1/2 inch space. One-half inch below the aircraft designation, center the contractor's name using 18 point Futura Demibold or equivalent.

3.2.1.2 Page 2. Drawings. The three-view drawings shall be drawn in ink on suitable drawing material and may be made oversize at whatever scale the manufacturer deems suitable. This over-size ink drawing shall then be photographically reduced and inserted on the appropriate block within the format sheet. Full advantage shall be taken of the space allotted so as to provide the largest three-view arrangement attainable within the 7 1/8" x 10 7/8" block in keeping with the positioning guidelines of paragraph 3.2.1.2.a and 3.2.1.2.b. The line weights used on the three-view drawings must be suitable to provide reproductionof the format page when reduced to 9 1/2" wide. All dimensions and text entered on this format page shall be typeset using 10 point Futura Medium or equivalent.

a. Descriptive arrangement drawing. In top of block give top view drawing; in middle of block give front view drawing; in bottom of block give side view drawings. Folded wings and extended tail hook shall be shown with dotted lines. Dimension in feet and fractions: wing span extended and folded, horizontal tail span, length, height, wheel base, wheel tread. A scale should be included. Describe wing airfoil shape at wing root and wing tip. Give wing planform area, mean aerodynamic chord (M.A.C.) and aspect ratio.

b. Armament and tankage drawing. In top of block give top view drawing; in middle of block give front view drawing; in bottom of block give side view drawing. Drawings shall be shown with external fuel tanks mounted. Internal fuel tank locations shall be shown by means of cross hatching. Tanks with survivability enhancements, i.e. foam, should be designated. Tank capacities shall be given. A scale should be included.

3.2.1.3 Page 3. Mission, Description and Principal Characteristics. The mission and description page shall include the information given below.

a. Mission and Description. The first paragraph in this block shall describe the primary and secondary missions of the aircraft. The second paragraph shall describe general design features, such as configuration, type of structure (use of composites, etc.), powered wing fold mechanism, etc. The third paragraph shall describe features of the propulsion and fuel systems, such as turbofan engine bypass ratio, number and capacity of external fuel tanks, self sealing fuel tanks, retractable refueling probe, etc. The fourth paragraph shall describe armament features, such as number of external store stations, gun caliber, forward looking IR, chaff dispensers, etc. The fifth paragraph shall describe control system features, such as type of high lift system, digital fly-by-wire, mechanical backup to primary control surfaces, rudder aileron interconnect, etc. The sixth paragraph shall describe avionic suite features, such as multi-mode radar, central digital computer, inertial navigation, etc. The seventh paragraph shall describe crew system features, such as ejection seat, anti-G system, etc.; if cabin is pressurized, the airplane altitude at which a 10,000 foot cabin altitude is reached shall be stated. Following the above descriptions, a sub-heading DEVELOPMENT shall give important dates: contract date, first flight, initial carrier sea trials, initial service date, etc.

b. Power Plant. Data to be listed shall include: number and model of engines, manufacturer, engine specification number, type, augmentation, length with afterburner, inlet diameter, dry weight, etc. If propellers are used, give the following data: manufacturer, propeller specification number, diameter, number of blades, gear ratio.

c. Ratings. Engine ratings shall include thrust or power, rpm, altitude(s) and time limits or deviations, as applicable. Engine ratings and auxiliary thrust device (ATD) ratings shall conform to those established in the officially approved engine specifications. Ratings with an augmentation shall be identified by note. If performance items are based on thrusts (powers) which differ appreciably from the listed specification ratings due to flight or engine laboratory test results or restrictions, such thrusts (powers) with explanations will be listed under notes. Reference to source of such thrust (power) shall be clearly stated in the performance data report.

d. Weight and Load Factors. The gross weights and the corresponding allowable load factors shall not exceed the limits established by the latest applicable technical orders, design requirements, or other specific recommendation of the Naval Air Systems Command. Maximum weights for which a mission is shown on the Standard Aircraft Characteristics Charts to illustrate maximum combat capabilities, but which may involve non-standard operating procedure and/or special operating techniques associated with such weight may be given, provided such weights are clearly identified with a note defining the limitations on usage. The following weights with corresponding load factors for both land based and carrier based aircraft as applicable, shall be given:

LOADING	POUNDS	LOAD FACTOR	REFERENCE
EMPTY			3.5.1.1
BASIC			3.5.1.2
DESIGN			3.5.1.4
COMBAT (BASIC MISSION)			3.5.1.6
MAXIMUM TAKEOFF			3.5.1.7.1
OVERLOAD MAXIMUM TAKEOFF			3.5.1.7.2
MAXIMUM IN-FLIGHT			3.5.1.8
MAXIMUM LANDING			3.5.1.9.2

NOTE:

Basis of Weight Data. The weights given shall correspond to the definitions of Paragraph 3.5.1. Weight empty shall be identified by the symbols "E": (estimated), "C": (calculated), or "A": (actual). As applicable, notation shall be made immediately below the takeoff weight of the immediate factor(s) limiting takeoff weight.

e. Fuel and Oil. The number of fuel and oil tanks, their usable capacities and locations, extent of self sealing provisions, together with grade and specification of fuel and oil used, shall be listed. Fuel tanks shall be grouped by fuel system.

f. Electronics. Sub-headings for airborne weapons control, electronic warfare, navigation and flight aids, communication and identification, control and display, and flight control shall be given. Under each sub-heading, list item and military model number in tabular form.

g. Ordnance. Data concerning the standard size and number of each type of droppable ordnance items such as bombs, torpedoes, mines, rockets, missiles and the maximum bomb load which may be accommodated by the aircraft. Ordnance carried externally shall be identified. The number and caliber of guns, the number of turrets, rounds of ammunition per gun, and the gun stations shall be listed.

h. Cargo. Maximum cargo load, clear space dimensions, limit floor loads, door size and location, usable cubage, etc. are to be given as applicable. Additional cargo information may be entered on a supplemental "NOTES" page.

i. Dimensions. Overall dimensions, in agreement with the general arrangement drawings of the basic aircraft in the three point position, such as length, height, width, maximum tread, and propeller ground clearance shall be given. Dimensions should be given in the wings folded and flight condition. Also include wing area and Aspect Ratio. Dimensions shall be given in feet and tenths of a foot.

3.2.1.4 Page 4. Performance Summary. Tabulated performance for the clean mission, basic mission, ferry mission, other typical missions (Paragraphs 3.5.10 to 3.5.10.4) shall include applicable loading and performance items. (See Page 4 of sample chart in Appendix I). Columns 1 and 2 of Page 4 are restricted to the clean and basic missions, as defined in Paragraph 3.5.10.1 and 3.5.10.2, respectively. Other columns, except the last column are restricted for the contractor's use in presenting performance data depicting the mission for which the vehicle was designed; requirement for compliance with ground rules outlined in this specification is waived for presentation of data on these typical missions (See Paragraph 3.5.10.5). Criteria (ground rules) for the typical missions shall be presented on Page 9. The last column used is restricted for use in depicting data for the Ferry Mission (See Paragraph 3.5.10.4).

a. The format of the performance summary page is shown on page I-4 in Appendix I. Show tabulated performance data for no more than six missions on each page. Data for all missions for which Navy requests are submitted shall be placed on the performance summary. A second performance summary page shall be used if the Navy requests data for more than 6 missions.

b. For each mission, divide the takeoff loading condition block into upper and lower sections; in the upper section give the name of the mission, in the lower section on the left side give the loading number in a circle, and to the right of that, show the missile, bomb and external tank loadings with the number of each item in parentheses. In the combat loading condition block on the left side, show the loading number in a circle, and to the right of that, describe the armament and external tank configuration (tanks off, missiles, retained, etc.). The takeoff loading condition for mission 1 is loading number 1; the combat loading condition for mission 1 is loading number 2; the takeoff loading condition for mission 2 is loading number 3; the combat loading condition for mission 2 is loading number 4; etc.

c. The space at the bottom of the page shall be used for footnotes lettered (A), (B), (C) etc. The applicability of the notes shall be shown by placing the appropriate letter behind the wording of the item affected; for example, the letter (A) placed behind the words "Takeoff Run at S.L." could be used along with the footnote, "(A) Intermediate Thrust (Power), Standard Day," to denote the thrust (power) setting for takeoff data. The last footnote shall be, "( ) Performance Basis: wind tunnel or flight test (as appropriate) followed by contractor's report number for the substantiating performance data report."

3.2.1.5 Page 5. Mission Summary - Alternate Loadings. For the basic mission and several secondary missions, show external store loading, takeoff gross weight, combat radius and mission time in tabular form. Data for various combinations of missiles, bombs, rocket packages and external fuel tanks shall be shown. Data should be given to demonstrate the capabilities of fighter, attack, patrol and anti-submarine warfare aircraft across a broad spectrum of loadings. Data may be given for missions not covered in the Performance Summary (Paragraph 3.2.1.4).

3.2.1.6 Page 6. Performance Graphs. Performance data shall be shown graphically on the appropriate grids provided. Curves shall not extend beyond any applicable limit.

a. Speed. As a function of altitude, plot maximum speed at basic mission combat weight with maximum, intermediate, and normal thrust (power), as applicable. Show maximum speed for several alternate mission loadings at the same power settings to show the effects of drag of significant external stores and/or important weight changes.

b. Climb. As a function of altitude, plot rate of climb at basic mission combat weight with maximum, intermediate, or normal thrust (power), as applicable. Show rates of climb for alternate loadings in order to show the effects of drag changes with various external stores and/or important weight changes. The effects of weight reduction during climb shall not be considered.

c. Takeoff. Plot gross weight versus takeoff distance for sea level, zero wind, standard day and tropical day. Show lines for ground run distance, total distance over 50-foot obstacle and critical field length.

d. Fourth Block. Data shown here should depend on type of aircraft. For fighter aircraft, show maneuverability; i.e. Mach number versus load factor in a constant altitude turn for the basic mission at a typical combat altitude; show load factor at various rates of longitudinal acceleration. For attack aircraft, patrol aircraft, anti-submarine aircraft, early warning aircraft and mission-dedicated electronic aircraft, show search time; i.e., radius versus time on station; show lines for basic mission and for several typical missions. For trainer aircraft, plot range versus cruise altitude; show lines for basic mission and for several typical missions. For cargo aircraft, plot range versus cargo weight; show lines for normal and overload takeoff gross weights. For tanker aircraft, plot radius versus pounds of fuel transferred; show data for loiter times of 0.5, 1.0, 1.5 hours, etc.

3.2.1.7 Page 7. Trade-Off Graphs.

a. This page shall contain up to four graphs, showing performance trade-offs for fighter, attack, patrol and anti-submarine warfare aircraft (See page I-7 of Appendix I).

b. The trade-offs shown may be selected from the following or be special graphs designed by the contractor to more aptly display the capabilities of the aircraft: combat radius versus combat time, combat radius versus combat patrol time, combat radius versus dash radius, combat radius versus combat loiter time. On each graph, lines for several loadings from the Performance Summary (Paragraph 3.2.1.4) shall be given.

3.2.1.8 Page 8. Carrier Suitability Graphs.

a. For carrier based aircraft, performance graphs are required as follows: gross weight versus minimum wind over deck required for catapulting shown for catapult gear selected by the Navy, gross weight versus minimum wind over deck required for arrestment shown for arresting gear selected by the Navy, gross weight versus single engine rate of climb at V_{PA} approach speed, gross weight versus V_{PA} and versus V_{SPA} stall speed at approach power. Both standard and tropic day values shall be shown.

3.2.1.9 Page 9. External Store Loadings.

a. This page shall contain a simplified front view drawing of the aircraft with landing gear retracted showing external store stations. Under the drawing, a table shall be given with columns numbered corresponding to external store stations. The left hand column of the table shall contain a list of all possible external stores. Within the table, the number of each external store that can be carried at each external store station shall be given with the number 1, 2, etc.

3.2.1.10 Page 10. Notes.

a. For each mission, a sketch shall be given showing combat radius versus altitude with lines drawn showing climb, cruise to target, action over target, return cruise and descent. Altitude at significant points shall be called out in feet.

b. Above each sketch, the name of the mission shall be given with notes underneath. Notes for a typical mission are as follows:

1. For Taxi, warmup, takeoff and acceleration to best climb speed: Fuel allowance equal to 4.6 minutes at intermediate thrust plus 30 seconds afterburner thrust if afterburner is used for takeoff.

2. CLIMB: On course at best climb speed at intermediate thrust to best cruise altitude (not to exceed cruise ceiling).

3. CRUISE OUT: At speeds and altitudes for best range, using a cruise climb flight path (not to exceed cruise ceiling).

4. DESCENT: Descend to sea level (no fuel used, no distance gained).

5. COMBAT: Fuel allowance equal to 5 minutes at maximum speed with intermediate thrust at sea level. No distance is credited (drop bombs, retain mounting hardware and missiles after combat).

6. CLIMB: On course at best climb speed at intermediate thrust from sea level to best cruise altitude (not to exceed cruise ceiling).

7. CRUISE BACK: At speeds and altitudes for best range, using a cruise climb flight path (not to exceed cruise ceiling).

8. DESCENT: Descend to sea level (no fuel used, no distance gained).

9. RESERVE: Fuel allowance equal to 20 minutes loiter at sea level at speeds for maximum endurance with all engines operating plus 5% of initial total fuel (internal plus external).

   a. Mission Time: Items 2 through 8.
   b. Cycle Time: Items 2 through 9.

3.3 SUBSTANTIATING DATA. All data presented on the charts shall be substantiated by reports which shall be submitted with the charts. The reports may be in legible rough draft form utilizing the contractor's worksheet copy, but they shall be complete and shall contain a list of adequate references, authority and justification for all data used. Contractors are free to use calculation methods of their own selection, but such methods shall be fully explained and sample calculations shall be given. Calculations shall be presented in sufficient detail to permit ready review and check of conclusions and to enable additional calculations to be made by the Navy as required.

3.3.1 Basic Aerodynamic Data Report. Prior to preparation of the formal Substantiating Data Report, the approval of the Navy shall be obtained for the data which will form the basis for the Standard Aircraft Characteristics Charts. These basic data, including adequate calculations and material for verification shall include those data described in Appendix II of this report. Data not accepted by the Navy shall be replaced after conference with the contractor by similar data to be designated by the Navy.

3.3.1.1 Revisions. The Basic Aerodynamic Data Report shall be revised under the same criteria as the charts (Paragraph 3.1.1).

3.3.2 Substantiating Performance Data Report. The Basic Aerodynamic Data (Paragraph 3.3.1) shall, after verification and approval by the Navy, form the basis for the detailed preparation of the formal Substantiating Data Report. These data shall be expanded as necessary and used to prepare the detailed performance data required to substantiate the validity of the Standard Aircraft Characteristics Charts. The Substantiating Data Report also serves as the data base for the Naval Air Training and Operating Procedures Standardization (NATOPS) Flight Manual.

3.3.2.1 Revisions. The substantiating data report shall be revised under the same criteria as the charts (Paragraph 3.1.1).

3.3.2.2 Text. The arrangement of the substantiating data report shall be arranged as shown in Appendix III.

3.4 STANDARDS. Characteristics and performance data shall be based on practical engineering analysis which produce results consistent with flight test results of vehicles of like types using standard operating procedures.

3.4.1 Basis for Data. All characteristics and performance data shall be based on the latest reliable aerodynamic, power plant and weight information available. The information given shall include the effect on weight and/or performance of all authorized contract and service changes, together with important changes assured of authorization but pending at the date of chart issue.

3.4.1.1 Changes in Characteristics. Changes in aircraft characteristics which do not result in a significant performance change (Paragraph 3.1.1) need not be justification for a revision by the contractor. However, the Navy shall be notified by correspondence so that proper notation may be appended to the published chart.

3.4.1.2 Flight Tests. Latest approved flight test data shall be used, as soon as available, as a basis for performance. While official military flight test results are to be preferred, contractor flight test results shall be considered, provided:

1. The contractor submits his method of flight test, instrumentation used and analysis leading to reduction of test results to standard conditions for review and approval by the Navy.

2. Specific "raw" test data and data reduced to standard conditions are provided to the Navy for approval prior to use in chart preparation.

3.4.1.3 Guarantees. The data quoted need not necessarily reflect contractor's aircraft performance guarantees.

3.4.2 Limitations. Performance data shall fall within all established limitations on the vehicle and its components, except as specifically provided herein.

3.4.3 Aircraft Condition. Performance shall be presented in such a manner as to show clearly the applicable aerodynamic configuration, power plant and loading information. Aircraft configurations shall include the installation of complete service equipment applicable to that particular aircraft model for the mission concerned. No special sealing of doors or cracks, filling of seams, waxing, or polishing shall be allowed, unless this is standard practice and is so stated on the charts. Flight performance shall be presented with guns, rotatable enclosures, bomb bay doors, etc., in position of least drag, retractable enclosures and wheels in retracted or closed position and external bombs or other armament in position for each condition, as noted. Fuel loadings shall comprise only those for which service approval has been obtained.

3.4.4 Atmosphere. Performance shall be based on the latest approved standard atmospheric tables as specified by the Navy.

3.4.4.1 Standard Day. Unless otherwise specified, performance shall be based on the latest approved ICAO standard atmosphere (59°F @ S.L.) as tabulated and described in Appendix IV.

3.4.4.2 Non-Standard Day. Unless otherwise specified, non-standard day performance shall be based on MIL-STD-210 Tropical (89.8°F @ S.L.) and Hot (103°F @ S.L.) conditions tabulated and described in Appendix IV.

3.5 DEFINITIONS. The following definitions are used for the various data on the charts and shall be strictly adhered to.

3.5.1 Weights. Weights used in preparation of and presented on the charts shall conform with the following definitions and be consistent with MIL-STD-1374, MIL-W-25140 and Technical Manual 01-1B-40.

3.5.1.1 Weight Empty. The weight empty condition shall be as defined in the latest model detail specification (does not include crew, fuel, armament, cargo, bombs, disposable or special equipment). The empty weight to be used in preparation of the SAC Chart shall be, in order of preference, the actual empty weight, the latest available calculated or estimated empty weight.

3.5.1.2 Basic Weight. Configuration for operating purposes, as defined in Technical Manual of Weight and Balance Data, NAVAIR 01-1B-40 and AIR FORCE Technical Order 01-1B-40 (empty weight plus trapped fuel and all fixed armament and equipment for normal operation).

3.5.1.3 Operating Weight. Zero fuel and zero payload weight - a convenience weight to which operators need add only fuel and payload for gross weight. (Basic weight plus crew and any special equipment that may be required. Does not include usable fuel, ammo, bombs, or auxiliary fuel tanks if such tanks are to be dropped in flight).

3.5.1.4 Design Weight. Weight at which specified flight structural design requirements are met or are required to be met.

3.5.1.5 Ramp Weight. Maximum in-flight weight unrefueled plus fuel, water, etc., used during takeoff. Shall not exceed other limits, such as maximum taxi weight, ground handling, wheel jacking, etc.; as specified in MIL-A-008860.

3.5.1.6 Combat Weight. Weight over the target for the mission presented with fuel, ammunition (including missile ordnance) used for air-to-air combat but without bombs, missiles (used for attack of surface targets), torpedoes, mines, cargo or droppable tanks unless otherwise noted.

1. For aircraft without external tanks, fuel load shall be 60 percent of initial usable fuel.

2. For aircraft with external drop tanks, fuel load shall be 60 percent of initial usable fuel load, or full internal fuel, whichever is less.

3.5.1.7 Takeoff Weight. Takeoff weight is the total weight of the aircraft with the fuel and payload for the mission presented. The takeoff weight normally shall be determined prior to start of engines, except in specially approved cases when weight expended during taxi and takeoff are excluded (Paragraph 3.5.1.5). Takeoff weight shall not exceed maximum takeoff weight.

3.5.1.7.1 Maximum Takeoff Weight. Maximum takeoff weight is the greatest weight for takeoff established by Technical Orders, design requirements, or other specific recommendations of the Navy.

3.5.1.7.2 Overload. Unless otherwise specified by the Navy, the maximum (overload) takeoff weight shall not exceed the least determined by the following:

a. The weight of the aircraft fully loaded with fuel, bombs and cargo to capacity for which space and/or tankage is normally provided. Bearing capacity for the floor and/or supporting structure shall not be exceeded. The expendable weight of ATD and water used for takeoff may be added to the quoted maximum takeoff weight provided the criteria of Paragraph 3.5.1.7.2.b is satisfied and a qualifying note appears on the chart.

b. The aircraft and its components (wing, landing gear, supporting structure for ordnance, cargo, etc.) shall sustain at least a 2.0g normal load factor for each phase of operation and shall meet the minimum criteria of the applicable specifications for taxi and ground handling (MIL-A-008860).

c. The maximum rate of climb at Sea Level altitude under standard atmospheric conditions shall not be less than 500 ft/min with all engines operating at normal (maximum continuous) rating.

d. For multi-engine aircraft without ejection seats, the rate of climb with one engine inoperative at Sea Level altitude under standard atmospheric conditions shall not be less than 100 ft/min at the 50 feet obstacle, out of ground effect, in takeoff configuration and at maximum takeoff engine rating minus easily jettisonable items (i.e., external fuel tanks and bombs). For multi-engine aircraft with ejection seats, the required rate of climb will depend on the mission and will be specified by the Naval Air Systems Command.

e. Throughout the flight, the center of gravity shall remain within the limits for satisfactory ground handling and flight.

f. Such other criteria as may be specified by the Navy for the specific aircraft model presented.

g. The following takeoff criteria will be based on Sea Level altitude and standard atmospheric conditions:

1. For all vehicles (single and multi-engine), critical field length shall not exceed 8,000 feet.
2. The maximum tow force for carrier operation and maximum acceptable wind-over-deck, as defined by the Naval Air Systems Command, shall not be exceeded.

3.5.1.7.3 Normal. The maximum (normal takeoff weight) shall not exceed the least weight determined by criteria of Paragraph 3.5.1.7.2 and the following additional criteria:

a. For multi-engine aircraft without ejection seats, the maximum thrust (power) rate of climb with one engine inoperative (propeller feathered or rotor windmilling) shall not be less than 100 ft/min at takeoff speed, in takeoff configuration at sea level under a 103°F atmospheric temperature minus easily jettisonable items (i.e., external fuel tanks and bombs). For multi-engine aircraft with ejection seats, the required rate of climb will depend on the mission and will be specified by the Naval Air Systems Command.

b. The aircraft shall be capable of cruising at airspeeds of maximum range at 5,000 feet altitude (pressure) on a 103°F day with power not exceeding 70 percent of normal (maximum continuous) rating for reciprocating engines and 85 percent for gas turbine engines.

c. The takeoff distance over 50 feet height at sea level on a 103°F day shall not exceed 10,000 feet.

3.5.1.8 Maximum In-Flight Weight. Weight at which the aircraft is authorized to be airborne. It is possible to be greater than maximum takeoff weight if in-flight refueling is utilized.

3.5.1.9 Landing Weight.

3.5.1.9.1 Normal. The weight as determined by the computation of the mission ground rules. It shall include the fuel reserve as specified in Paragraph 3.6.4.

3.5.1.9.2 Maximum. Maximum landing weight is the greatest weight established for landing by flight restrictions, detailed specifications, or specific recommendations of the Navy.

3.5.1.10 Payload. The load which justifies the mission. Payload includes cargo, personnel other than crew (passengers), bombs, chaff, missiles (offensive and decoy), reconnaissance cameras, photo flash flares, bombs, fuel carried for transfer by tankers, ammunition and air-to-air missiles carried by fighter aircraft and gunnery trainers. Special equipment required for the mission, such as winterization, rescue equipment (except that carried for drop by "H" type aircraft [search-rescue]), cargo handling, etc., shall not be included in payload. The maximum zero fuel weight limitations must be observed when selecting payload.

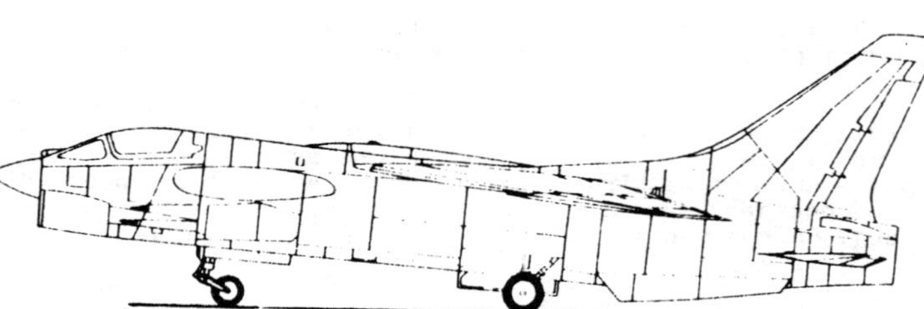

3.5.1.11 Weight Definition Guide. For the information of the contractor, the following guide (ref. MIL-W-25140) is given to the above weight definitions:

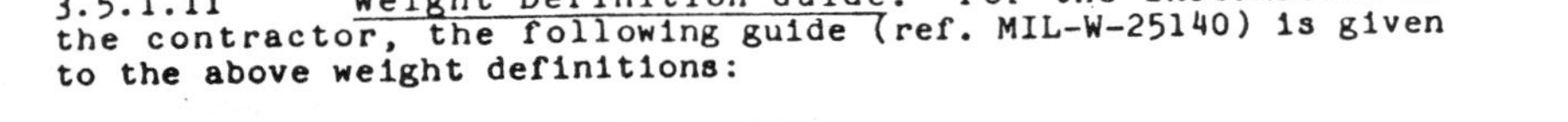

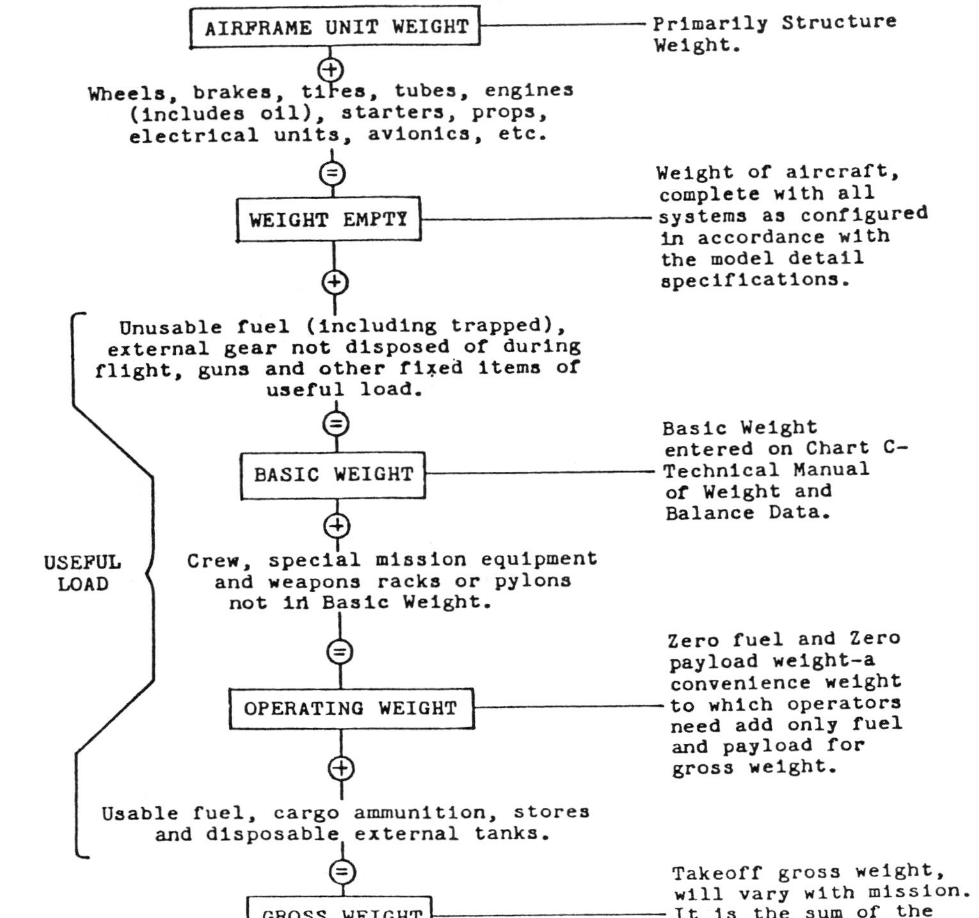

3.5.1.12 Fuel. Standard weight of fuel in pounds per U.S. gallon shall be as follows:

a. MIL-G-5572, Gasoline in all grades - 6.0 lbs/gal.

b. MIL-T-5624, JP-4, Jet Fuel - 6.5 lbs/gal.

c. MIL-T-5624, JP-5, Jet Fuel - 6.8 lbs/gal.

d. MIL-T-83133, JP-8, Jet Fuel - 6.7 lbs/gal.

3.5.2 Speed. All speeds shall be true airspeeds in knots and Mach number as applicable (Mach number for jet aircraft, true airspeed for propeller aircraft).

3.5.2.1 Maximum Speed. Highest speed obtainable in level flight. State the weight, altitude and engine-power rating. Such maximum speed shall be within all operating restrictions (i.e., thrust, structural, heating limitations), with the limiting restriction noted. For the Performance Summary, maximum speed shall be at specified weight, maximum thrust (power) and the altitude for best speed (or Navy designated conditions).

3.5.2.1.1 Level Flight Maximum Speed (V_H). The maximum speed attainable at the basic flight design gross weight in the basic configuration in level flight with maximum available thrust (power) including use of afterburners, rocket thrust augmentation considering engine limitations, or afterburners and rocket thrust augmentation considering engine limitations, whichever is applicable.

3.5.2.1.2 Limit Speed (V_L). For the basic and high drag configurations, the maximum attainable speed commensurate with the operational use of the airplane considering shallow and steep dive angles, thrust, operation and nonoperation of speed brakes, and inadvertent upsets from gusts.

3.5.2.2 Combat Speed. Highest speed obtainable in level flight at combat weight with maximum thrust (power) at combat altitude.

3.5.2.3 Stall Speed. The stall speed shall be computed on the basis of 1.0g flight with the maximum trimmed lift coefficient established by computation or wind tunnel testing. Upon availability of flight test results, stall speed shall be changed to the highest of the speeds for steady straight 1.0g flight at C_L maximum, the speed at which abrupt loss of control occurs about any of the pitch, roll or yaw axes, the speed at which intolerable buffet or structural vibration is encountered, or other minimum permissible speed as defined in MIL-F-8785.

3.5.2.3.1 Power-Off. The stall speed without thrust (power) or, if significantly affected, with flight idle thrust (power).

3.5.2.3.2 Power-On. The stall speed using approach power which is defined as the thrust (power) required for level flight at 1.15 times the power-off stall speed in the landing configuration (Reference MIL-F-8785C).

3.5.2.4 Takeoff Speed

3.5.2.4.1 Takeoff Speed Criteria. Takeoff speed shall be the highest of the speeds specified by the following:

a. 1.1 times the speed represented by 90 percent maximum lift coefficient, power-on, including ground effects in the takeoff configuration.

b. A speed determined by the lift coefficient, in ground effect, for the maximum angle of attack attainable with the main landing gear oleo in the static position with aircraft on ground.

c. Minimum speed at which the aircraft has a climb gradient potential of 1/2 percent (0.005), with takeoff thrust (power), in the takeoff configuration, out-of-ground effect. For multi-engine aircraft, this potential shall be obtainable with the most critical engine inoperative (with rotor windmilling or propeller feathered). Where;

$$\text{gradient} = \frac{[\text{Vertical Height in Climb (ft)}]}{[\text{Horizontal Distance in Climb (ft)}]} \quad (1)$$

d. 1.05 times air minimum control speed as specified in Paragraph 3.5.2.8.2.

e. The speed which permits attaining obstacle climb-out speed, as defined in Paragraph 3.5.2.6, at or before reaching 50 feet height above the runway.

3.5.2.4.1.1 Typical Design Criteria. For design purposes, consideration may be made of alternate definitions of takeoff speed such as: a higher or lower percentage of stall speed, a higher climb gradient potential or other criteria which optimizes the design.

3.5.2.4.2 Refusal Speed. The maximum speed during takeoff which will allow the aircraft to stop within the available remaining runway length.

3.5.2.5 Catapult End Airspeed (V_C). The airspeed required at the end of the catapult stroke to support the airplane under the conditions of attitude, lift, and longitudinal acceleration specified for catapulting. An example would be where the c.g. position of the aircraft shall sink no more than 10 feet from its position at the end of the power stroke, with a deck run not to exceed 32 feet (distance from the end of the power stroke to round-down), without exceeding the angle of attack for 0.9 $C_{L_{max}}$, power off, and with cockpit control position fixed for a specified loading, weight and thrust (power) setting. The aircraft is also required to have a longitudinal acceleration of $a/g > .065$ at zero flight path angle at the catapult end airspeed.

3.5.2.6 Obstacle Climb-Out Speed. The climb speed at the 50-foot obstacle shall not be less than the highest of the speeds specified below.

a. 1.2 times power-off stall speed with flaps in takeoff position, landing gear retracted.

b. 1.1 times air minimum control speed.

c. Speed at which the aircraft has a climb gradient of 2.5 percent (0.025) with gear up, flaps in takeoff position, with maximum thrust (power), out-of-ground effect. For multi-engine aircraft, this potential shall be obtainable with the most critical engine inoperative (rotor windmilling or propeller feathered).

d. If gear retraction results in a transient drag increase over that for gear down, the speed at which the aircraft has a 1/2 percent (0.005) climb gradient potential with flaps in takeoff setting, gear in transit, with maximum thrust (power) out-of-ground effect. For multi-engine aircraft, the most critical engine shall be inoperative (with propeller feathered or rotor windmilling).

3.5.2.7 Climb Speed. The climb speed shall be the airspeed at which the optimum rate-of-climb is attained for the given configuration, weight, altitude and power. Consideration shall be made for kinetic energy corrections in optimizing the climb speed schedule. When authorized in the applicable Flight Manual, a simplified, non-optimum speed schedule may be used.

3.5.2.8 Critical Engine Failure Speed. The critical engine failure speed shall be the speed occurring during the takeoff run at which an engine can fail and the same distance is required to either continue the takeoff to lift off or to stop the aircraft.

3.5.2.9 Minimum Engine-Out Control Speed.

3.5.2.9.1 Ground. The minimum control speed, ground, shall be the minimum speed during the takeoff run where the engine most critical to directional stability can fail and directional control can be maintained.

3.5.2.9.2 Air. The minimum control speed, air, shall be the minimum airborne speed with maximum thrust (power) where the engine most critical to stability can fail and control can be maintained under the conditions specified in MIL-F-8785.

3.5.2.10 Cruise Speed.

3.5.2.10.1 Maximum Range Cruise Speed. The speed for maximum range operation shall be the speed at which maximum nautical miles per pound of fuel are attainable at the momentary weight and altitude conditions.

3.5.2.10.2 Long Range Cruise Speed. The higher of the two airspeeds which give nautical miles per pound of fuel equal to 99 percent of the maximum nautical miles per pound of fuel for momentary weight and altitude unless otherwise limited by handling characteristics. For propeller driven aircraft, long range cruise speed is used in lieu of maximum range cruise speed.

3.5.2.10.3 Maximum Cruise Speed. The highest speed that can be maintained with stated thrust (power), altitude, weight and configuration.

3.5.2.10.4 Average Cruise Speed. Total distance covered in cruise divided by time for cruise (distance and time for climb, acceleration to combat speed, combat time and loiter time are not included).

3.5.2.11 Loiter Speed

3.5.2.11.1 Maximum Endurance (Loiter) Speed. The airspeed for maximum endurance shall correspond to the speed for minimum fuel flow attainable at momentary weight and altitude, except as limited by acceptable handling characteristics of the aircraft.

3.5.2.11.2 Combat Loiter Speed. The airspeed for combat loiter shall correspond to the speed for minimum fuel flow attained at momentary weight and altitude, except that the airspeed must be adequate to allow an instantaneous load factor of a specified value.

3.5.2.11.3 Corner Speed. The lowest airspeed at which the lift and structural lines intersect. This is the speed at which the maximum turn rate and minimum turn radius exists for the specified altitude.

3.5.2.12 Landing Speed. The landing speed shall be determined by the maximum angle of attack attainable with the main landing gear oleo strut positioned for the static condition. The landing speed shall not be less than 110 percent of power-off stall speed for the landing configuration. The speed over a 50-foot height shall be at least 120 percent of power-off stall speed in the landing configuration.

3.5.2.13 Landing Touchdown Speed. For design purposes landing touchdown speed is that speed equal to 1.05 times approach speed. For operational aircraft, landing touchdown speed will be determined using fleet survey data.

3.5.2.13.1 Approach Speed. With the aircraft in the landing configuration and on a 4° glide slope on a 89.8°F day, the minimum usable approach speed V_{PAMIN}, shall be the highest of the airspeeds defined by the following:

a. The lowest speed at which it is possible to achieve a level flight longitudinal acceleration of 5 ft/sec^2 within 2.5 seconds after initiation of throttle movement and speed brake retraction.

b. V_{SPA} x 1.1 where V_{SPA} is the power-on stall speed using the thrust (power) required for level flight at 1.15 V_{SL}, the power-off stall speed.

c. The lowest level flight speed at which the pilot, at the design eye position, can see the stern of the carrier at the waterline when intercepting a 4° glide slope at an altitude of 600 feet. The origin of the glide slope is 500 feet forward of the stern and 63 feet above the waterline.

d. The lowest speed at which all stability and control requirements are satisfied (MIL-F-8785).

e. The lowest speed at which the aircraft is capable of making a glide path correction from stabilized flight at V_{PAMIN} to a new glide path 50 feet above the original glide path within five (5) seconds after initiation of the maneuver. The maneuver shall be performed without change in thrust settings, and the aircraft angle of attack during the maneuver shall not exceed that necessary to achieve 50 percent of the maximum positive delta load factor available, based on static lift coefficient, at the initiation of the maneuver. Control rate input for simulation of V_{PAMIN} shall not exceed control system limits. The maneuver shall be considered complete when a glide path correction of 50 feet has been reached. After completion of this maneuver, the aircraft shall be capable of maintaining a new glide path at least 50 feet above and parallel to the initial glide path, with the pilot permitted to change thrust setting as required.

f. To insure rapid aircraft response to step throttle commands corresponding to + 3.86 ft/sec^2 longitudinal acceleration, such throttle inputs shall result in achieving 90 percent of the commanded acceleration within 1.2 seconds. This requirement shall apply in the approach configuration throughout the range of all throttle settings required for operations over the usable approach configuration weight/drag levels while trimmed on a 4° glide slope.

Note: Control rate input for simulation of V_{PAMIN} shall not exceed control system limits. Calculation of V_{PAMIN} shall be based on static lift coefficient.

3.5.3 Ceiling

3.5.3.1 Service Ceiling. Service ceiling is that altitude at which the rate of climb at subsonic speed is 100 ft/min at stated loading, weight and engine thrust (power).

3.5.3.2 Combat Ceiling.

3.5.3.2.1 Subsonic Vehicles. Combat ceiling for subsonic vehicles is that altitude at which the rate of climb is 500 ft/min at the stated loading, weight and thrust (power).

3.5.3.2.2 Supersonic Vehicles. Combat ceiling for supersonic vehicles is the highest altitude at which the vehicle can fly supersonically and have a 500 ft/min rate of climb at the stated loading, weight and thrust (power).

3.5.3.3 Cruise Ceiling

3.5.3.3.1 Subsonic Vehicles. Cruise ceiling for subsonic cruise vehicles is that altitude at which the rate of climb is 300 ft/min at normal (maximum continuous) engine rating at stated weight and loading.

3.5.3.3.2 Supersonic Vehicles. Cruise ceiling for supersonic cruise vehicles is that altitude at which the rate of climb is 300 ft/min at normal (maximum continuous) engine rating at stated weight and loading.

3.5.4 Altitude.

3.5.4.1 Cruise Altitude. The cruise altitude is the altitude at which the cruise portion of the missions is computed. Depending on the mission ground rules, the cruise altitude may be assigned. Otherwise, it is governed by the following limitations: for pressurized aircraft, cruise ceiling shall not exceed the altitude where cabin altitude is 10,000 feet. For unpressurized aircraft with oxygen masks, cruise ceiling shall not exceed 20,000 feet (Reference OPNAVINST 3710.7K Paragraph 714). In no case shall cruise altitude exceed cruise ceiling.

3.5.4.2 Optimum Cruise Altitude. The altitude at which the aircraft attains the maximum nautical miles per pound of fuel for the momentary weight and configuration. If this altitude exceeds cruise ceiling, the latter shall be used for cruise.

3.5.4.3 Combat Altitude. Combat altitude is the altitude at the target for the specific mission shown.

3.5.5 Takeoff. Criteria for conventional takeoff aircraft shall comply with the following: (For STOL aircraft the criteria shall be determined by design criteria.) (Vertical components of thrust may be used in takeoff computation.)

3.5.5.1 Ground Run Distance (i.e., Takeoff Distance). Takeoff ground run distance shall be that normally obtainable in service operation at Sea Level with standard atmospheric conditions, zero wind, no runway slope on hard (concrete or asphalt) surfaced runways. For estimated data, the takeoff speed criteria of Paragraph 3.5.2.4 shall be used.

3.5.5.1.1 Typical Design Criteria. For design purposes, consideration may be made of alternate definitions of takeoff ground run such as: non-standard atmospheric conditions, higher pressure altitudes, alternate runway surfaces (hard, sod, etc.), head or tail-wind or other criteria in keeping with the operational concept of the design.

3.5.5.2 Distance To 50 Feet. The distance to clear a 50-foot obstacle shall be the sum of takeoff ground run distance of 3.5.5.1 plus the airborne distance required to accelerate and climb to arrive at the 50-foot height at the speed specified in 3.5.2.6.

3.5.5.3 Takeoff Time. The takeoff time shall be that normally obtainable in service operation at Sea Level under standard day atmospheric conditions with no wind. The time is measured from start of takeoff (brake release) to start of enroute climb (attainment of climb speed).

3.5.5.4 Critical Field Length. Critical field length is defined as the total length of runway required to accelerate on all engines to the critical engine failure speed, experience an engine failure, and either continue to takeoff or stop.

3.5.5.4.1 Data Basis. The data basis for the computation of the stopping distance for critical field length shall be as follows:

a. At engine failure speed, the aircraft continues to accelerate for 3 seconds with remaining engine(s) operating at maximum thrust (power) and with zero thrust on the inoperative engine.

b. At the end of the 3-second acceleration time, thrust (power) on all engines is instantaneously reduced to idle, brakes applied and deceleration devices deployed.

c. Sufficient time after b, above, shall be allowed for deployment of the deceleration device(s) or for reverse thrust to reach maximum before including its effect on deceleration.

3.5.5.5 Coefficient of Friction. The coefficient, μ, as used in this document is defined as the ratio of the total retardation force attributable to the braking system to the momentary gross weight of the aircraft (momentary gross weight defined as weight on wheels which is weight minus lift). The following values will be used unless ground or flight test data are available.

3.5.5.5.1 Rolling. The rolling (unbraked) coefficient of friction for a dry, hard runway shall be equal to 0.025.

3.5.5.5.2 Braking. The braking coefficient of friction for a dry, hard runway shall be equal to 0.3. Application of anti-skid criteria will be specified by the Navy.

3.5.5.5.3 Test Data. Test μ values may be either the results of tests conducted on the specific aircraft or similar types, i.e. commerical aircraft.

3.5.5.5.4 Typical Design Criteria. For design purposes, the following coefficient of friction values should be used for the conditions specified on a hard surfaced runway:

RUNWAY CONDITION	ROLLING UNBRAKED	BRAKES	ANTI-SKID BRAKES
Dry	.025	.30	.38
Wet (Rain)	.05	.14	.20
Snow	.09	.10	.15
Ice	.05	.07	.09

3.5.6 Climb. Climb after takeoff may be divided into two segments: initial climbout and enroute climb.

3.5.6.1 Initial Climb-Out. Climb-out shall be at a speed which shall not be less than that limited by the criteria of 3.5.2.6. Gear retraction shall be initiated as soon as an adequate positive climb gradient (3.5.2.6.c and d), using applicable power, has been established and maintained while accelerating to climb-out speed. Flaps shall be in the takeoff position. Enroute climb speed shall be reached at a height no greater than 1,000 feet above ground.

3.5.6.1.1 All Engines Operating. Initial climb-out with all engines operating shall be based on all engines operating from brake release to takeoff. Acceleration to climb-out speed and climb-out shall be based on the thrust (power) available with all available engines.

3.5.6.1.2 One Engine Inoperative. Initial climb-out with one engine inoperative shall be based on all engines operating from brake release to critical engine failure speed and with the critical engine inoperative from critical engine failure speed to takeoff. Acceleration to climb-out speed and climb-out shall be based upon the thrust (power) available with the remaining engines at takeoff thrust (power) and the drag of the inoperative engine. If means of reducing drag of the inoperative engine are a design feature, such drag reduction shall be utilized with a time allowance for activation.

3.5.6.2 Enroute Climb. Except for point intercept missions, all climbs shall be enroute with thrust (power) and speed schedules optimized to maximize mission range. Point intercept missions shall be optimized to obtain minimum time to combat altitude.

3.5.6.2.1 Enroute Climb Data. Enroute climb data shall be based on the appropriate configuration, thrust (power) and weight. The aircraft shall have the landing gear and flaps retracted and have attained the airspeed for best climb for the applicable condition.

3.5.6.2.2 Enroute Climb Power. For jet (fighter, attack, trainers, etc.) aircraft enroute climb to cruise altitude shall be at intermediate (military) thrust. For propeller (patrol, transport, etc.) aircraft use maximum continuous power.

3.5.6.2.3 Typical Design Criteria. For design purposes, consideration may be given to alternate climb schedules to more adequately portray the desired operational capability of the design. For example, the following schedules could apply: minimum time, minimum fuel, maximum range, specified thrust (power) or speed, accelerate during climb, etc.

3.5.6.3 Time to Climb. The time to climb to a specified altitude(s) shall be expressed in minutes from start of enroute climb. Weight reduction as a result of fuel consumption shall be applied to the calculations.

3.5.6.4 Combat Climb. Combat climb is the instantaneous maximum vertical speed capability in feet per minute at combat conditions, such as, weight, configuration, altitude, and thrust (power).

3.5.7 Landing Distance. The following criteria are for conventional aircraft. (For STOL aircraft, the criteria shall be as established by design requirements). Landing distance includes: (a) landing ground roll and (b) distance over a 50-foot height. Distances shall be for the landing configuration and weight and shall be based on the landing speeds defined in 3.5.2.12. Unless otherwise specified, ground roll deceleration shall be based on operation at Sea Level, standard day, zero wind, no runway slope, on hard (concrete or asphalt) surfaced runways, idle thrust (power) and a braking coefficient as defined in 3.5.5.5.2. Factors that should be considered are pilot reaction time, thrust decay, aerodynamic and mechanical braking, and maximum brake capacity.

3.5.7.1 Typical Design Criteria. For design purposes, consideration may be given to alternate definitions of landing distance such as: reverse thrust, atmospheric conditions alternate runway surfaces, runway slopes and winds of a non-standard nature, a rigid computer analysis of the air distance and other similar criteria selected to optimize the design of the airplane.

3.5.8 Thrust (Power). The term thrust (power) is used to mean thrust (jet engine) and/or brake horsepower (shaft engines) as applicable with due consideration for installation effects and limitations. Engine and ATD ratings as defined in Paragraph 3.2.1.3.c shall be those which appear in the approved engine model specification without regard to installation effects or limitations.

3.5.8.1 Maximum Thrust (Power). Maximum thrust (power) is the highest thrust (power) which the engine will consistently deliver at specific ground or flight conditions for the durations (incremental and total) specified in the model specification for demonstration during the qualification or preliminary flight rating tests.

3.5.8.2 Intermediate Thrust (Power). Intermediate thrust (power) is the highest thrust (power) which the engine will consistently deliver at specific ground or flight conditions for an incremental duration of at least 30 minutes, and a total duration as specified in the engine model specification for demonstration during qualification or preliminary flight rating tests. Intermediate thrust is equivalent to the old term military thrust.

3.5.8.3 Maximum Continuous Thrust (Power). Maximum continuous thrust (power) is the highest thrust (power) which the engine will consistently deliver at specific ground or flight conditions for an unlimited time period.

3.5.8.4 Cruise Thrust (Power). The thrust (power) required to fly the aircraft at cruise speed for the configuration, altitude and weight designated.

3.5.8.5 Idle Thrust (Power). Idle thrust (power) is the lowest thrust (power) which the engine will consistently deliver at specific ground or flight conditions for an unlimited duration or as defined in the engine model specification for demonstration during qualification or preliminary flight rating tests.

3.5.9 Fuel Consumption Service Tolerance. Unless authorized otherwise, for proposal aircraft, all fuel consumption data, regardless of source, shall be increased by 5 percent for all engine thrust (power) conditions as a service tolerance to allow for practical operation. In addition, corrections or allowances to engine fuel flow shall be made for all power plant installation losses such as accessory drives, ducts, fans, cabin pressure bleed, etc. Fuel consumption data will not be increased by 5 percent for service aircraft, if verified by Navy approved flight test.

3.5.10 Mission Types. For pre-service and service SAC Charts (1.4.3 and 1.4.4), the tabulated performance data of SAC Chart page 4 shall show performance data for missions designated by the Navy. Typical missions for various types of aircraft are shown in Appendix V for use in Proposal SAC Charts (1.4.1). Unless otherwise specified, reserve fuel shall conform to the allowances shown in Appendix V.

3.5.10.1 Clean Mission. The first mission to be described in the Standard Aircraft Characteristics Charts will be the Clean Mission. This mission is intended to show the maximum capabilities of the aircraft (usually a high-high-high profile).

3.5.10.2 Basic Mission. The basic mission is the mission profile detailed in Appendix V which most nearly depicts the primary intended operational use of the aircraft. To maintain the capability of presenting a direct comparison between similar type aircraft, no deviation from the ground rules of Appendix V can be allowed.

3.5.10.3 Design Mission. The design mission is defined as the primary mission for which the aircraft was specifically procured. This mission will normally be defined in procurement documents such as the statement of work and will include the flight profile, allowances, fuel (clean or external tanks) and payload. Ground rules and allowances for the design mission are dictated by the specific operational requirements and will be used in describing the mission capabilities in the Standard Aircraft Characteristics Charts.

3.5.10.4 Ferry Mission. Ferry range is the greatest distance attainable on a practicable one-way mission with maximum authorized fuel and no pay load according to a specified sequence of operations, allowances and reserves. External fuel tanks may be carried and must be retained for the duration of the flight.

3.5.10.5 Typical Missions. Any missions, preferably from Appendix V, which would present the additional capabilities of the aircraft. If different from Appendix V, the mission definitions should be coordinated with the Navy.

3.5.10.6 In-Flight Refueled Mission. For aircraft capable of in-flight refueling, a refueled mission is the greatest distance (radius or range) attainable through receipt of replacement fuel during flight. A single refueling operation is required although multiple refueling operations may be used if considered to be feasible. Basic ground rules from Appendix V shall apply.

3.5.11 Combat Radius. Combat radius is the distance (including distance covered in climb) attainable on a practicable flight to the target and return a distance equal to that flown out, carrying a specific load (bombs, cargo, personnel, etc.), to or from the target according to a sequence of operations specified under "Mission Types" (Paragraph 3.5.10). Droppable fuel tanks are discussed in Paragraph 3.6.1.6.

3.5.12 Combat Range. Combat range is the distance (including distance covered in climb) attainable on a practicable one-way flight carrying payload (bombs, cargo, personnel) the entire distance. Droppable fuel tanks are not dropped when empty.

3.6 MISSION DETAILED REQUIREMENTS.

3.6.1 General Mission Requirements. Unless otherwise specified, the following general ground rules shall apply:

3.6.1.1 Standard Atmosphere. Data shall be presented for standard day atmosphere.

3.6.1.2 Wind. Data shall be for a no-wind condition.

3.6.1.3 Formation Flight. Data shall be for a single aircraft only.

3.6.1.4 Ordnance Expenditure. Ammunition and air-to-air missiles shall not be expended during the mission.

3.6.1.5 Off-Loading Fuel. Fuel may be off-loaded to avoid exceeding the maximum allowable takeoff weight.

3.6.1.6 External Fuel Tanks. For combat radius missions only, external fuel tanks shall be dropped when empty or prior to combat unless such tanks are designed to be carried during combat. Unless otherwise restricted (e.g. CG, etc.), dropping of external tanks shall be sequenced to provide maximum range. Cargo, tanker and training missions for Attack and Fighter aircraft shall not drop external tanks.

3.6.1.7 Pylons/Racks. Bomb racks, etc. shall not be jettisoned with the external stores. Pylons shall be retained during return to base.

3.6.1.8 Reduced Engine Operation. When applicable, a minimum number of engines may be used to increase range or loiter time if such operation would represent normal service usage. However, such action shall conform to Paragraph 3.6.1.9.

3.6.1.9 Authorized Operation. No operational technique shall be utilized that is not, or is not intended to be included as a recommended procedure in the applicable flight manual.

3.6.1.10 Trainer Aircraft. The trainer basic missions, as defined in Appendix V is applicable to basic and advanced trainer airplanes. Combat and tactical trainer airplanes fly the basic mission for the appropriate parent-type airplane.

3.6.1.11 Variable Geometry Wing (VGW) Aircraft. For VGW aircraft, the automatic sweep program will be clearly defined and used unless otherwise noted. If not automatic, the VGW aircraft will be assumed to have wings in the unswept position for takeoff and subsonic flight and swept for supersonic dash unless footnoted otherwise.

3.6.2 Mission Loading Requirements. In order to facilitate and expedite the make-up and delivery of the charts, it is suggested that the contractor contact the procuring service to discuss the various mission loadings prior to submission. In the absence of special instructions, the following shall apply:

3.6.2.1 Basic Mission Loading. The fuel and payload loading for the basic mission shall be the basic loading condition as defined by the first load condition given in the detail specification weight statement for the aircraft.

3.6.2.2 Typical Mission Loadings. Loadings shall be selected from those included in the detail specification or other approved loadings which depict a particular capability of the aircraft. At least one mission shall conform to the maximum (overload) gross weight (Paragraph 3.5.1.7.2).

3.6.2.3 Ferry Mission Loadings. Loading shall consist of maximum authorized fuel and no payload.

3.6.2.4 In-Flight Refueling Mission Loading. One mission shall be for the same loading as the basic mission. Other loadings may be selected by the typical missions.

3.6.2.5 Combat Range Mission Loading. Identical to the loading of the associated combat radius mission.

3.6.3 Mission Segments. Rationale for mission segments is presented in the following:

3.6.3.1 Takeoff. Ground operation, including starting engines, warm-up, taxi, takeoff and acceleration to climb speed are variable. An arbitrary fuel allowance, based on statistical analysis, must be used. The takeoff fuel allowance used for gas turbine engine and turboprop powered aircraft is a quantity of fuel equal to the fuel used during 4.6 minutes of intermediate thrust operation at Sea Level Standard Day (10 minutes maximum continuous power for reciprocating engines). If afterburners are required for use during takeoff, a fuel allowance equal to 30 seconds of operation at maximum thrust at Sea Level Standard Day must be used along with fuel for 4.6 minutes operation at intermediate thrust.

3.6.3.2 Climb. See Paragraph 3.5.6.

3.6.3.2.1 Typical Design Criteria. For design purposes, consideration may be given to defining the takeoff allowance to fully utilize the state-of-the-art. Some typical examples are:

a. Specify engine operation for specific time periods at specified powers. Such as, fuel used during 4.6 minutes of intermediate thrust operation at Sea Level, on a standard day plus 30 seconds of maximum thrust operation if afterburner is used during takeoff.

b. Estimate fuel required to start the engine(s), run-up, taxi a specified distance at a specified thrust (power) setting and to accelerate from brake release to climb speed at a specified power.

c. Estimate fuel for a specified time at a specified thrust (power)/weight ratio to account for starting and taxi plus fuel for takeoff and acceleration to climb speed computed from the following:

$$W_{f_{TO}} = \frac{V_c W_{TO}}{2g} \cdot \frac{(\dot{W}_o + \dot{W}_c)}{T-D} \qquad (2)$$

When:

$W_{f_{TO}}$ = takeoff and acceleration fuel, lbs.

V_c = initial climb speed, ft/sec.

W_{TO} = takeoff weight, lbs.

$\dot{W}_o$ = static fuel flow at takeoff power, lbs/sec.

$\dot{W}_c$ = fuel flow at initial climb speed at takeoff power, lbs/sec.

$T-D$ = thrust minus drag at V_c, lbs.

g = acceleration of gravity, Sea Level, ft/sec^2

NOTE:

If thrust (power) is to be varied between lift-off and climb speed, this equation can be so modified.

d. Other specific criteria may be selected to more accurately portray the operational characteristics of the specific design.

3.6.3.3 Cruise. Unless specifically assigned, aircraft shall cruise at the speed and altitude for maximum specific range (optimum cruise altitude) for the applicable configuration, thrust (power) and weight. This altitude shall not exceed cruise ceiling. For aircraft having a low optimum altitude (e.g.: Reciprocating Engine Aircraft), the cruise altitude shall not be less than 5,000 feet for terrain clearance over land or 1,500 feet over water. Except where the altitude is specified, the aircraft may utilize a cruise climb to optimize cruise distance. Turbojet and turbofan driven aircraft shall cruise at maximum range cruise speed (Paragraph 3.5.2.10.1) and propeller driven aircraft shall cruise at long range cruise speed (Paragraph 3.5.2.10.2).

3.6.3.3.1 Typical Design Criteria. For design purposes, consideration may be given to specifying a cruise technique selected to optimize the desired characteristics of the design. Techniques to be considered include: constant altitude cruise, constant speed cruise, cruise climb profile, step climb, cruise at specified power, cruise with reduced number of engines, cruise altitude in excess of cruise ceiling, fixed distance segment, headwinds or tail winds, non-standard temperatures, etc.

3.6.3.4 Combat. Combat shall be considered by setting aside a quantity of fuel to be used for that purpose if required. Normally, fuel flow for this allowance shall be based on the level flight stabilized speeds for the altitude and thrust (power) stated in Appendix V. The change in speed due to weight reduction during the combat period shall be ignored. When more than one thrust (power) setting is used, the lesser thrust (power) will be used first and each treated independently. For task-oriented fuel allowances, computation shall be based upon weight at start of combat period with benefit due to weight reduction credited; change in speed due to weight reduction shall be ignored.

3.6.3.4.1 Escape and Evasion. Escape and evasion shall be considered by setting aside a quantity of fuel based upon a specified measure of performance.

3.6.3.4.2 Typical Design Criteria. For design purposes, consideration may be given to various methods of accounting for the fuel to be used during combat or escape and evasion action. Some examples of methods are:

a. Fuel required for a specified time with a specified thrust (power) at a specified speed and a specified altitude.

b. Fuel consumed in expending a specified quantity of energy. For example:

$$\text{Combat Fuel} = \frac{E_s \dot{W}_f}{P_s} \qquad (3)$$

When:

E_s = specific energy, feet.

W_f = fuel flow at combat speed, power, and altitude, lbs/sec.

P_s = excess energy or $\frac{(T-D)V_c}{W_{T_c}}$, ft/sec.

V_c = combat true airspeed, ft/sec.

W_{T_c} = combat weight, lbs.

(T-D) = thrust minus drag, lbs.

c. The quantity of fuel determined as the sum of the fuel required to accelerate from cruise speed to a specified speed, plus fuel required to make a specified number of sustainable turns at a specified speed or speeds. These operations shall be performed at a selected thrust (power)(s) and altitude(s).

d. All or a portion of the armament may be expended.

e. Other specific criteria selected to more accurately portray the operational characteristics of the specific design.

3.6.3.5 Search and Loiter. Speed shall be as given in Paragraph 3.5.2.11.

3.6.3.6 Descent. For vehicles whose best cruise is subsonic, no time, fuel or distance will be credited for descent. For supersonic cruise vehicles, credit may be taken for descent and deceleration to an altitude of 25,000 feet and a specified speed. Aircraft which conduct a supersonic runout from the target may, if the cruise altitude and speed are lower than the runout altitude and speed, account for distance in descent and deceleration to cruise.

3.6.3.6.1 Typical Design Criteria. For design purposes, consideration may be given to alternate definitions of descent. For example: time, fuel and distance could be credited, descent could be a long range (airline) approach, use of thrust (power) could vary from none to full, speeds could vary from near stall to redline, altitudes could be reduced in step increments, etc. For gas turbine powered aircraft, the criteria will usually be idle thrust (power) descent to a given altitude at a given speed, i.e., M=0.8 to Sea Level (outbound leg to target area), 250 KCAS to 20,000 feet (return leg to land).

3.6.4 Landing Reserve. Fuel onboard at landing shall be the greater of the following:

a. Fuel allowance equal to 10 percent of initial usable fuel as required by OPNAVINST 3710.7K Paragraph 326.

b. Fuel allowance equal to 20 minutes loiter (30 minutes for cargo and transport aircraft) at sea level at speeds for maximum endurance with all engines operating plus 5% of initial total usable fuel (internal plus external).

3.6.4.1 Typical Design Criteria. For design purposes, consideration may be given to defining the landing reserves to fully utilize the state-of-the-art. Some examples are:

a. The fuel required for a ground controlled approach; a wave-off, go-around and a second, successful landing. This could be approximated by using the equivalent of fuel consumed during a specified time at maximum endurance at Sea Level with all engines operating.

b. A specified percentage of initial fuel load.

c. Fuel consumed during a specified time of operation at a specified power at a specified altitude.

d. The greater of the fuel required for 10 percent of mission time or 20 minutes at maximum endurance speed at 10,000 feet.

e. Fuel required to fly to an alternate field (specify distance) plus a specified time at a specified speed at a specified altitude to account for landing.

f. Combinations of the above or other criteria selected to optimize the design.

3.6.5 Mission Time. Time in air (excludes time before start of initial climb and reserve).

3.6.6 Cycle Time. The time of flight from the start of enroute climb (omitting takeoff time) to stopping engines after landing.

3.6.7 Block Time. The total time of flight from start engines to stop engines after landing.

3.6.8 Intercept Time. The time from engine start until initiation of combat at the intercept altitude. This time includes the period required for takeoff and acceleration to climb speed.

SECTION 1

BASIC AERODYNAMIC DATA REPORT

INTRODUCTION

SECTION 1. INTRODUCTION
2. THRUST/LIFT/DRAG BOOKKEEPING PROCEDURE FOR PERFORMANCE CALCULATIONS
3. EXAMPLE TABLE OF CONTENTS
4. EXAMPLE PLOTS

INTRODUCTION

Prior to proceeding with the initial performance calculations for the Standard Aircraft Characteristics Charts, the following basic data, including all calculations and materials necessary to substantiate these data, shall be submitted to NAVAIR (AIR-53012) for acceptance [normally not later than sixty (60) days following receipt of Authority to Proceed unless specifically extended by NAVAIR (AIR-53012)]. The aerodynamic and propulsion system thrust/drag bookkeeping procedures for performance calculations are outlined in Section 2 of this Appendix and shall be utilized, where applicable to the particular design, in the presentation of basic data and for performance calculations. Prior to subsequent performance calculations, these basic data shall be submitted.

1. Low speed drag analysis itemized according to various aircraft components (wing, fuselage, drag devices, etc.).

2. Plots of parasitic drag coefficient, $C_{D_{min}}$; incremental skin friction drag coefficient due to variation of flat plate skin friction drag with Reynolds number (fully turbulent boundary layer case adjusted for the effects of compressibility should be utilized); lift coefficient for minimum drag, C_{L_B}, as a function of Mach number; and trimmed airplane efficiency factor "e" versus Mach number for various values of lift coefficient. Trimmed airplane drag polars at various values of Mach number may be submitted in lieu of the "e" and C_{L_B} curves. Incremental drag coefficient, ΔC_D, versus Mach number for drag devices and for each required external store and combination of stores shall be presented.

3. Standard Day net thrust available and fuel flow variation with altitude and Mach number for maximum afterburner, intermediate and normal engine operation (including idle power) with all losses (induction system, nozzle, compressor bleed and accessory drive power extraction) indicated. The variation of fuel flow with net thrust as a function of Mach number and altitude for partial thrust operation shall be presented. Also, intermediate and maximum (afterburner) thrust available at Sea Level, 89.8°F, between Mach equal 0 and 0.3. Engine ram drag shall also be presented for all of the above engine conditions. When applicable, one engine inoperative data and partial afterburner net thrust versus fuel flow should be presented at specific altitudes/conditions.

4. Untrimmed lift coefficient plotted against pitching moment, angle-of-attack and drag coefficient for three horizontal tail positions, without thrust effect, in the takeoff and landing configurations, and both in and out of ground effect. Trimmed lift coefficient versus angle-of-attack and drag coefficient, without thrust effect, for the takeoff and approach configuration (in and out of ground effect) and for the clean configuration.

5. Breakout of wetted areas and aircraft dimensional data.

6. Area distribution for MN = 1.0 (Total and broken down by components).

7. Catapult:

a. Load-stroke data for main and nose gear.

b. Load-tire deflection data for main and nose gear. For 7.a and 7.b, specify if load is total load, load on one side, or load on one wheel.

c. Moment of inertia about Y-Y axis (pitch).

d. CM $\dot{\alpha}$ and CM $\dot{\theta}$.

8. Drawings:

a. General Arrangement, 1/20 scale dimensioned, including CG and thrust line locations.

b. Landing gear (side view) showing main and nose gear hub locations (station and waterline) in extended and compressed position; tow bar attachment point and tow bar length.

NOTE: Data not accepted by NAVAIR shall be replaced, after conference with the contractor, by similar data designated by NAVAIR.

Section 3 presents an example "Table of Contents" that illustrates the format for the Basic Aerodynamic Data Report. It is required that this format be used unless exempted by NAVAIR (AIR-53012).

Section 4 presents example plot formats to be used in the graphical presentation of data for the Basic Aerodynamic Data Report. The aircraft and configuration should be noted where applicable. This includes maneuver devices and schedules (Mach and angle-of-attack) for these devices. For maximum lift coefficient, include maximum defensive and offensive limits, maximum tracking and buffet onset. On all external stores show effect of C_L on drag coefficient. Also, effect of speed brakes should be shown, where applicable.

SECTION 2

BASIC AERODYNAMIC DATA REPORT

THRUST/LIFT/DRAG BOOKKEEPING PROCEDURES FOR PERFORMANCE CALCULATIONS

1. This Appendix discusses the requirements for the presentation and calculation of aircraft performance. These procedures outlined in Figure II-1, are intended for use during design, development and test of the aircraft (whether performance calculations are based on analytical, wind tunnel or flight analysis) and shall be utilized, where applicable to the particular design, (a) in the presentation of basic data, (b) for aircraft performance calculations, and (c) to enhance generalization of aerodynamic data obtained from flight test.

2. The basis for the thrust/lift/drag bookkeeping procedures and attendant list of symbols and definitions is:

a. Realism in the allocation of aerodynamic and propulsion system force components to thrust and drag.

b. The inclusion of all force components independent of engine power setting in the aircraft lift/drag characteristics.

c. The inclusion of all force components which are functions of engine throttle setting and/or induction and exhaust system geometry in installed propulsion system characteristics.

d. The availability of aerodynamic/propulsion system interaction effects and Reynolds number effects to generalize flight-measured lift/drag data for correlation of flight-measured and wind-tunnel-derived full-scale lift/drag characteristics.

3. The "reference" configuration between aerodynamic force and moment and propulsion wind tunnel tests shall be as follows:

Inlet: Inlet(s) operating at the critical mass flow ratio or the Mach number being tested. Inlet drag for this condition will be included in aircraft drag.

Nozzle/Afterbody: The nozzle(s) should be in the full-open position, with P_{EXIT}/P_a = 1.0. Nozzle/afterbody drag for this condition is included in aircraft drag.

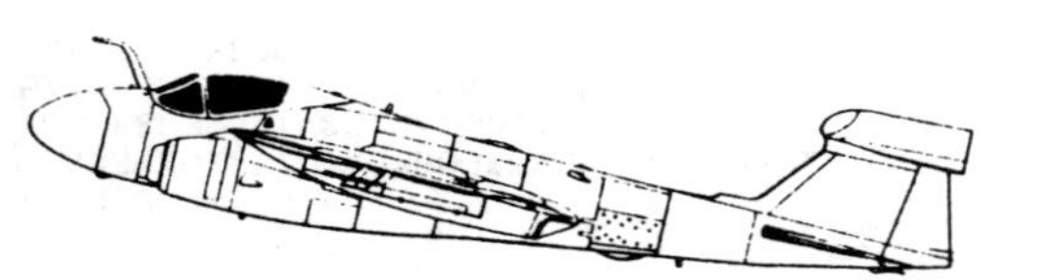

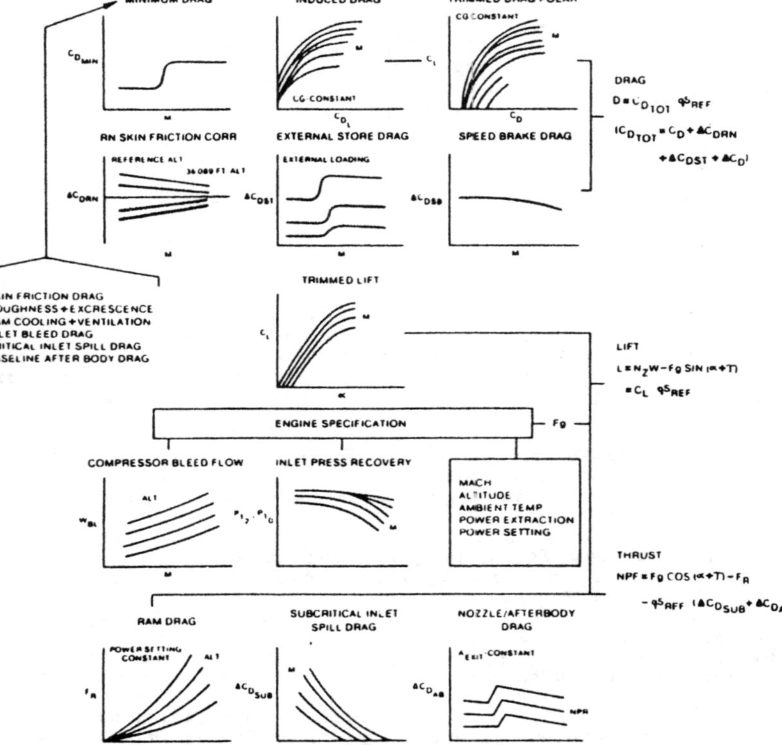

FIGURE II-1. THRUST/LIFT/DRAG BOOKKEEPING PROCEDURES FOR PERFORMANCE CALCULATIONS

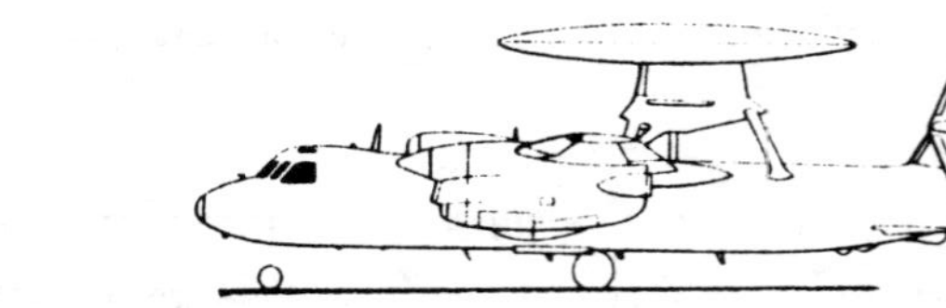

LIST OF SYMBOLS AND DEFINITION OF TERMS

Alt	ALTITUDE
A_{EXIT}	NOZZLE EXIT AREA
C_D	DRAG COEFFICIENT (CLEAN CONFIGURATION)
C_{Di}	INDUCED DRAG COEFFICIENT
$\Delta C_{D_{AB}}$	INCREMENTAL NOZZLE/AFTERBODY DRAG COEFFICIENT THAT IS A FUNCTION OF ENGINE THROTTLE POSITION
$C_{D_{min}}$	MINIMUM DRAG COEFFICIENT (INCLUDING SEA LEVEL SKIN FRICTION DRAG, ROUGHNESS AND EXCRESCENCE, RAM COOLING AND VENTILATION, INLET BLEED DRAG, SUPERCRITICAL INLET SPILLAGE DRAG AND BASELINE NOZZLE/AFTERBODY DRAG)
$\Delta C_{D_{RN}}$	INCREMENTAL SKIN FRICTION DRAG COEFFICIENT DUE TO VARIATION OF FLAT PLATE SKIN FRICTION DRAG WITH REYNOLDS NUMBER
$\Delta C_{D_{SB}}$	INCREMENTAL DRAG COEFFICIENT DUE TO SPEEDBRAKE DEFLECTION
$\Delta C_{D_{ST}}$	INCREMENTAL DRAG COEFFICIENT DUE TO CARRIAGE OF EXTERNAL STORES
$\Delta C_{D_{SUB}}$	INCREMENTAL SUBCRITICAL INLET SPILLAGE DRAG COEFFICIENT
$C_{D_{TOT}}$	TOTAL DRAG COEFFICIENT (C_D AND $C_{D_{RN}}$ AND $C_{D_{ST}}$ AND $C_{D_{SB}}$)
C_L	LIFT COEFFICIENT
CG	CENTER OF GRAVITY POSITION
D	DRAG
F_g	INSTALLED ENGINE GROSS THRUST
F_R	ENGINE RAM DRAG
L	LIFT
M	MACH NUMBER
m	INLET MASS FLOW OF OPERATING ENGINE CONDITION

LIST OF SYMBOLS AND DEFINITION OF TERMS

m_o	THEORETICAL MAXIMUM MASS FLOW FOR REFERENCE INLET CAPTURE AREA
$(m/m_o)_{oper}$	INLET OPERATING MASS FLOW RATIO
NPF	NET PROPULSIVE FORCE ($F_g \cos(\alpha + \tau) - F_R - qS_{REF}(C_{D_{SUB}} + C_{D_{AB}})$)
NPR	NOZZLE PRESSURE RATIO (P_{EXIT}/P_a)
N_z	AIRCRAFT ACCELERATION ALONG VERTICAL AXIS
P_a	AMBIENT PRESSURE
P_{EXIT}	NOZZLE EXIT STATIC PRESSURE
$P_{T_{EXIT}}$	NOZZLE EXIT TOTAL PRESSURE
P_{T_o}	FREESTREAM TOTAL PRESSURE
P_{T_2}	TOTAL PRESSURE AT ENGINE COMPRESSOR FACE
P_{T_2}/P_{T_o}	INLET PRESSURE RECOVERY
q	DYNAMIC PRESSURE
RN	REYNOLDS NUMBER
S.L.	SEA LEVEL
S_{REF}	REFERENCE WING AREA FOR AERODYNAMIC COEFFICIENTS
W	AIRPLANE GROSS WEIGHT
W_a	INLET AIRFLOW
W_{BL}	ENGINE COMPRESSOR BLEED AIRFLOW
α	ANGLE-OF-ATTACK
δ	RATIO OF AMBIENT TO STANDARD SEA LEVEL STATIC PRESSURE
θ	RATIO OF AMBIENT TO STANDARD SEA LEVEL STATIC TEMPERATURE
τ	LONGITUDINAL THRUST LINE INCLINATION

SECTION 3

BASIC AERODYNAMIC DATA REPORT

EXAMPLE TABLE OF CONTENTS

1.0 INTRODUCTION

2.0 AIRCRAFT DESCRIPTION AND TABULATED DATA

- 2.1 Three View Drawing and Configuration Schematic Drawings
- 2.2 Tabulated Aircraft Dimensional Data
- 2.3 Catapulting Geometry
- 2.4 Wetted Area
- 2.5 Cross Sectional Area
- 2.6 Weight, Center of Gravity and Inertia Data Summary
- 2.7 Powerplant and Propeller (if required) Data

3.0 AERODYNAMIC DATA

- 3.1 Source of Data
- 3.2 Thrust Drag Bookkeeping
- 3.3 High Speed and Maneuvering Configuration (Flaps and Gear Up)
  - 3.3.1 Drag Substantiation
  - 3.3.2 Lift Data
- 3.4 Delta Drag Coefficients for Pylons and External Stores
- 3.5 Miscellaneous Drag, i.e., Speed Brake, etc.
- 3.6 High Lift Configuration Characteristics
  - 3.6.1 General
  - 3.6.2 Catapult and Approach Configuration In and Out of Ground Effects
  - 3.6.3 Landing Gear Drag Coefficients
  - 3.6.4 Delta Drag for Single Engine Trim

4.0 PROPULSION DATA

- 4.1 Source of Data
- 4.2 Installation Effects
- 4.3 Installed Performance
  - 4.3.1 Standard Day
  - 4.3.2 Tropical Day Takeoff Data (Mach Number $\leq$ 0.4)

5.0 AERODYNAMIC ENVELOPE

- 5.1 Structural Limits (V_H and Load Factor)
- 5.2 Engine Limitations
- 5.3 Alpha Restrictions

6.0 ANGLE-OF-ATTACK AND AIRSPEED CORRECTIONS

- 6.1 Angle-of-Attack (Degrees to Units)
- 6.2 Position Error (Mach Number and Airspeed)

7.0 ABBREVIATIONS AND SYMBOLS

8.0 REFERENCES

SECTION 4

BASIC AERODYNAMIC DATA REPORT

EXAMPLE PLOTS

HIGH SPEED LIFT & DRAG CHARACTERISTICS

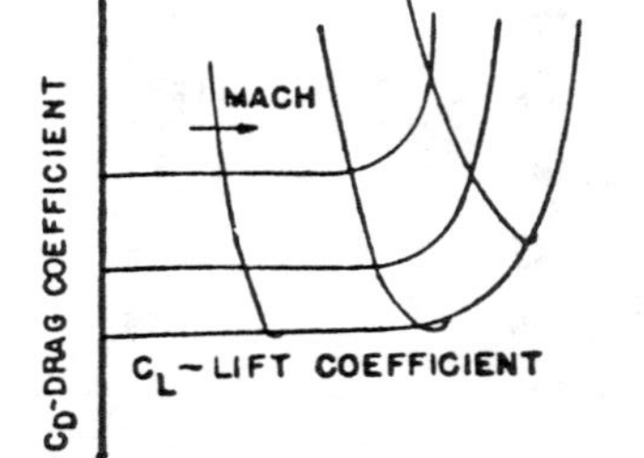

FIGURE - 1

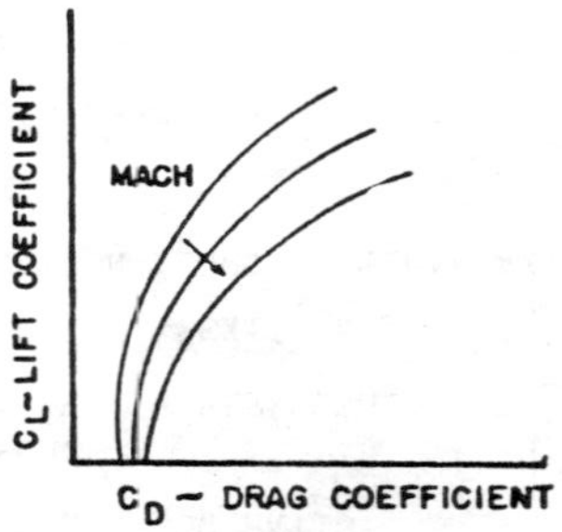

MACH

C_L–LIFT COEFFICIENT

C_D – DRAG COEFFICIENT

FIGURE - 2

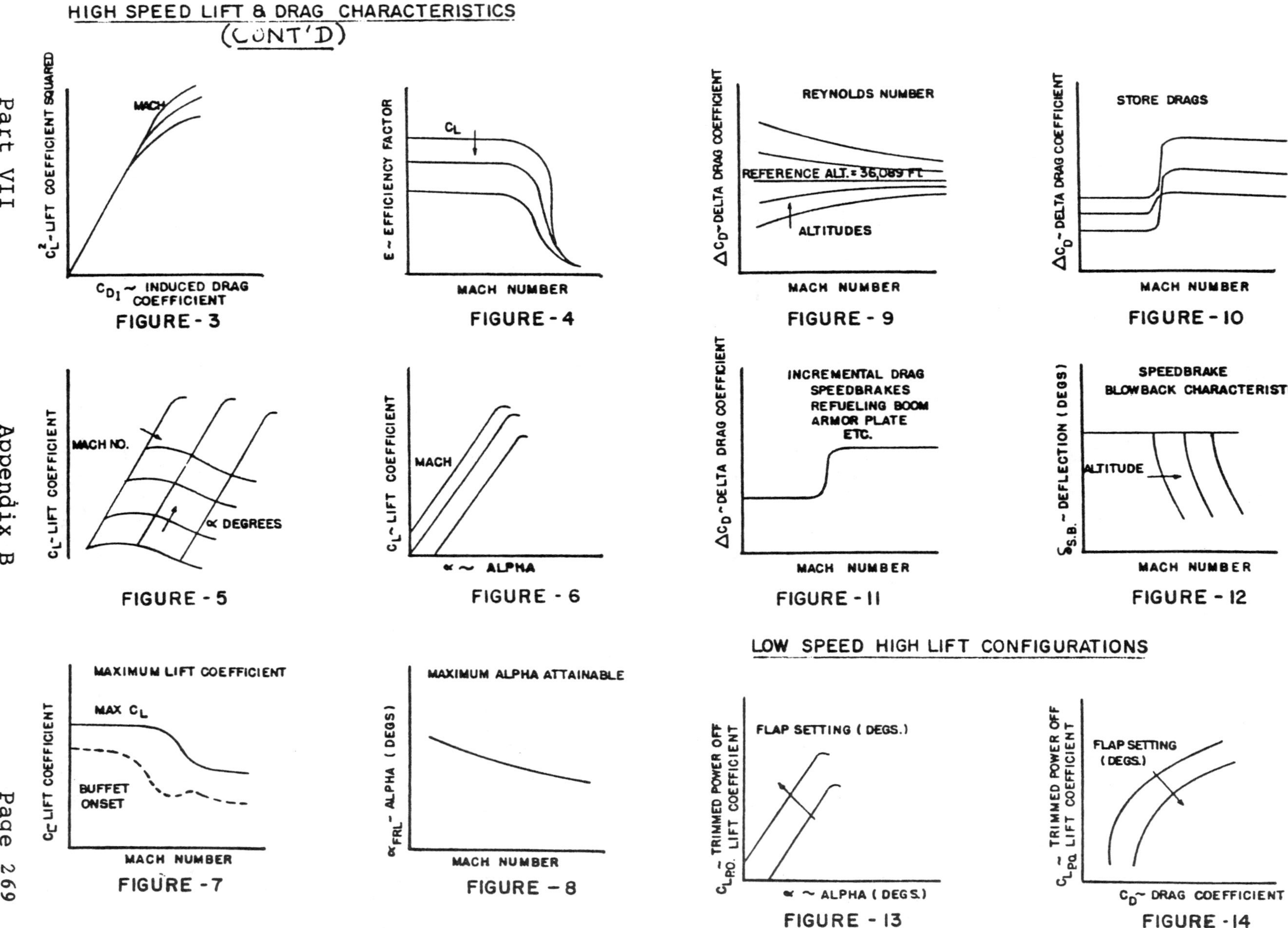
HIGH SPEED LIFT & DRAG CHARACTERISTICS
(CONT'D)
C_L^2 - LIFT COEFFICIENT SQUARED
MACH
C_{D_I} ~ INDUCED DRAG COEFFICIENT
FIGURE - 3
E ~ EFFICIENCY FACTOR
C_L
MACH NUMBER
FIGURE - 4
ΔC_D ~ DELTA DRAG COEFFICIENT
REYNOLDS NUMBER
REFERENCE ALT. = 36,089 FT.
ALTITUDES
MACH NUMBER
FIGURE - 9
ΔC_D ~ DELTA DRAG COEFFICIENT
STORE DRAGS
MACH NUMBER
FIGURE - 10
C_L - LIFT COEFFICIENT
MACH NO.
α DEGREES
FIGURE - 5
C_L ~ LIFT COEFFICIENT
MACH
α ~ ALPHA
FIGURE - 6
ΔC_D ~ DELTA DRAG COEFFICIENT
INCREMENTAL DRAG
SPEEDBRAKES
REFUELING BOOM
ARMOR PLATE
ETC.
MACH NUMBER
FIGURE - 11
$\delta_{S.B.}$ ~ DEFLECTION (DEGS)
SPEEDBRAKE
BLOWBACK CHARACTERISTICS
ALTITUDE
MACH NUMBER
FIGURE - 12
C_L LIFT COEFFICIENT
MAXIMUM LIFT COEFFICIENT
MAX C_L
BUFFET ONSET
MACH NUMBER
FIGURE - 7
α_{FRL} ~ ALPHA (DEGS)
MAXIMUM ALPHA ATTAINABLE
MACH NUMBER
FIGURE - 8
LOW SPEED HIGH LIFT CONFIGURATIONS
$C_{L_{P.O.}}$ ~ TRIMMED POWER OFF LIFT COEFFICIENT
FLAP SETTING (DEGS.)
α ~ ALPHA (DEGS.)
FIGURE - 13
$C_{L_{P.O.}}$ ~ TRIMMED POWER OFF LIFT COEFFICIENT
FLAP SETTING (DEGS.)
C_D ~ DRAG COEFFICIENT
FIGURE - 14

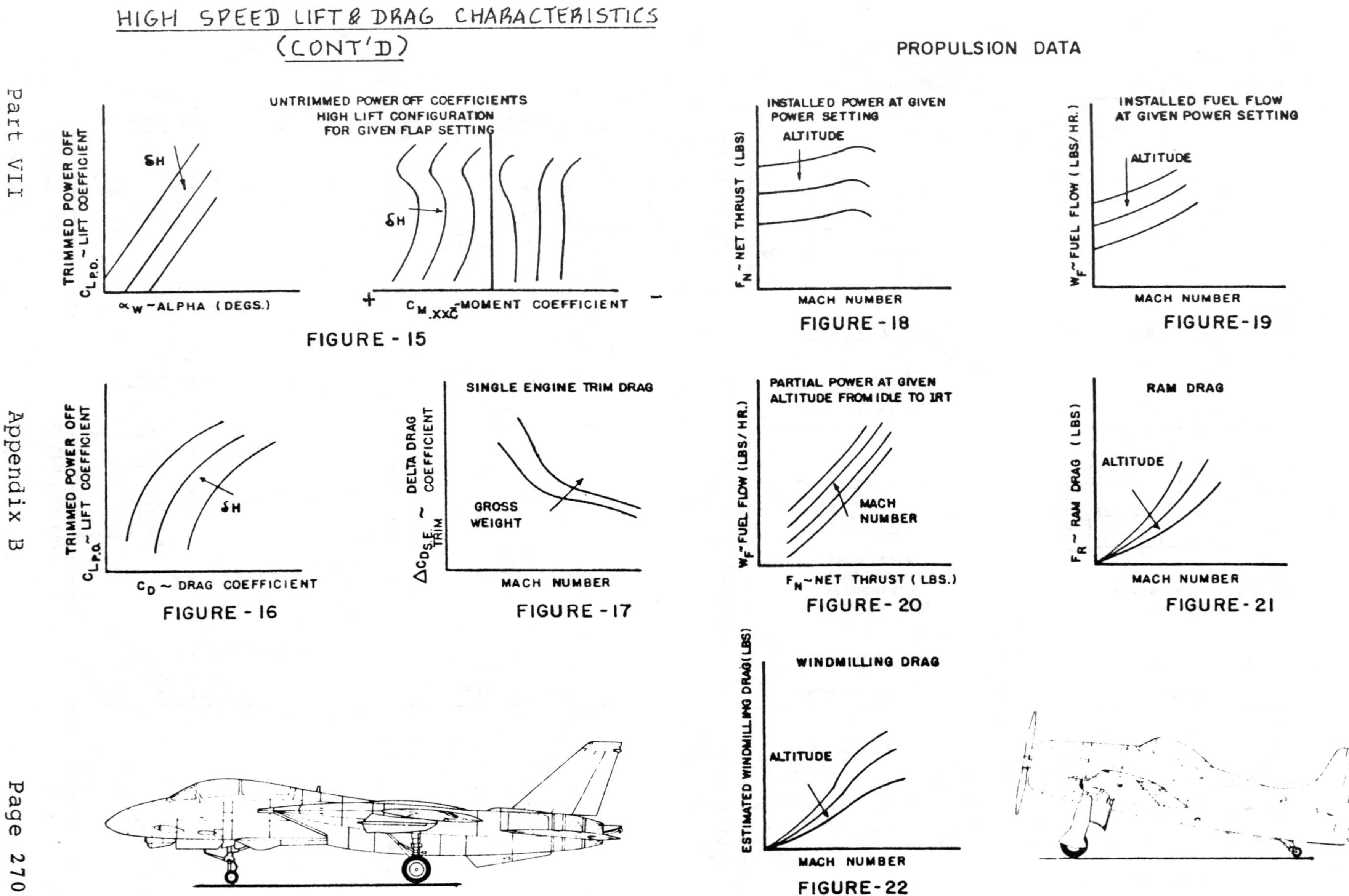
HIGH SPEED LIFT & DRAG CHARACTERISTICS
(CONT'D)
UNTRIMMED POWER OFF COEFFICIENTS
HIGH LIFT CONFIGURATION
FOR GIVEN FLAP SETTING
TRIMMED POWER OFF $C_{L_{P.O.}}$ ~ LIFT COEFFICIENT
δ_H
α_W ~ ALPHA (DEGS.)
δ_H
+
$C_{M.XX\bar{C}}$ ~ MOMENT COEFFICIENT
−
FIGURE - 15
TRIMMED POWER OFF $C_{L_{P.O.}}$ ~ LIFT COEFFICIENT
δ_H
C_D ~ DRAG COEFFICIENT
FIGURE - 16
SINGLE ENGINE TRIM DRAG
$\Delta C_{D_{S.E.\,TRIM}}$ ~ DELTA DRAG COEFFICIENT
GROSS WEIGHT
MACH NUMBER
FIGURE - 17
PROPULSION DATA
INSTALLED POWER AT GIVEN POWER SETTING
ALTITUDE
F_N ~ NET THRUST (LBS)
MACH NUMBER
FIGURE - 18
INSTALLED FUEL FLOW AT GIVEN POWER SETTING
ALTITUDE
W_F ~ FUEL FLOW (LBS/HR.)
MACH NUMBER
FIGURE - 19
PARTIAL POWER AT GIVEN ALTITUDE FROM IDLE TO IRT
W_F ~ FUEL FLOW (LBS/HR.)
MACH NUMBER
F_N ~ NET THRUST (LBS.)
FIGURE - 20
RAM DRAG
ALTITUDE
F_R ~ RAM DRAG (LBS)
MACH NUMBER
FIGURE - 21
WINDMILLING DRAG
ALTITUDE
ESTIMATED WINDMILLING DRAG (LBS)
MACH NUMBER
FIGURE - 22

SPECIALIZED PROPELLER AIRCRAFT

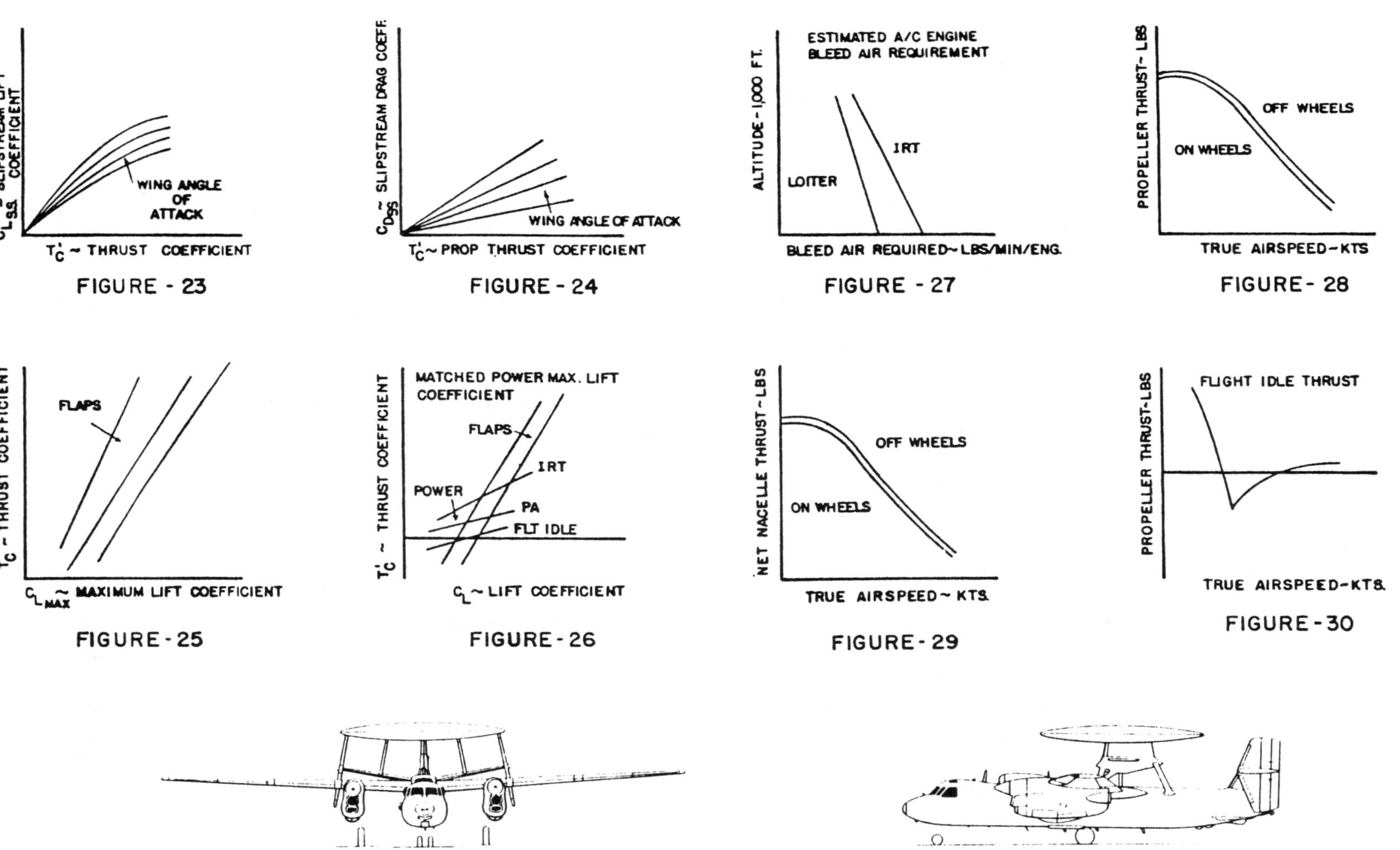

FIGURE - 23

FIGURE - 24

FIGURE - 27

FIGURE - 28

FIGURE - 25

FIGURE - 26

FIGURE - 29

FIGURE - 30

SECTION 1

SUBSTANTIATING DATA REPORT

INTRODUCTION

SECTION 1. INTRODUCTION
2. EXAMPLE TABLE OF CONTENTS
3. EXAMPLE PLOTS

INTRODUCTON

The performance Substantiating Data Report shall be prepared using the data contained in the Basic Aerodynamic Data Report which has been accepted by NAVAIR (AIR-53012). It shall include data to substantiate the information given in the Standard Aircraft Characteristics Charts and must be sufficiently complete to expedite a prompt investigation and review of the derived performance and to permit additional calculations to be made by NAVAIR (AIR-53012). The report also provides the general basis for and should be consistent with the Flight Manual Performance Data.

Section 2 presents an example "Table of Contents" that illustrates the format for the performance Substantiating Data Report. This format outlines the pertinent data to be provided and should be used unless exempted by NAVAIR (AIR-53012).

Section 3 presents example plot formats to be used in the graphical presentation of data for the performance Substantiating Data Report. Where applicable, one engine inoperative data should be provided in addition to the all engines operating condition. In the high lift configuration, data should be provided for all normal and emergency conditions. These include the various flap settings, lift devices (slats, etc.), and drag devices (speed brakes, etc.) available for pilot use. Field stopping/landing distance should be determined with and without reverse thrust, if appropriate.

The graphical presentation should be clear and concise with scales easy to read. Any questions concerning scales or format should be directed to NAVAIR (AIR-53012).

SECTION 2

SUBSTANTIATING DATA REPORT

EXAMPLE TABLE OF CONTENTS

1.0 SUMMARY (INCLUDING SAC CHARTS)

2.0 INTRODUCTION (INCLUDES DATA SOURCE)

3.0 TABULATED DATA

- 3.1 Aircraft General Arrangement
- 3.2 Aircraft Dimensional Data
- 3.3 Weight and Configuration Summary
(Includes tabulation of weight used in SAC Chart)
- 3.4 Aircraft Basic Useful Load
- 3.5 Fuel and Oil
- 3.6 Propulsion System
(Reference Engine Specification) Dimensions, Capture Area, Uninstalled Thrust, RPM (N_2), SFC, Airflow, Time Limit for Various Power Settings

4.0 MISSION AND TRADE-OFF SUMMARIES

5.0 PERFORMANCE DATA PRESENTATION METHOD

6.0 MAXIMUM MACH NUMBER
(Includes V_L, V_H and other limits)

7.0 CEILINGS
(Absolute, Service, Cruise and Combat Ceilings for Applicable Power Settings)

8.0 CLIMB PERFORMANCE

- 8.1 Climb - Speed Schedule
- 8.2 Rate-of-Climb
- 8.3 Time, Distance and Fuel to Climb
(Maximum Range and Minimum Time)
  - 8.3.1 Intermediate Power
  - 8.3.2 Maximum Power

9.0 CRUISE PERFORMANCE

- 9.1 Optimum Cruise
- 9.2 Cruise at Constant Mach and Altitude

10.0 ENDURANCE AND LOITER

- 10.1 Optimum Loiter
- 10.2 Specific Endurance at Constant Altitude

11.0 SPECIALIZED PERFORMANCE

- 11.1 Buddy Refueling
- 11.2 Search Performance (Flat Turning and Orbiting)
- 11.3 Loiter at Corner Speeds
- 11.4 Bingo
- 11.5 Single Engine Cruise

12.0 DESCENT PERFORMANCE

12.1 Rate of Descent

12.2 Fuel, Distance and Time to Descend (Optimum and Tactical)

13.0 ACCELERATION AND DECELERATION

13.1 Acceleration to Climb Speed

13.2 Level Acceleration at Applicable Power Settings (Intermediate and Maximum Power)

13.3 Deceleration Performance

14.0 MANEUVERABILITY

14.1 Specific Excess Power

14.2 Maneuverability Envelopes

14.2.1 Sustained

14.2.2 Instantaneous

15.0 LONGITUDINAL ACCELERATION FOR CATAPULT TAKEOFF

16.0 CATAPULT PERFORMANCE

17.0 CARRIER APPROACH SPEED AND ARRESTING WIND-OVER-DECK

18.0 STALL SPEEDS

19.0 FIELD TAKEOFF

20.0 FIELD LANDING

21.0 SINGLE ENGINE RATE-OF-CLIMB

22.0 ABBREVIATIONS AND SYMBOLS

23.0 REFERENCES

SECTION 3

SUBSTANTIATING DATA REPORT

EXAMPLE PLOTS

PLOTS ARE ARRANGED TO CONFORM WITH SECTION 2:
ITEMS 5, 22 AND 23 OMITTED

4.0 MISSION TRADEOFF SUMMARIES

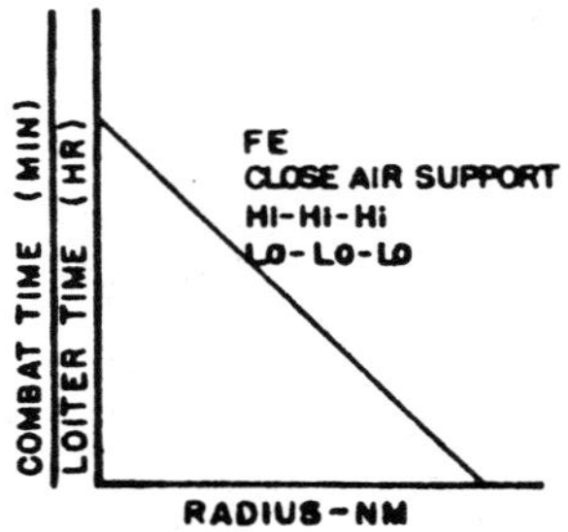

FIGURE - 1

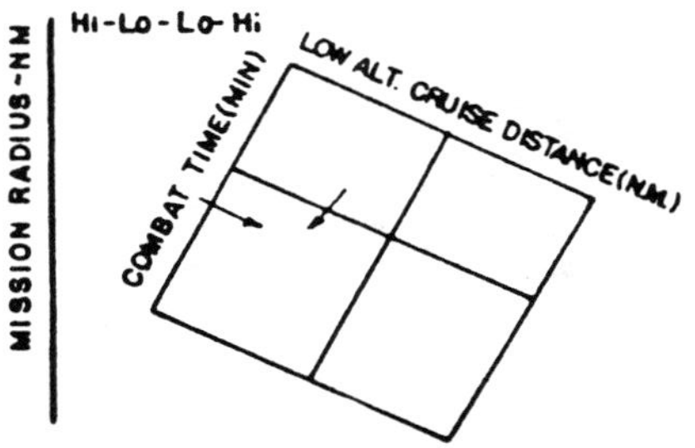

FIGURE - 2

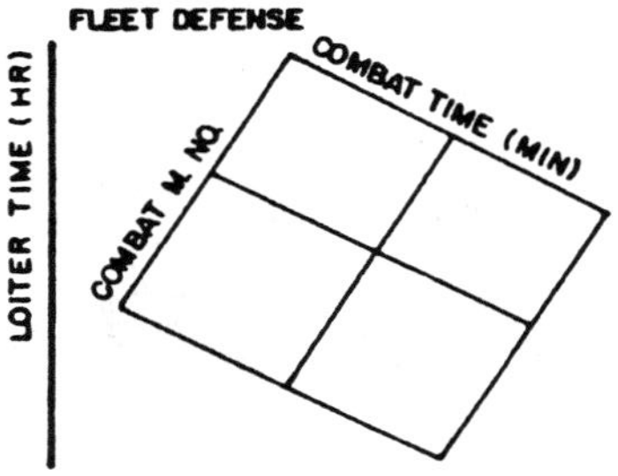

FIGURE - 3

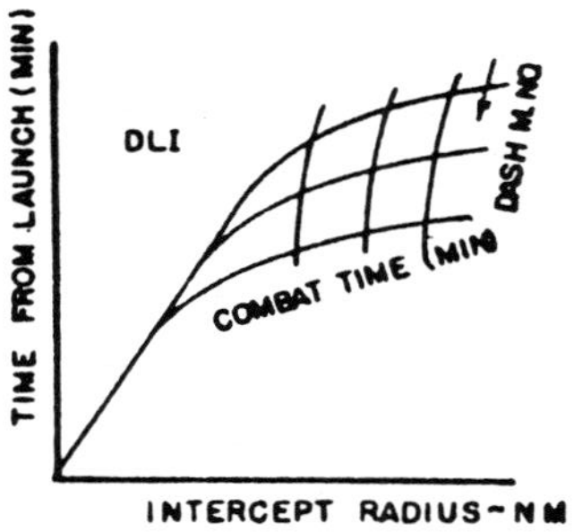

FIGURE - 4

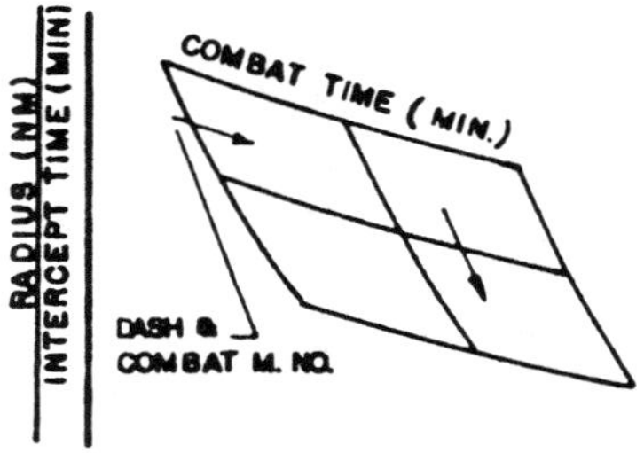

FIGURE - 5

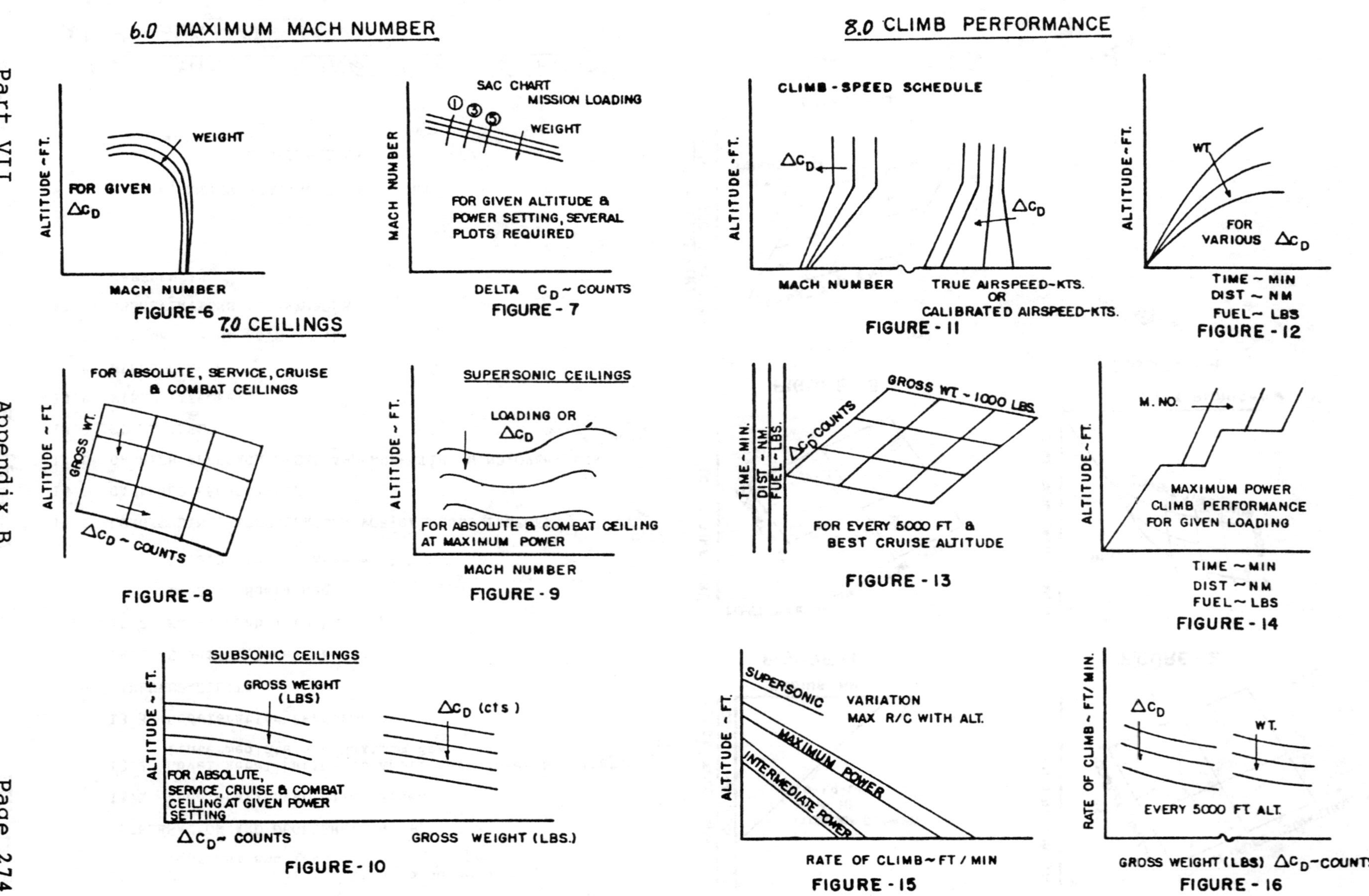

6.0 MAXIMUM MACH NUMBER
ALTITUDE-FT.
WEIGHT
FOR GIVEN ΔC_D
MACH NUMBER
FIGURE-6
MACH NUMBER
SAC CHART
MISSION LOADING
① ③ ⑤
WEIGHT
FOR GIVEN ALTITUDE & POWER SETTING, SEVERAL PLOTS REQUIRED
DELTA C_D ~ COUNTS
FIGURE - 7
7.0 CEILINGS
FOR ABSOLUTE, SERVICE, CRUISE & COMBAT CEILINGS
ALTITUDE ~ FT
GROSS WT.
ΔC_D ~ COUNTS
FIGURE-8
SUPERSONIC CEILINGS
ALTITUDE ~ FT.
LOADING OR ΔC_D
FOR ABSOLUTE & COMBAT CEILING AT MAXIMUM POWER
MACH NUMBER
FIGURE - 9
SUBSONIC CEILINGS
ALTITUDE ~ FT.
GROSS WEIGHT (LBS)
ΔC_D (cts)
FOR ABSOLUTE, SERVICE, CRUISE & COMBAT CEILING AT GIVEN POWER SETTING
ΔC_D~ COUNTS
GROSS WEIGHT (LBS.)
FIGURE - 10
8.0 CLIMB PERFORMANCE
CLIMB-SPEED SCHEDULE
ALTITUDE-FT.
ΔC_D
ΔC_D
MACH NUMBER
TRUE AIRSPEED-KTS. OR CALIBRATED AIRSPEED-KTS.
FIGURE - 11
ALTITUDE-FT.
WT.
FOR VARIOUS ΔC_D
TIME ~ MIN
DIST ~ NM
FUEL~ LBS
FIGURE - 12
TIME-MIN.
DIST-NM.
FUEL-LBS.
ΔC_D-COUNTS
GROSS WT - 1000 LBS
FOR EVERY 5000 FT & BEST CRUISE ALTITUDE
FIGURE - 13
ALTITUDE-FT.
M. NO.
MAXIMUM POWER CLIMB PERFORMANCE FOR GIVEN LOADING
TIME ~ MIN
DIST ~ NM
FUEL ~ LBS
FIGURE - 14
ALTITUDE - FT.
SUPERSONIC
VARIATION MAX R/C WITH ALT.
MAXIMUM POWER
INTERMEDIATE POWER
RATE OF CLIMB ~ FT / MIN
FIGURE - 15
RATE OF CLIMB ~ FT/MIN.
ΔC_D
WT.
EVERY 5000 FT ALT.
GROSS WEIGHT (LBS) ΔC_D-COUNTS
FIGURE - 16

9.0 CRUISE PERFORMANCE

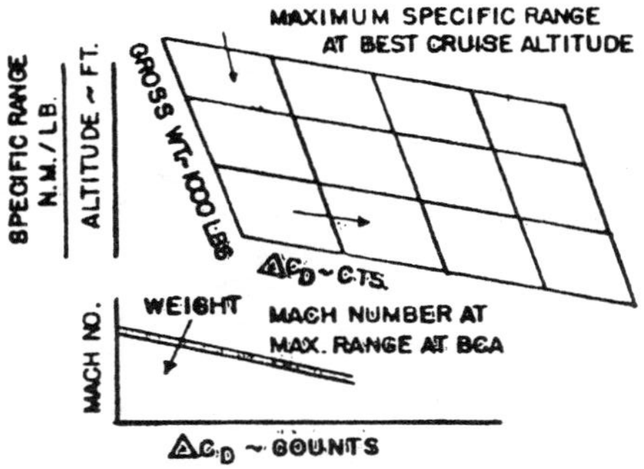

MAXIMUM SPECIFIC RANGE AT BEST CRUISE ALTITUDE

SPECIFIC RANGE N.M./LB.
ALTITUDE ~ FT.
GROSS WT-1000 LBS
ΔC_D ~ CTS.

MACH NUMBER AT MAX. RANGE AT BCA

MACH NO.
WEIGHT
ΔC_D ~ COUNTS

FIGURE - 17

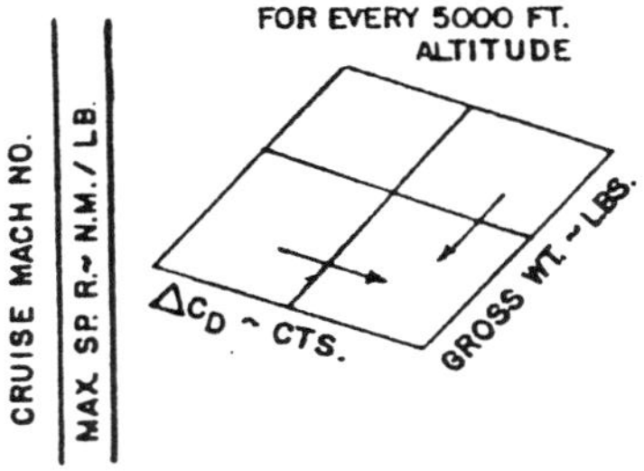

FOR EVERY 5000 FT. ALTITUDE

CRUISE MACH NO.
MAX. SP. R.~ N.M./LB.
ΔC_D ~ CTS.
GROSS WT. ~ LBS.

FIGURE - 18

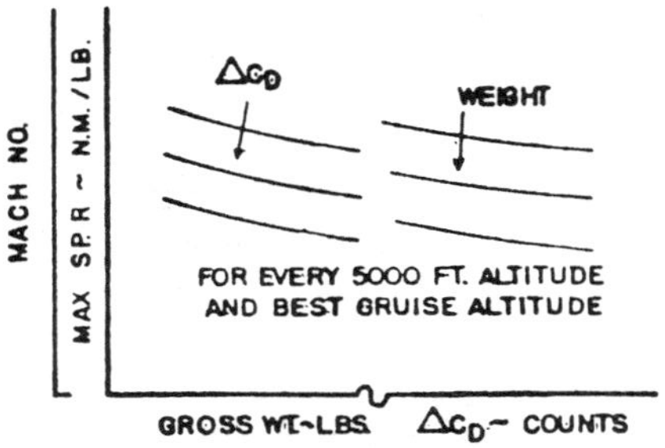

MACH NO.
MAX SP. R ~ N.M./LB.
ΔC_D
WEIGHT
FOR EVERY 5000 FT. ALTITUDE AND BEST CRUISE ALTITUDE
GROSS WT-LBS. ΔC_D ~ COUNTS

FIGURE - 19

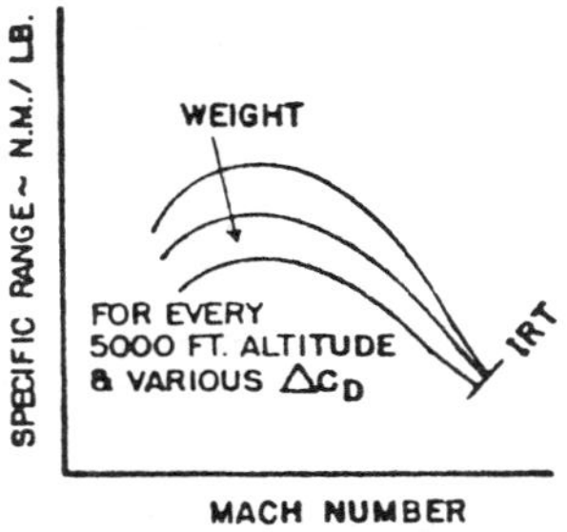

SPECIFIC RANGE ~ N.M./LB.
WEIGHT
FOR EVERY 5000 FT. ALTITUDE & VARIOUS ΔC_D
IRT
MACH NUMBER

FIGURE - 20

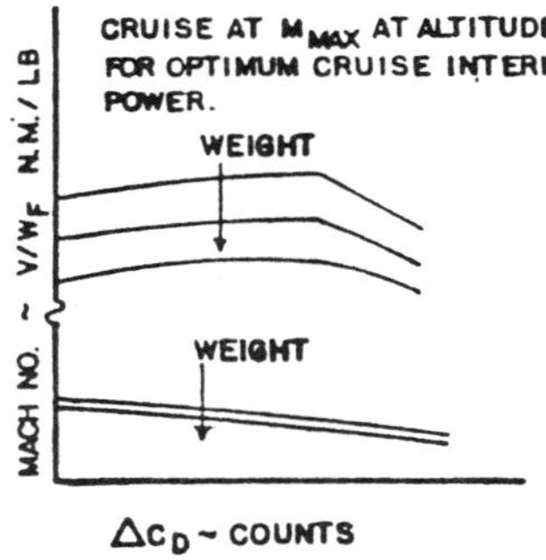

CRUISE AT M_{MAX} AT ALTITUDE FOR OPTIMUM CRUISE INTERMEDIATE POWER.

MACH NO. ~ V/W_F N.M./LB
WEIGHT
WEIGHT
ΔC_D ~ COUNTS

FIGURE - 21

CRUISE AT M_{MAX} AT SEA LEVEL INTERMEDIATE POWER.

MACH NO. · V/W_F N.M./LB.
ALL WEIGHTS
ALL WEIGHTS
ΔC_D ~ COUNTS

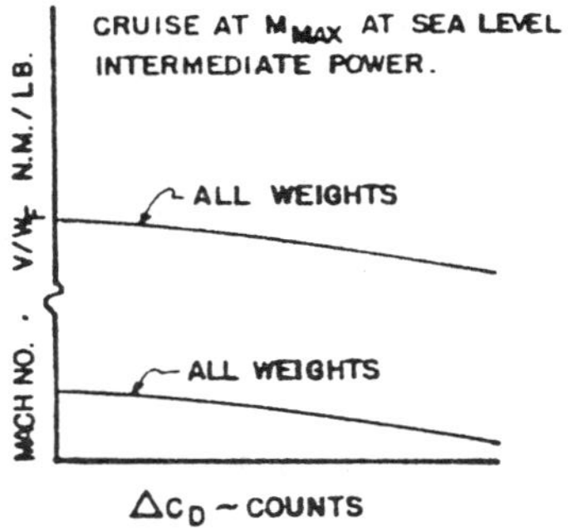

FIGURE - 22

9.0 CRUISE PERFORMANCE CONT'D

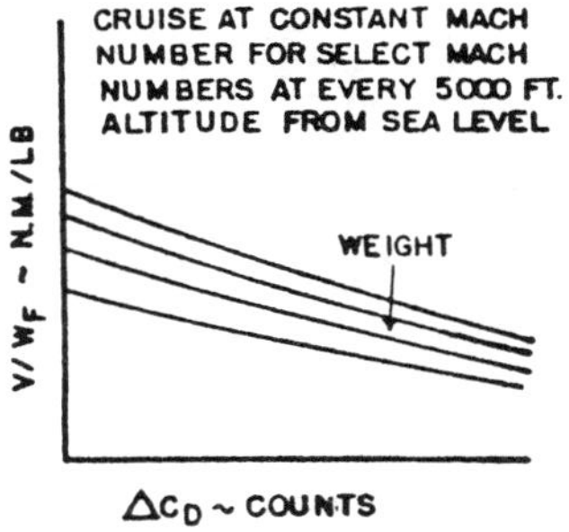

CRUISE AT CONSTANT MACH NUMBER FOR SELECT MACH NUMBERS AT EVERY 5000 FT. ALTITUDE FROM SEA LEVEL

V/W_F ~ N.M./LB
WEIGHT
ΔC_D ~ COUNTS

FIGURE - 23

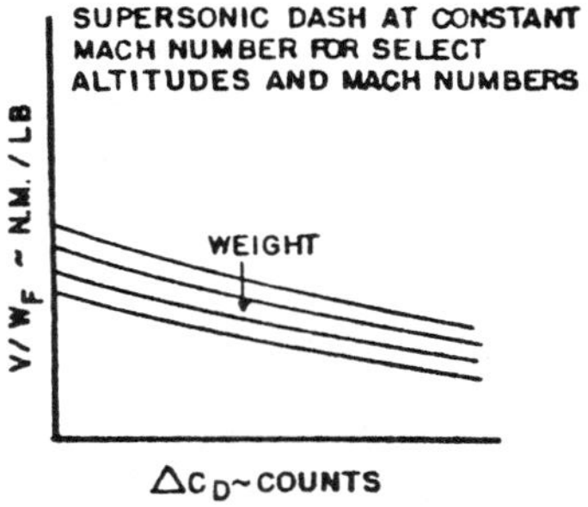

SUPERSONIC DASH AT CONSTANT MACH NUMBER FOR SELECT ALTITUDES AND MACH NUMBERS

V/W_F ~ N.M./LB
WEIGHT
ΔC_D ~ COUNTS

FIGURE - 24

PARTIAL AFTERBURNER POWER SPECIFIC RANGE FOR SELECT LOADINGS AND ALTITUDES

SPECIFIC RANGE ~ N.M./LB
MACH NUMBER
M FOR MIN. A/B
WEIGHT
M_{MAX}

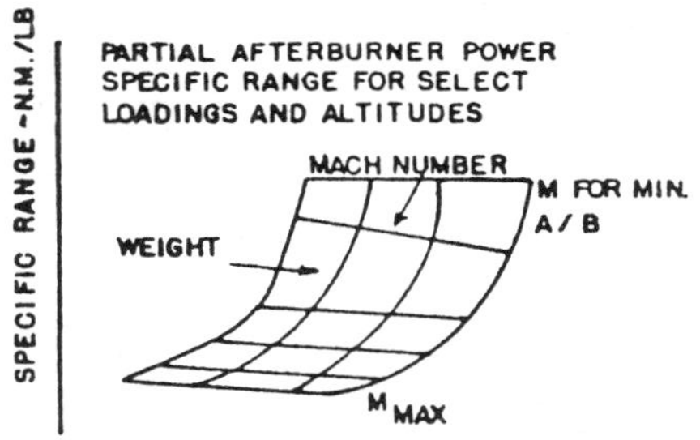

FIGURE - 25

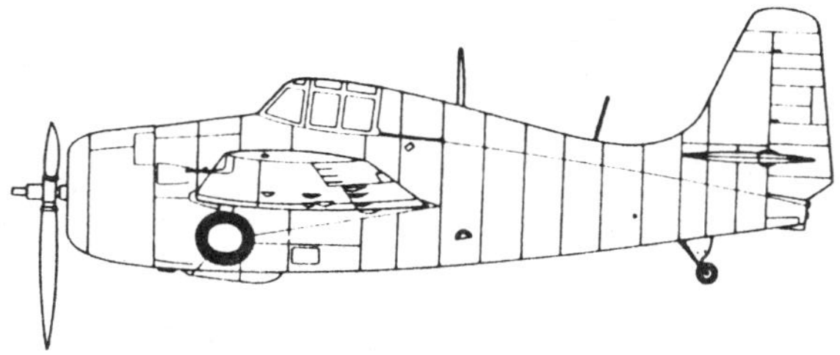

10. ENDURANCE & LOITER

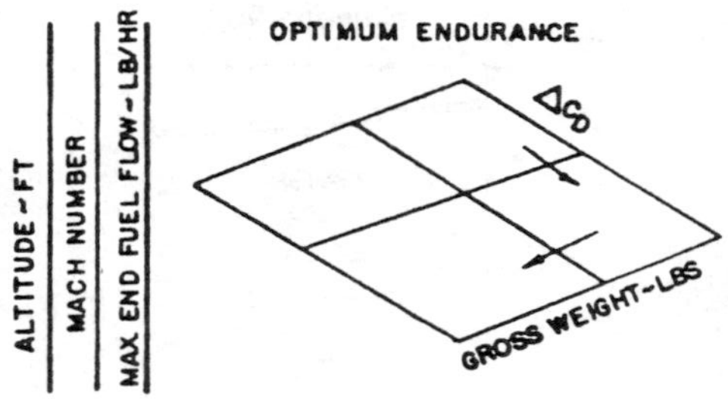

OPTIMUM ENDURANCE
ALTITUDE ~ FT
MACH NUMBER
MAX END FUEL FLOW ~ LB/HR
ΔC_D
GROSS WEIGHT ~ LBS

FIGURE - 26

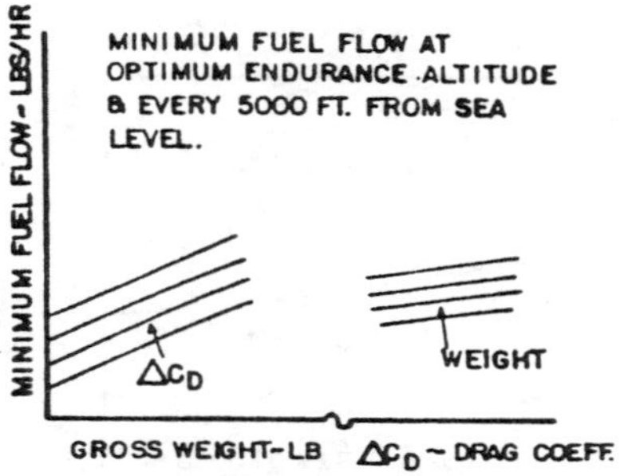

MINIMUM FUEL FLOW AT OPTIMUM ENDURANCE ALTITUDE & EVERY 5000 FT. FROM SEA LEVEL.
MINIMUM FUEL FLOW ~ LBS/HR
ΔC_D
WEIGHT
GROSS WEIGHT-LB
ΔC_D ~ DRAG COEFF.

FIGURE - 27

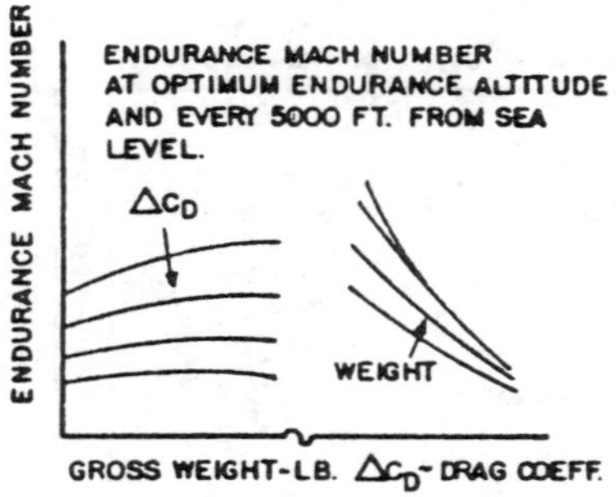

ENDURANCE MACH NUMBER AT OPTIMUM ENDURANCE ALTITUDE AND EVERY 5000 FT. FROM SEA LEVEL.
ENDURANCE MACH NUMBER
ΔC_D
WEIGHT
GROSS WEIGHT-LB.
ΔC_D ~ DRAG COEFF.

FIGURE - 28

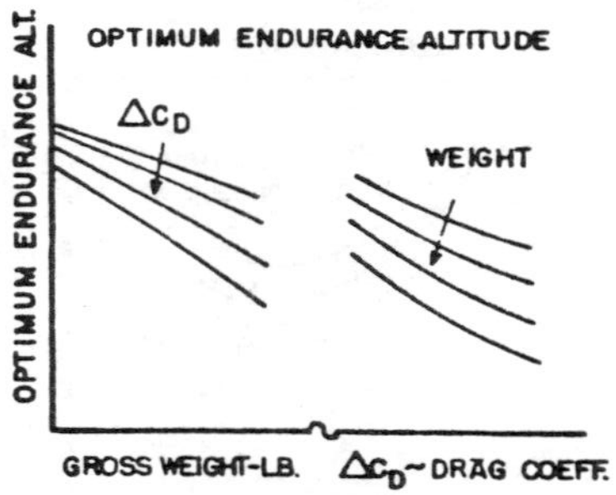

OPTIMUM ENDURANCE ALTITUDE
OPTIMUM ENDURANCE ALT.
ΔC_D
WEIGHT
GROSS WEIGHT-LB.
ΔC_D ~ DRAG COEFF.

FIGURE - 29

AT VARIOUS ALTITUDES AND LOADINGS
FUEL FLOW ~ LB/HR
WEIGHT
MAX ENDURANCE
MACH NUMBER

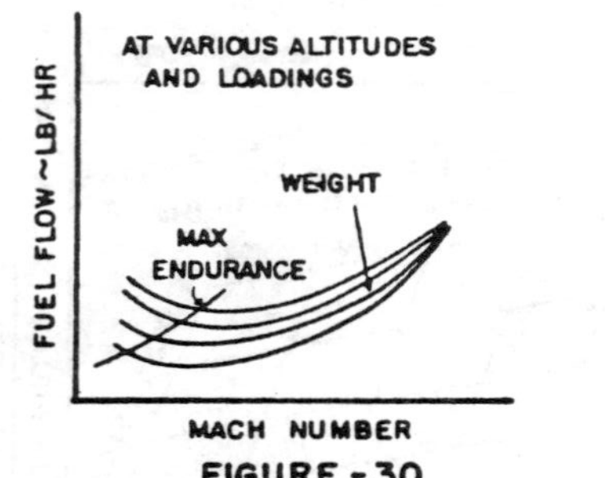

FIGURE - 30

12.0 DESCENT PERFORMANCE

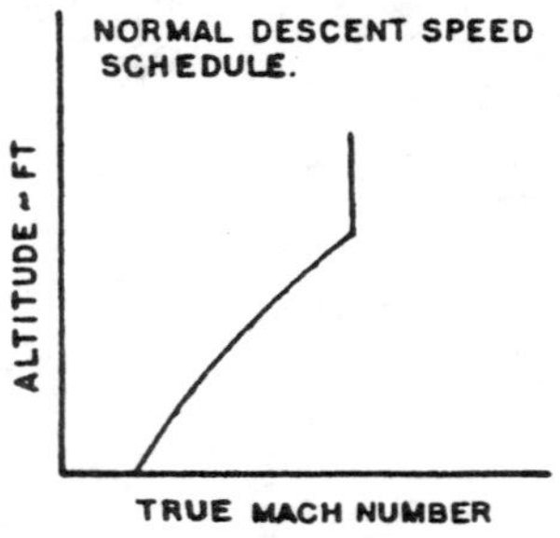

NORMAL DESCENT SPEED SCHEDULE.
ALTITUDE ~ FT
TRUE MACH NUMBER

FIGURE - 31

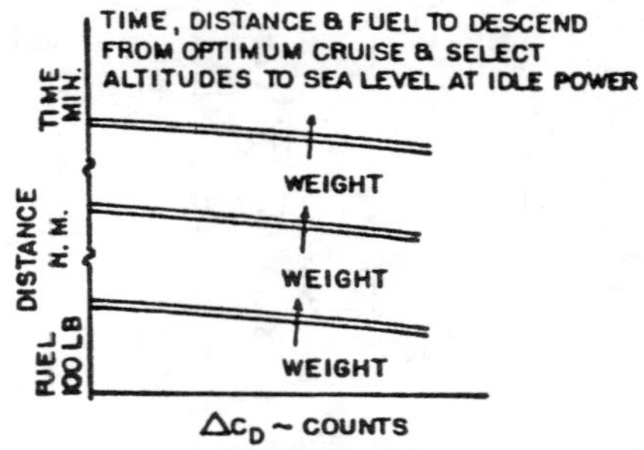

TIME, DISTANCE & FUEL TO DESCEND FROM OPTIMUM CRUISE & SELECT ALTITUDES TO SEA LEVEL AT IDLE POWER
TIME MIN.
DISTANCE N. M.
FUEL 100 LB
WEIGHT
WEIGHT
WEIGHT
ΔC_D ~ COUNTS

FIGURE - 32

13.0 ACCELERATION PERFORMANCE

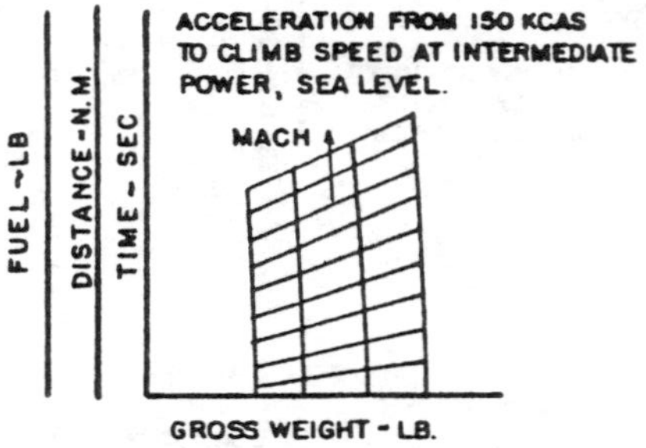

ACCELERATION FROM 150 KCAS TO CLIMB SPEED AT INTERMEDIATE POWER, SEA LEVEL.
FUEL ~ LB
DISTANCE ~ N.M.
TIME ~ SEC
MACH
GROSS WEIGHT - LB.

FIGURE - 33

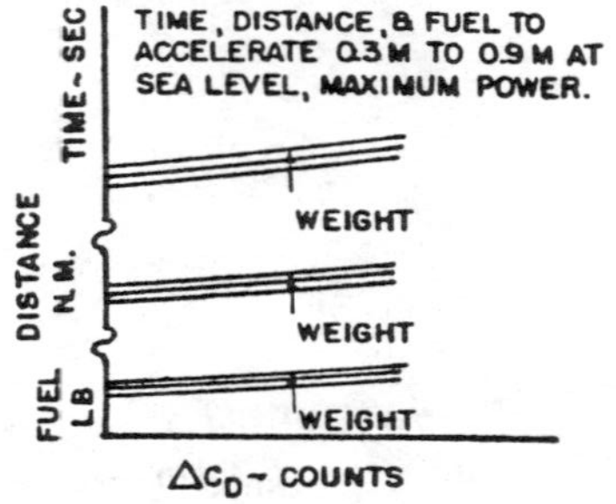

TIME, DISTANCE, & FUEL TO ACCELERATE 0.3 M TO 0.9 M AT SEA LEVEL, MAXIMUM POWER.
TIME ~ SEC
DISTANCE N. M.
FUEL LB
WEIGHT
WEIGHT
WEIGHT
ΔC_D ~ COUNTS

FIGURE - 34

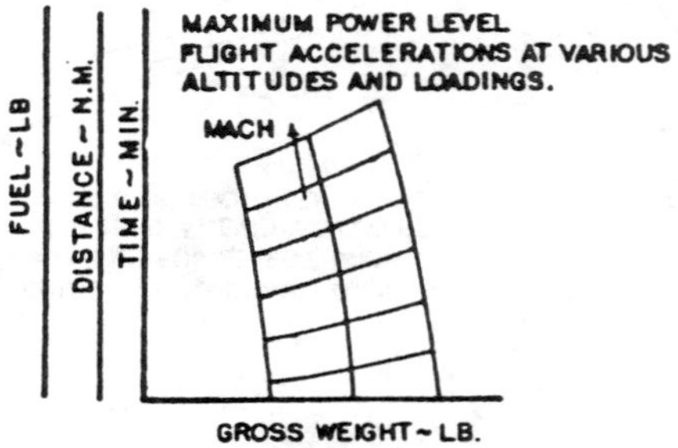

MAXIMUM POWER LEVEL FLIGHT ACCELERATIONS AT VARIOUS ALTITUDES AND LOADINGS.
FUEL ~ LB
DISTANCE ~ N.M.
TIME ~ MIN.
MACH
GROSS WEIGHT ~ LB.

FIGURE - 35

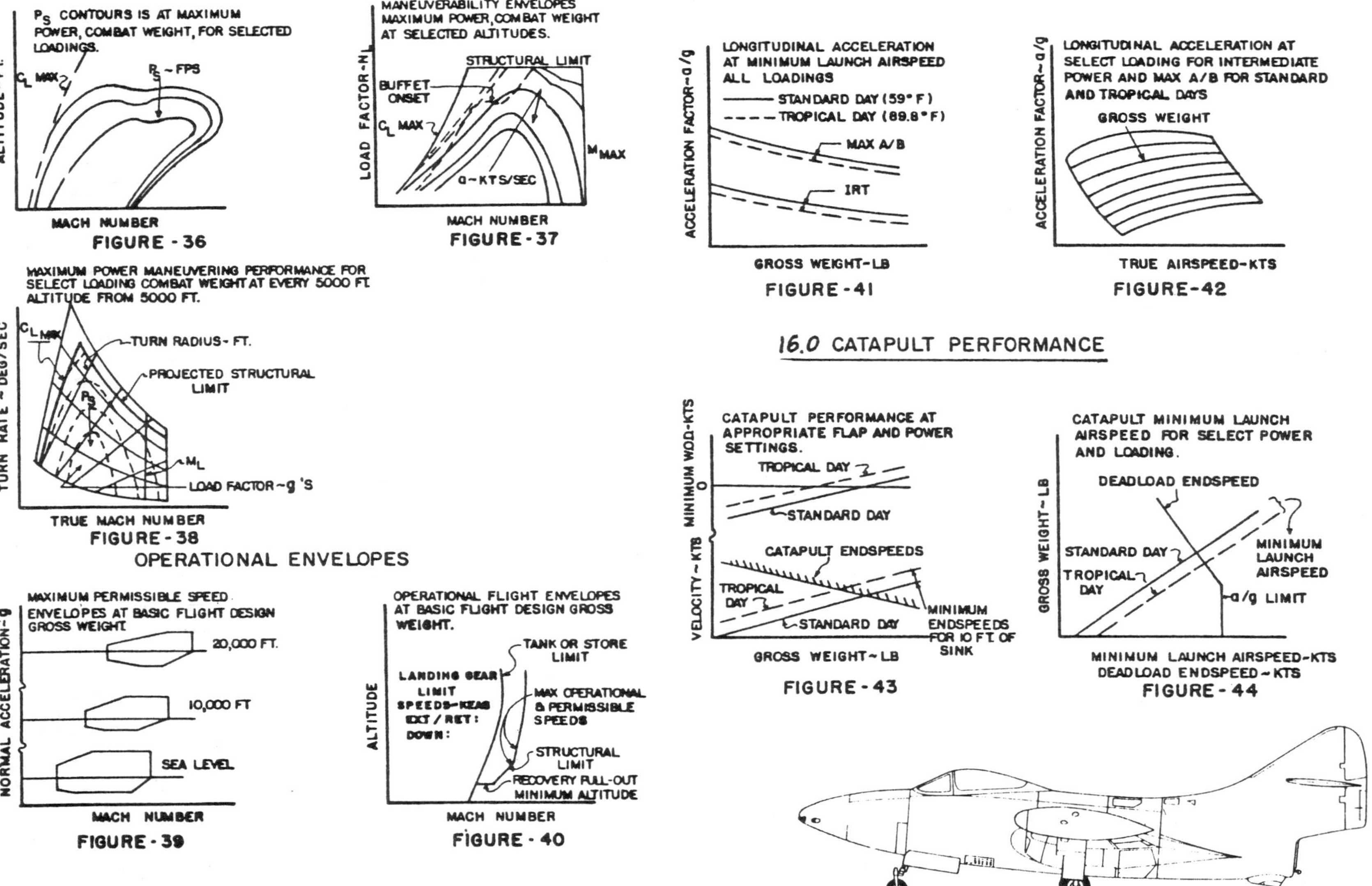
14.0 MANEUVERABILITY COMBAT PERFORMANCE
P_S CONTOURS IS AT MAXIMUM POWER, COMBAT WEIGHT, FOR SELECTED LOADINGS.
ALTITUDE-FT.
C_L MAX
P_S ~ FPS
MACH NUMBER
FIGURE - 36
MANEUVERABILITY ENVELOPES MAXIMUM POWER, COMBAT WEIGHT AT SELECTED ALTITUDES.
LOAD FACTOR-N_L
STRUCTURAL LIMIT
BUFFET ONSET
C_L MAX
M_{MAX}
a ~ KTS/SEC
MACH NUMBER
FIGURE - 37
MAXIMUM POWER MANEUVERING PERFORMANCE FOR SELECT LOADING COMBAT WEIGHT AT EVERY 5000 FT. ALTITUDE FROM 5000 FT.
TURN RATE ~ DEG/SEC
C_L MAX
TURN RADIUS- FT.
PROJECTED STRUCTURAL LIMIT
P_S
M_L
LOAD FACTOR ~ g 'S
TRUE MACH NUMBER
FIGURE - 38
OPERATIONAL ENVELOPES
MAXIMUM PERMISSIBLE SPEED ENVELOPES AT BASIC FLIGHT DESIGN GROSS WEIGHT
NORMAL ACCELERATION ~ g
20,000 FT.
10,000 FT
SEA LEVEL
MACH NUMBER
FIGURE - 39
OPERATIONAL FLIGHT ENVELOPES AT BASIC FLIGHT DESIGN GROSS WEIGHT.
ALTITUDE
LANDING GEAR LIMIT SPEEDS-KEAS EXT / RET: DOWN:
TANK OR STORE LIMIT
MAX OPERATIONAL & PERMISSIBLE SPEEDS
STRUCTURAL LIMIT
RECOVERY PULL-OUT MINIMUM ALTITUDE
MACH NUMBER
FIGURE - 40
15.0 LONGITUDINAL ACCELERATION
LONGITUDINAL ACCELERATION AT MINIMUM LAUNCH AIRSPEED ALL LOADINGS
STANDARD DAY (59° F)
TROPICAL DAY (89.8° F)
ACCELERATION FACTOR-a/g
MAX A/B
IRT
GROSS WEIGHT-LB
FIGURE - 41
LONGITUDINAL ACCELERATION AT SELECT LOADING FOR INTERMEDIATE POWER AND MAX A/B FOR STANDARD AND TROPICAL DAYS
ACCELERATION FACTOR ~ a/g
GROSS WEIGHT
TRUE AIRSPEED-KTS
FIGURE - 42
16.0 CATAPULT PERFORMANCE
CATAPULT PERFORMANCE AT APPROPRIATE FLAP AND POWER SETTINGS.
MINIMUM WOD-KTS
VELOCITY ~ KTS
0
TROPICAL DAY
STANDARD DAY
CATAPULT ENDSPEEDS
TROPICAL DAY
STANDARD DAY
MINIMUM ENDSPEEDS FOR 10 FT. OF SINK
GROSS WEIGHT ~ LB
FIGURE - 43
CATAPULT MINIMUM LAUNCH AIRSPEED FOR SELECT POWER AND LOADING.
GROSS WEIGHT ~ LB
DEADLOAD ENDSPEED
STANDARD DAY
TROPICAL DAY
MINIMUM LAUNCH AIRSPEED
a/g LIMIT
MINIMUM LAUNCH AIRSPEED-KTS
DEADLOAD ENDSPEED ~ KTS
FIGURE - 44

17.0 CARRIER APPROACH SPEED & ARRESTING WIND-OVER-DECK

18.0 STALL SPEEDS

19.0 FIELD TAKE-OFF

20.0 FIELD LANDING

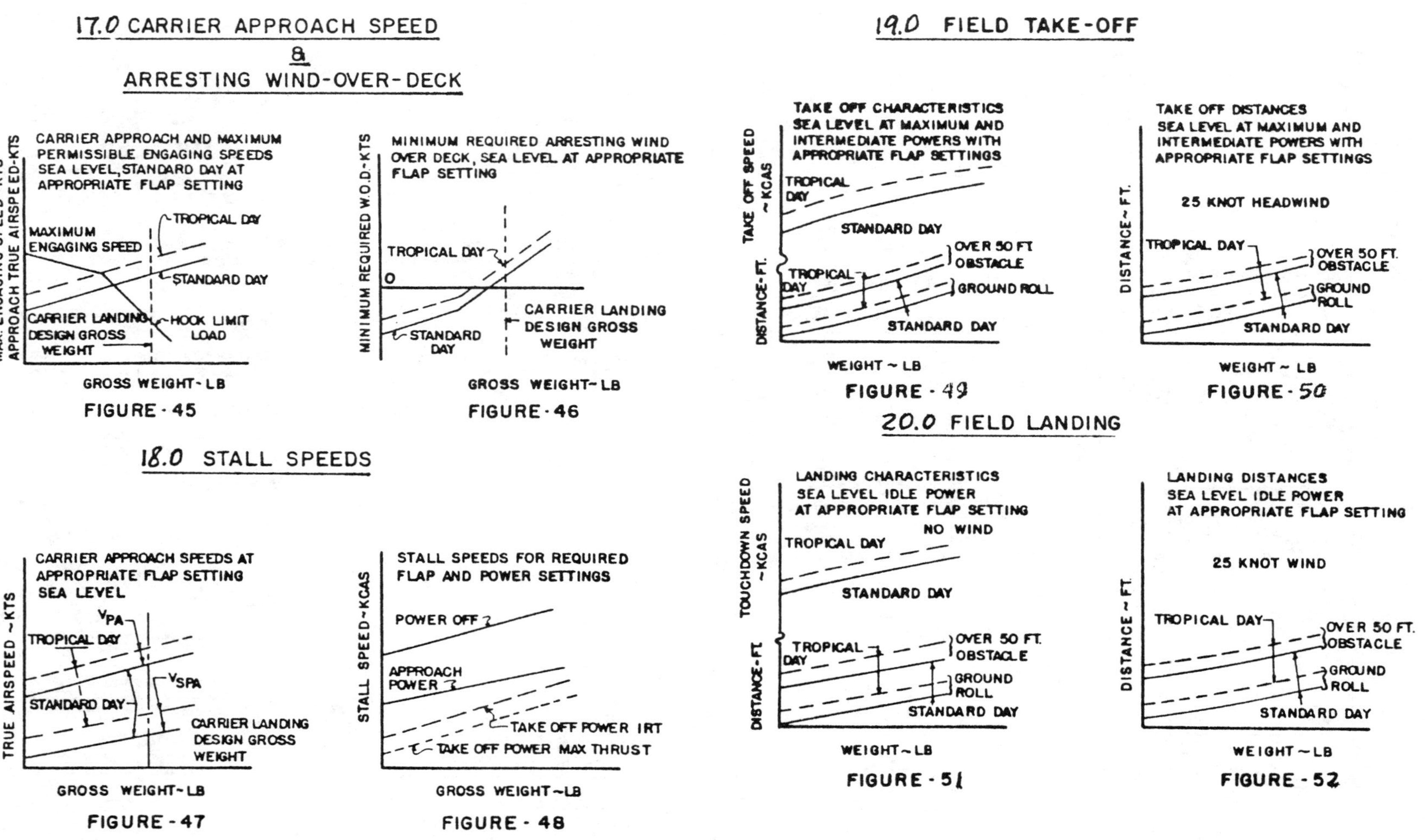

FIGURE - 45

FIGURE - 46

FIGURE - 47

FIGURE - 48

FIGURE - 49

FIGURE - 50

FIGURE - 51

FIGURE - 52

21.0 SINGLE ENGINE RATE-OF-CLIMB

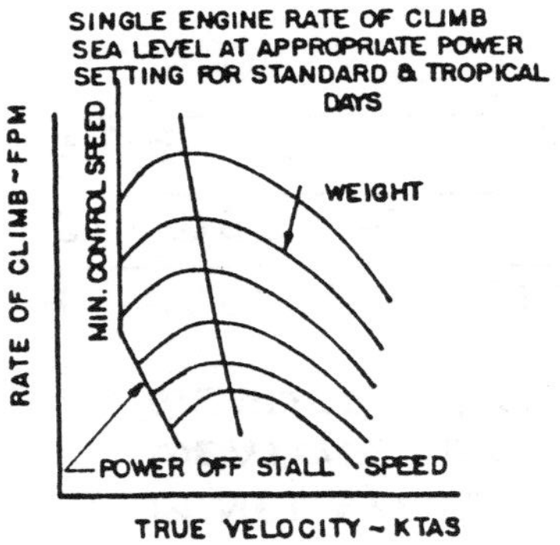

SINGLE ENGINE RATE OF CLIMB SEA LEVEL AT APPROPRIATE POWER SETTING FOR STANDARD & TROPICAL DAYS

RATE OF CLIMB~FPM
MIN. CONTROL SPEED
WEIGHT
POWER OFF STALL SPEED
TRUE VELOCITY ~ KTAS

FIGURE- 53

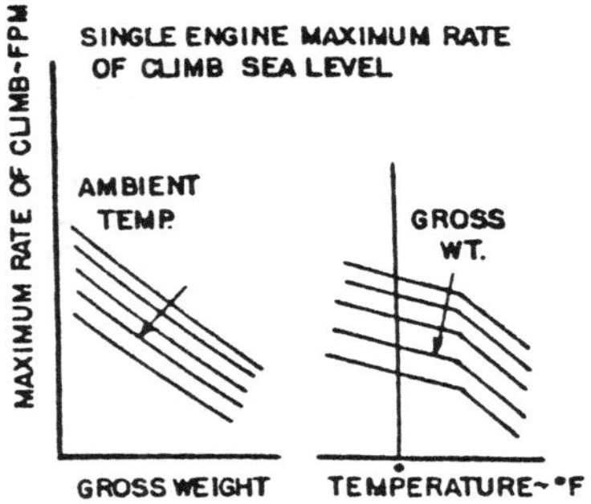

SINGLE ENGINE MAXIMUM RATE OF CLIMB SEA LEVEL

MAXIMUM RATE OF CLIMB~FPM
AMBIENT TEMP.
GROSS WEIGHT
GROSS WT.
TEMPERATURE~°F

FIGURE- 54

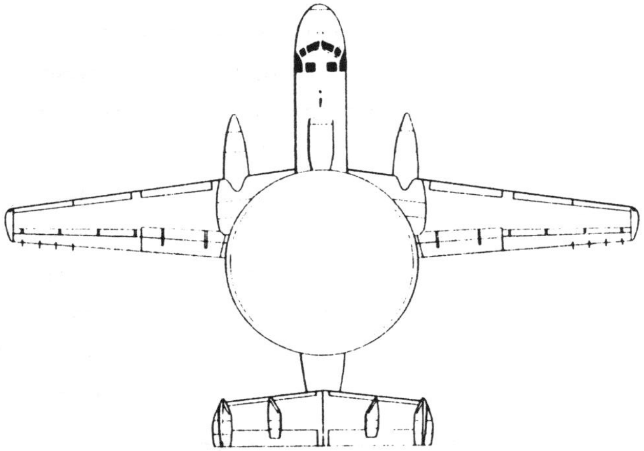

MISCELLANEOUS PROPULSION DATA

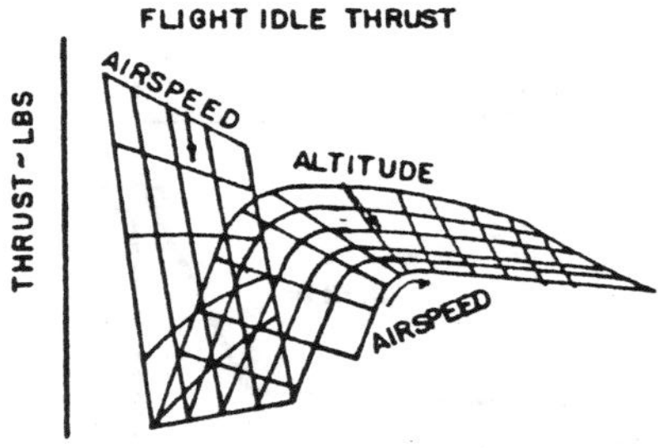

FLIGHT IDLE THRUST

THRUST~LBS
AIRSPEED
ALTITUDE
AIRSPEED

FIGURE -55

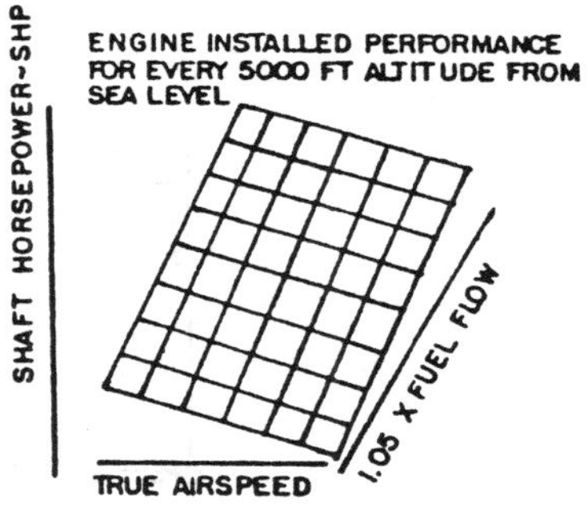

ENGINE INSTALLED PERFORMANCE FOR EVERY 5000 FT ALTITUDE FROM SEA LEVEL

SHAFT HORSEPOWER~SHP
1.05 X FUEL FLOW
TRUE AIRSPEED

FIGURE-56

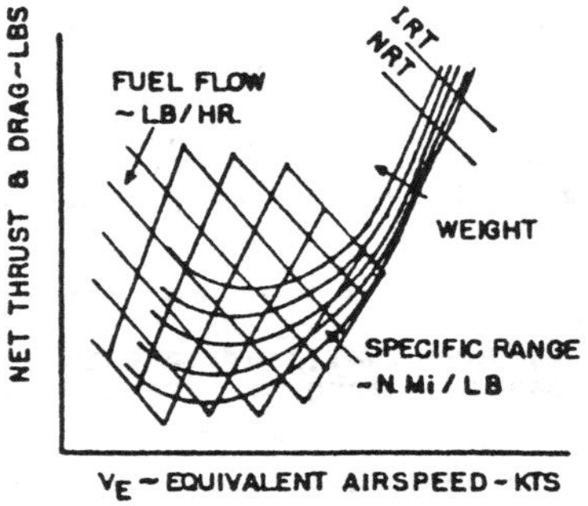

FOR EVERY 5000 FT ALTITUDE FROM SEA LEVEL

NET THRUST & DRAG~LBS
FUEL FLOW ~LB/HR.
IRT
NRT
WEIGHT
SPECIFIC RANGE ~N.Mi/LB
V_E ~ EQUIVALENT AIRSPEED-KTS

FIGURE -57

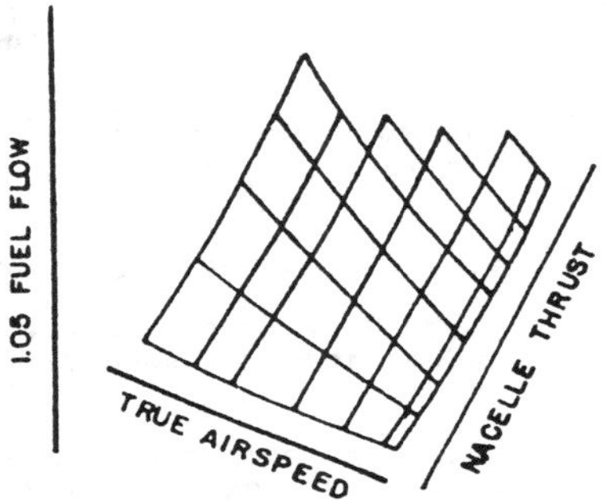

ENGINE INSTALLED PERFORMANCE FOR EVERY 5000 FT ALTITUDE FROM SEA LEVEL

1.05 FUEL FLOW
TRUE AIRSPEED
NACELLE THRUST

FIGURE-58

APPENDIX V

MISSION PROFILES

GENERAL MISSIONS

* 1. HI-HI-HI
2. Fighter Escort
3. Fighter Escort (Alternate)
* 4. Deck Launched Intercept
5. Deck Launched Intercept (Alternate)
* 6. Combat Air Patrol
* 7. Close Support
8. Ferry/Cross Country Navigation
* 9. Interdiction (HI-LO-LO-HI)
10. Interdiction (Alternate)
11. HI-LO-HI
12. LO-LO-LO
13. LO-LO-LO-HI
* 14. ASW SEARCH
* 15. ASW
* 16. MINELAYING
* 17. WEAPONS DELIVERY/ GUNNERY (TRAINING)

* MISSION PROFILES INCLUDED IN THIS TEXT. FOR OTHERS SEE AS-5263

HI-HI-HI
(High Altitude Subsonic)

1. For taxi, warmup, takeoff and acceleration to best climb speed: Fuel allowance at sea level static equal to 4.6 minutes at intermediate thrust plus 30 seconds afterburner thrust if afterburner is used for takeoff.

2. Climb: On course at best climb speed at intermediate power to best cruise altitude (not to exceed cruise ceiling).

3. Cruise Out: To target at speed and altitudes for best range, using a cruise climb flight path (not to exceed cruise ceiling).

4. Combat: Fuel allowance equal to 5 minutes at maximum speed with intermediate thrust at best cruise altitude. No distance is credited (drop bombs, retain mounting hardware and missiles after combat).

5. Cruise Back: To base at speed and altitudes for best range, using a cruise climb flight path (not to exceed cruise ceiling).

6. Descent: Descend to sea level (no fuel used, no distance gained).

7. Reserve: Fuel allowance equal to 20 minutes loiter at sea level at speeds for maximum endurance with all engines operating plus 5% of initial total fuel (internal plus external).

(a) Mission Time: Items 2 through 6.
(b) Cycle Time: Items 2 through 7.

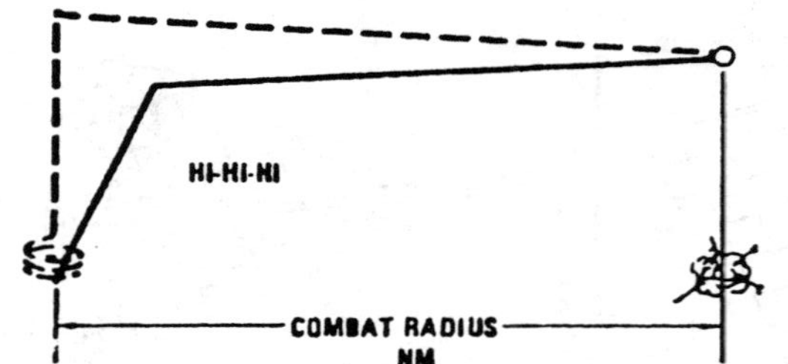

DECK LAUNCHED INTERCEPT

1. For taxi, warmup, takeoff and acceleration to Mach 0.3: Fuel allowance at sea level static equal to 4.6 minutes at intermediate thrust plus 30 seconds afterburner thrust if afterburner is used for takeoff.

2. Acceleration: Maximum power acceleration from Mach 0.3 to Mach 0.9 at sea level.

3. Climb: On course at Mach 0.9 at maximum power to 35,000 feet.

4. Acceleration: Maximum power acceleration from Mach 0.9 to Mach 1.35 at 35,000 feet.

5. Dash Out: Mach 1.35 dash at 35,000 feet.

6. Combat: Fuel allowance equal to 1 minute at maximum power, Mach 1.35 at 35,000 feet (no distance is credited, missiles are retained).

7. Climb: On course at best climb speed at intermediate power to best cruise altitude (not to exceed cruise ceiling).

8. Cruise Back: To base at speed and altitudes for best range, using a cruise climb flight path (not to exceed cruise ceiling).

9. Descent: Descend to sea level (no fuel used, no distance gained).

10. Reserve: Fuel allowance equal to 20 minutes loiter at sea level at speeds for maximum endurance with all engines operating plus 5% of initial total fuel (internal plus external).

(a) Mission Time: Items 2 through 9.
(b) Cycle Time: Items 2 through 10.

NOTE: Dash Mach and Altitude variations should be considered for this mission.

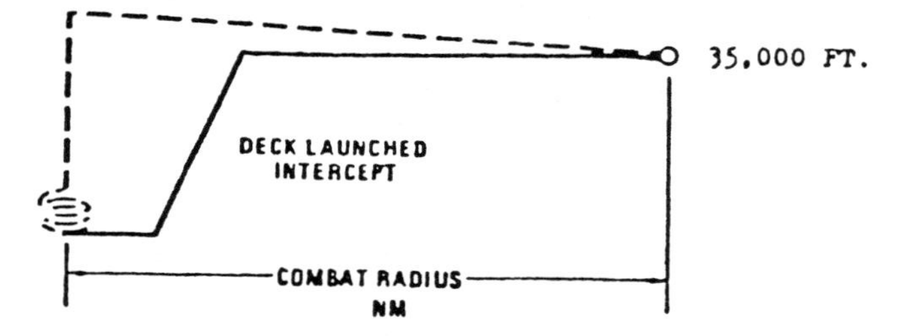

COMBAT AIR PATROL

1. For taxi, warmup, takeoff and acceleration to best climb speed: Fuel allowance at sea level static equal to 4.6 minutes at intermediate thrust plus 30 seconds afterburner thrust if afterburner is used for takeoff.

2. Climb: On course at best climb speed at intermediate thrust to best cruise altitudes (not to exceed cruise ceiling).

3. Cruise Out: To 150 nautical miles at speed and altitudes for best range, using a cruise climb flight path (not to exceed cruise ceiling).

4. Descent: Descend to 35,000 feet (no fuel used, no distance gained).

5. Loiter: Loiter at speed for maximum endurance at 35,000 feet (no distance is credited).

6. Combat: Fuel allowance equals that used to accelerate from loiter speed at 35,000 feet to Mach 1.2 plus 2 minutes at maximum power, Mach 1.2 at 35,000 feet (no distance is credited, missiles are retained).

7. Climb: On course at best climb speed at intermediate thrust to best cruise altitude (not to exceed cruise ceiling).

8. Cruise Back: To base at speed and altitudes for best range, using a cruise climb flight path (not to exceed cruise ceiling).

9. Descent: Descend to sea level (no fuel used, no distance gained).

10. Reserve: Fuel allowance equal to 20 minutes loiter at sea level at speeds for maximum endurance with all engines operating plus 5% of initial total fuel (internal plus external).

(a) Mission Time: Items 2 through 9.
(b) Cycle Time: Items 2 through 10.

NOTE: Loiter altitude and combat variations should be considered for this mission.

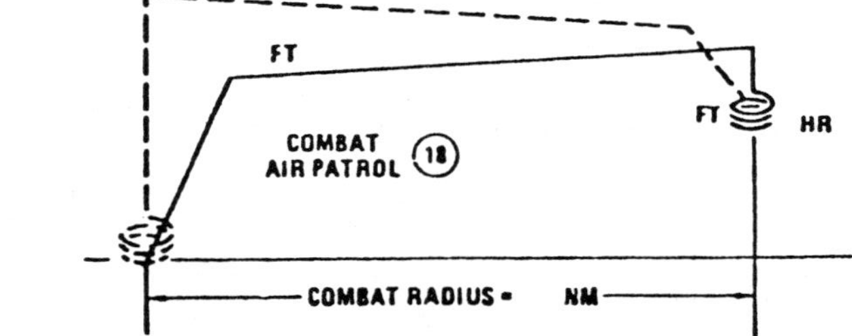

CLOSE SUPPORT

1. For taxi, warmup, takeoff and acceleration to best climb speed: Fuel allowance at sea level static equal to 4.6 minutes at intermediate thrust plus 30 seconds afterburner thrust if afterburner is used for takeoff.

2. Climb: On course at best climb speed at intermediate thrust to best cruise altitude (not to exceed cruise ceiling).

3. Cruise Out: To target at speed and altitudes for best range, using a cruise climb flight path (not to exceed cruise ceiling).

4. Descent: Descend to 5,000 feet (no fuel used, no distance gained).

5. Loiter: Loiter for 1 hour at speed for maximum endurance at 5,000 feet (no distance is credited, drop bombs after loiter, retain mounting hardware and missiles).

6. Climb: On course at best climb speed at intermediate thrust from 5,000 feet to best cruise altitude (not to exceed cruise ceiling).

7. Cruise Back: To base at speed and altitudes for best range, using a cruise climb flight path (not to exceed cruise ceiling).

8. Descent: Descend to sea level (no fuel used, no distance gained).

9. Reserve: Fuel allowance equal to 20 minutes loiter at sea level at speeds for maximum endurance with all engines operating plus 5% of initial total fuel (internal plus external).

(a) Mission Time: Items 2 through 8.
(b) Cycle Time: Items 2 through 9.

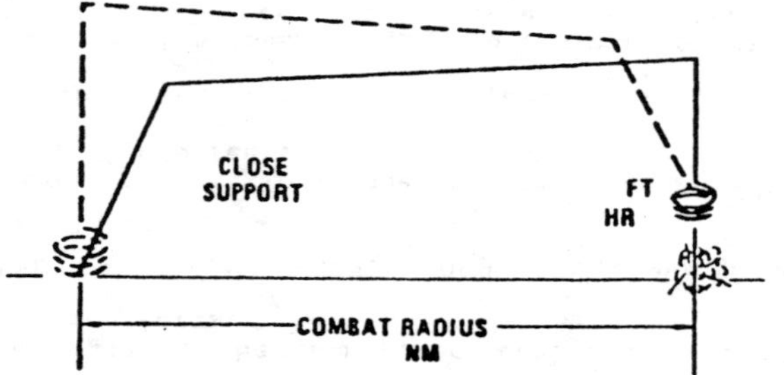

INTERDICTION

1. For taxi, warmup, takeoff and acceleration to best climb speed: Fuel allowance at sea level static equal to 4.6 minutes at intermediate thrust plus 30 seconds afterburner thrust if afterburner is used for takeoff.

2. Climb: On course at best climb speed at intermediate thrust to best cruise altitude (not to exceed cruise ceiling).

3. Cruise Out: At speeds and altitudes for best range, using a cruise climb flight path (not to exceed cruise ceiling).

4. Descent: Descend to sea level (no fuel used, no distance gained).

5. Run-in to Target: Sea level dash for 50 nautical miles at Mach 0.8 (or maximum speed at intermediate thrust if less than Mach 0.8).

6. Combat: Fuel allowance equal to 5 minutes at intermediate thrust, Mach 0.8 (or maximum speed if less than Mach 0.8) at sea level. No distance is credited (drop bombs, retain mounting hardware and missiles after combat).

7. Run-out from Target: Sea level dash for 50 nautical miles at Mach 0.8 (or maximum speed at intermediate thrust if less than Mach 0.8).

8. Climb: On course at best climb speed at intermediate thrust from sea level to best cruise altitude (not to exceed cruise ceiling).

9. Cruise Back: At speeds and altitudes for best range, using a cruise climb flight path (not to exceed cruise ceiling).

10. Descent:, Descend to sea level (no fuel used, no distance gained).

11. Reserve: Fuel allowance equal to 20 minutes loiter at sea level at speeds for maximum endurance with all engines operating plus 5% of initial total fuel (internal plus external).

(a) Mission Time: Items 2 through 10.
(b) Cycle Time: Items 2 through 11.

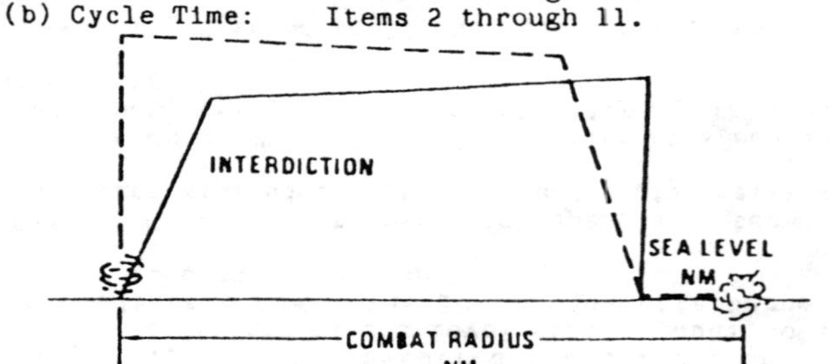

<u>ASW SEARCH</u>

1. For Taxi, warmup, takeoff and acceleration to best climb speed: Fuel allowance at sea level static equal to 4.6 minutes at intermediate thrust (10 minutes for propeller engine aircraft at normal power) plus 30 seconds afterburner thrust if afterburner is used for takeoff.

2. Climb: On course at best climb speed at intermediate thrust (normal power for props) to search altitude (not to exceed cruise ceiling).

3. Cruise Out: At search altitude at speed for maximum endurance (unless otherwise limited by handling qualities).

4. Cruise Back: At search altitude at speed for maximum endurance (unless otherwise limited by handling qualities).

5. Descent: Descend to sea level (no fuel used, no distance gained).

6. Reserve: Fuel allowance equal to 20 minutes (30 minutes for props) loiter at sea level at speeds for maximum endurance (maximum range for props) with all engines operating plus 5% of initial total fuel (internal plus external).

(a) Mission Time: Items 2 through 5.
(b) Cycle Time: Items 2 through 6.

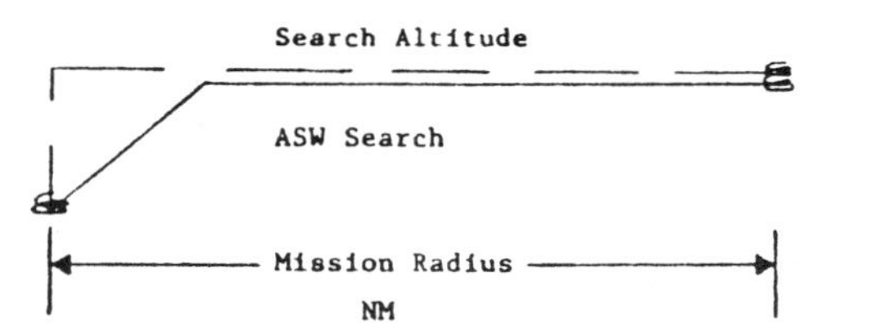

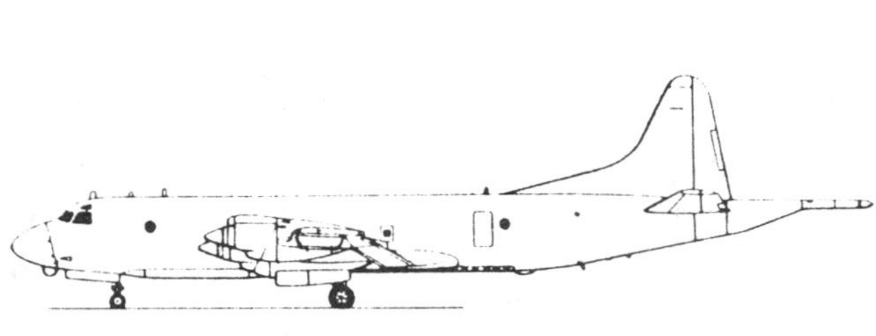

<u>ASW</u>

1. For Taxi, warmup, takeoff and acceleration to best climb speed: Fuel allowance at sea level static equal to 4.6 minutes at intermediate thrust (10 minutes for propeller engine aircraft at normal power) plus 30 seconds afterburner thrust if afterburner is used for takeoff.

2. Climb: On course at best climb speed at intermediate thrust (normal power for props) to best cruise altitude (not to exceed cruise ceiling).

3. Cruise Out: At speeds and altitudes for best range, using a cruise climb flight path (not to exceed cruise ceiling).

4. Descent: Descend to 20,000 feet (no fuel used, no distance gained).

5. Search: Search for 3 hours at speed for maximum endurance at 20,000 feet.

6. Descent: Descend to 200 feet (no fuel used, no distance gained).

7. Search: Search for 1 hour at speed for maximum endurance at 200 feet.

8. Climb: On course at best climb speed at intermediate thrust (normal power for props) to best cruise altitude (not to exceed cruise ceiling).

9. Cruise Back: At speeds and altitudes for best range, using a cruise climb flight path (not to exceed cruise ceiling).

10. Descent: Descend to sea level (no fuel used, no distance gained).

11. Reserve: Fuel allowance equal to 20 minutes (30 minutes for props) loiter at sea level at speeds for maximum endurance (maximum range for props) with all engines operating plus 5% of initial total fuel (internal plus external).

(a) Mission Time: Items 2 through 10.
(b) Cycle Time: Items 2 through 11.

ASW

20,000 ft

Mission Radius

NM

MINELAYING

1. For Taxi, warmup, takeoff and acceleration to best climb speed: Fuel allowance at sea level static equal to 4.6 minutes at intermediate thrust (10 minutes for propeller engine aircraft at normal power) plus 30 seconds afterburner thrust if afterburner is used for takeoff.

2. Climb: On course at best climb speed at intermediate thrust (normal power for props) to best cruise altitude (not to exceed cruise ceiling).

3. Cruise Out: At speeds and altitudes for best range, using a cruise climb flight path (not to exceed cruise ceiling).

4. Descent: Descend to 200 feet (no fuel used, no distance gained).

5. Penetrate: At maximum continuous power for 300 nautical miles at 200 feet.

6. Attack: At maximum continuous power for 100 nautical miles at 200 feet.

7. Release Mines.

8. Escape: On course at maximum continuous power for 300 nautical miles.

9. Climb: On course at best climb speed at intermediate thrust (normal power for props) from 200 feet to best cruise altitude (not to exceed cruise ceiling).

10. Cruise Back: At speeds and altitudes for best range, using a cruise climb flight path (not to exceed cruise ceiling).

11. Descent: Descend to sea level (no fuel used, no distance gained).

12. Reserve: Fuel allowance equal to 20 minutes (30 minutes for props) loiter at sea level at speeds for maximum endurance (maximum range for props) with all engines operating plus 5% of initial total fuel (internal plus external).

(a) Mission Time: Items 2 through 11.
(b) Cycle Time: Items 2 through 12.

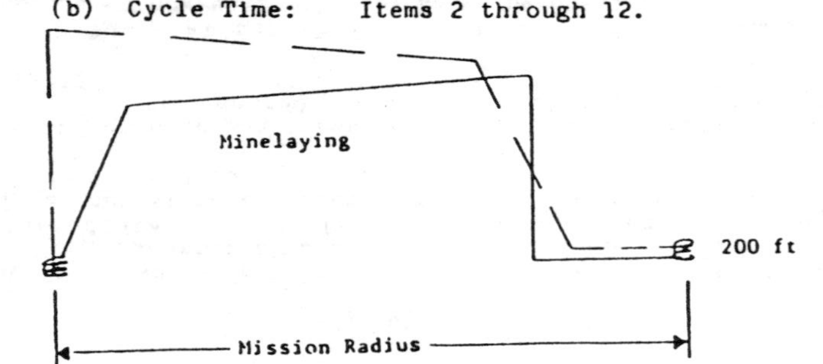

WEAPONS DELIVERY/GUNNERY

1. For Taxi, warmup, takeoff and acceleration to best climb speed: Fuel allowance at sea level static equal to 4.6 minutes at intermediate thrust plus 30 seconds afterburner thrust if afterburner is used for takeoff.

2. Climb: On course at best climb speed at intermediate thrust to 20,000 feet.

3. Cruise Out: 60 nautical miles from initial climb point at speed for best range at 20,000 feet.

4. Descent: Descend to gunnery altitude (10,000 feet) or weapons delivery altitude (sea level), (no fuel used, no distance gained).

5a. Gunnery Option: Time for gunnery shall be allocated as follows: 60% at intermediate thrust (Mach to be designated by NAVAIR), 25% at 80% intermediate thrust fuel flow (Mach to be designated by NAVAIR), and 15% at speed for best range. (no distance gained).

5b. Weapons Delivery Option: Time for weapons delivery shall be allocated as follows: 50% at intermediate thrust (Mach to be designated by NAVAIR), and 50% at 80% intermediate thrust fuel flow (Mach to be designated by NAVAIR). (no distance gained).

6. Climb: On course at best climb speed at intermediate thrust from gunnery (10,000 feet) or weapons delivery (sea level) altitude.

7. Cruise Back: 60 nautical miles from climb point at speed for best range at 20,000 feet.

8. Descent: Descend to sea level (no fuel used, no distance gained).

9. Reserve: Fuel allowance equal to 20 minutes loiter at sea level at speeds for maximum endurance with all engines operating plus 5% of initial total fuel (internal plus external).

(a) Mission Time: Items 2 through 8.
(b) Cycle Time: Items 2 through 9.

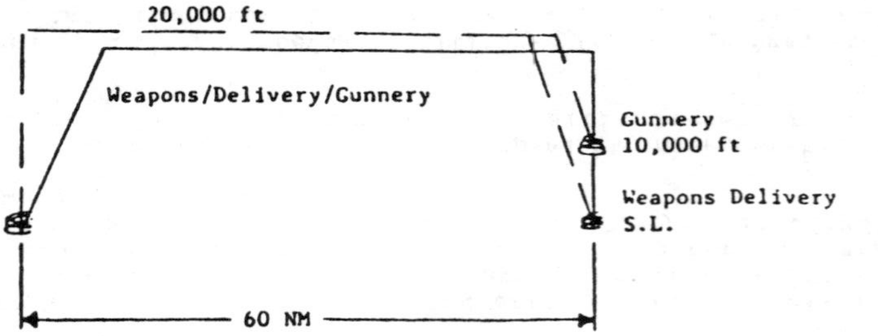

32. Airplane Stability, Control and Flying Qualities

NOTES: 1. FOR SYMBOLS SEE P. 330-341
2. FOR CONTENTS SEE P. 341-343

32.1 MIL-F-8785C: Military Specification, Flying Qualities of Piloted Airplanes, November 1980.

This specification is approved for use by all Departments and Agencies of the Department of Defense.

1. SCOPE

1.1 Scope. This specification contains the requirements for the flying and handling qualities, in flight and on the ground, of U.S. Military, manned, piloted airplanes except for flight at airspeeds below V_{con} (MIL-F-83300).

It is intended to assure flying qualities that provide adequate mission performance and flight safety regardless of design implementation or flight control system mechanization. The structure of the specification allows its use to guide these aspects in design tradeoffs, analyses and tests.

1.2 Application. The flying qualities of all airplanes proposed or contracted for shall be in accordance with the provisions of this specification. The requirements apply as stated to the combination of airframe and related subsystems. Stability augmentation and control augmentation are specifically to be included when provided in the airplane. The automatic flight control system is also to be considered to the extent stated in MIL-F-9490 or MIL-C-18244, whichever applies. The requirements are written in terms of cockpit flight controls that produce essentially pitching, yawing and rolling moments. This approach is not meant to preclude other modes of control for special purposes. Additional or alternative requirements may be imposed by the procuring activity in order to fit better the intended use or the particular design.

1.3 Classification of airplanes. For the purpose of this specification, an airplane shall be placed in one of the following Classes:

Class I Small, light airplanes such as:
- Light utility
- Primary trainer
- Light observation

Class II Medium weight, low-to-medium maneuverability airplanes such as:
- Heavy utility/search and rescue
- Light or medium transport/cargo/tanker
- Early warning/electronic countermeasures/airborne command, control or communications relay
- Antisubmarine
- Assault transport
- Reconnaissance
- Tactical bomber
- Heavy attack
- Trainer for Class II

Class III Large, heavy, low-to-medium maneuverability airplanes such as:
- Heavy transport/cargo/tanker
- Heavy bomber
- Patrol/early warning/electronic countermeasures/airborne command, control, or communications relay
- Trainer for Class III

Class IV High-maneuverability airplanes such as:
- Fighter/interceptor
- Attack
- Tactical reconnaissance
- Observation
- Trainer for Class IV

The procuring activity will assign an airplane to one of these Classes, and the requirements for that Class shall apply. When no Class is specified in a requirement, the requirement shall apply to all Classes. When operational missions so dictate, an airplane of one Class may be required by the procuring activity to meet selected requirements ordinarily specified for airplanes of another Class.

1.3.1 Land- or carrier-based designation. The letter -L following a Class designation identifies an airplane as land-based. Carrier-based airplanes are similarly identified by -C. When no such differentiation is made in a requirement, the requirement shall apply to both land-based and carrier-based airplanes.

1.4 Flight Phase Categories. The Flight Phases have been combined into three Categories which are referred to in the requirement statements. These Flight Phases shall be considered in the context of total missions so that there will be no gap between successive Phases of any flight and so that transition will be smooth. In certain cases, requirements are directed at specific Flight Phases identified in the requirement. When no Flight Phase or Category is stated in a requirement, that requirement shall apply to all three Categories. Flight Phases descriptive of most military airplane missions are:

Nonterminal Flight Phases:

Category A: Those nonterminal Flight Phases that require rapid maneuvering, precision tracking, or precise flight-path control. Included in this Category are:

a. Air-to-air combat (CO)
b. Ground Attack (GA)
c. Weapon delivery/launch (WD)
d. Aerial recovery (AR)
e. Reconnaissance (RC)
f. In-flight refuelling (receiver) (RR)
g. Terrain following (TF)
h. Antisubmarine search (AS)
i. Close formation flying (FF)

Category B: Those nonterminal Flight Phases that are normally accomplished using gradual maneuvers and without precision tracking, although accurate flight-path control may be required. Included in this Category are:

a. Climb (CL)
b. Cruise (CR)
c. Loiter (LO)
d. In-flight refueling (tanker) (RT)
e. Descent (D)
f. Emergency descent (ED)
g. Emergency deceleration (DE)
h. Aerial delivery (AD)

Terminal Flight Phases:

Category C: Terminal Flight Phases are normally accomplished using gradual maneuvers and usually require accurate flight-path control. Included in this category are:

a. Takeoff (TO)
b. Catapult takeoff (CT)
c. Approach (PA)
d. Wave-off/go-around (WO)
e. Landing (L)

When necessary, recategorization or addition of Flight Phases or delineation of requirements for special purpose situations, e.g. zoom climbs, will be accomplished by the procuring activity.

1.5 Levels of flying qualities. Where possible, the requirements of Section 3 have been stated in terms of three values of the stability or control parameter being specified. Each value is a minimum condition to meet one of three Levels of acceptability related to the ability to complete operational missions for which the airplane is designed. The Levels are:

Level 1: Flying qualities clearly adequate for the mission Flight Phase.

Level 2: Flying qualities adequate to accomplish the mission Flight Phase, but some increase in pilot workload or degradation in mission effectiveness, or both, exists.

Level 3: Flying qualities such that the airplane can be controlled safely, but pilot workload is excessive or mission effectiveness is inadequate, or both. Category A Flight Phases can be terminated safely, and Category B and C Flight Phases can be completed.

2. APPLICABLE DOCUMENTS

2.1 Issues of documents. The following documents, of the issue in effect on the date of invitation for bids or request for proposal, form a part of this specification to the extent specified herein:

SPECIFICATIONS

MILITARY

MIL-D-8708 Demonstration Requirements for Airplanes

MIL-A-8861 Airplane Strength and Rigidity Flight Loads

MIL-F-9490 Flight Control Systems- Design, Installation and Test of, Piloted Aircraft, General Specification for

MIL-C-18244 Control and Stabilization Systems, Automatic, Piloted Aircraft, General Specification for

MIL-F-18372 Flight Control Systems, Design, Installation and Test of, Aircraft, General Specification for

MIL-W-25140 Weight and Balance Control Data (for Airplanes and Rotorcraft)

MIL-F-83300 Flying Qualities of Piloted V/STOL Aircraft

MIL-S-83691 Stall/Post-Stall/Spin Flight Test Demonstration Requirements for Airplanes

STANDARDS

MIL-STD-756 Reliability Prediction

(Copies of specifications and standards required by contractors in connection with specific procurement functions should be obtained from the procuring activity or as directed by the contracting officer).

3. REQUIREMENTS

3.1 General Requirements

3.1.1 Operational missions. The procuring activity will specify the operational missions to be considered by the contractor in designing the airplane to meet the flying quality requirements of this specification. These missions will include all associated Flight Phases and tasks, such as takeoff, takeoff abort, landing and missed approach. Operational missions include the entire spectrum of intended usage including aircrew upgrade and training.

3.1.2 Loadings. The contractor shall define the envelopes of center-of-gravity and corresponding weights that will exist for each Flight Phase. These envelopes shall include the most forward and aft center-of-gravity positions as defined in MIL-W-25140. In addition, the contractor shall determine the maximum center-of-gravity excursions attainable through failures in systems or components, such as fuel sequencing, hung stores, etc., for each Flight Phase to be considered in the Failure States of 3.1.6.2. Within these envelopes, plus a growth margin to be specified by the procuring activity, and for the excursions cited above, this specification shall apply.

3.1.3 Moments and products of inertia. The contractor shall define the moments and products of inertia of the airplane associated with all loadings of 3.1.2. The requirements of this specification shall apply for all moments and products of inertia so defined.

3.1.4 External stores. The requirements of this specification shall apply for all combinations of external stores required by the operational missions. The effects of external stores on the weight, moments of inertia, center-of-gravity position, and aerodynamic characteristics of the airplane shall be considered for each mission Flight Phase. When the stores contain expendable loads, the requirements of this specification apply throughout the range of store loadings. The external stores and store combinations to be considered for flying qualities design will be specified by the procuring activity. In establishing external store combinations to be investigated, consideration shall be given to asymmetric as well as to symmetric combinations.

3.1.5 Configurations. The requirements of this specification shall apply for all configurations required or encountered in the applicable Flight Phases of 1.4. A (crew-) selected configuration is defined by the positions and adjustments of the various selectors and controls available to the crew except for pitch, roll, yaw, throttle and trim controls. Examples are: the flap control setting and the yaw damper ON or OFF. The selected configurations to be examined must consist of those required for performance and mission accomplishment. Additional configurations to be investigated may be defined by the procuring activity.

3.1.6 State of the airplane. The State of the airplane is defined by the selected configuration together with the functional status of each of the airplane components or systems, throttle setting, weight, moments of inertia, center-of-gravity position, and external store complement. The trim setting and the positions of the pitch, roll and yaw controls are not included in the definition of Airplane State since they are often specified by the requirements.

3.1.6.1 Airplane Normal States. The contractor shall define and tabulate all pertinent items to describe the Airplane Normal (no component or system failure) State(s) associated with each of the applicable Flight Phases. This tabulation shall be in the format and shall use the nomenclature specified in 6.2. Certain items, such as weight, moments of inertia, center-of-gravity position, wing sweep, or thrust setting may vary continuously over a range of values during a Flight Phase. The contractor shall replace this continuous variation by a limited number of values of the parameter in question which will be treated as specific States, and which include the most critical values and extremes encountered during the Flight Phase in question.

3.1.6.2 Airplane Failure States. The contractor shall define and tabulate all Airplane Failure States, which consist of Airplane Normal States modified by one or more malfunctions in airplane components or systems, for example, a discrepancy between a selected configuration and an actual configuration. Those malfunctions that result in center-of-gravity positions outside the center-of-gravity envelope defined in 3.1.2 shall be included. Each mode of failure shall be considered. Failures occurring in any Flight Phase shall be considered in all subsequent Flight Phases.

3.1.6.2.1 Airplane Special Failure States. Certain components, systems, or combinations thereof may have extremely remote probability of failure during a given flight. These failure probabilities may, in turn, be very difficult to predict with any degree of accuracy. Special Failure States of this type need not be considered in complying with the requirements of Section 3 if justification for considering the Failure States as Special is submitted by the contractor and approved by the procuring activity.

3.1.7 Operational Flight Envelopes. The Operational Flight Envelopes define the boundaries in terms of speed, altitude and load factor within which the airplane must be capable of operating in order to accomplish the missions of 3.1.1. Envelopes for each applicable Flight Phase shall be established with the guidance and approval of the procuring activity. In the absence of specific guidance, the contractor shall use the representative conditions of Table I for the applicable flight phases.

TABLE I OPERATIONAL FLIGHT ENVELOPES

Flight Phase Category: A

Flight Phase	Airspeed $V_{o_{min}}$ $(M_{o_{min}})$	$V_{o_{max}}$ $(M_{o_{max}})$	Altitude $h_{o_{min}}$	$h_{o_{max}}$	Load Factor $n_{o_{min}}$	$n_{o_{max}}$
Air-to-air Combat (CO)	$1.4V_S$	V_{MAT}	MSL	Combat Ceiling	-1.0	n_L
Ground Attack (GA)	$1.3V_S$	V_{MRT}	MSL	Medium	-1.0	n_L
Weapon Delivery/ Launch (WD)	V_{range}	V_{MAT}	MSL	Combat Ceiling	0.5	•
Aerial Recovery (AR)	$1.2V_S$	V_{MRT}	MSL	Combat	0.5	n_L
Reconnaissance (RC)	$1.3V_S$	V_{MAT}	MSL	Combat Ceiling	•	•
In-Flight Refuel (Receiver) (RR)	$1.2V_S$	V_{MRT}	MSL	Combat Ceiling	0.5	2.0
Terrain Following (TF)	V_{range}	V_{MAT}	MSL	10,000 ft	0	3.5
Antisubmarine Search (AS)	$1.2V_S$	V_{MRT}	MSL	Medium	0	2.0
Close Formation Flying (FF)	$1.4V_S$	V_{MAT}	MSL	Combat Ceiling	-1.0	n_L

Flight Phase Category: B

Flight Phase	Airspeed $V_{o_{min}}$ $(M_{o_{min}})$	$V_{o_{max}}$ $(M_{o_{max}})$	Altitude $h_{o_{min}}$	$h_{o_{max}}$	Load Factor $n_{o_{min}}$	$n_{o_{max}}$
Climb (CL)	$0.85V_{R/C}$	$1.3V_{R/C}$	MSL	Cruise Ceiling	0.5	2.0
Cruise (CR)	V_{range}	V_{NRT}	MSL	Cruise Ceiling	-1.0	2.0
Loiter (LO)	$0.85V_{end}$	$1.3V_{end}$	MSL	Cruise Ceiling	0.5	2.0
In-Flight Refuel (Tanker) (RT)	$1.4V_S$	V_{MAT}	MSL	Cruise Ceiling	0.5	2.0
Descent (D)	$1.4V_S$	V_{MAT}	MSL	Cruise Ceiling	0.5	2.0
Emergency Descent (ED)	$1.4V_S$	V_{max}	MSL	Cruise Ceiling	0.5	2.0
Emergency Decelera-tion(DE)	$1.4V_S$	V_{max}	MSL	Cruise Ceiling	0.5	2.0
Aerial Delivery (AS)	$1.2V_S$	200 kts	MSL	10,000 ft	0	2.0

TABLE I OPERATIONAL FLIGHT ENVELOPES (Cont'd)

Flight Phase Category: C

Flight Phase	Airspeed $V_{o_{min}}$ $(M_{o_{min}})$	Airspeed $V_{o_{max}}$ $(M_{o_{max}})$	Altitude $h_{o_{min}}$	Altitude $h_{o_{max}}$	Load Factor $n_{o_{min}}$	Load Factor $n_{o_{max}}$
Takeoff (TO)	Minimum Normal Takeoff Speed	V_{max}	MSL	10,000 ft	0.5	2.0
Catapult Takeoff (CT)	Min. Catapult End Airspeed	$V_{o_{min}}$ + 30 kts	MSL		0.5	n_L
Approach (PA)	Minimum Normal Approach Speed	V_{max}	MSL	10,000 ft	0.5	2.0
Wave-off/Go-around (WO)	Minimum Normal Approach Speed	V_{max}	MSL	10,000 ft	0.5	2.0
Landing (L)	Minimum Normal Approach Speed	V_{max}	MSL	10,000 ft	0.5	2.0

• Appropriate to the operational mission

3.1.8 Service Flight Envelopes. For each Airplane Normal State the contractor shall establish, subject to the approval of the procuring activity, Service Flight Envelopes showing combinations of speed, altitude and normal acceleration derived from airplane limits as distinguished from mission requirements. For each applicable Flight Phase and Airplane Normal State, the boundaries of the Service Flight Envelopes can be coincident with or lie outside the corresponding Operational Flight Envelopes, but in no case shall they fall inside those Operational boundaries. The boundaries of the Service Flight Envelopes shall be based on considerations discussed in 3.1.8.1, 3.1.8.2, 3.1.8.3 and 3.1.8.4.

3.1.8.1 Maximum service speed. The maximum service speed, V_{max} or M_{max}, for each altitude is the lowest of:

a. The maximum permissible speed

b. A speed which is a safe margin below the speed at which intolerable buffet or structural vibration is encountered

c. The maximum airspeed at MAT, for each altitude, for dives (at all angles) from V_{MAT} at all altitudes, from which recovery can be made at 2,000 ft above MSL or higher without penetrating a safe margin from loss of control, other dangerous behavior or intolerable buffet, and without exceeding structural limits.

3.1.8.2 Minimum service speed. The minimum service speed, V_{min} or M_{min}, for each altitude is the highest of:

a. $1.1V_S$

b. V_S + 10 knots equivalent airspeed

c. The speed below which full airplane-nose-up pitch control power and trim are insufficient to maintain steady, straight flight.

d. The lowest speed at which level flight can be maintained with MRT and, for Category C Flight Phases:

e. A speed limited by reduced visibility or an extreme pitch attitude that would result in the tail or aft fuselage contacting the ground.

3.1.8.3 Maximum service altitude. The maximum service altitude, h_{max} for a given speed is the maximum altitude at which a rate of climb of 100 feet per minute can be maintained in unaccelerated flight with MAT.

3.1.8.4 Service load factors. Maximum and minimum service load factors, n(+) [n(-)], shall be established as a function of speed for several significant altitudes. The maximum [minimum] service load factor, when trimmed for 1g flight at a particular speed and altitude, is the lowest [highest] algebraically of:

a. The positive [negative] structural limit load factor

b. The steady load factor corresponding to the minimum allowable value of lift coefficient for stall warning (3.4.2.1.1.2)

c. The steady load factor at which the pitch control is in the full airplane-nose-up [nose-down] position

d. A safe margin below [above] the load factor at which intolerable buffet or structural vibration is encountered.

3.1.9 Permissible Flight Envelopes. The contractor shall define Permissible Flight Envelopes which encompass all regions in which operation of the airplane is both allowable and possible, consistent with 3.1.10.3.3. These Envelopes define boundaries in terms of speed, altitude and load factor.

3.1.10 Application of Levels. Levels of flying qualities as indicated in 1.5 are employed in this specification in realization of the possibility that the airplane may be required to operate under abnormal conditions. Such abnormalities that may occur as a result of either flight outside the Operational Flight Envelope, failure of airplane components, or both, are permitted to comply with a degraded Level of flying qualities as specified in 3.1.10.1 through 3.1.10.3.3 (see also 4.1.1).

3.1.10.1 Requirements for Airplane Normal States. The minimum required flying qualities for Airplane Normal States (3.1.6.1) are as specified in Table II.

TABLE II LEVELS FOR AIRPLANE NORMAL STATES

Within Operational Flight Envelope	Within Service Flight Envelope
Level 1	Level 2

3.1.10.2 Requirements for Airplane Failure States. When Airplane Failure States exist (3.1.6.2), a degradation in flying qualities is permitted only if the probability of encountering a lower Level than specified in 3.1.10.1 is sufficiently small. At intervals established by the procuring activity, the contractor shall determine, based on the most accurate available data, the probability of occurrence of each Airplane Failure State per flight and the effect of that Failure State on the flying qualities within the Operational and Service Flight Envelopes. These determinations shall be based on MIL-STD-756 except that:

a. All airplane components and systems are assumed to be operating for a time period, per flight, equal to the longest operational mission time to be considered by the contractor in designing the airplane, and

b. Each specific failure is assumed to be present at whichever point in the Flight Envelope being considered is the most critical (in the flying qualities sense). From these Failure State probabilities and effects, the contractor shall determine the overall probability, per flight, that one or more flying qualities are degraded to Level 2 because of one or more failures. The contractor shall also determine the probability that one or more flying qualities are degraded to Level 3. These probabilities shall be less than the values specified in Table III.

In no case shall a Failure State (except an approved Special Failure State) degrade any flying quality parameter outside the Level 3 limit.

TABLE III LEVELS FOR AIRPLANE FAILURE STATES

Probability of Encountering	Within Operational Flight Envelope	Within Service Flight Envelope
Level 2 after failure	$< 10^{-2}$ per flight	
Level 3 after failure	$< 10^{-4}$ per flight	$< 10^{-2}$ per flight

3.1.10.2.1 Requirements for specific failures. The requirements on the effects of specific types of failures, e.g. propulsion or flight control system, shall be met on the basis that the specific type of failure has occurred, regardless of its probability of occurrence.

3.1.10.3 Exceptions

3.1.10.3.1 Ground operation and terminal flight phases. Some requirements pertaining to takeoff, landing and taxiing involve operations outside the Operational, Service and Permissible Flight Envelopes, such as at V_S or on the ground. When requirements are stated at conditions such as these, the Levels shall be applied as if the conditions were in the Operational Flight Envelope.

3.1.10.3.2 When Levels are not specified. Within the Operational and Service Flight Envelopes, all requirements that are not identified with specific Levels shall be met under all conditions of component and system failure except approved Airplane Special Failure States (3.1.6.2.1).

3.1.10.3.3 Flight outside the Service Flight Envelope. From all points in the Permissible Flight Envelopes, it shall be possible readily and safely to return to the Service Flight Envelope without exceptional pilot skill or technique, regardless of component failure or system failures. The requirements on flight at high angle of attack, dive characteristics, dive recovery devices and dangerous flight conditions shall also apply.

3.1.11 Interpretation of subjective requirements. In several instances throughout the specification subjective terms, such as objectionable flight characteristics, realistic time delay, normal pilot technique and excessive loss of altitude or buildup of speed, have been employed to permit latitude where absolute quantitative criteria might be unduly restrictive. Final determination of compliance with requirements so worded will be made by the procuring activity (1.5).

3.1.12 Interpretation of quantitative requirements. The numerical requirements of this specification generally are stated in terms of a linear description of the airplane. Certain factors, for example flight control system nonlinearities and higher-order characteristic or aerodynamic nonlinearities, can cause the aircraft response to differ significantly from that of the linear model. The contractor shall define equivalent classical systems which have responses most closely matching those of the actual aircraft. Then those numerical requirements of section 3 which are stated in terms of linear system parameters (such as frequency, damping ratio and modal phase angles) apply to the parameters of that equivalent system rather than to any particular modes of the actual higher-order system. The procuring activity shall be the judge of the adequacy of the response match between equivalent and actual aircraft.

3.2 Longitudinal flying qualities. For Levels 1 and 2 there shall be no tendency for airspeed to diverge aperiodically when the airplane is disturbed from trim with the cockpit controls fixed and with them free. This requirement will be considered satisfied if the variations of pitch control force and pitch control position with airspeed are smooth and the local gradients stable, with:

a. Trimmer and throttle controls not moved from the trim setting by the crew, and

b. 1g acceleration normal to the flight path, and

c. constant altitude

over a range about the trim speed of +/- 15 percent or +/- 50 knots equivalent airspeed, whichever is less (except where limited by the boundaries of the Service Flight Envelopes). Alternatively, this requirement will be considered satisfied if stability with respect to speed is provided through the flight control system, even though the resulting pitch control force and deflection gradients may be zero. For Level 3 the requirements may be relaxed, subject to approval by the procuring activity of the maximum instability to be allowed for the particular case. In no event shall its time to double amplitude be less than 6 seconds. In the presence of one or more other Level 3 flying qualities, no static longitudinal instability will be permitted unless the flight safety of that combination of characteristics has been demonstrated to the satisfaction of the procuring activity. Stable gradients mean that the pitch controller deflection and force increments required to maintain straight, steady flight at a different speed are in the same sense as those required to initiate the speed change, that is, airplane-nose-down control to fly at a faster speed, airplane-nose-up control to fly at a slower speed. The term gradient does not include that portion of the control force or control position versus airspeed curve within the breakout force range.

3.2.1.1.1 Relaxation in transonic flight. The requirements of 3.2.1.1 may be relaxed in the transonic speed range provided any divergent airplane motions or reversals in slope of pitch control force and position with speed are gradual and not objectionable to the pilot. In no case, however, shall the requirements of 3.2.1.1 be relaxed more than the following:

a. Levels 1 and 2 - For center-stick controllers, no local force gradient shall be more unstable than 3 lbs per 0.01 M nor shall the force change exceed 10 lbs in the unstable direction. The corresponding limits for wheel controllers are 5 lbs per 0.01 M and 15 lbs, respectively.

b. Level 3- For center-stick controllers, no local force gradient shall be more unstable than 6 lbs per 0.01 M nor shall the force ever exceed 20 lbs in the unstable direction. The corresponding limits for wheel controllers are 10 lbs per 0.01 M and 30 lbs respectively.

This relaxation does not apply to Level 1 for any Flight Phase which requires prolonged transonic operation.

3.2.1.1.2 Pitch control force variations during rapid speed changes. When the airplane is accelerated and decelerated rapidly through the operational speed range and through the transonic speed range by the most critical combination of changes in power, actuation of deceleration devices, steep turns and pullups, the magnitude and rate of the associated trim change shall not be so great as to cause difficulty in maintaining the desired load factor by normal pilot techniques.

3.2.1.2 Phugoid stability. The long-period airspeed oscillations which occur when the airplane seeks a stabilized airspeed following a disturbance shall meet the following requirements:

a. Level 1 ----- ζ_p at least 0.04

b. Level 2 ----- ζ_p at least 0

c. Level 3 ----- T_2 at least 55 seconds

These requirements apply with the pitch control free and also with it fixed. They need not be met transonically in cases where 3.2.1.1.1 permits relaxation of the static stability requirement.

3.2.1.3 Flight-path stability. Flight-path stability is defined in terms of flight-path-angle change where the airspeed is changed by the use of pitch control only (throttle setting not changed by the crew). For the landing approach Flight Phase, the curve of flight-path angle versus true airspeed shall have a local slope at $V_{o_{min}}$ which is negative or less positive than:

a. Level 1 ----- 0.06 degrees/knot

b. Level 2 ----- 0.15 degrees/knot

c. Level 3 ----- 0.24 degrees/knot

The thrust setting shall be that required for the normal approach glide path at $V_{o_{min}}$. The slope of the curve of flight-path angle versus airspeed at 5 knots slower than $V_{o_{min}}$ shall not be more than 0.05 degrees/knot more positive than the slope at $V_{o_{min}}$, as illustrated by:

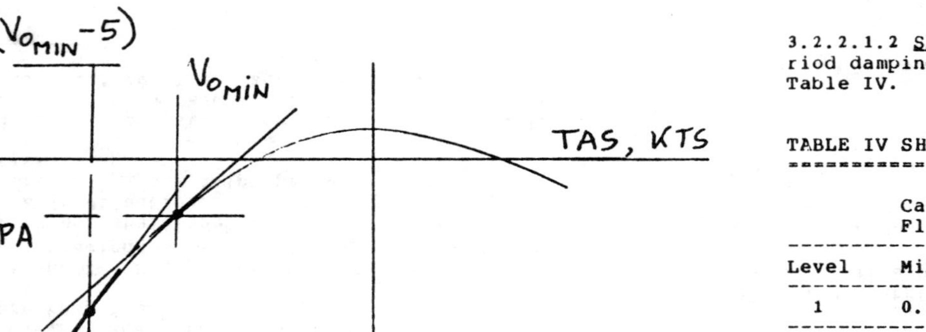

3.2.2 Longitudinal maneuvering characteristics

3.2.2.1 Short-period response. The short-period response of angle-of-attack which occurs at approximately constant speed, and which may be produced by abrupt control inputs, shall meet the requirements of 3.2.2.1.1 and 3.2.2.1.2. These requirements apply, with the cockpit control free and with it fixed, for responses of any magnitude that might be experienced in service use. If oscillations are nonlinear with amplitude, the requirements shall apply to each cycle of the oscillation. In addition to meeting the numerical requirements of 3.2.2.1.1 and 3.2.2.1.2, the contractor shall show that the airplane has suitable response characteristics in atmospheric disturbances (3.7 and 3.8).

3.2.2.1.1 Short-period frequency and acceleration sensitivity. The equivalent short-period undamped natural frequency, $\omega_{n_{sp}}$, shall be within the limits shown on Figures B1, B2 and B3. If suitable means of directly controlling normal force are provided, the lower bounds on $\omega_{n_{sp}}$ and n/α of Figure B3 may be relaxed if approved by the procuring activity.

3.2.2.1.2 Short-period damping. The equivalent short-period damping ratio, ζ_{sp} shall be within the limits of Table IV.

TABLE IV SHORT-PERIOD DAMPING RATIO LIMITS

Level	Category A and C Flight Phases		Category B Flight Phases	
	Minimum	Maximum	Minimum	Maximum
1	0.35	1.30	0.30	2.00
2	0.25	2.00	0.20	2.00
3	0.15*	-	0.15*	-

*May be reduced at altitudes above 20,000 ft if approved by the procuring activity.

3.2.2.1.3 Residual oscillations. Any sustained residual oscillations in calm air shall not interfere with the pilot's ability to perform the tasks required in service use of the airplane. For Levels 1 and 2, oscillations in normal acceleration at the pilot's station greater than +/-0.05g will be considered excessive for any Flight Phase, as will pitch attitude oscillations greater than +/-3 mils for Category A Flight Phases requiring precise control of pitch attitude. These requirements shall apply with the pitch control fixed and with it free.

3.2.2.2 Control feel and stability in maneuvering flight at constant speed. In steady turning flight and in pullups at constant speed, there shall be no tendency for the airplane pitch attitude or angle of attack to diverge aperiodically with controls fixed or with controls free. For the above conditions, the incremental force and control deflection required to maintain a change in normal load factor and pitch rate shall be in the same sense (aft-more positive, forward-more negative) as those required to initiate the change. These requirements apply for all local gradients throughout the range of service load factors defined in 3.1.8.4.

3.2.2.2.1 Control forces in maneuvering flight. At constant speed in steady turning flight, pullups and pushovers, the variation in pitch controller force with steady-state normal acceleration shall have no objectionable non-linearities within the following load factor ranges:

Class	Minimum	Maximum
I, II and III	0.5	$0.5(n_o(+)+1)$ or 3
IV	0	whichever is less

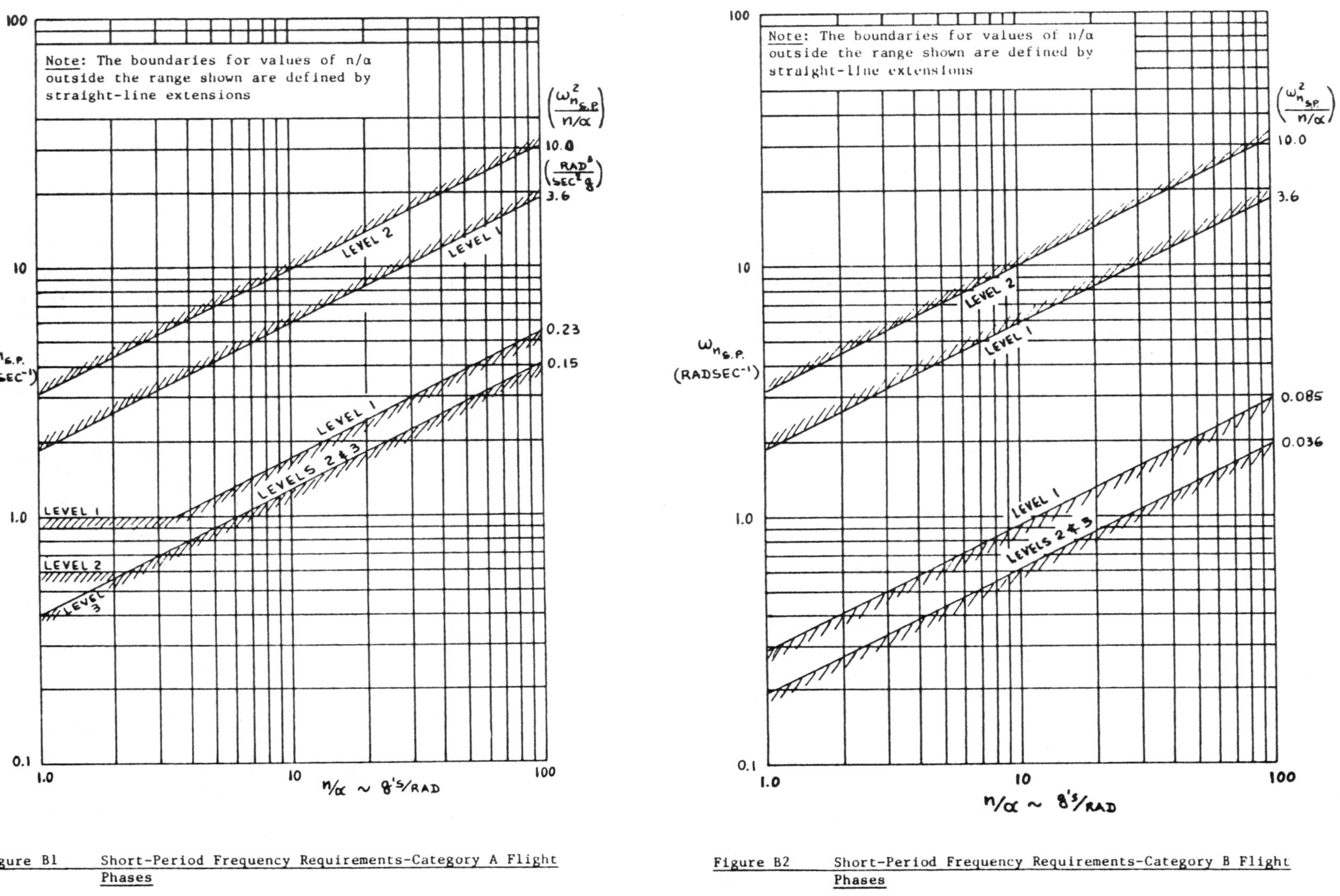

Figure B1 Short-Period Frequency Requirements-Category A Flight Phases

Figure B2 Short-Period Frequency Requirements-Category B Flight Phases

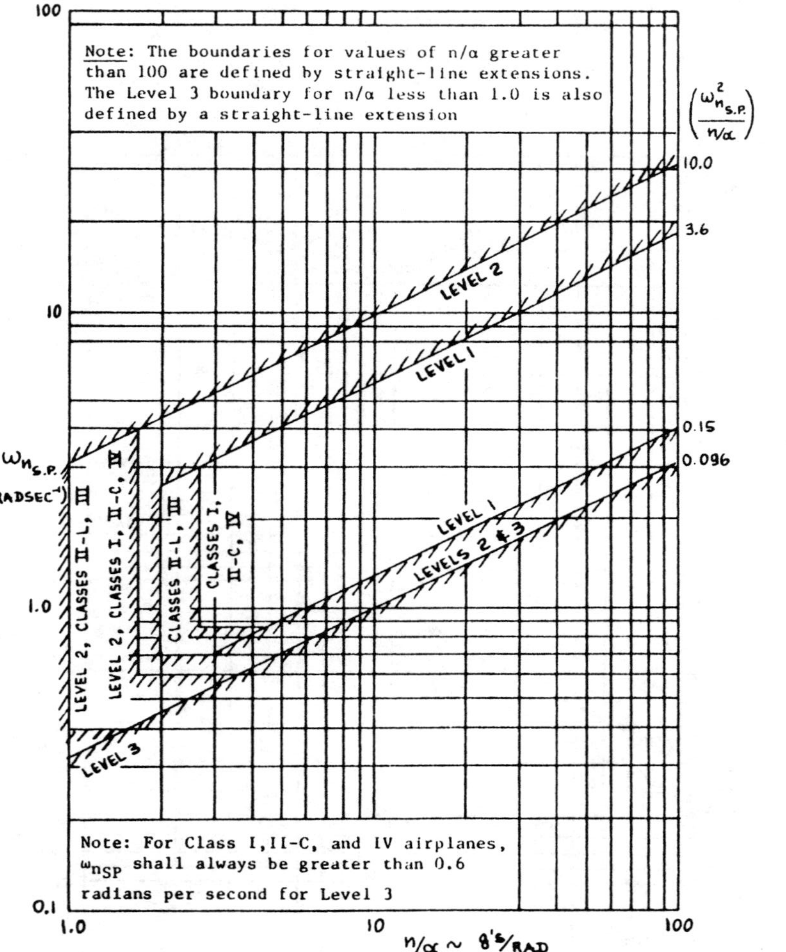

Figure B3 Short-Period Frequency Requirements-Category C Flight Phases

Outside this range, a departure from linearity resulting in a local gradient which differs from the average gradient for the maneuver by more than 50 percent is considered excessive, except that larger increases in force gradient are permissible at load factors greater than $0.85n_L$. All local force gradients shall be within the limits of Table V. In addition, F_s/n_z should be near the Level 1 upper boundaries of Table V for combinations of high frequency and low damping. The term gradient does not include that portion of the force versus n_z curve within the breakout force.

Since the range of acceptable force gradients for side stick controllers varies with the control deflection gradient and the task to be performed, the contractor shall show that the control force gradients will provide suitable flying qualities.

3.2.2.2.2 Control motions in maneuvering flight. For all types of pitch controllers, the control motions in maneuvering flight shall not be so large or so small as to be objectionable. For Category A Flight Phases, the average gradient of pitch-control force per unit of pitch-control deflection at constant speed shall not be less than 5.0 pounds per inch for wheel and center-stick controllers or 2.0 pounds per degree for side-stick controllers for Levels 1 and 2.

3.2.2.3 Longitudinal pilot-induced oscillations. There shall be no tendency for pilot-induced oscillations, that is, sustained or uncontrollable oscillations resulting from the efforts of the pilot to control the airplane. The pitch attitude response dynamics of the airplane plus control system shall not change abruptly with the motion amplitudes of pitch, pitch rate or normal acceleration unless it can be shown that this will not result in a pilot-induced oscillation. The requirements of 3.2.2.3.1 and 3.2.2.3.2 shall be met for all expected airplane motion amplitudes and frequencies, starting at any service load factor.

3.2.2.3.1 Dynamic control forces in maneuvering flight. The frequency response of normal acceleration at the pilot to pitch control force shall be such that the inverse amplitude is greater than the following for all frequencies greater than 1.0 rad/sec. Units are pounds per g.

Controller Type	Level 1	Level 2	Level 3
One-handed Controllers	$14/(n_L - 1)$	$12/(n_L - 1)$	$8/(n_L - 1)$
Two-handed Controllers	$30/(n_L - 1)$	$25/(n_L - 1)$	$17/(n_L - 1)$

3.2.2.3.2 Control feel. The deflection of the pilot's control must not lead the control force throughout the frequency range of pilot control inputs. In addition, the peak control forces developed during abrupt maneuvers shall not be objectionably light, and the buildup of control force during the maneuver entry shall lead the buildup of normal acceleration.

TABLE V PITCH MANEUVERING FORCE GRADIENT LIMITS

For Center Stick Controllers:

Level	Maximum Gradient, $(F_s/n)_{max}$, lbs/g	Minimum Gradient, $(F_s/n)_{min}$, lbs/g
1	$240/(n/\alpha)$ but not more than 28.0 nor less than $56/(n_L - 1)$*	The higher of $21/(n_L - 1)$ and 3.0
2	$360/(n/\alpha)$ but not more than 42.5 nor less than $85/(n_L - 1)$	The higher of $18/(n_L - 1)$ and 3.0
3	56.0	The higher of $12/(n_L - 1)$ and 2.0

*For $n_L < 3$, $(F_s/n)_{max}$ is 28.0 for Level 1, and 42.5 for Level 2.

For Wheel Controllers:

Level	Maximum Gradient, $(F_s/n)_{max}$, lbs/g	Minimum Gradient, $(F_s/n)_{min}$, lbs/g
1	$500/(n/\alpha)$ but not more than 120.0 nor less than $120/(n_L - 1)$	The higher of $35/(n_L - 1)$ and 6.0
2	$775/(n/\alpha)$ but not more than 182.0 nor less than $182/(n_L - 1)$	The higher of $30/(n_L - 1)$ and 6.0
3	240.0	5.0

3.2.3 Longitudinal control

3.2.3.1 Longitudinal control in unaccelerated flight. In erect unaccelerated flight at all service altitudes, the attainment of speed between V_S and V_{max} shall not be limited by the effectiveness of the longitudinal control or controls.

3.2.3.2 Longitudinal control in maneuvering flight. Within the Operational Flight Envelope, it shall be possible to develop, by use of the pitch control alone, the following range of load factors:

Levels 1 and 2 ----- $n_o(-)$ to $n_o(+)$

Level 3 ----- $n = 0.5g$ to the lower of:

a) $n_o(+)$

b) $n = 2.0$ for $n_o(+) \leq 3g$

$= 0.5(n_o(+) + 1)$ for $n_o(+) > 3g$

This maneuvering capability is required at the 1g trim speed and, with trim and throttle settings not changed by the crew, over a range about the trim speed the lesser of +/-15 percent or +/-50 knots equivalent airspeed (except where limited by the boundaries of the Operational Flight Envelope). Within the Service and Permissible Flight Envelopes, the dive-recovery requirements of 3.2.3.5 and 3.2.3.6, respectively, shall be met.

3.2.3.3 Longitudinal control in takeoff. The effectiveness of the pitch control shall not restrict the takeoff performance of the airplane and shall be sufficient to prevent over-rotation to undesirable attitudes during takeoffs. Satisfactory takeoffs shall not be dependent upon use of the trimmer control during takeoff or on complicated control manipulation by the pilot. For nose-wheel airplanes it shall be possible to obtain, at $0.9V_{min}$, the pitch attitude which will result in takeoff at V_{min}. For tail-wheel airplanes, it shall be possible to maintain any pitch attitude up to that for a level thrust-line at $0.5V_S$ for Class I airplanes and at V_S for Class II, III and IV airplanes. These requirements shall be met on hard-surfaced runways. In the event that an airplane has a mission requirement for operation from unprepared fields, these requirements shall be met on such fields.

3.2.3.3.1 Longitudinal control in catapult takeoff. On airplanes designed for catapult takeoff, the effectiveness of the pitch control shall be sufficient to prevent the airplane from pitching up or down to undesirable attitudes in catapult takeoffs at speeds ranging from the minimum safe launching speed to launching speed 30 knot higher than the minimum. Satisfactory catapult takeoffs shall not depend upon complicated control manipulation by the pilot.

3.2.3.3.2 Longitudinal control force and travel in takeoff. With the trim setting optional but fixed, the pitch-control forces required during all types of takeoffs for which the airplane is designed, including short-field takeoffs and assisted takeoffs such as catapult or rocket-augmented, shall be within the following limits:

Nose-wheel and bicycle-gear airplanes

Classes I, IV-C -------- 20 pounds pull to 10 pounds push

Classes II-C, IV-L ----- 30 pounds pull to 10 pounds push

Classes II-L, III ------ 50 pounds pull to 20 pounds push

Tail-wheel airplanes

Classes I, II-C, IV ---- 20 pounds push to 10 pounds pull

Classes II-L, III ------ 35 pounds push to 15 pounds pull

The pitch-control travel during takeoffs shall not exceed 75 percent of the total travel, stop-to-stop. Here the term takeoff includes the ground run, rotation and lift-off, the ensuing acceleration to V_{max}(TO), and the transient caused by assist cessation. Takeoff power shall be maintained until V_{max}(TO) is reached, with the landing gear and high-lift devices retracted in the normal manner at speeds from $V_{o_{min}}$(TO) to V_{max}(TO).

3.2.3.4 Longitudinal control in landing. The pitch control shall be sufficiently effective in the landing Flight Phase in close proximity to the ground, that in calm air:

a. The geometry-limited touchdown attitude can be maintained in level flight or

b. The lower of V_S(L) or the guaranteed landing speed can be obtained.

This requirement shall be met with the airplane trimmed for the approach Flight Phase at the recommended approach speed. The requirements of 3.2.3.4 and 3.2.3.4.1 define Levels 1 and 2, and the requirements of 3.4.10 define Level 3.

3.2.3.4.1 Longitudinal control forces in landing. The pitch-control forces required to meet the requirements of 3.2.3.4 shall be pull forces and shall not exceed:

Classes I, II-C ----- 35 pounds

Classes II-L -------- 50 pounds

3.2.3.5 Longitudinal control forces in dives - Service Flight Envelope. With the airplane trimmed for level flight at speeds throughout the Service Flight Envelope, the control forces in dives to all attainable airspeeds within the Service Flight Envelope shall not exceed 50 pounds push or 10 pounds pull for center-stick controllers, nor 75 pounds push or 15 pounds pull for wheel controllers. In similar dives, but with trim optional following the dive entry, it shall be possible with normal piloting techniques to maintain the forces within the limits of 10 pounds push or pull for center-stick controllers, and 20 pounds push or pull for wheel controllers. In event that operation of the trim system requires removal of one hand from a wheel control the force limits shall be as for a center-stick. The forces required for recovery from these dives shall be in accordance with the gradients specified in 3.2.2.2.1 although speed may vary during the pullout.

3.2.3.6 Longitudinal control forces in dives - Permissible Flight Envelope. With the airplane trimmed for level flight at V_{MAT} but with trim optional in the dive, it shall be possible to maintain the pitch control force within the limits of 50 pounds push or 35 pounds pull in dives to all attainable speeds within the Permissible Flight Envelope. The force required for recovery from these dives shall not exceed 120 pounds. Trim and deceleration devices, etc., may be used to assist in recovery if no unusual pilot technique is required.

3.2.3.7 Longitudinal control in sideslips. With the airplane trimmed for straight, level flight with zero sideslip, the pitch-control force required to maintain constant speed in steady sideslips with up to 50 pounds of pedal force in either direction shall not exceed the pitch-control force that would result in a 1g change in normal acceleration. In no case, however, shall the pitch-control force exceed:

Center-stick controllers ----- 10 lbs pull to 3 lbs push

Wheel controllers ------------ 15 lbs pull to 10 lbs push

If a variation of pitch-control force with sideslip does exist, it is preferred that increasing pull force accompany increasing sideslip, and that the magnitude and direction of the force change be similar for right and left sideslips. These requirements define Levels 1 and 2. For Level 3 there shall be no uncontrollable pitching motions associated with the sideslips discussed above.

3.3 Lateral-directional flying qualities

3.3.1 Lateral-directional mode characteristics

3.3.1.1 Lateral-directional oscillations (Dutch roll). The frequency, ω_{n_d}, and damping ratio, ξ_d, of the lateral-directional oscillations following a yaw disturbance input shall exceed the minimum values in Table VI. The requirements shall be met in trimmed and in maneuvering flight with the cockpit controls fixed and with them free, in oscillations of any magnitude that might be expected in operational use. If the oscillation is nonlinear with amplitude, the requirements shall apply to each cycle of the oscillation. In calm air residual oscillations may be tolerated only if the amplitude is sufficiently small that the motions are not objectionable and do not impair mission performance. For Category A Flight Phases, angular deviations shall be less than +/- 3 mils.

3.3.1.2 Roll mode. The roll-mode time constant, T_r, shall be no greater than the appropriate value in Table VII.

TABLE VI MINIMUM DUTCH ROLL FREQUENCY AND DAMPING

Level	Flight Phase Category	Class	Min. ξ_d *	Min. $\xi_d \omega_{n_d}$ * rad/sec.	Min. ω_{n_d} rad/sec.
1	A (CO and GA)	IV	0.4	-	1.0
	A	I, IV	0.19	0.35	1.0
		II, III	0.19	0.35	0.4**
	B	All	0.08	0.15	0.4**
	C	I, II-C, IV	0.08	0.15	1.0
		II-L, III	0.08	0.10	0.4**
2	All	All	0.02	0.05	0.4**
3	All	All	0	-	0.4**

* The governing damping requirement is that yielding the larger value of ξ_d, except that a ξ_d of 0.7 is the maximum required for Class III.

** Class III airplanes may be excepted from the minimum ω_{n_d} requirement, subject to approval by the procuring activity, if the requirements of 3.3.2 through 3.3.2.4.1, 3.3.5 and 3.3.9.4 are met.

When $(\omega_{n_d})^2 |\phi/\beta|_d$ is greater than 20 $(\text{rad/sec})^2$, the minimum $\xi_d \omega_{n_d}$ shall be increased above the $\xi_d \omega_{n_d}$ minimums listed in Table VI by:

Level 1 - $\Delta\xi_d\omega_{n_d} = 0.014((\omega_{n_d})^2 |\phi/\beta|_d - 20)$

Level 2 - $\Delta\xi_d\omega_{n_d} = 0.009((\omega_{n_d})^2 |\phi/\beta|_d - 20)$

Level 3 - $\Delta\xi_d\omega_{n_d} = 0.005((\omega_{n_d})^2 |\phi/\beta|_d - 20)$

with ω_{n_d} in rad/sec.

TABLE VII MAXIMUM ROLL-MODE TIME CONSTANT, T_r, SECONDS

Flight Phase Category	Class	Level 1	Level 2	Level 3
A	I, IV	1.0	1.4	
	II, III	1.4	3.0	
B	All	1.4	3.0	10.0
C	I, II-C, IV	1.0	1.4	
	II-L, III	1.4	3.0	

3.3.1.3 <u>Spiral stability</u>. The combined effects of spiral stability, flight-control-system characteristics and rolling moment change with speed shall be such that following a disturbance in bank of up to 20 degrees, the time for the bank angle to double shall be greater than the values in Table VIII. This requirement shall be met with the airplane trimmed for wings-level, zero-yaw-rate flight with the cockpit controls free.

TABLE VIII SPIRAL STABILITY - MINIMUM TIME TO DOUBLE AMPLITUDE, T_{2_s}

Flight Phase Category	Level 1	Level 2	Level 3
A and C	12 sec.	8 sec.	4 sec.
B	20 sec.	8 sec.	4 sec.

3.3.1.4 <u>Coupled roll-spiral oscillation</u>. For Flight Phases which involve more than gentle maneuvering, such as CO and GA, the airplane characteristics shall not exhibit a coupled roll-spiral mode in response to the pilot roll control commands. A coupled roll-spiral mode will be permitted for Category B and C Flight Phases provided the product of frequency and damping ratio exceeds the following requirements:

Level	$\xi_{rs}\omega_{n_{rs}}$, rad/sec
1	0.5
2	0.3
3	0.15

3.3.2 Lateral-directional dynamic response characteristics. Lateral-directional dynamic response characteristics are stated in terms of response to atmospheric disturbances and in terms of allowable roll rate and bank angle oscillations, sideslip excursions, roll control forces and yaw control forces that occur during specified rolling and turning maneuvers to the right and to the left. The requirements of 3.3.2.2, 3.3.2.3 and 3.3.2.4 apply for roll commands of all magnitudes needed to meet the roll performance requirements of 3.3.4 and 3.3.4.1.

3.3.2.1 Lateral-directional response to atmospheric disturbances. The combined effect of ω_{n_d}, ζ_d, T_r, $|\phi/\beta|_d$, $\angle(p/\beta)$, gust sensitivity, and flight-control-system nonlinearities on response and controllability characteristics in atmospheric disturbances shall be considered (see 3.8.3). In particular, the roll acceleration, rate and displacement responses to side gusts shall be investigated for airplanes with large rolling moment due to sideslip (i.e. large dihedral effect).

3.3.2.2 Roll rate oscillations. Following a yaw-control-free step roll control command, the roll rate at the first minimum following the first peak shall be of the same sign and not less than the following percentage of the roll rate at the first peak:

Level	Flight Phase Category	Percent
1	A and C	60
	B	25
2	A and C	25
	B	0

For all Levels, the change in bank angle shall always be in the direction of the roll control command. The roll command shall be held fixed until the bank angle has changed at least 90 degrees.

3.3.2.2.1 Additional roll rate requirement for small inputs. The value of the parameter p_{osc}/p_{av} following a yaw-control-free step roll command shall be within the limits shown on Figure B4 for Levels 1 and 2. This requirement applies for step roll-control commands up to the magnitude which causes a 60-degree bank angle change in $1.7T_d$ seconds.

3.3.2.3 Bank angle oscillations. The value of the parameter ϕ_{osc}/ϕ_{av} following a yaw-control-free impulse roll control command shall be within the limits as shown on Figure B5 for Levels 1 and 2. The impulse shall be as abrupt as practical within the strength limits of the pilot and the rate limits of the roll control system.

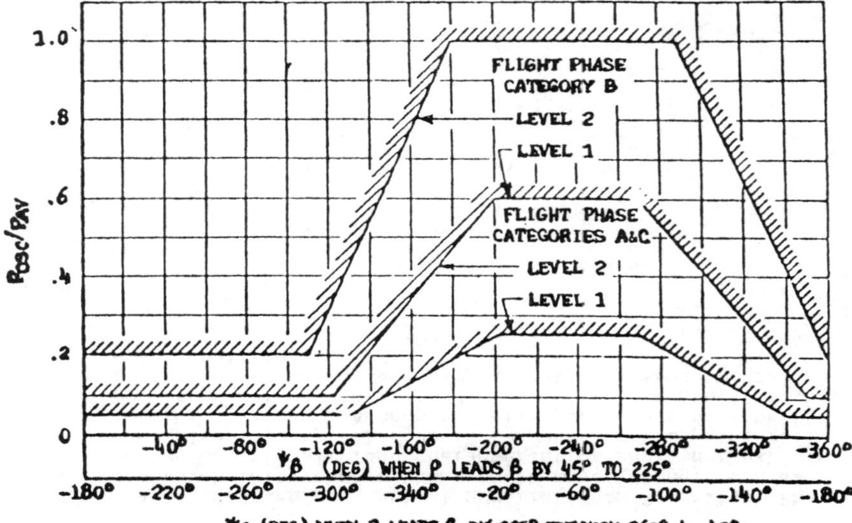

Figure B4 Roll Rate Oscillation Limitations

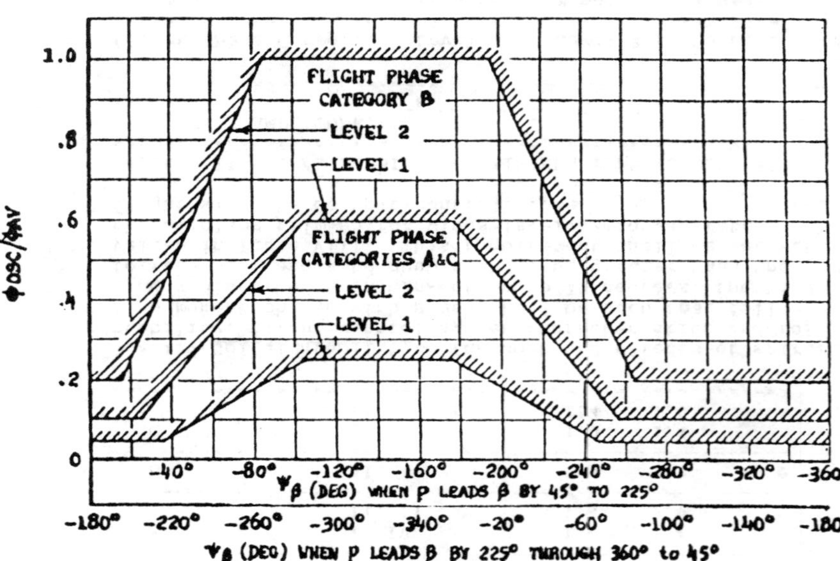

Figure B5 Bank Angle Oscillation Limittions

3.3.2.4 Sideslip excursions. Following a yaw-control-free step roll control command, the ratio of the sideslip increment, $\Delta\beta$ to the parameter k (6.2.6) shall be less than the values specified herein. The roll command shall be held fixed until the bank angle has changed at least 90 degrees.

Level	Flight Phase Category	Adverse Sideslip (Right roll command causes RIGHT sideslip	Proverse Sideslip (Right roll command causes LEFT sideslip
1	A	6 degrees	2 degrees
	B and C	10 degrees	3 degrees
2	All	15 degrees	4 degrees

3.3.2.4.1 Additional sideslip requirement for small inputs. The amount of sideslip following a yaw-control-free step roll control command shall be within the limits shown on Figure B6 for Levels 1 and 2. This requirement shall apply for step roll control commands up to the magnitude which causes a 60-degree bank angle change within T_d or 2 seconds, whichever is longer.

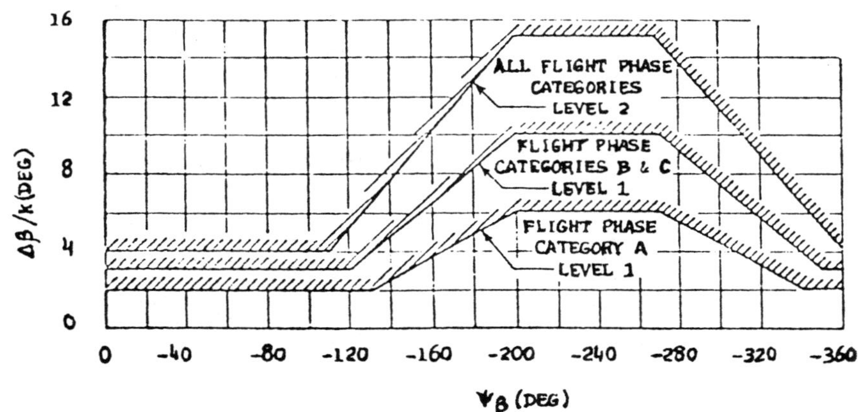

Figure B6 Sideslip Excursion Limitations

3.3.2.5 Control of sideslip in rolls. In the rolling maneuvers described in 3.3.4, but with coordination allowed for all Classes, directional-control effectiveness shall be adequate to maintain zero sideslip with pedal force not greater than 50 pounds for Class IV airplanes in Flight Phase Category A, Level 1, and 100 pounds for all other combinations of Class, Flight Phase Category and Level.

3.3.2.6 Turn coordination. It shall be possible to maintain steady coordinated turns in either direction, using 60 degrees of bank for Class IV airplanes, 45 degrees of bank for Class I and II airplanes, and 30 degrees of bank for Class III airplanes, with a pedal force not exceeding 40 pounds. It shall be possible to perform steady turns at the same bank angles with yaw-controls-free, with a roll-stick force not exceeding 5 pounds or a roll-wheel force not exceeding 10 pounds. These requirements constitute Levels 1 and 2, with the airplane trimmed for wings-level straight flight.

3.3.3 Pilot-induced oscillations. There shall be no tendency for sustained or uncontrollable lateral-directional oscillations resulting from efforts of the pilot to control the airplane.

3.3.4 Roll control effectiveness. Roll performance in terms of a bank angle change in a given time, ϕ_t, is specified in Table IXa for Class I and Class II airplanes, in 3.3.4.1 for Class IV airplanes, and in 3.3.4.2 for Class III airplanes. For rolls from banked flight, the initial condition shall be coordinated, that is, zero lateral acceleration. The requirements apply to roll commands to the right and to the left, initiated both from steady bank angles and from wings-level flight except as otherwise stated. Inputs shall be abrupt, with the time measured from the initiation of control force application. The pitch control shall be fixed throughout the maneuver. Yaw control pedals shall remain free for Class IV airplanes for Level 1, and for all carrier-based airplanes in Category C Flight Phases for Levels 1 and 2, but otherwise, yaw control pedals may be used to reduce sideslip that retards roll rate (not to produce sideslip which augments roll rate) if such control inputs are simple, easily coordinated with roll control inputs and consistent with piloting techniques for the airplane class and mission. For Flight Phase TO, the time required to bank may be increased proportional to the ratio of the rolling moment of inertia at takeoff to the largest rolling moment of inertia at landing, for weights up to the maximum authorized landing weight.

TABLE IXa ROLL PERFORMANCE FOR CLASS I AND II AIRPLANES

Time to Achieve the Following Bank Angle Change (Seconds)

Class	Level	Category A		Category B		Category C	
		60°	45°	60°	45°	30°	25°
I	1	1.3		1.7		1.3	
I	2	1.7		2.5		1.8	
I	3	2.6		3.4		2.6	
II-L	1		1.4		1.9	1.8	
II-L	2		1.9		2.8	2.5	
II-L	3		2.8		3.8	3.6	
II-C	1		1.4		1.9		1.0
II-C	2		1.9		2.8		1.5
II-C	3		2.8		3.8		2.0

TABLE IXb ROLL PERFORMANCE FOR CLASS IV AIRPLANES

Time to Achieve the Following Bank Angle Change (Seconds)

Level	Speed Range	Category A 30°	Category A 50°	Category A 90°	Category B 90°	Category C 30°
1	VL	1.1			2.0	1.1
	L	1.1			1.7	1.1
	M			1.3	1.7	1.1
	H		1.1		1.7	1.1
2	VL	1.6			2.8	1.3
	L	1.5			2.5	1.3
	M			1.7	2.5	1.3
	H		1.3		2.5	1.3
3	VL	2.6			3.7	2.0
	L	2.0			3.4	2.0
	M			2.6	3.4	2.0
	H		2.6		3.4	2.0

3.3.4.1 Roll performance for Class IV airplanes. Roll performance in terms of ϕ_t for Class IV airplanes is

specified in Table IXb. Additional or alternate roll performance requirements are specified in 3.3.4.1.1 and 3.3.4.1.2: these requirements take precedence over those in Table IXb. Roll performance for Class IV airplanes is specified over the following ranges of airspeeds:

Speed Range		Equivalent Airspeed Range
VL	Level 1:	$V_{o_{min}} \leq V < V_{min} + 20$ kts
	Levels 2 and 3:	$V_{min} \leq V \leq V_{min} + 20$ kts
L	Level 1:	$V_{min} + 20\ kts^{(1)} \leq V < 1.4V_{min}$
	Levels 2 and 3:	$V_{min} + 20$ kts $\leq V < 1.4V_{min}$
M	Level 1:	$1.4V_{o_{min}} \leq V < 0.7V_{max}^{(2)}$
	Levels 2 and 3:	$1.4V_{min} \leq V < 0.7V_{max}$
H	Level 1:	$0.7V_{max}^{(2)} < V \leq V_{o_{max}}$
	Levels 2 and 3:	$0.7V_{max} \leq V \leq V_{max}$

(1) or $V_{o_{min}}$ whichever is greater

(2) or $V_{o_{max}}$ whichever is less

3.3.4.1.1 Roll performance in Flight Phase CO. Roll performance for Class IV airplanes in Flight Phase CO is specified in Table IXc in terms of ϕ_t for 360 degree

rolls initiated at 1g, and in Table IXd for rolls initiated at load factors between $0.8n_o(-)$ and $0.8n_o(+)$.

3.3.4.1.2 Roll performance in Flight Phase GA. The roll performance requirements for Class IV airplanes in Flight Phase GA with large complements of external stores may be relaxed from those specified in Table IXb, subject to approval by the procuring activity. For any external loading specified in the contract, however, the roll performance shall not be less than that in Table IXe where the roll performance is specified in terms of ϕ_t for rolls

initiated at load factors between $0.8n_o(-)$ and $0.8n_o(+)$.

For any asymmetric loading specified in the contract, roll control power shall be sufficient to hold the wings level at the maximum load factors specified in 3.2.3.2 with adequate control margin (3.4.10).

3.3.4.1.3 Roll response. Stick-controlled Class IV airplanes in Category A Flight Phase shall have a roll response to control force not greater than 15 degrees in 1 second per pound for Level 1, and not greater than 25 degrees in 1 second per pound for Level 2. For Category C

TABLE IXc FLIGHT PHASE CO ROLL PERFORMANCE IN 360° ROLLS

Time to Achieve the Following Bank Angle Change (Seconds)

Level	Speed Range	30°	90°	180°	360°
1	VL	1.0			
	L		1.4	2.3	4.1
	M		1.0	1.6	2.8
	H		1.4	2.3	4.1
2	VL	1.6			
	L	1.3			
	M		1.3	2.0	3.4
	H		1.7	2.6	4.4
3	VL	2.5			
	L	2.0			
	M		1.7	3.0	
	H		2.1		

TABLE IXd FLIGHT PHASE CO ROLL PERFORMANCE

Time to Achieve the Following Bank Angle Change (Seconds)

Level	Speed Range	30°	50°	90°	180°
1	VL	1.0			
	L		1.1		
	M			1.1	2.2
	H		1.0		
2	VL	1.6			
	L	1.3			
	M			1.4	2.8
	H		1.4		
3	VL	2.5			
	L	2.0			
	M			1.7	3.4
	H		1.7		

Flight Phases, the roll sensitivity shall be not greater than 7.5 degrees in 1 second per pound for Level 1, and not greater than 12.5 degrees in 1 second per pound for Level 2. In case of conflict between the requirements of 3.3.4.1.3 and 3.3.4.3, the requirements of 3.3.4.1.3 shall govern. The term sensitivity does not include breakout force.

TABLE IXe FLIGHT PHASE GA ROLL PERFORMANCE

Time to Achieve the Following Bank Angle Change (Seconds)

Level	Speed Range	30°	50°	90°	180°
1	VL	1.5			
	L		1.7		
	M			1.7	3.0
	H		1.5		
2	VL	2.8			
	L	2.2			
	M			2.4	4.2
	H		2.4		
3	VL	4.4			
	L	3.8			
	M			3.4	6.0
	H		3.4		

TABLE IXf CLASS III ROLL PERFORMANCE

Time to Achieve 30° Bank Angle Change (Seconds)

Level	Speed Range	Category A	Category B	Category C
1	L	1.8	2.3	2.5
	M	1.5	2.0	2.5
	H	2.0	2.3	2.5
2	L	2.4	3.9	4.0
	M	2.0	3.3	4.0
	H	2.5	3.9	4.0
3	All	3.0	5.0	6.0

3.3.4.2 Roll performance for Class III airplanes. Roll performance in terms of ϕ_t for Class III airplanes is

specified in Table IXf over the following ranges of air-speeds:

Speed Range		Equivalent Airspeed Range
L	Level 1:	$V_{o_{min}} \leqslant V < 1.8V_{min}$
	Levels 2 and 3:	$V_{min} \leqslant V < 1.8V_{min}$
M	Level 1:	$1.8V_{min}^{(1)} \leqslant V < 0.7V_{max}^{(2)}$
	Levels 2 and 3:	$1.8V_{min} \leqslant V < 0.7V_{max}$
H	Level 1:	$0.7V_{max}^{(2)} \leqslant V \leqslant V_{o_{max}}$
	Levels 2 and 3:	$0.7V_{max} \leqslant V \leqslant V_{max}$

(1) or $V_{o_{min}}$ whichever is greater

(2) or $V_{o_{max}}$ whichever is less

3.3.4.3 Roll control forces. The stick or wheel force required to obtain the rolling performance specified in 3.3.4, 3.3.4.1 and 3.3.4.2 shall be neither greater than the maximum in Table X nor less than the breakout force plus:

a. Level 1 ----- one-fourth the values in Table X

b. Level 2 ----- one-eighth the values in Table X

c. Level 3 ----- zero

TABLE X MAXIMUM ROLL CONTROL FORCES

Level	Class	Flight Phase Category	Maximum Stick Force (lbs)	Maximum Wheel Force (lbs)
1	I, II-C, IV	A, B	20	40
		C	20	20
	II-L, III	A, B	25	50
		C	25	25
2	I, II-C, IV	A, B	30	60
		C	20	20
	II-L, III	A, B	30	60
		C	30	30
3	All	All	35	70

3.3.4.4 Linearity of roll response. There shall be no objectionable nonlinearities in the variation of rolling response with roll control deflection or force. Sensitivity or sluggishness in response to small control deflections or force shall be avoided.

3.3.4.5 Wheel control throw. For airplanes with wheel controllers, the wheel throw necessary to meet the roll performance requirements specified in 3.3.4 and 3.3.4.2 shall not exceed 60 degrees in either direction. For completely mechanical systems, the requirement may be relaxed to 80 degrees.

3.3.5 Directional control characteristics. Directional stability and control characteristics shall enable the pilot to balance yawing moments and control yaw and sideslip. Sensitivity to yaw control pedal forces shall be sufficiently high that directional control and force requirements can be met and satisfactory coordination can be achieved without unduly high pedal forces, yet sufficiently low that occasional improperly coordinated control inputs will not seriously degrade the flying qualities.

3.3.5.1 Directional control with speed change. When initially trimmed directionally with symmetric power, the trim change of propeller-driven airplanes with speed shall be such that wings-level straight flight can be maintained over a speed range of +/- 30 percent of the trim speed or +/- 100 knots equivalent airspeed, whichever is less (except where limited by boundaries of the Service Flight Envelope) with yaw-control-pedal forces not greater than 100 pounds for Levels 1 and 2 and not greater than 180 pounds for Level 3, without retrimming. For other airplanes, yaw-control-pedal forces shall not exceed 40 pounds at the specified conditions for Levels 1 and 2 or 180 pounds for Level 3.

3.3.5.1.1 Directional control with asymmetric loading. When initially trimmed directionally with each asymmetric loading specified in the contract at any speed in the Operational Flight Envelope, it shall be possible to maintain a straight flight path throughout the Operational Flight Envelope with yaw-control-pedal forces not greater than 100 pounds for Levels 1 and 2 and not greater than 180 pounds for Level 3, without retrimming.

3.3.5.2 Directional control in wave-off (go-around). For propeller-driven Class IV, and all propeller-driven carrier-based airplanes the response to thrust, configuration and airspeed change shall be such that the pilot can maintain straight flight during wave-off (go-around) initiated at speeds down to V_s (PA) with yaw-control-pedal forces not exceeding 100 lbs when trimmed at $V_{o_{min}}$ (PA). For other airplanes, yaw-control-pedal forces shall not exceed 40 pounds for the specified conditions. The preceding requirements apply for Levels 1 and 2. For all airplanes the Level 3 requirement is to maintain straight flight in these conditions with yaw-control-pedal forces not exceeding 180 pounds. For all Levels, bank angles up to 5 degrees are permitted.

3.3.6 Lateral-directional characteristics in steady sideslips. The requirements of 3.3.6.1 through 3.3.6.3.1 and 3.3.7.1 are expressed in terms of characteristics in yaw-control-induced steady, zero-yaw-rate sideslips with the airplane trimmed for wings-level straight flight. Requirements of 3.3.6.1 through 3.3.6.3 apply at sideslip angles up to those produced or limited by:

a. Full yaw-control-pedal deflection, or

b. 250 pounds of yaw-control-pedal force, or

c. Maximum roll control or surface deflection,

except that for single-propeller-driven airplanes during wave-off (go-around), yaw-control-pedal deflection in the direction opposite to that required for wings-level straight flight need not be considered beyond the deflection for a 10-degree change in sideslip from the wings-level straight flight condition.

3.3.6.1 Yawing moments in steady sideslips. For sideslips specified in 3.3.6, right yaw-control-pedal deflection and force shall produce left sideslips and left yaw-control-pedal deflection and force shall produce right sideslips. For Levels 1 and 2 the following requirements shall apply. The variation of sideslip angle with yaw-control-pedal deflection shall be essentially linear for sideslip angles between +15 degrees and -15 degrees. For larger sideslip angles, an increase in yaw-control-pedal deflection shall always be required for an increase in sideslip. The variation of sideslip angle with yaw-control-pedal force shall be essentially linear for sideslip angles between +10 degrees and -10 degrees. Although a lightening of pedal force is acceptable for sideslip angles outside this range, the pedal force shall never reduce to zero.

3.3.6.2 Side forces in steady sideslips. For the sideslips of 3.3.6, an increase in right bank angle shall accompany an increase in right sideslip, and an increase in left bank angle shall accompany an increase in left sideslip.

3.3.6.3 Rolling moments in steady sideslips. For the sideslips of 3.3.6, left roll-control deflection and force shall accompany left sideslips, and right roll-control deflection and force shall accompany right sideslips. For Levels 1 and 2, the variation of roll-control deflection and force with sideslip angle shall be essentially linear.

3.3.6.3.1 Exception for wave-off (go-around). The requirement of 3.3.6.3 may, if necessary, be excepted for wave-off (go-around) if task performance is not impaired and no more than 50 percent of roll control power available to the pilot, and no more than 10 pounds of roll-control force, are required in a direction opposite to that specified in 3.3.6.3.

3.3.6.3.2 Positive effective dihedral limit. For Levels 1 and 2, positive effective dihedral (right roll control for right sideslip and left roll control for left sideslip) shall never be so great that more than 75 percent of roll control power available to the pilot, and no more than 10 pounds of roll-stick force or 20 pounds of roll-wheel force, are required for sideslip angles which might be experienced in service employment.

3.3.7 Lateral-directional control in crosswinds. It shall be possible to take off and land with normal pilot skill and technique in 90-degree crosswinds, from either side, of velocities up to those specified in Table XI. Roll-control force shall be within the limits specified in 3.3.4.2, and yaw-control-pedal forces shall not exceed 100 pounds for Level 1 or 180 pounds for Levels 2 and 3. This requirement can normally be met through compliance with 3.3.7.1 and 3.3.7.2.

TABLE XI CROSSWIND VELOCITY

Level	Class	Crosswind
1 and 2	I	20 knots
	II, III, and IV	30 knots
	Water-based airplanes	20 knots
3	All	One half the values for Levels 1 and 2

3.3.7.1 Final approach in crosswinds. For all airplanes except land-based airplanes equipped with crosswind landing gear, or otherwise constructed to land in a large crabbed attitude, yaw- and roll-control power shall be adequate to develop at least 10 degrees of sideslip (3.3.6) in the power approach with yaw-control-pedal forces not exceeding the values specified in 3.3.7. For Level 1, roll control shall not exceed either 10 pounds of force or 75 percent of control power available to the pilot. For Levels 2 and 3, roll-control force shall not exceed 20 pounds.

3.3.7.2 Takeoff run and landing rollout in crosswinds. Yaw and roll control power, in conjunction with other normal means of control, shall be adequate to maintain a straight flight path on the ground or other landing surface. This requirement applies in calm air and in crosswinds up to the values specified in Table XI with cockpit control forces not exceeding the values specified in 3.3.7.

3.3.7.2.1 Cold- and wet-weather operation. The requirements of 3.3.7.2 apply on wet runways for all airplanes, and on snow-packed and icy runways for airplanes intended to operate under such conditions. If compliance is not demonstrated under these adverse runway conditions, directional control shall be maintained by use of aerodynamic controls alone at all airspeeds above 50 knots for Class IV airplanes and above 30 knots for all others. For very slippery runways, the requirement need not apply for crosswind components at which the force tending to blow the airplane off the runway exceeds the opposing tire-runway frictional force with the tires supporting the entire weight of the airplane.

3.3.7.2.2 Carrier-based airplanes. All carrier-based airplanes shall be capable of maintaining a straight path on the ground without the use of wheel brakes, at airspeeds of 30 knots and above, during takeoffs and landings in a 90-degree crosswind of at least 10 percent $V_S(L)$. Cockpit control forces shall be as specified in 3.3.7.

3.3.7.3 Taxiing wind speed limits. It shall be possible to taxi at any angle to a 35-knot wind for Class I airplanes and to a 45-knot wind for Class II, III and IV airplanes.

3.3.8 Lateral-directional control in dives. Yaw and roll control power shall be adequate to maintain wings level and sideslip zero, without retrimming, throughout the dives and pullouts of 3.2.3.5 and 3.2.3.6. In the Service Flight Envelope, roll control forces shall not exceed 20 pounds for propeller-driven airplanes or 10 pounds for other airplanes. Yaw-control-pedal forces shall not exceed 180 pounds for propeller-driven airplanes or 50 lbs for other airplanes.

3.3.9 Lateral-directional control with asymmetric thrust. Asymmetric loss of thrust may be caused by many factors including engine failure, inlet unstart, propeller failure or propeller-drive failure. Following sudden asymmetric loss of thrust from any factor, the airplane shall be safely controllable in the crosswinds of Table XI from the unfavorable direction. The requirements of 3.3.9.1 through 3.3.9.4 apply for the appropriate Flight Phases when any single failure or malperformance of the propulsive system, including inlet or exhaust, causes loss of thrust on one or more engines or propellers, considering also the effect of the failure or malperformance on all subsystems or driven by the failed propulsive system.

3.3.9.1 Thrust loss during takeoff run. It shall be possible for the pilot to maintain control of an airplane on the takeoff surface following sudden loss of thrust from the most critical factor. Thereafter, it shall be possible to achieve and maintain a straight path on the takeoff surface without a deviaton of more than 30 feet from the path originally intended, with yaw-control-pedal forces not exceeding 180 pounds. For the continued takeoff, the requirement shall be met when thrust is lost at speeds from the refusal speed (based on the shortest runway from which the airplane is designed to operate) to the maximum takeoff speed, with takeoff thrust maintained on the operative engine(s), using only controls not dependent upon friction against the takeoff surface or upon release of the pitch, roll, yaw or throttle controls. For the aborted takeoff, the requirement shall be met at all speeds below the maximum takeoff speed, however, additional controls such as nosewheel steering and differential braking may be used. Automatic devices which normally operate in the event of a thrust failure may be used in either case.

3.3.9.2 Thrust loss after takeoff. During takeoff it shall be possible without a change in selected configuration to achieve straight flight following sudden asymmetric loss of thrust from the most critical factor at speeds from V_{min} (TO) to V_{max} (TO), and thereafter to maintain straight flight throughout the climbout. The yaw-control-pedal force required to maintain straight flight with asymmetric thrust shall not exceed 180 lbs. Roll control shall not exceed either the force limits specified in 3.3.4.3 or 75 percent of available control power, with takeoff thrust maintained on the operative engine(s) and trim at normal setting for takeoff with symmetric thrust. Automatic devices which normally operate in the event of a thrust failure may be used, and the airplane may be banked up to 5 degrees away from the inoperative engine.

3.3.9.3 Transient effects. The airplane motions following sudden asymmetric loss of thrust shall be such that dangerous conditions can be avoided by pilot corrective action. A realistic time delay (3.4.8) of at least 1 second shall be incorporated.

3.3.9.4 Asymmetric thrust - yaw controls free. The static directional stability shall be such that at all speeds above $1.4V_{min}$, with asymmetric loss of thrust from the most critical factor while the other engine(s) develop normal rated thrust, the airplane with yaw-control-pedals free may be balanced directionally in steady straight flight. The trim settings shall be those required for wings-level straight flight prior to the engine failure. Roll-control forces shall not exceed the Level 2 upper limits specified in 3.3.4.2 for Levels 1 and 2 and shall not exceed the Level 3 upper limits for Level 3.

3.3.9.5 Two engines inoperative. At the one-engine-out speed for maximum range with any engine initially failed, it shall be possible upon failure of the most critical remaining engine to stop the transient motion and thereafter to maintain straight flight from that speed to the speed for maximum range with both engines failed. In addition, it shall be possible to effect a safe recovery at any service speed above $V_{o_{min}}$ (CL) following sudden simultaneous failure of the two most critical engines.

3.4 Miscellaneous flying qualities. Dangerous conditions may exist where the airplane should not be flown. When approaching these flight conditions, it shall be possible by clearly discernible means for the pilot to recognize the impending dangers and take corrective action. Final determination of the adequacy of all warning of impending dangerous flight conditions will be made by the procuring activity, considering functional effectiveness and reliability.

3.4.1.1 Warning and indication. Warning and indication of approach to a dangerous condition shall be clear and unambiguous. For example, a pilot must be able to distinguish readily among stall warning (which requires pitching down or increasing speed), Mach buffet (which may indicate a need to decrease speed), and normal airplane vibration (which indicates no need for pilot action).

3.4.1.2 Devices for indication, warning, prevention, recovery. It is intended that dangerous flight conditions be eliminated and the requirements of this specification met by appropriate aerodynamic design and mass distribution, rather than through incorporation of a special device or devices. Such devices may be used only if the procuring activity approves the need, the design criteria, possible Special Failure States (3.1.6.2.1) and the devices themselves. As a minimum, these devices shall perform their function whenever needed but shall not limit flight within the Operational Flight Envelope. Neither normal nor inadvertent operation of such devices shall create a hazard to the airplane. For Levels 1 and 2, nuisance operation shall not be possible. Functional failure of the devices shall be indicated to the pilot.

3.4.2 Flight at high angle of attack. The requirements of 3.4.2 through 3.4.2.2.2 concern stall warning, stalls, departure from controlled flight, post-stall gyrations, spins, recoveries and related characteristics. They apply at speeds and angles of attack which in general are outside the Service Flight Envelope. They are intended to assure safety and the absence of mission limitations due to high angle of attack characteristics.

3.4.2.1 Stalls. The stall is defined in terms of airspeed and angle of attack in 6.2.2 and 6.2.5 respectively. It usually is a phenomenon caused by airflow separation induced by high angle of attack, but it may instead be determined by some limit on usable angle of attack. The stall requirements apply for all Airplane Normal States in straight unaccelerated flight and in turns and pullups with attainable normal accelerations up to n_L. Specifically, the Airplane Normal States associated with the configurations, throttle settings and trim settings of 6.2.2 shall be investigated. Also, the requirements apply to Airplane Failure States that affect stall characteristics.

3.4.2.1.1 Stall approach. The stall approach shall be accompanied by an easily perceptible warning consisting of shaking of the cockpit controls, buffeting or shaking of the airplane, or a combination of both. The onset of this warning shall occur within the ranges specified in 3.4.2.1.1.1 and 3.4.2.1.1.2 but not within the Operational Flight Envelope. The increase in buffeting intensity with further increase in angle of attack shall be sufficiently marked to be noted by the pilot. The warning shall continue until the angle of attack is reduced to a value less than that for warning onset. At all angles of attack up to the stall, the cockpit controls shall remain effective in their normal sense, and small control inputs shall not result in departure from controlled flight. Prior to the stall, uncommanded oscillations shall not be objectionable to the pilot.

3.4.2.1.1.1 Warning speed for stalls at 1g normal to the flight path. Warning onset for stalls at 1g normal to the flight path shall occur between the following limits when the stall is approached gradually:

Flight Phase	Minimum Speed for Onset	Maximum Speed for Onset
Approach	Higher of $1.05V_S$ or V_S + 5 knots	Higher of $1.10V_S$ or V_S + 10 knots
All other	Higher of $1.05V_S$ or V_S + 5 knots	Higher of $1.15V_S$ or V_S + 15 knots

3.4.2.1.1.2 Warning range for accelerated stalls. Onset of stall warning shall occur outside the Operational Flight Envelope associated with the Airplane Normal State and within the following range or fraction of lift at stall at that airspeed, in that Airplane State, when the stall is approached gradually:

Flight Phase	Minimum Lift at Onset	Maximum Lift at Onset
Approach	$0.82C_{L_{stall}}$	$0.90C_{L_{stall}}$
All other	$0.75C_{L_{stall}}$	$0.90C_{L_{stall}}$

3.4.2.1.2 Stall characteristics. In the unaccelerated stalls of 3.4.2.1, the airplane shall not exhibit rolling, yawing or downward pitching at the stall which cannot be controlled to stay within 20 degrees for Classes

I, II and III or 30 degrees for Class IV airplanes. It is desired that no pitchup tendencies occur in unaccelerated or accelerated stalls. In unaccelerated stalls, mild nose-up pitch may be acceptable if no pitch control force reversal occurs and if no dangerous, unrecoverable flight conditions result. A mild nose-up tendency may be acceptable in accelerated stalls if the operational effectiveness of the airplane is not compromised and:

a. The airplane has adequate stall warning

b. Pitch control effectiveness is such that it is possible to stop the pitchup promptly and reduce the angle of attack and

c. At no point during the stall, stall approach or recovery does any portion of the airplane exceed structural limit loads.

The requirements apply for all stalls, including stalls entered abruptly.

3.4.2.1.3 Stall prevention and recovery. It shall be possible to prevent the stall by moderate use of the pitch control alone at the onset of the stall warning. It shall be possible to recover from a stall by simple use of the pitch, roll and yaw controls with cockpit control forces not to exceed those of 3.4.4.1, and to regain level flight without excessive loss of altitude or buildup of speed. Throttles shall remain fixed until speed has begun to increase and an angle of attack below the stall has been regained unless compliance would result in exceeding engine operating limitations. In the straight-flight stalls of 3.4.2.1, with the airplane trimmed at an airspeed not greater than $1.4V_S$, pitch control power

shall be sufficient to recover from any attainable angle of attack.

3.4.2.1.3.1 One-engine-out stalls. On multi-engine airplanes, it shall be possible to recover safely from stalls with the critical engine inoperative. This requirement applies with the remaining engines at up to:

Flight Phase	Thrust
TO	Takeoff
CL	Normal climb
PA	Normal approach
WO	Waveoff

3.4.2.2 Post-stall gyrations and spins. The post-stall gyration and spin requirements apply to all modes of motion that can be entered from upsets, decelerations, and extreme maneuvers appropriate to the Class and Flight Phase Category. Entries form inverted flight shall be included for Class I and IV airplanes. Entry angles of attack and sideslip up to maximum control capability and under dynamic flight conditions are to be included, except as limited by structural considerations. For all Classes and Flight Phase Categories, thrust settings up to and including MAT shall be included, with and without one critical engine inoperative at entry. The requirements hold for all Airplane Normal States and for all states of stability and control augmentation systems, except approved Special Failure States. Store release shall not be allowed during loss of control, spin or gyration, recovery, or subsequent dive pullout. Automatic disengagement of augmentation systems, however, is permissible if it is necessary and does not prevent meeting any other requirements. Re-engagement shall be possible in flight following recovery.

3.4.2.2.1 Departure from controlled flight. All Classes of airplanes shall be extremely resistant to departure from controlled flight, post-stall gyrations and spins. The airplane shall exhibit no uncommanded motion which cannot be arrested promptly by simple appropriate application of pilot control. In addition, the procuring activity may designate that certain training airplanes shall be capable of a developed spin and consistent recovery.

3.4.2.2.2 Recovery from post-stall gyrations and spins. For airplanes which, according to MIL-A-8861 must be structurally designed for spinning, the following requirements apply. The proper recovery technique(s) must be readily ascertainable by the pilot, and simple and easy to apply under the motions encountered. Whatever the motions, safe consistent recovery and pullout shall be possible without exceeding the control forces of 3.4.4.1 and without exceeding structural limitations. A single technique shall provide prompt recovery from all post-stall gyrations and incipient spins, without requiring the pilot to determine the direction of motion and without tendency to develop a spin. The same technique used to recover from post-stall gyrations and incipient spins, or at least a compatible one, is also desired for spin recovery. For all modes of spin that can occur, these recoveries shall be attainable within the number of turns, measured from the initiation of recovery action as follows:

Class	Flight Phase Category	Turns for Recovery
I	A, B	1.5
I	PA	1
Others	PA	1
Others	A, B	2

Avoidance of a spin reversal or an adverse mode change shall not depend upon precise pilot control timing or deflection. It is desired that all airplanes be readily recoverable from all attainable attitudes and motions. The post-stall characteristics of those airplanes not required to comply with requirements of this paragraph shall be determined by analysis and model test.

3.4.3 Cross-axis coupling in roll maneuvers. For Class I and IV airplanes in yaw-control-free, pitch-control-fixed, maximum performance rolls through 360 degrees, entered from straight flight or from turns, pushovers, or pullups ranging from 0g to $0.8n_L$, the resulting yaw or

pitch motions and sideslip or angle of attack changes shall neither exceed structural limits nor cause other dangerous flight conditions such as uncontrollable motions or roll autorotation.

During combat-type maneuvers involving rolls through angles up to 360 degrees and rolls which are checked at a given bank angle, the yawing and pitching shall not be so severe as to impair the tactical effectiveness of the maneuver. These requirements define Level 1 and 2 operation. For Class II and III airplanes, these requirements apply in rolls through 120 degrees and rolls which are checked at a given bank angle.

3.4.4 Control harmony. The pitch- and roll-control force and displacement sensitivities and breakout forces shall be compatible so that intentional inputs to one control axis will not cause inadvertent inputs to the other.

3.4.4.1 Control force coordination. The cockpit control forces required to perform maneuvers which are normal for the airplane should have magnitudes which are related to the pilot's capability to produce such forces in combination. The following control force levels are considered to be limiting values compatible with pilot's capability to apply simultaneous forces:

Control Type	Pitch	Roll	Yaw
Side-stick or Center-stick	50 lbs	25 lbs	
Wheel	75 lbs	40 lbs	
Pedal			175 lbs

3.4.5 Buffet. Within the boundaries of the Operational Flight Envelope, there shall be no objectionable buffet which might detract from the effectiveness of the airplane in executing its intended missions.

3.4.6 Release of stores. The intentional release of any stores shall not result in objectionable flight characteristics for Levels 1 and 2. However, the intentional release of stores shall never result in dangerous or intolerable flight characteristics. This requirement applies for all flight conditions and store loadings at which normal or emergency store release is permissible.

3.4.7 Effects of armament delivery and special equipment. Operation of moveable parts such as bomb bay doors, cargo doors, armament pods, refueling devices and rescue equipment, or firing of weapons, release of bombs, or delivery or pickup of cargo shall not cause buffet, trim changes, or other characteristics which impair the tactical effectiveness of the airplane under any pertinent flight condition. These requirements shall be met for Level 1 and for Level 2.

3.4.8 Transients following failures. The airplane motions following sudden system or component failures shall be such that dangerous conditions can be avoided by pilot corrective action. A realistic time delay between the failure and initiation of pilot corrective action shall be incorporated when determining compliance. This time delay should include an interval between the occurrence of the failure and the occurrence of a cue such as acceleration, rate, displacement, or sound that will definitely indicate to the pilot that a failure has occurred, plus an additional interval which represents the time required for the pilot to diagnose the situation and initiate corrective action.

3.4.9 Failures. No single failure of any component or system shall result in dangerous or intolerable flying qualities, Special Failure States (3.1.6.2.1) are excepted. The crew member concerned shall be provided with immediate and easily interpreted indications whenever failures occur that require or limit any flight crew action or decision.

3.4.10 Control margin. Control authority, rate and hinge moment capability shall be sufficient to assure safety throughout the combined range of all attainable angles of attack (both positive and negative) and sideslip. This requirement applies to the prevention of loss of control and to recovery from any situation for all maneuvering, including pertinent effects of factors such as regions of control-surface-fixed instability, inertial coupling, fuel slosh, the influence of symmetric and asymmetric stores (3.1.4), stall/post-stall/spin characteristics (3.4.2 through 3.4.2.2.2), atmospheric disturbances (3.8) and Airplane Failure States (3.1.10.1 and 3.1.10.2 with maneuvering flight appropriate to the Failure State to be included). Consideration shall be taken of the degrees of effectiveness and certainty of operation of limiters, c.g. control malfunction or mismanagement, and transients from failures in the propulsion, flight control and other relevant systems.

3.4.11 Direct force controls. Use of devices for direct normal-force control and direct side-force control shall not produce objectionable changes in attitude for any amount of control up to the maximum available. This requirement shall be met for Levels 1 and 2.

3.5 Characteristics of the primary flight control system

3.5.1 General characteristics. As used in this specification, the term primary flight control system includes the pitch, roll and yaw controls, stability augmentation systems, and all mechanisms and devices which they operate. The requirements of this section are concerned with those aspects of the primary flight control system which are directly related to the flying qualities. These requirements are in addition to the requirements of the applicable control system design specifications, e.g.: MIL-F-9490 or MIL-C-18244.

3.5.2 Mechanical characteristics. Some of the important mechanical characteristics of control systems (including servo valves and actuators) are: friction and preload, lost motion, flexibility, mass imbalance and inertia, nonlinear gearing, and rate limiting. Requirements for some of these characteristics are contained in 3.5.2.1 through 3.5.2.4. Meeting these separate requirements, however, will not necessarily ensure that the overall system will be adequate, the mechanical characteristics must be compatible with the nonmechanical portions of the control system as well as with the airframe dynamic characteristics.

3.5.2.1 Control centering and breakout forces. Longitudinal, lateral and directional controls should exhibit positive centering in flight at any normal trim setting. Although absolute centering is not required, the combined effects of centering, breakout force, stability and force gradient shall not produce objectionable flight characteristics, such as poor precision-tracking ability, or permit large departures from trim conditions with controls free. Breakout forces, including friction, preload, etc., shall be within the limits of Table XII. The values in Table XII refer to the cockpit control force required to start movement of the control surface in flight for Levels 1 and 2, the upper limits are doubled for Level 3.

Measurement of breakout forces on the ground will ordinarily suffice in lieu of actual flight measurement, provided that the qualitative agreement between ground measurement and flight observation can be established.

3.5.2.2 Cockpit control free play. The free play in each cockpit control, that is, any motion of the cockpit control which does not move the control surface in flight, shall not result in objectionable flight characteristics, particularly for small-amplitude control inputs.

3.5.2.3 Rate of control displacement. The ability of the airplane to perform the operational maneuvers required of it shall not be limited in the atmospheric disturbances specified in 3.7 by control surface deflection rates (3.8.3.1, 3.8.3.2 and 3.4.10). For powered or boosted controls, the effect of engine speed and the duty cycle

TABLE XII ALLOWABLE BREAKOUT FORCES, POUNDS

Control		Classes I, II-C, IV Min.	Classes I, II-C, IV Max.	Classes II-L, III Min.	Classes II-L, III Max.
Pitch	Stick	0.5	3.0	0.5	5.0
	Wheel	0.5	4.0	0.5	7.0
Roll	Stick	0.5	2.0	0.5	4.0
	Wheel	0.5	3.0	0.5	6.0
Yaw	Pedal	1.0	7.0	1.0	14.0

of both primary and secondary control together with the pilot control technique shall be included when establishing compliance with this requirement.

3.5.2.4 Adjustable controls. When a cockpit control is adjustable for pilot physical dimensions and comfort, the control forces defined in 6.2 refer to the mean adjustment. A force referred to any other adjustment shall not differ by more than 10 percent from the force referred to the mean adjustment.

3.5.3 Dynamic characteristics. A linear or smoothly varying airplane response to cockpit-control deflection and to control force shall be provided for all amplitudes of control input. The response of the control surfaces in flight shall not lag the cockpit-control force inputs by more than the angles specified in Table XIII, for frequencies equal to or less than the frequencies specified in Table XIII.

TABLE XIII ALLOWABLE CONTROL SURFACE LAGS

Allowable Lag, degrees

Level	Flight Phase Category A and C	Flight Phase Category B
1	15	30
2	30	45
3	60	60

Control	Upper Frequency, rad/sec
Pitch	the larger of $\omega_{n_{sp}}$ and 2.0
Roll and Yaw	the largest of ω_{n_d}, $1/T_r$ and 2.0

In addition, the response of the airplane motion shall not exhibit a time delay longer than the values given in Table XIV for a pilot-initiated step control force input.

Further, the values of the equivalent time delay derived from equivalent system match of the aircraft response to cockpit controls shall not exceed the values given in Table XIV.

TABLE XIV ALLOWABLE AIRPLANE RESPONSE DELAY

Level	Allowable Delay, Seconds
1	0.10
2	0.20
3	0.25

3.5.3.1 Damping. All control system oscillations shall be well damped, unless they are of such an amplitude, frequency and phasing that they do not result in objectionable oscillations of the cockpit controls or the airframe during abrupt maneuvers and during flight in atmospheric disturbances.

3.5.4 Augmentation systems. Operation of stability augmentation and control augmentation systems and devices shall not introduce any objectionable flight or ground handling characteristics.

3.5.5 Failures. The following events shall not cause dangerous or intolerable flying qualities:

a. Complete or partial loss of any function of the augmentation system following a single failure

b. Failure-induced transient motions and trim changes either immediately after failure or upon subsequent transfer to alternate control modes

c. Configuration changes required or recommended following failure.

3.5.5.1 Failure transients. With controls free, the airplane motions due to failures described in 3.5.5 shall not exceed the following limits for at least 2 seconds following the failure, as a function of the Level of flying qualities after the failure transient has subsided:

Levels 1 and 2 (after failure)	+/- 0.5g incremental normal or lateral acceleration at the pilot's station and +/- 10 degrees per second roll rate, except that neither stall angle of attack nor structural limits shall be exceeded. In addition for Category A, vertical or lateral excursions of 5 feet, +/- 2 degrees bank angle
Level 3 (after failure)	No dangerous attitude or structural limit is reached, and no dangerous alteration of the flight path results from which recovery is impossible.

3.5.5.2 Trim changes due to failures. The changes in control forces required to maintain attitude and sideslip for the failures described in 3.5.5 shall not exceed the following limits for at least 5 seconds following the failure:

Pitch------------------------20 pounds
Roll-------------------------10 pounds
Yaw--------------------------50 pounds

3.5.6 Transfer to alternate control modes. The transient motions and trim changes resulting from the intentional engagement or disengagement of any portion of the primary flight control system by the pilot shall be such that dangerous flying qualities never result.

3.5.6.1 Transfer transients. With controls free, the transients resulting from the situations described in 3.5.6 shall not exceed the following limits for at least 2 seconds following the transfer:

Within the Operational Flight Envelope	+/- 0.1g normal or lateral acceleration at the pilot's station and +/- 3 deg/sec roll
Within the Service Flight Envelope	+/- 0.5g at the pilot's station, +/- 5 deg/sec roll, the lesser of +/- 5 degrees sideslip and the structural limits.

These requirements apply only for Airplane Normal States.

3.5.6.2 Trim changes. The changes in control forces required to maintain attitude and sideslip for the situations described in 3.5.6 shall not exceed the following limits for at least 5 seconds following the transfer:

Pitch-----------------------20 pounds
Roll------------------------10 pounds
Yaw-------------------------50 pounds

These requirements apply only for Airplane Normal States.

3.6 Characteristics of secondary control systems

3.6.1 Trim system. In straight flight, throughout the Operational Flight Envelope the trimming devices shall be capable of reducing all the cockpit control forces to zero for Levels 1 and 2. For Level 3 the untrimmed steady-state cockpit-control forces shall not exceed 10 pounds in pitch, 5 pounds in roll and 20 pounds in yaw (pedal). The failures to be considered in applying the Level 2 and 3 requirements shall include trim sticking and runaway in either direction. It is permissible to meet the Level 2 and 3 requirements by providing the pilot with alternate trim mechanisms or override capability. Additional requirements on trim rate and authority are contained in Mil-F-9490 and Mil-F-18372.

3.6.1.1 Trim for asymmetric thrust. For all multi-engine airplanes, it shall be possible to trim the cockpit-control forces to zero in straight flight with up to two engines inoperative following asymmetric loss of thrust from the most critical factors (3.3.9). This requirement defines Level 1 in level-flight cruise at speeds from the maximum-range speed for the engine(s)-out configuration to the speed obtainable with normal rated thrust on the functioning engine(s). Systems completely dependent on the failed engine(s) shall also be considered failed.

3.6.1.2 Rate of trim operation. Trim devices shall operate rapidly enough to enable the pilot to maintain low control forces under changing conditions normally encountered in service, yet not so rapidly as to cause oversensitivity or trim precision difficulties under any conditions. Specifically, it shall be possible to trim the pitch control forces to less than +/- 10 pounds for center-stick airplanes and +/- 20 pounds for wheel-control airplanes throughout:

a. dives and ground attack maneuvers required in normal service operation and

b. level-flight acceleration at maximum augmented thrust from 250 knots or $V_{R/C}$, whichever is less, to V_{max} at any altitude when the airplane is trimmed for level flight prior to initiation of the maneuver.

In the event that operation of the trim system requires removal of one hand from the wheel-control, Level 1 force limits shall be as for a center-stick.

3.6.1.3 Stalling of trim systems. Stalling of a trim system due to aerodynamic loads during maneuvers shall not result in an unsafe condition. Specifically, the longitudinal trim system shall be capable of operating during the dive recoveries of 3.2.3.6 at any attainable permissible n, at any possible position of the trimming device.

3.6.1.4 Trim system irreversibility. All trimming devices shall maintain a given setting indefinitely unless changed by the pilot, or by a special automatic interconnect (such as to the landing flaps), or by the operation of an augmentation device. If an automatic interconnect or augmentation device is used in conjunction with a trim device, provision shall be made to ensure the accurate return of the device to its initial trim position on removal of each interconnect or augmentation command.

3.6.2 Speed and flight-path control devices. The effectiveness and response times of the longitudinal controls shall be sufficient to provide adequate control of flight path and airspeed at any flight condition within the Operational Flight Envelope. This requirement may be met by use of devices such as throttles, thrust reversers, auxiliary drag devices and flaps.

3.6.3 Transients and trim changes. The transients and steady-state trim changes for normal operation of secondary control devices (such as throttle, thrust reversers, flaps, slats, speed brakes, deceleration devices, dive recovery devices, wing sweep and landing gear) shall not impose excessive control forces to maintain the desired heading, altitude, attitude, rate of climb, speed or load factor without use of trimmer control. This requirement applies to all in-flight configuration changes and combinations of changes made under service conditions, including the effects of asymmetric operations such as unequal operation of the landing gear, speed brakes, slats or flaps. In no case shall there be any objectionable buffeting or oscillation caused by such devices. More specific requirements on secondary control devices are contained in 3.6.3.1, 3.6.4 and 3.6.5 and in Mil-F-9490 and Mil-F-18372.

3.6.3.1 Pitch trim changes. The pitch trim changes caused by operation of secondary control devices shall not be so large that a peak pitch control force in excess of 10 lbs for center-stick controllers or 20 lbs for wheel controllers is required when such configuration changes are made in flight under conditions representative of operational procedure. Generally, the conditions listed in Table XV will suffice for determination of compliance with this requirement. (For airplanes with variable-sweep wings, additional requirements will be imposed consistent with operational employment of the vehicle). With the airplane trimmed for each specified initial condition, the peak force required to maintain the specified parameter constant following the specified configuration change shall not exceed the stated value for a time interval of at least 5 seconds following the completion of the pilot action initiating the configuration change. The magnitude and rate of trim change subsequent to this time period shall be such that the forces are easily trimmable by use of the normal trimming devices. These requirements define Level 1. For Levels 2 and 3, the allowable forces are increased by 50 percent.

3.6.4 Auxiliary dive recovery devices. Operation of any auxiliary device intended solely for dive recovery shall always produce a positive increment of normal acceleration, but the total normal load factor shall never exceed $0.8n_L$, controls free.

TABLE XV PITCH TRIM CHANGE CONDITIONS

No.	Flight Phase	Initial Trim Condition: Altitude	Speed	Landing Gear	High Lift Devices and Wing Flaps	Thrust	Configuration Change	Parameter held constant
1	Approach	$h_{o_{min}}$	Normal pattern entry speed	Up	Up	TLF	Gear down	Altitude and airspeed*
2	Same	Same	Same	Up	Up	TLF	Gear Down	Altitude
3	Same	Same	Same	Down	Up	TLF	Extend high-lift devices and wing flaps	Altitude and airspeed*
4	Same	Same	Same	Down	Up	TLF	Extend high-lift devices and wing flaps	Altitude
5	Same	Same	Same	Down	Down	TLF	Idle thrust	Airspeed
6	Same	Same	$V_{o_{min}}$	Down	Down	TLF	Extend approach drag device	Airspeed
7	Same	Same	Same	Down	Down	TLF	Takeoff thrust	Airspeed
8	Same	Same	Same	Down	Down	TLF	Takeoff thrust plus normal cleanup for wave-off (go-around)	Airspeed
9	Takeoff	$h_{o_{min}}$	$V_{o_{min}}$	Down	Takeoff	Takeoff thrust	Gear up	Pitch attitude
10	Same	Same	Minimum flap re-tract speed	Up	Takeoff	Takeoff thrust	Retract high lift devices and wing flaps	Airspeed
11	Cruise and air-to-air combat	$h_{o_{min}}$ and $h_{o_{max}}$	Speed for level flight	Up	Up	MRT	Idle thrust	Pitch Attitude
12	Same	Same	Same	Up	Up	MRT	Actuate deceleration device	Same
13	Same	Same	Same	Up	Up	MRT	Maximum augmented thrust	Same
14	Same	Same	Speed for best range	Up	Up	TLF	Actuate deceleration device	Same

Notes: 1. Auxiliary drag devices are initially retracted, and all details of configuration not specifically mentioned are normal for the Flight Phase.

2. If power reduction is permitted in meeting the deceleration requirements established for the mission, actuation of the deceleration device in Numbers 12 and 14 shall be accompanied by the allowable power reduction.

* Throttle may be changed during the maneuver

3.7 Atmospheric disturbances

3.7.1 Form of the disturbance models. Where feasible, the Von Karman form shall be used for the continuous turbulence model, so that the flying qualities analyses will be consistent with comparable structural analyses. When no comparable structural analysis is performed or when it is not feasible to use the Von Karman form, use of the Dryden form will be permissible. In general, both the continuous turbulence model and the discrete gust model shall be used. The scales and intensities used in determining the gust magnitudes for the discrete gust model shall be the same as those in the continuous model.

3.7.1.1 Continuous turbulence model (Von Karman form). The Von Karman form of the spectra for the turbulence velocities is:

$$\phi_{u_g}(\Omega) = \frac{(\sigma_u)^2 (2L_u/\pi)}{[1 + (1.339 L_u \Omega)^2]^{5/6}}$$

$$\phi_{v_g}(\Omega) = \frac{(\sigma_v)^2 (L_v/\pi)[1 + (8/3)(1.339 L_v \Omega)^2]}{[1 + (1.339 L_v \Omega)^2]^{11/6}}$$

$$\phi_{w_g}(\Omega) = \frac{(\sigma_w)^2 (L_w/\pi)[1 + (8/3)(1.339 L_w \Omega)^2]}{[1 + (1.339 L_w \Omega)^2]^{11/6}}$$

3.7.1.2 Continuous turbulence model (Dryden form). The Dryden form of the spectra of turbulence velocities is:

$$\phi_{u_g}(\Omega) = \frac{(\sigma_u)^2 (2L_u/\pi)}{[1 + (L_u \Omega)^2}$$

$$\phi_{v_g}(\Omega) = \frac{(\sigma_v)^2 (L_v/\pi)[1 + 3(L_v \Omega)^2}{[1 + (L_v \Omega)^2]^2}$$

$$\phi_{w_g}(\Omega) = \frac{(\sigma_w)^2 (L_w/\pi)[1 + 3(L_w \Omega)^2}{[1 + (L_w \Omega)^2]^2}$$

3.7.1.3 Discrete gust model. The discrete gust model may be used for any of the three gust-velocity components and, by derivation, any of the three angular components. The discrete gust has the '(1 - cosine)' shape given by:

$v = 0$ for $x < 0$

$v = (v_m/2)(1 - \cos(\pi x/d_m))$, for $0 < x < d_m$

$v = v_m$ for $x > d_m$

In graphical form this is:

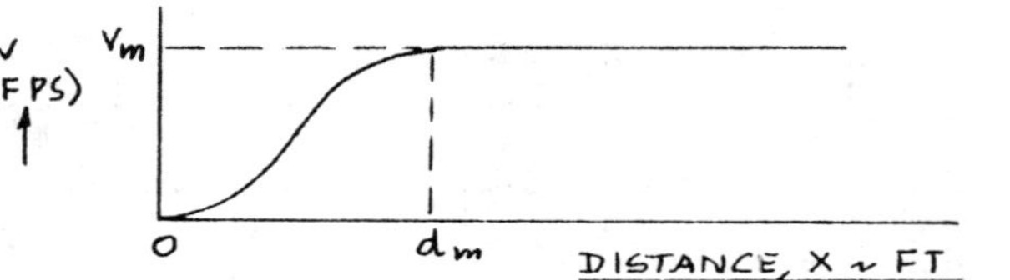

The discrete gust above may be used singly or in multiples to assess airplane response to, or pilot control of, large disturbances. Step function or linear ramp gusts may also be used.

3.7.2 Medium/high-altitude model. The scales and intensities are based on the assumption that turbulence above 2,000 feet is isotropic. Then:

$$\sigma_u = \sigma_v = \sigma_w$$

and:

$$L_u = L_v = L_w$$

3.7.2.1 Turbulence scale lengths. The scales to be used are:

$L_u = L_v = L_w = 2{,}500$ feet using the Von Karman form, or

$L_u = L_v = L_w = 1{,}750$ feet using the Dryden form.

3.7.2.2 Turbulence intensities. Root-mean-square turbulence intensities are shown in Figure B7 as functions of altitude and probability of exceedance. Simplified variations for application to the requirements of this specification are indicated.

3.7.2.3 Gust lengths. Several values of d_m shall be used, each chosen so that the gust is tuned to each of the natural frequencies of the airplane and its flight control system (higher-frequency structural modes may be excepted). The magnitude of v_m shall be determined from Figure B8.

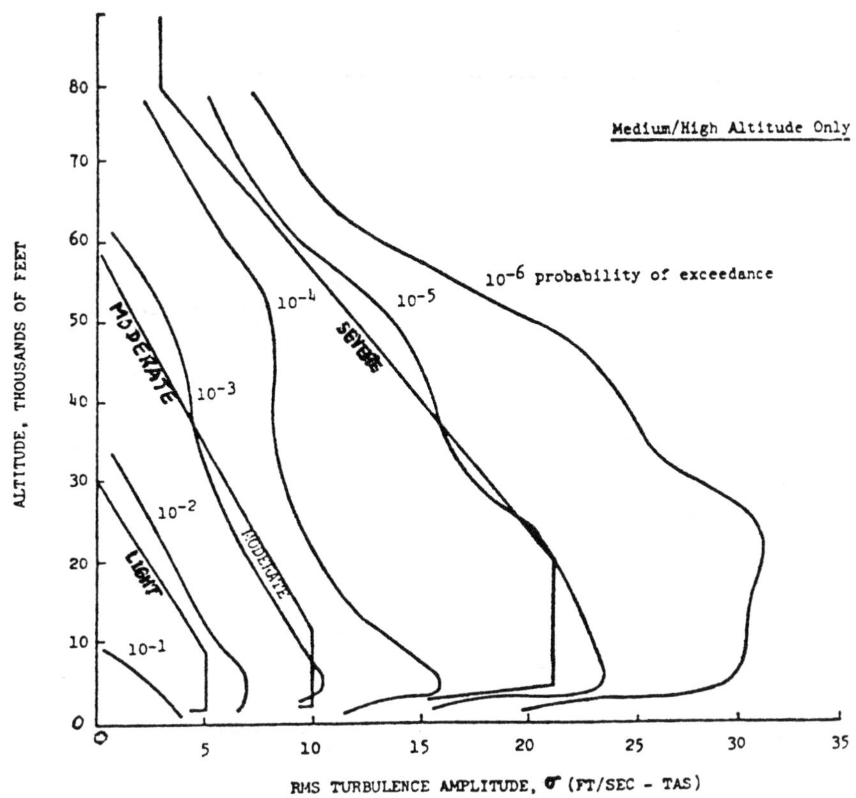

Figure B7 Turbulence Exceedance Probability

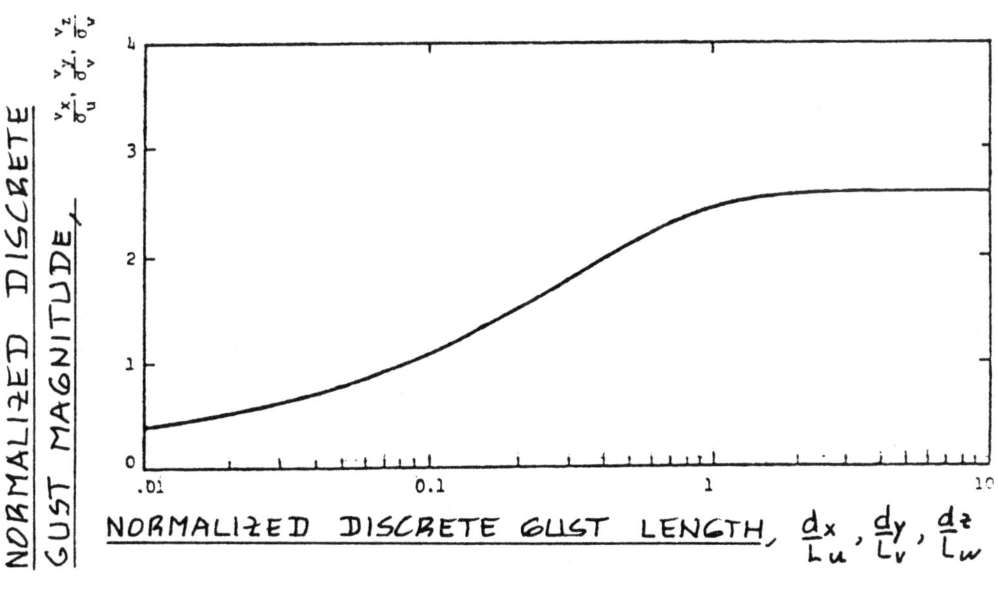

Figure B8 Magnitude of Discrete Gusts

3.7.2.4 Gust magnitudes. The Light and Moderate gust magnitudes u_g, v_g and w_g shall be determined from Figure B8 using the values of d_x, d_y and d_z determined according to 3.7.2.3, and the appropriate RMS turbulence intensities from Figure B7. Severe gusts shall be:

a. 66 ft/sec EAS at V_G, gust penetration speed

b. 50 ft/sec EAS at $V_{o_{max}}$

c. 25 ft/sec EAS at V_{max}

d. 50 ft/sec EAS at speeds up to V_{max} (PA) with the landing gear and other devices which are open or extended in their maximum open or maximum extended positions

e. For altitudes above 20,000 feet the gust magnitudes may be reduced linearly from:

(1) 66 ft/sec EAS at 20,000 feet to 38 ft/sec EAS at 50,000 feet for the V_G condition

(2) 50 ft/sec EAS at 20,000 feet to 25 ft/sec EAS at 50,000 feet for the $V_{o_{max}}$ condition

(3) 25 ft/sec EAS at 20,000 feet to 12.5 ft/sec EAS at 50,000 feet for the V_{max} condition

f. For altitudes above 50,000 feet the equivalent gust velocity specified at 50,000 feet shall be multiplied by the factor $(\rho/\rho_{50})^{1/2}$, the square root of the ratio of air density at altitude to standard atmospheric density at 50,000 feet.

3.7.3 Low-altitude disturbance model. This section specifies the model of atmospheric disturbances to be used for all Category C operations. The effects of wind shear, turbulence and gusts may be analyzed separately. Some analysis and piloted simulation is required considering a complete environmental representation, demonstrating compliance with the requirements with the cumulative effects of wind shear, turbulence and gusts. A non-Gaussian turbulence representation together with a wind model may also be used to represent the patchy, intermittent nature of actual measured turbulence.

3.7.3.1 Wind speeds. The wind speed at 20 feet above the ground, u_{20}, is shown in Figure B9 as a function of probability of occurrence. The values to be used for the different intensities of atmospheric disturbance are indicated.

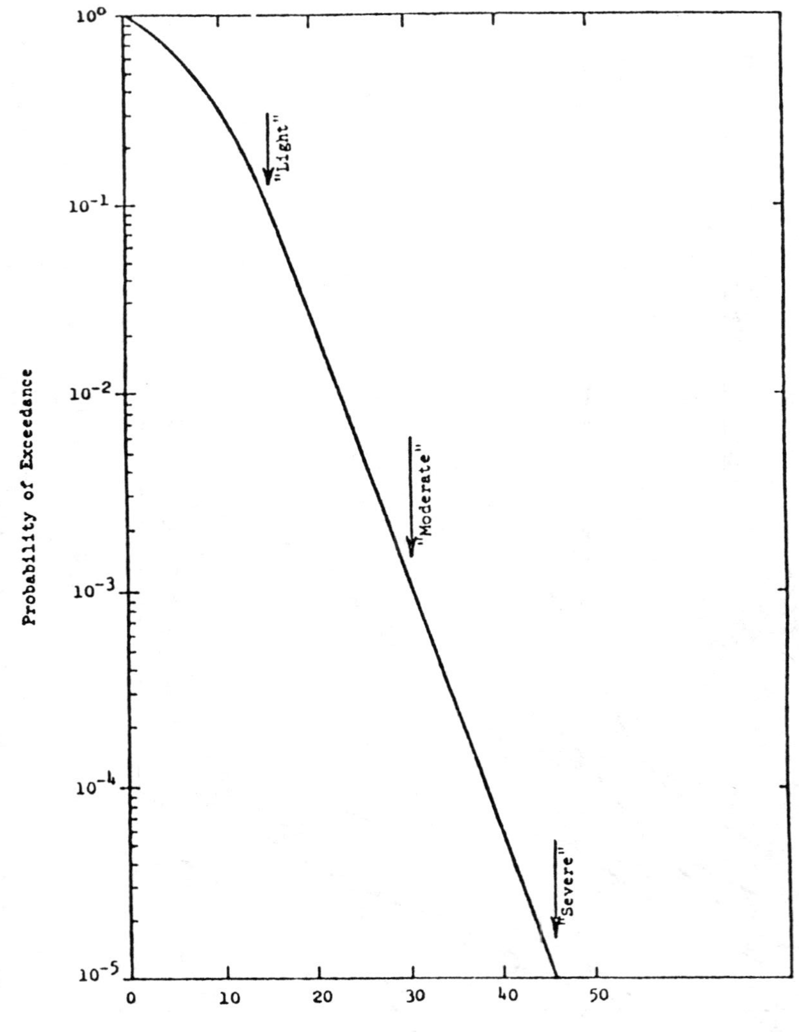

Figure B9 Probability of Exceeding Mean Wind Speed at 20 Feet

3.7.3.2 Wind shear. The magnitude of the wind scalar shear is defined by the use of the following expression for the mean wind profile as a function of altitude:

$$u_w = u_{20}(\ln(h/z_o))/(\ln(20/z_o))$$

where: z_o = 0.15 feet for Category C Flight Phase

= 2.0 feet for other Flight Phases.

3.7.3.3 Vector shear. Different orientations of the mean wind relative to the runway for Category C, or relative to the aircraft flight path for other Flight Phases, shall be considered. In addition, changes in direction of the mean wind speed over a given height change shall be considered as follows:

Disturbance intensity	Change in mean wind heading, degrees	Height of vector shear, feet
LIGHT	0	----
MODERATE	90	600
SEVERE	90	300

A range of values for the initial wind orientation and the initial altitude for onset of the shear shall be considered. Relative to the runway, magnitudes of $u_{20}\sin\Psi_w$ greater than the crosswind values in 3.3.7 or tailwind component at 20 feet greater than 10 knots need not be considered. At any altitude other than 20 feet these limits do not apply.

3.7.3.4 Turbulence. The turbulence models of 3.7.1.1 or 3.7.1.2 shall be used. The appropriate scale lengths are shown in Figure B10 as functions of altitude. The turbulence intensities to be used are:

$\sigma_w = 0.1u_{20}$, and σ_u and σ_v given by Figure B11 as functions of σ_w and altitude.

3.7.3.5 Gusts. Discrete gusts of the form specified in 3.7.2.3 shall be used, with both single and double ramps to be considered. Several values of d_m shall be used, each chosen so that the gust is tuned to each of the natural frequencies of the airplane and its flight control system. The gust magnitudes shall be determined from Figure B8 using the appropriate values from Figures B10 and B11. The two halves of a double gust do not have to be the same length or magnitude.

3.7.4 Carrier landing disturbance model. This section specifies the model of atmospheric disturbances to be used for carrier landing operations. This model shall be used in analysis and piloted simulation to determine aircraft control response and path control accuracy during carrier landing. This model supplements but does not replace the low-altitude model of 3.7.3.

The terminal approach carrier landing disturbance model shall be used during simulation of the last 1/2 mile of the carrier approach. The u velocity component is aligned with the wind over the deck. Total disturbance velocities are computed by adding segments caused by random free-air turbulence, u_1, v_1, w_1, staedy ship-wake disturbance, u_2, w_2, periodic ship-motion-induced turbulence, u_3, w_3, and random ship-wake disturbance, u_4, v_4, w_4.

The total air disturbance components u_g, v_g and w_g are then computed as:

$$u_g = u_1 + u_2 + u_3 + u_4$$

$$v_g = v_1 + v_4$$

$$w_g = w_1 + w_2 + w_3 + w_4$$

The input to all of the random disturbance filters shall be generated by filtering the wide-band, Gaussian output of zero-mean, unit-variance random-number generators.

3.7.4.1 Free-air turbulence components. The free-air turbulence components which are independent of aircraft relative position are represented by filtering the output of white-noise generators described in 3.7.4 to produce the following spectra:

$$\phi_{u_1}(\Omega) = \frac{200}{(1 + (100\Omega)^2)} \quad \text{per radian/ft}$$

$$\phi_{v_1}(\Omega) = \frac{5900(1 + (400\Omega)^2)}{(1 + (1000\Omega)^2)(1 + (400\Omega/3)^2)} \quad \text{per radian/ft}$$

$$\phi_{w_1}(\Omega) = \frac{71.6}{(1 + (100\Omega)^2)} \quad \text{per radian/ft}$$

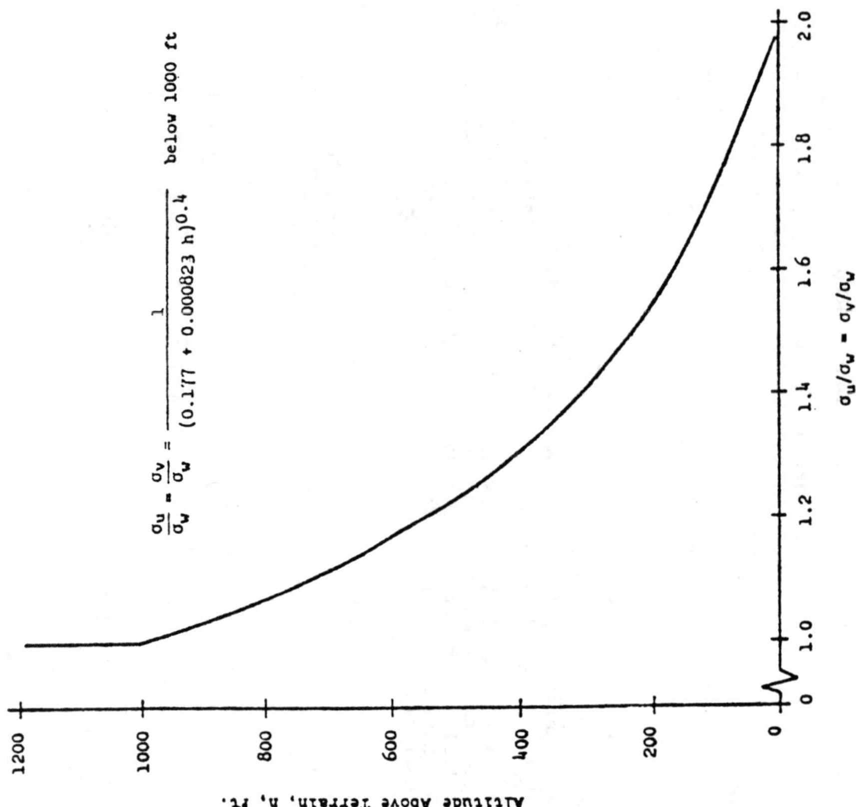

Figure B11 Horizontal Turbulence RMS Intensities

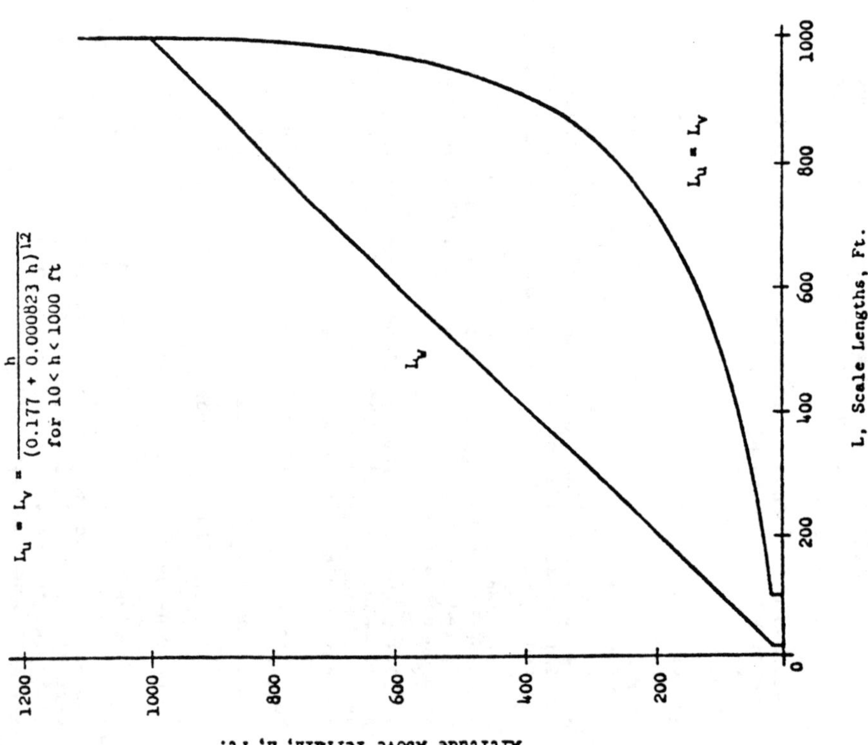

Figure B10 Low Altitude Turbulence Intensity Scales

3.7.4.2 Steady component of carrier airwake. The steady components of the carrier airwake consist of a reduction in the steady wind and a predominant upwash aft of the ship which are functions of range. Figure B12 illustrates the steady wind functions $u_2/V_{w/d}$ and $w_2/V_{w/d}$ as functions of position aft of the ship center of pitch.

3.7.4.3 Periodic component of carrier airwake. The periodic component of the airwake varies with ship pitching frequency, pitch magnitude, wind over deck and aircraft range. These components are computed as follows:

$$u_3 = \theta_s V_{w/d}(2.22 + 0.0009X)C$$

$$w_3 = \theta_s V_{w/d}(4.98 + 0.0018X)C$$

with: C =

$$\cos[\omega_p(t + t(V - V_{w/d})/(0.85V_{w/d}) + X/(0.85V_{w/d})) + P]$$

where: ω_p = Ship pitch frequency, rad/sec.

θ_s = Ship pitch amplitude, rad.

P = Random phase, rad.

X = the distance from the ship center of pitch, in ft, as defined in Figure B12.

Notes from the author: 1. The center of pitch location depends on the type of carrier. In preliminary design, the center of pitch may be assumed to be at one half the length of the carrier.

2. Values for ship pitch frequency, pitch amplitude and random phase must be obtained from the procuring activity. These values depend on ship type and on sea state.

The u component is set to zero for $X < -2236$ feet, and the w component is set to zero for $X < -2536$ feet.

3.7.4.4 Random component of carrier air wake. The ship-related random velocity components are computed by filtering white noise (3.7.4) as follows:

$$u_4 = \frac{\sigma(X)\{2\tau(X)\}^{1/2}(\text{Input})}{\{\tau(X)j\omega + 1\}}$$

$$w_4 = v_4 = \frac{0.035V_{w/d}(6.66)^{1/2}(\text{Input})}{(3.33j\omega + 1)}$$

where:

$\sigma(X)$ = RMS Amplitude in ft/sec., see Figure B13

$\tau(X)$ = Time constant in sec., see Figure B13

Input = (Random number output)$\{j\omega/(j\omega + 0.1)\}\sin(10\pi t)$

3.7.5 Application of the disturbance model in analyses. The gust and turbulence velocities shall be applied to the airplane equations of motion through the aerodynamic terms only, and the direct effect on the aerodynamic sensors shall be included when such sensors are part of the airplane augmentation system. When using the discrete gust model, all significant aspects of the penetration of the gust by the airplane shall be incorporated in the analyses. Application of the disturbance model depends on the range of frequencies of concern in the analyses of the airframe. When structural modes are significant, the exact distribution of turbulence velocities should be considered. For this purpose, it is acceptable to consider u_g and v_g as being one-dimensional functions only of x, but w_g shall be considered two-dimensional, a function of both x and y, for the evaluation of aerodynamic forces and moments.

When structural modes are not significant, airframe rigid-body responses may be evaluated by considering uniform gust or turbulence immersion along with linear gradients of the disturbance velocities. The uniform immersion is accounted for by u_g, v_g and w_g defined at the airplane center of gravity. The angular velocities due to turbulence are equivalent in effect to airplane angular velocities. Approximations for these angular velocities are defined (precisely at very low frequencies only) as follows:

$$\dot{\alpha}_g = q_g = \partial w_g/\partial x,\quad p_g = \partial w_g/\partial y,\quad r_g = \partial v_g/\partial x$$

The spectra of the angular velocity disturbances due to turbulence are then given by:

$$\phi_{p_g}(\Omega) = ((\sigma_w)^2/L_w)\frac{(0.8(\pi L_w/4b)^{1/3})}{(1 + (4b\Omega/\pi)^2)}$$

$$\phi_{q_g}(\Omega) = [(\Omega)^2/(1 + (4b\Omega/\pi)^2)]\phi_{w_g}(\Omega)$$

$$\phi_{r_g}(\Omega) = [(\Omega)^2/(1 + (3b\Omega/\pi)^2)]\phi_{v_g}(\Omega)$$

where: b is the wing span.

The turbulence components u_g, v_g, w_g and p_g shall be considered mutually independent (uncorrelated) in a statistical sense. However, q_g is correlated with w_g, and r_g is correlated with v_g. For the discrete gusts the linear gradient gives angular velocity perturbations of the following form:

$$p_g = p_m \sin(\pi x/d_m) \qquad 0 \leq x \leq d_m$$

For the low-altitude model, the turbulence velocity components u_g, v_g and w_g are to be taken along axes with u_g aligned along the relative mean wind vector and with w_g vertical.

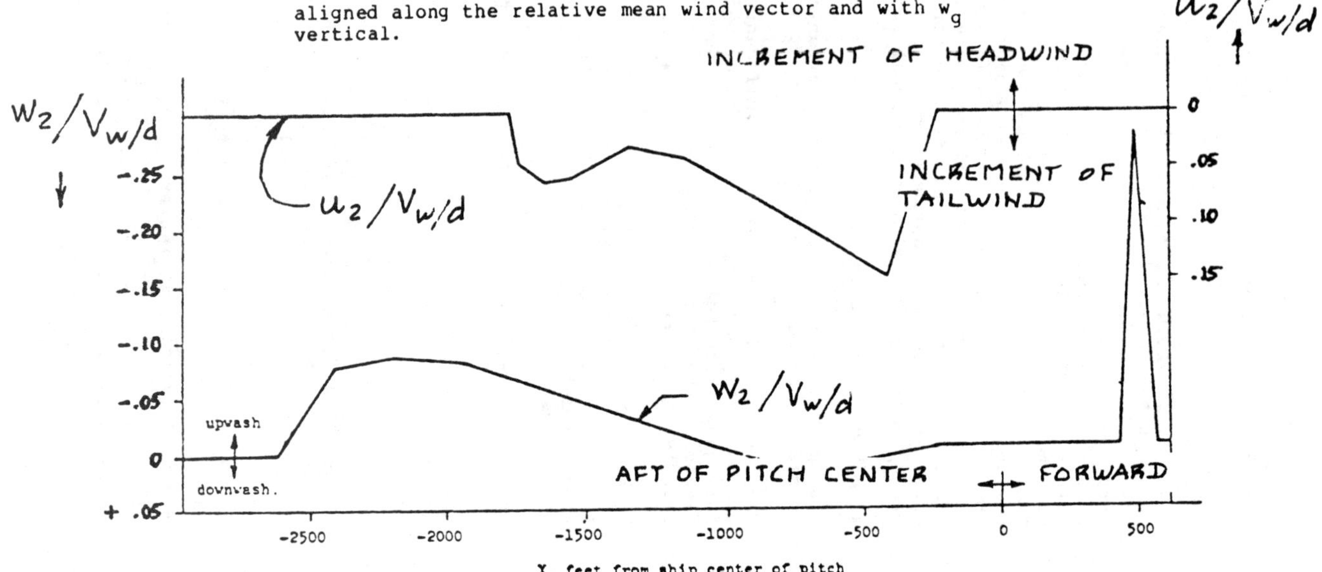

Figure B12 CVA Ship Burble Steady Wind Ratios

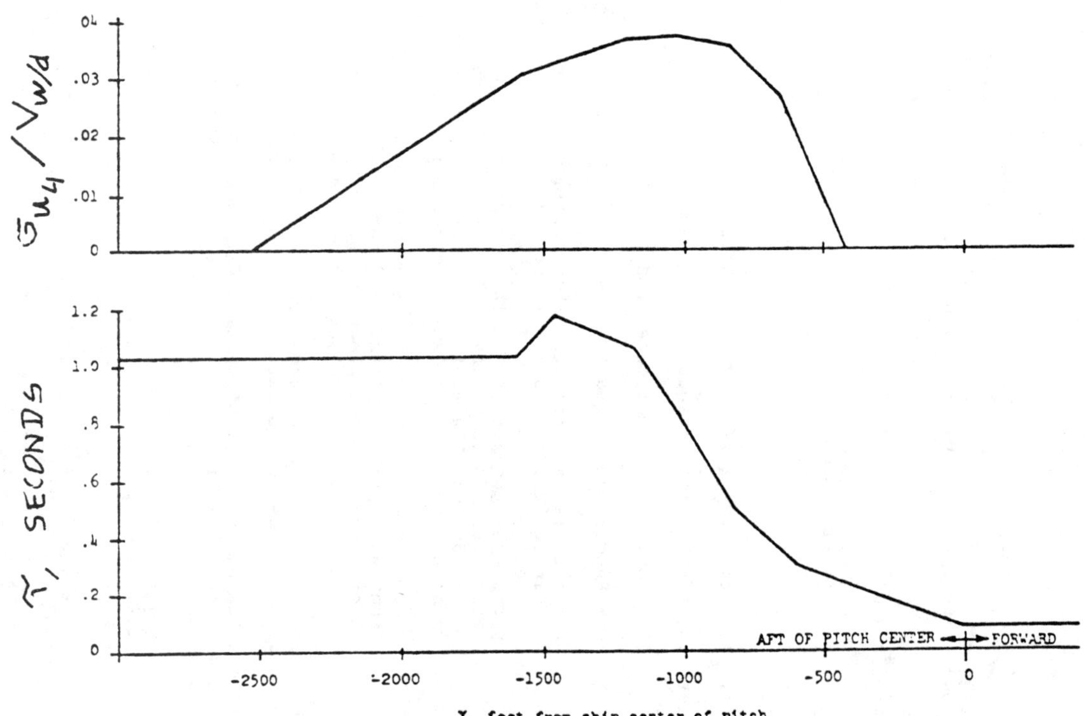

Figure B13 u-Component Burble Time Constant and Variance

3.8 Requirements for use of the disturbance models

Explicit consideration of the effects of disturbances on flying qualities, if required by the procuring activity, shall be in accordance with requirements in 3.8.2 through 3.8.3.2. In particular, 3.8.3.1 will replace 3.1.10.1 and 3.8.3.2 will replace 3.1.10.2.

3.8.1 Use of disturbance models. Paragraphs 3.7.1 through 3.7.4.4 specify models of wind shear, continuous random turbulence and discrete gusts that shall be used to assess:

a. The effects of certain environmental conditions on the flying qualities of the airplane.

b. The ability of the pilot to recover from upsets caused by environmental conditions.

c. Flight path control precision during manual and automatic carrier landing.

For the purpose of this specification the atmosphere shall be considered to consist of three regions:

(1) low-altitude (ground level to approximately 2,000 feet AGL),

(2) medium/high-altitude (above approximately 2,000 feet) and,

for carrier landing only,

(3) terminal approach (0 - 300 feet altitude and 1/2 mile to touchdown).

The low-altitude model shall apply to Category C and any other Flight Phase (e.g. ground attack, terrain following) designated by the procuring activity. The medium/high-altitude model is intended to apply to those Flight Phases where proximity to the ground is not a factor, generally Categories A and B. In application it will be permissible to use conditions at an average altitude for the medium/high-altitude model only. The carrier landing disturbance model will apply to carrier-based aircraft only.

3.8.2 Qualitative degrees of suitability. In assessing the qualitative suitability of flying qualities three intensities and disturbances shall be considered. These intensities are Light, Moderate and Severe as defined in 3.7. The requirements for the effects of these disturbances are contained in 3.8.3.1 and 3.8.3.2 for the different Flight Envelopes and Airplane States.

The qualitative degrees of suitability of flying qualities are categorized as follows:

Satisfactory	Flying qualities clearly adequate for the mission Flight Phase
Acceptable	Flying qualities adequate to accomplish the mission Flight Phase, but some increase in pilot workload or degradation in mission effectiveness, or both, exists
Controllable	Flying qualities such that the airplane can be controlled safely, but pilot workload is excessive or mission effectiveness is inadequate, or both. Category A Flight Phases can be terminated safely, and Category B and C Flight Phases can be completed.
Recoverable	Flying qualities such that control can be maintained long enough to fly out of a disturbance. All Flight Phases can be terminated safely and a wave-off/go-around can be accomplished.

3.8.3 Effects of atmospheric disturbances. Levels of flying qualities as indicated in 1.5 are employed in this specification in realization of the possibility that the airplane may be required to operate under abnormal conditions. Such abnormalities may occur also as a result of extreme atmospheric disturbances, or some combination of conditions. For these factors a degradation of flying qualities is permitted as specified in 3.8.3.1 and in 3.8.3.2 (see also 4.1.1).

3.8.3.1 Requirements for Airplane Normal States. In atmospheric disturbances the minimum required flying qualities for Airplane Normal States (3.1.6.1) are as specified in Table XVI.

3.8.3.2 Requirements for Airplane Failure states. When Airplane Failure States exist (3.1.6.2), a degradation in flying qualities is permitted only if the probability of encountering a lower Level than specified in 3.8.3.1 is sufficiently small. At intervals established by the procuring activity, the contractor shall determine, based on the most accurate available data, the probability of occurrence of each Airplane Failure State per flight and the effect of that Failure State on the flying qualities within the Operational and Service Flight Envelopes. These determinations shall be based on Mil-STD-756 except that:

a. All airplane components and systems are assumed to be operating for a time period, per flight, equal to the longest operational mission time to be considered by the contractor in designing the airplane, and

b. Each specific failure is assumed to be present at whichever point in the Flight Envelope being considered is most critical (in the flying qualities sense).

From these Failure State probabilities and effects, the contractor shall determine the overall probability, per flight, that one or more flying qualities are degraded to Level 2 because of one or more failures. The contractor shall also determine the probability that one or more flying qualities are degraded to Level 3. Table XVII specifies the requirements as functions of the probabili t' of encountering the degradation in flying qualities

TABLE XVI LEVELS FOR AIRPLANE NORMAL STATES

Atmospheric Disturbances	Within Operational Flight Envelope	Within Service Flight Envelope
LIGHT to CALM	Quantitative requirements Level 1, Qualitative requirements Satisfactory	Quantitative requirements Level 2, Qualitative requirements Acceptable
MODERATE to LIGHT	Quantitative requirements Level 1, Qualitative requirements Acceptable or better	Quantitative requirements Level 2, Qualitative requirements Controllable or better
SEVERE to MODERATE	Qualitative requirements Controllable or better	Qualitative requirements Recoverable or better

TABLE XVII LEVELS FOR AIRPLANE FAILURE STATES

Atmospheric Disturbances	Failure State I*	Failure State II**
LIGHT to CALM	Quantitative requirements Level 2 and qualitative requirements Acceptable or better	Quantitative requirements Level 3 and qualitative requirements Controllable or better
MODERATE to LIGHT	Quantitative requirements Level 2 and qualitative requirements Controllable or better	Quantitative requirements Level 3 and qualitative requirements Recoverable or better
SEVERE to MODERATE	Qualitative requirements Recoverable or better	

* For flight in the Operational Flight Envelope: Probability of encountering degraded levels of flying qualities due to failure(s) < 1 per 100 flights

** For flight in the Operational Flight Envelope: Probability of encountering degraded levels of flying qualities due to failure(s): < 1 per 10,000 flights, and for flight in the Service Flight Envelope: Probability of encountering degraded levels of flying qualities due to failure(s): < 1 per 100 flights

4. QUALITY ASSURANCE

4.1 Compliance demonstration. Compliance with all requirements of section 3 shall be demonstrated through analysis. In addition, compliance with many of the requirements will be demonstrated by simulation, flight test or both. The methods for demonstrating compliance shall be established by agreement between the procuring activity and the contractor. Representative flight conditions, configurations, external store complements, loadings, etcetera, shall be determined for detailed investigations in order to restrict the number of design and test conditions. The selected design points must be sufficient to alow accurate extrapolation to other conditions at which the requirements apply.

Table XVIII specifies the general guidelines but the peculiarities of the specific airplane design may require additional or alternate test conditions. The required failure analyses shall be thorough, excepting only approved Special Failure States (3.1.6.2.1).

4.1.1 Analytical compliance

4.1.1.1 Effects of Failure States. To determine theoretical compliance with the requirements of 3.1.10.2, the following steps must be performed:

a. Identify those Airplane Failure States which have a significant effect on flying qualities (3.1.6.2)

b. Define the longest flight duration to be encountered during operational missions (3.1.1)

c. Determine the probability of encountering various Airplane Failure States per flight, based on the above flight duration (3.1.10.2)

d. Determine the degree of flying qualities degradation associated with each Airplane Failure State in terms of Levels as defined in the specific requirements

e. Determine the most critical Airplane Failure States (assuming the failures are present at whichever point in the Flight Envelope being considered is most critical in a flying qualities sense), and compute the total probability of encountering Level 2 flying qualities in the Operational Flight Envelope due to equipment failures. Likewise, compute the probability of encountering Level 3 flying qualities in the Operational Flight Envelope, etc.

f. Compare the computed values above with the requirements specified in 3.1.10.2 and 3.1.10.3. An example which illustrates an approximate estimate of the probabilities of encounter follows: if the failures are all statistically independent, determine the sum of the probabilities of encountering all Airplane Failure

States which degrade flying qualities to Level 2 in the Operational Flight Envelope. This sum must be less than 1 per 100 flights.

If the requirements are not met, the designer must consider alternate courses such as:

a. Improve the airplane flying qualities associated with the more probable Failure States, or

b. Reduce the probability of encountering the more probable Failure States through equipment redesign, redundancy, etc.

Regardless of the probability of encountering any given Airplane Failure States (with the exception of Special Failure States) the flying qualities shall not degrade below Level 3.

4.1.1.2 Effects of atmospheric disturbances. Paragraph 4.1.1.1 indicates a procedure for satisfying the requirements on the degrading effects of Airplane Failure States, without consideration of atmospheric disturbances. Atmospheric disturbances also may cause a degradation in pilot opinion as specified in 3.8.2. In application, numerical values of control force and deflection, and of steady-state and dynamic response parameters (for example $n_{o_{max}}$, $\partial F_s/\partial n$, θ_t) are to be considered as mean values in the presence of atmospheric disturbances. These are frequently equivalent to the values in calm air. Numerical values of frequency-response parameters and of control authority are effective values for the airplane in each particular intensity of atmospheric disturbance. The qualitative requirements of 3.8.3.1 and 3.8.3.2 should then be assessed for both Airplane Normal States and critical Failure States identified in 4.1.1.1.

4.1.1.3 Computational assumptions. Assumptions a and b of 3.1.10.2 are somewhat conservative, but they simplify the required computations in 3.1.10.2 and provide a set of workable ground rules for theoretical predictions. The reasons for these assumptions are:

a. '...components and systems are ... operating for a time period per flight equal to the longest operational mission time ...'. Since most component failure data are in terms of failures per flight hour, even though continuous operation may not be typical (e.g. yaw damper ON during supersonic flight only), failure probabilities must be predicted on a per flight basis using 'typical' total flight time. The 'longest operational mission time' as 'typical' is a natural result. If acceptance cycles-to-failure reliability data are available (MIL-STD-756), these data may be used for prediction purposes based on maximum cycles per operational mission, subject to procuring activity approval. In any event, compliance with the requirements of 3.1.10.2, as determined in accordance with Section 4, is based on the probability of encounter per flight.

b. '... failure is assumed to be present at whichever point ... is most critical ...'. This assumption is in keeping with the requirements of 3.1.6.2 regarding Flight Phases subsequent to the actual failure in question. In cases that are unrealistic from the operational standpoint, the specific Airplane Failure States might fall in the Airplane Special Failure State classification (3.1.6.2.1).

4.1.2 Simulation. The danger, extent or difficulty of flight testing may dictate simulation rather than flight test to evaluate some conditions and events, such as the influence of Severe disturbances, events close to the ground (except 3.2.3.4 shall be demonstrated in flight), combined Failure States and disturbances, etc. In addition, by agreement with the procuring activity, piloted simulation shall be performed before first flight of a new airplane design in order to demonstrate compliance with qualitative requirements in atmospheric disturbances and in the critical conditions identified in 4.1.1.1. Where simulation is the ultimate method of demonstrating compliance for a requirement, the simulation model shall be validated with flight test data and approved by the procuring activity.

4.1.3 Flight test demonstration. The required flight tests will be defined by operational, technical and safety considerations as decided jointly by the procuring activity, the test agency and the contractor using results from 4.1.1 and 4.1.2. It is not expected that flight test demonstration of the requirements in Moderate and Severe disturbances will be done unless required by the airplane mission. Some flights can be expected to encounter actual disturbances. Then the qualitative requirements would apply if the disturbance intensity could be categorized.

4.2 Airplane States. The parameters defining Airplane States shall be tabulated. Table XIX illustrates an acceptable format.

4.2.1 Weights and moments of inertia. Terms specified in Table XVIII such as 'heaviest weight' and 'greatest moment of inertia' mean the heaviest and greatest consistent with 3.1.2 and 3.1.3. When a critical center-of-gravity position is identified, the airplane weight and associated moments of inertia shall correspond to the most adverse service loading in which that critical center-of-gravity position is obtained.

4.2.2 Center-of-gravity positions. Terms specified in Table XVIII such as 'most forward c.g.' and 'most aft c.g.' mean the most forward or aft consistent with 3.1.2. When a critical weight or inertia is identified, the center-of-gravity position shall correspond to the most adverse service loading in which that critical weight or moment of inertia is obtained.

4.2.3 Thrust settings. Thrust settings shall be as listed in Table XIX.

TABLE XVIII DESIGN AND TEST CONDITION GUIDELINES

Requirement Number	Title	Critical Loading (4.2.1 and 4.2.2)	Load Factor	Altitude (4.3.1)	Speed	Flight Phase
Section 3.2	**Longitudinal Flying Qualities**					
3.2.1.1	Longitudinal static stability	Most aft c.g.	1.0	$h_{o_{min}}$, medium, $h_{o_{max}}$	V_{min} to V_{max}, transonic	CO, CR, LO, RR, FF, RT, PA, L. WO TO, CT
3.2.1.1.1	Relaxation in transonic flight	Same	Same	Same	Same	Same
3.2.1.1.2	Elevator control force variations during rapid speed changes	----	As reqd	Same	Same	CO, GA, DE
3.2.1.2	Phugoid stability	Most fwd c.g.*	1.0	Same	V_{min} to V_{max}	CR, LO, PA, RT
3.2.1.3	Flight-path stability	----	Same	Same	$V_{o_{min}}$, $V_{o_{min}}$ - 5 kts	PA
3.2.2.1.1	Short period frequency and acceleration sensitivity	Most fwd* and most aft** c.g.	Same	Same	V_{min} to V_{max}	(*), CR, RT, PA, L, CT
3.2.2.1.2	Short period damping	Most fwd c.g.	1.0	$h_{o_{min}}$, medium, $h_{o_{max}}$	V_{min} to V_{max}	(*), CR, RT, PA, CT
3.2.2.1.3	Residual oscillations	----	Same	Same	$V_{o_{min}}$ to $V_{o_{max}}$	(*), PA
3.2.2.2	Control feel and stability in maneuvering flight	Most aft c.g.	n(-) to n(+)	Same	V_{min} to V_{max}	(*), RT, CR, PA, L, CT
3.2.2.2.1	Control forces in maneuvering flight	Most fwd* and most aft** c.g.	$n_o(-)$ to $n_{(+)}$	Same	Same	Same
3.2.2.2.2	Control motions in maneuvering flight	Most fwd c.g.*	Same	Same	Same	Same
3.2.2.3	Longitudinal pilot-induced oscillations	----	Min. to max. permissible	Same	Same	(*), RT, CR, PA, L, CT
3.2.2.3.1	Dynamic control forces in maneuvering flight	Most fwd c.g.*	1.0	$h_{o_{min}}$, medium, $h_{o_{max}}$	V_{min} to V_{max}	----
3.2.2.3.2	Control feel	Most aft c.g.**	Same	Same	Same	----
3.2.3.1	Longitudinal control in unaccelerated flight	Most fwd c.g.	Same	Same	Same	----

* Combined with heaviest weight   ** Combined with lightest weight

TABLE XVIII (CONT'D) DESIGN AND TEST CONDITION GUIDELINES

Requirement Number	Title	Critical Loading (4.2.1 and 4.2.2)	Load Factor	Altitude (4.3.1)	Speed	Flight Phase
3.2.3.2	Longitudinal control in maneuvering flight	Most fwd c.g.*	As reqd	Same	$V_{o_{min}}$ to $V_{o_{max}}$	CO, GA, AR, TF, CR, PA
3.2.3.3	Longitudinal control in takeoff	Most fwd c.g. for nosewheel and most aft c.g. for tailwheel airplanes	1.0	Low	As reqd	TO
3.2.3.3.1	Longitudinal control in catapult takeoff	Most fwd and most aft c.g.	As reqd	Same	Min. safe launch speed to min. + 30 kts	CT
3.2.3.3.2	Longitudinal control force and travel in takeoff	Most fwd and most aft c.g.	As reqd	Low	0 to V_{max}(TO)	TO, CT
3.2.3.4	Longitudinal control in landing	Most fwd c.g.	1.0	Same	V_s(L) or geometric limit	L
3.2.3.4.1	Longitudinal control forces in landing	Same	Same	Same	Same	L
3.2.3.5	Longitudinal control forces in dives (SFE)	Most fwd* and most aft** c.g.	As reqd	2000 ft above MGL to h_{max}	V_{min} to V_{max}	D, ED, CO, CR
3.2.3.6	Longitudinal control forces in dives (PFE)	Same	Same	As reqd	V_{MAT} to max permissible	Same
3.2.3.7	Longitudinal control in sideslips	----	1.0	$h_{o_{min}}$, medium, $h_{o_{max}}$	V_{min} to V_{max}	CO, CR, PA, L
<u>Section 3.3</u>	<u>Lateral-Directional Flying Qualities</u>					
3.3.1.1	Lateral-directional oscillations (Dutch roll)	Greatest yawing moment of inertia	1.0 and $n_o(+)$	$h_{o_{min}}$, medium, $h_{o_{max}}$	V_{min} to $V_{o_{max}}$	(*), CR, RT, PA, L
3.3.1.2	Roll mode	Greatest rolling moment of inertia	Same	$h_{o_{max}}$	Same	(*), CR, PA, L
3.3.1.3	Spiral stability	----	1.0	Same	Same	(*), CL, CR, LO, RT, DE, PA, L
3.3.1.4	Coupled roll-spiral oscillations	----	1.0 and $n_o(+)$	Same	Same	(*), CR, PA, L
3.3.2.1	Lateral-directional response to atmospheric disturbances	----	1.0	Same	Same	----
3.3.2.2	Roll rate oscillations	----	1.0 and $n_o(+)$	Same	Same	(*), CR, PA, L
3.3.2.2.1	Additional roll rate reqm't for small inputs	----	Same	Same	Same	Same

* Combined with heaviest weight
SFE = Service Flight Envelope

** Combined with lightest weight
PFE = Permissible Flight Envelope

TABLE XVIII (CONT'D) DESIGN AND TEST CONDITION GUIDELINES

Requirement Number	Title	Critical Loading (4.2.1 and 4.2.2)	Load Factor	Altitude (4.3.1)	Speed	Flight Phase
3.3.2.3	Bank angle oscillations	----	1.0 and $n_o(+)$	$h_{o_{min}}$, medium, $h_{o_{max}}$	V_{min} to $V_{o_{max}}$	(*), CR, PA, L
3.3.2.4	Sideslip excursions	Greatest yawing and rolling moment of inertia	1.0	Same	Same	Same
3.3.2.4.1	Additional sideslip reqm't for small inputs	Same	1.0	Same	Same	Same
3.3.2.5	Control of sideslip in rolls	Greatest rolling moment of inertia	As reqd	Same	Same	CO, GA, AR, TF, CR, PA, L
3.3.2.6	Turn coordination	----	Same	Same	$V_{o_{min}}$	CO, CR, LO, PA
3.3.3	Pilot-induced oscillations	----	Min. to max. permissible	MSL to h_{max}	V_{min} to V_{max}	----
3.3.4	Roll control effectiveness	Greatest rolling moment of inertia	As reqd (not above $0.8n_L$)	$h_{o_{min}}$ medium, $h_{o_{max}}$	V_{min} to V_{max}	CO, GA, AR, TF, CR, PA, L
3.3.4.1	Roll performance for Class IV airplanes	Same	Same	Same	Same	Same
3.3.4.1.1	Roll performance in Flight Phase CO	Same	Same	$h_{o_{min}}$	Same	CO
3.3.4.1.2	Roll performance in Flight Phase GA	Same	Same	Same	Same	GA
3.3.4.1.3	Roll response	Smallest rolling moment of inertia	Same	$h_{o_{min}}$ medium $h_{o_{max}}$	Same	----
3.3.4.2	Roll performance for Class III airplanes	Greatest and smallest rolling moment of inertia	Same	Same	Same	CO, GA, AR, TF, CR, PA, L
3.3.4.3	Roll control force	Greatest rolling moment of inertia	As reqd (not above $0.8n_L$)	$h_{o_{min}}$ medium, $h_{o_{max}}$	V_{min} to V_{max}	----
3.3.4.4	Linearity of roll response	Same	Same	Same	Same	CO, GA, AR, TF, CR, PA, L
3.3.4.5	Wheel control throw	Same	Same	Same	Same	Same
3.3.5	Directional control characteristics	----	n(-) to n(+)	Same	Same	(*), CR, PA, L

* Combined with heaviest weight ** Combined with lightest weight

TABLE XVIII (CONT'D) DESIGN AND TEST CONDITION GUIDELINES

Requirement Number	Title	Critical Loading (4.2.1 and 4.2.2)	Load Factor	Altitude (4.3.1)	Speed	Flight Phase
3.3.5.1	Directional control with speed change	----	1.0	Same	Same	CO, GA, CR, D, PA, L
3.3.5.1.1	Directional control with asymmetric loading	----	Same	Same	$V_{o_{min}}$ to $V_{o_{max}}$	----
3.3.5.2	Directional control in wave-off (go-around)	Lightest weight	1.0	Low	V_{min} (PA) or guaranteed landing speed	WO
3.3.6 (3.3.6.1, 3.3.6.2, 3.3.6.3, 3.3.6.3.1, 3.3.6.3.2)	Lateral-directional characteristics in steady sideslips	Same	Same	$h_{o_{min}}$ medium, $h_{o_{max}}$	V_{min} to V_{max}	CO, CR, PA, L
3.3.7	Lateral-directinal control in cross winds	----	Same	Low	As reqd	TO, L
3.3.7.1	Final approach in cross winds	----	Same	Same	V_{min} to V_{max}	PA
3.3.7.2 (3.3.7.2.1, 3.3.7.2.2)	Takeoff run and landing rollout in cross wind	----	As reqd	Same	As reqd	TO, L
3.3.7.3	Taxiing wind speed limits	----	As reqd	Same	All taxiing speeds	TAXI
3.3.8	Lateral-directional control in dives	----	As reqd	2,000 ft above MSL to h_{max}	V_{MAT} to V_{max}	D, ED
3.3.9.1	Thrust loss during takeoff run	Lightest weight	1.0	$h_{o_{min}}$	0 to max. takeoff speed	TO
3.3.9.2	Thrust loss after takeoff	Same	Same	Same	Down to V_{min} (TO)	TO, CT
3.3.9.3	Transient effects	Same	Same	All	V_{min} to V_{max}	CO, GA, TF, CR, CL, TO, CT
3.3.9.4	Asymmetric thrust, rudder pedals free	Same	Same	$h_{o_{min}}$ medium, $h_{o_{max}}$	$1.4V_{min}$	CR
3.3.9.5	Two engines inoperative	----	Same	Same	V_{range} (1 and 2 engines out)	----

* Combined with heaviest weight ** Combined with lightest weight

TABLE XVIII (CONT'D) DESIGN AND TEST CONDITION GUIDELINES

Requirement Number	Title	Critical Loading (4.2.1 and 4.2.2)	Load Factor	Altitude (4.3.1)	Speed	Flight Phase
Section 3.4	**Miscellaneous Flying Qualities**					
3.4.2	Flight at high angle of attack	See MIL-S-83691 or MIL-D-8708, whichever is applicable for flight demonstration. More severe conditions generally will be investigated by analysis and by model testing. ***				
3.4.2.1	Stalls (3.4.2.1.1 through 3.4.2.1.3.1) See *** above					
3.4.2.2	Post-stall gyrations and spins (3.4.2.2.1, 3.4.2.2.2) See *** above					
3.4.3	Cross-axis coupling in roll maneuvers	----	0 to $0.8n_L$	$h_{o_{min}}$ medium $h_{o_{max}}$	$V_{o_{min}}$ to $V_{o_{max}}$	CO, GA, AR, TF
3.4.4 (3.4.4.1)	Control harmony	----	$n_o(-)$ to $n_o(+)$	Same	Same	----
3.4.5	Buffet	----	Same	Same	Same	(*)
3.4.6	Release of stores	----	Same	Same	Same	CO, GA, WD, D
3.4.7	Effects of armament delivery and special equipment	----	Same	Same	Same	(*), RT
3.4.8	Transients following failures	----	All	$h_{o_{min}}$ to $h_{o_{max}}$	All	----
3.4.10	Control margin	----	Same	Same	Same	----
3.4.11	Direct force control	----	1.0 +/- max. DLC authority	Same	$V_{o_{min}}$ to $V_{o_{max}}$	----
Section 3.5	**Characteristics of the Primary Flight Control System**					
3.5.2 (3.5.2.1, 3.5.2.2, 3.5.2.3)	Mechanical characteristics	----	$n_o(-)$ to $n_o(+)$	$h_{o_{min}}$ and $h_{o_{max}}$	V_{min} to V_{max}	----
3.5.3	Dynamic characteristics	Most fwd c.g. and lowest rolling and yawing moments of inertia	1.0			----
3.5.5 (3.5.5.1, 3.5.5.2)	Failures	----	All			----
3.5.6 (3.5.6.1, 3.5.6.2)	Transfer to alternate control modes	----	1.0	$h_{o_{min}}$ medium, $h_{o_{max}}$		----

NOTES: 1. ---- indicates that no general guidance can be provided.

2. The phrase 'As reqd' means the flight conditions are specified in the requirement or are determined by the nature of the test maneuver.

3. (*) means all applicable Category A Flight Phases.

TABLE XVIII (CONT'D) DESIGN AND TEST CONDITION GUIDELINES

Requirement Number	Title	Critical Loading (4.2.1 and 4.2.2)	Load Factor	Altitude (4.3.1)	Speed	Flight Phase
Section 3.6	Characteristics of Secondary Control Systems					
3.6.1	Trim system	Most fwd and most aft c.g.	1.0	$h_{o_{min}}$, medium, $h_{o_{max}}$	V_{min} to V_{max}	----
3.6.1.1	Trim for asymmetric thrust	Same	Same	$h_{o_{min}}$ and max. attainable	V_{range} to V_{MRT} (with 1 and 2 engines out)	CR
3.6.1.2	Rate of trim operation	----	Same	As reqd	As reqd	CO, GA, D, ED
3.6.1.3	Stalling of trim system	Most fwd c.g. combined with heaviest weight	As reqd	Same	Start of dive recovery to V_{max}	D, ED, CO, CR
3.6.1.4	Trim system irreversibility	----	1.0	MSL to h_{max}	V_{min} to V_{max}	----
3.6.2	Speed and flight-path control devices	----	1.0 to $n_o(+)$	$h_{o_{min}}$ medium, $h_{o_{max}}$	$V_{o_{min}}$ to $V_{o_{max}}$	(•), RT, ED, DE, PA, WO, GA
3.6.3	Transients and trim changes	----	$n_o(-)$ to $n_o(+)$	$h_{o_{min}}$, medium, $h_{o_{max}}$	V_{min} to V_{max}	----
3.6.3.1	Pitch trim changes	----	As reqd	As reqd	As reqd	CO, CR, PA TO, CT
3.6.4	Auxiliary dive recovery devices	Most aft c.g. combined with lightest weight	Same	MSL to to h_{max}	$V_{o_{min}}$ to V_{max}	D, ED
Section 3.7	Atmospheric Disturbances	----	1.0	Same	V_{min} to V_{max}	----
Section 3.8	Requirements for Use of the Disturbance Models	----	All	Same	Same	----

NOTES: 1. ---- indicates that no general guidance can be provided.

2. The phrase 'As reqd' means the flight conditions are specified in the requirement or are determined by the nature of the test maneuver.

3. (•) means all applicable Category A Flight Phases.

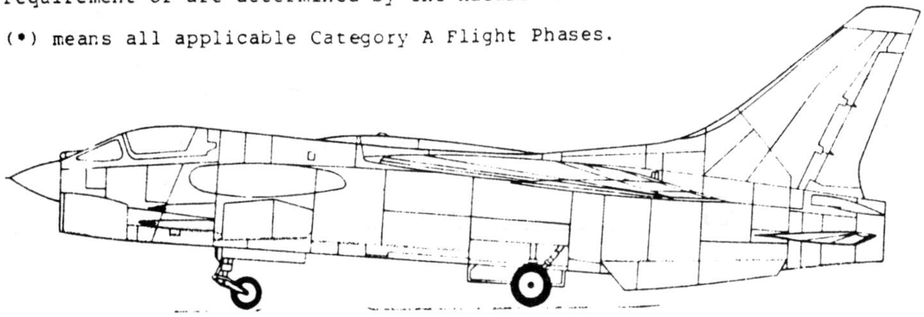

TABLE XIX DEFINITION OF AIRPLANE NORMAL STATES

Flight Phase	Symbol	Weight	C.G.	External Stores	Thrust	Thrust Vector Angle	High Lift Devices	Wing Sweep
Takeoff	TO							
Climb	CL							
Cruise	CR							
Loiter	LO							
Descent	D							
Emergency Descent	ED							
Emergency Deceleration	DE							
Approach	PA							
Wave-off/ Go-around	WO							
Landing	L							
Air-to-air Combat	CO							
Ground Attack	GA							
Weapon Delivery/ Launch	WD							
Aerial Delivery	AD							
Aerial Recovery	AR							
Reconnaissance	RC							
Refuel Receiver	RR							
Refuel Tanker	RT							
Terrain Following	TF							
Antisubmarine Search	AS							
Close Formation Flying	FF							
Catapult Takeoff	CT							

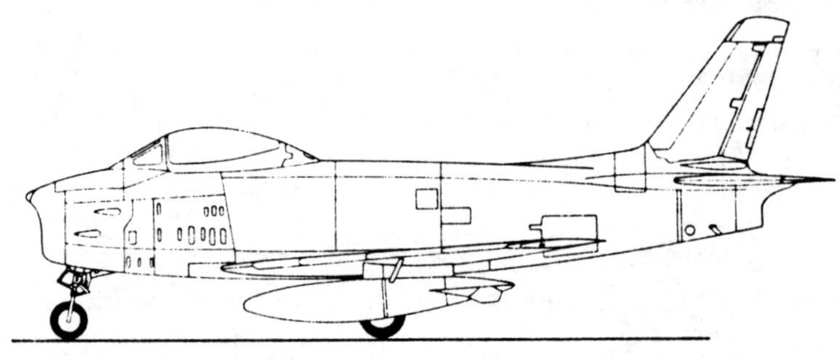

TABLE XIX (CONT'D) DEFINITION OF AIRPLANE NORMAL STATES

Flight Phase	Symbol	Wing Incidence	Landing Gear	Speed Brakes	Bomb Bay or Cargo Doors	Stability Augmentation	Other
Takeoff	TO						
Climb	CL						
Cruise	CR						
Loiter	LO						
Descent	D						
Emergency Descent	ED						
Emergency Deceleration	DE						
Approach	PA						
Wave-off/ Go-around	WO						
Landing	L						
Air-to-air Combat	CO						
Ground Attack	GA						
Weapon Delivery/ Launch	WD						
Aerial Delivery	AD						
Aerial Recovery	AR						
Reconnaissance	RC						
Refuel Receiver	RR						
Refuel Tanker	RT						
Terrain Following	TF						
Antisubmarine Search	AS						
Close Formation Flying	FF						
Catapult Takeoff	CT						

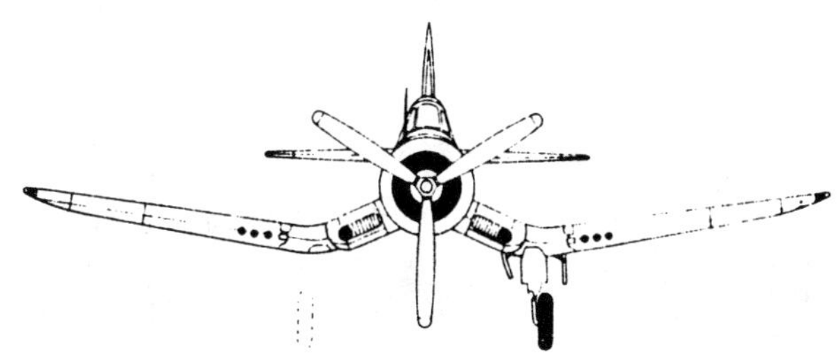

4.3 Design and test conditions

4.3.1 Altitudes. For terminal Flight Phases, it will normally suffice to examine the selected Airplane States at only one altitude below 10,000 feet (low altitude). For nonterminal Flight Phases, it will normally suffice to examine the selected Airplane States at one altitude below 10,000 feet or at the lowest operational altitude (low altitude), the maximum operational altitude ($h_{o_{max}}$), and one intermediate altitude. When the maximum operational altitude is above 40,000 feet or when stability or control characteristics vary rapidly with altitude, more intermediate altitudes than specified in Table XVIII shall be investigated. When the Service Flight Envelope extends far above or below the Operational Flight Envelope, the service-altitude extremes must be considered.

4.3.2 Special conditions. In addition to the flight conditions previously indicated, the speed-altitude combinations that result in the following shall be investigated, where applicable:

a. Maximum normal acceleration response per degree of controller deflection

b. Maximum normal acceleration response per pound of control force

c. Highest dynamic pressure and highest Mach Number.

4.4 Tests at specialized facilities. Certain tests, by their nature can be conducted only at specialized facilities which are not accessible to either the procuring activity or the contractor except at the option of a third organization. In such cases, when an agreement of test support at the specialized facility is obtained by the procuring activity, an analysis of results obtained in the tests, is a necessary part of the analytical compliance demonstration.

5. PREPARATION FOR DELIVERY

5.1 Section 5 is not applicable to this specification.

6. NOTES

6.1 Intended use. This specification contains the flying qualities requirements for piloted airplanes and forms one of the bases for determination by the procuring activity of airplane acceptability. The specification consists of design requirements in terms of criteria for use in stability and control calculations, analysis of wind tunnel test results, simulator evaluations, flight testing, etc. The requirements should be met as far as possible by providing an inherently good basic airframe. Cost, performance, reliability, maintenance, etc. tradeoffs are necessary in determining the proper balance between airframe characteristics and augmented dynamic response characteristics. The contractor should advise the procuring activity of any significant design penalties which may result from meeting any particular requirement.

6.2 Definitions. Terms and symbols used throughout this specification are defined as follows:

6.2.1 General.

S	wing area
s	Laplace operator
$\bar{q}$	dynamic pressure
MSL	mean sea level
T_2	time to double amplitude: $T_2 = -0.693/\zeta\omega_n$ for oscillations $T_2 = 0.693T_{s \text{ or } r}$ for first order divergences
Airplane Normal States	nomenclature and format of Table XIX shall be used in defining the Airplane Normal States (3.1.6.1)
Service ceiling	altitude at a given airspeed at which the rate of climb is 100 ft/min at the stated weight and engine thrust
Combat ceiling	altitude at a given airspeed at which the rate of climb is 500 ft/min at the stated weight and engine thrust
Cruising ceiling	altitude at a given airspeed at which the rate of climb is 300 ft/min at NRT at the stated weight
h_{max}	maximum service altitude (defined in 3.1.8.3)
$h_{o_{max}}$	maximum operational altitude (3.1.7)
$h_{o_{min}}$	minimum operational altitude (3.1.7)
c.g.	airplane center of gravity

6.2.2 Speeds.

Equivalent airspeed, EAS	true airspeed multiplied by $(\sigma)^{1/2}$, where σ is the ratio of free-stream density at the given altitude to standard sealevel air density
Calibrated airspeed	airspeed-indicator reading corrected for position and instrument error but NOT for compressibility
Refusal speed	the maximum speed to which the airplane can accelerate and then stop in the available runway length

M Mach number

V airspeed along the flight path (where appropriate, may be replaced by M in this specification)

V_S stall speed (equivalent airspeed), at 1g normal to the flight path, defined as the highest of:

a) speed for steady straight flight at $C_{L_{max}}$, the first local maximum of the curve of lift coefficient ($L/\bar{q}S$) versus angle of attack which occurs as C_L is increased from zero

b) speed at which uncommanded pitching, rolling or yawing occurs (3.4.2.1.2)

c) speed at which intolerable buffet or structural vibration is encountered

Conditions for determining V_S.

The airplane shall be initially trimmed at approximately $1.2V_S$ with the following settings, after which the trim and and throttle settings shall be held constant:

Flight Phase	Thrust Settings*	Trim Setting
Climb (CL)	Normal climb	For straight flight
Descent (D)	Normal Descent	For straight flight
Emergency descent (ED)	Idle	For straight flight
Emergency deceleration (DE)	Idle	For straight flight
Takeoff (TO)	Takeoff	Recommended takeoff setting
Approach (PA)	Normal approach	For normal approach
Wave-off/ Go-around (WO)	Takeoff	For normal approach
Landing (L)	Idle	For normal approach
All other	TLF at $1.2V_S$	For straight flight

* Either on all engines or on remaining engines with critical engine inoperative whichever yields the higher value of V_S.

In flight test, it is necessary to reduce speed very slowly (typically 0.5 knot per second or less) to minimize dynamic lift effects. The load factor will generally not be exactly 1g when stall occurs, when this is the case, V_S is defined as follows:

$$V_S = V/(n_f)^{1/2}$$

where V and n_f are the measured values at stall, n_f being the load factor normal to the flight path.

$V_S(X)$, $V_{min}(X)$, $V_{max}(X)$ short-hand notation for the speeds V_S, V_{min}, V_{max}, for a given configuration, weight, c.g. position, and external store combination associated with some Flight Phase X. For example, the designation $V_{max}(TO)$ is used in 3.2.3.3.2 to emphasize that the speed intended (for the weight, center of gravity, and external store combination under consideration) is V_{max} for the configuration associated with the takeoff Flight Phase. This is necessary to avoid confusion, since the configuration and the Flight Phase change from takeoff to climb during the maneuver.

V_{con} speed below which control is lost

V_{trim} trim speed

V_{end} speed for maximum endurance

$V_{L/D}$ speed for maximum lift-to-drag ratio

$V_{R/C}$ speed for maximum rate of climb

V_{range} speed for maximum range with zero wind

V_{NRT} high speed, level flight, normal rated thrust

V_{MRT} high speed, level flight, military rated thrust

V_{MAT} high speed, level flight, maximum augmented thrust

V_{max} maximum service speed (see 3.1.8.1)

V_{min} minimum service speed (see 3.1.8.2)

$V_{o_{max}}$	maximum operational speed (see 3.1.7)
$V_{o_{min}}$	minimum operational speed (see 3.1.7)
V_G	gust penetration speed

6.2.3 Thrust and power.

Thrust and power	for propeller-driven airplanes the word 'thrust' shall be replaced by the word 'power' throughout this specification
TLF	thrust for level flight
NRT	normal rated thrust, which is the maximum thrust at which the engine can operate continuously
MRT	military rated thrust, which is the maximum thrust at which the engine can be operated for a specified period
MAT	maximum augmented thrust: the maximum thrust, augmented by all means available for the Flight Phase
Takeoff thrust	maximum thrust available for takeoff

6.2.4 Control parameters.

Pitch, roll, yaw controls	the stick or wheel and pedals manipulated by the pilot to produce pitching, rolling and yawing moments respectively, the cockpit controls
Pitch control force, F_S	component of applied force, exerted by the pilot on the cockpit control, in or parallel to the plane of symmetry, acting at the center of the stick grip or wheel in a direction perpendicular to a line between the center of the stick grip and the stick or control column pivot
Roll control force	for a stick control, the component of control force exerted by the pilot in a plane perpendicular to the plane of symmetry, acting at the center of the stick grip in a direction perpendicular to a line between the center of the stick grip and the stick pivot. For a wheel control, the total moment applied by the pilot applied about the wheel axis in the plane of the wheel, divided by the average radius from the wheel pivot to the pilot's grip
Yaw-control pedal force	difference of push-force components of forces exerted by the pilot on the yaw-control pedals, lying in planes parallel to the plane of symmetry, measured perpendicular to the pedals at the normal point of application of the pilot's instep on the respective yaw-control pedals
Direct normal force control	a device producing direct normal force for the primary purpose of controlling the flight path of the airplane. Direct normal force control is the descriptive title given to the concept of directly modulating the normal force on the airplane by changing its lifting capabilities at a constant angle of attack and constant airspeed or by controlling the normal force component of such items as jet exhausts, propellers, and fans
Control power	effectiveness of control surfaces in applying forces or moments to an airplane. For example, 50 percent of available roll control power is 50 percent of the maximum rolling moment that is available to the pilot with allowable roll control force

6.3.5 Longitudinal parameters.

ζ_{sp}	damping ratio of the short-period oscillation
$\omega_{n_{sp}}$	undamped natural frequency of the short-period oscillation
ζ_p	damping ratio of the phugoid oscillation
ω_{n_p}	undamped natural frequency of the phugoid oscillation
n	normal acceleration or normal load factor, measured at the c.g.
n_L	symmetrical flight limit load factor for a given Airplane Normal State, based on structural considerations
n_{max}, n_{min}	maximum and minimum service load factors
$n(+)$, $n(-)$	for a given altitude, the upper and lower boundaries of n in the V-n diagrams depicting the Service Flight Envelope
$n_{o_{max}}$, $n_{o_{min}}$	maximum and minimum operational load factors

$n_o(+)$, $n_o(-)$	for a given altitude, the upper and lower boundaries of n in the V-n diagrams depicting the Operational Flight Envelope

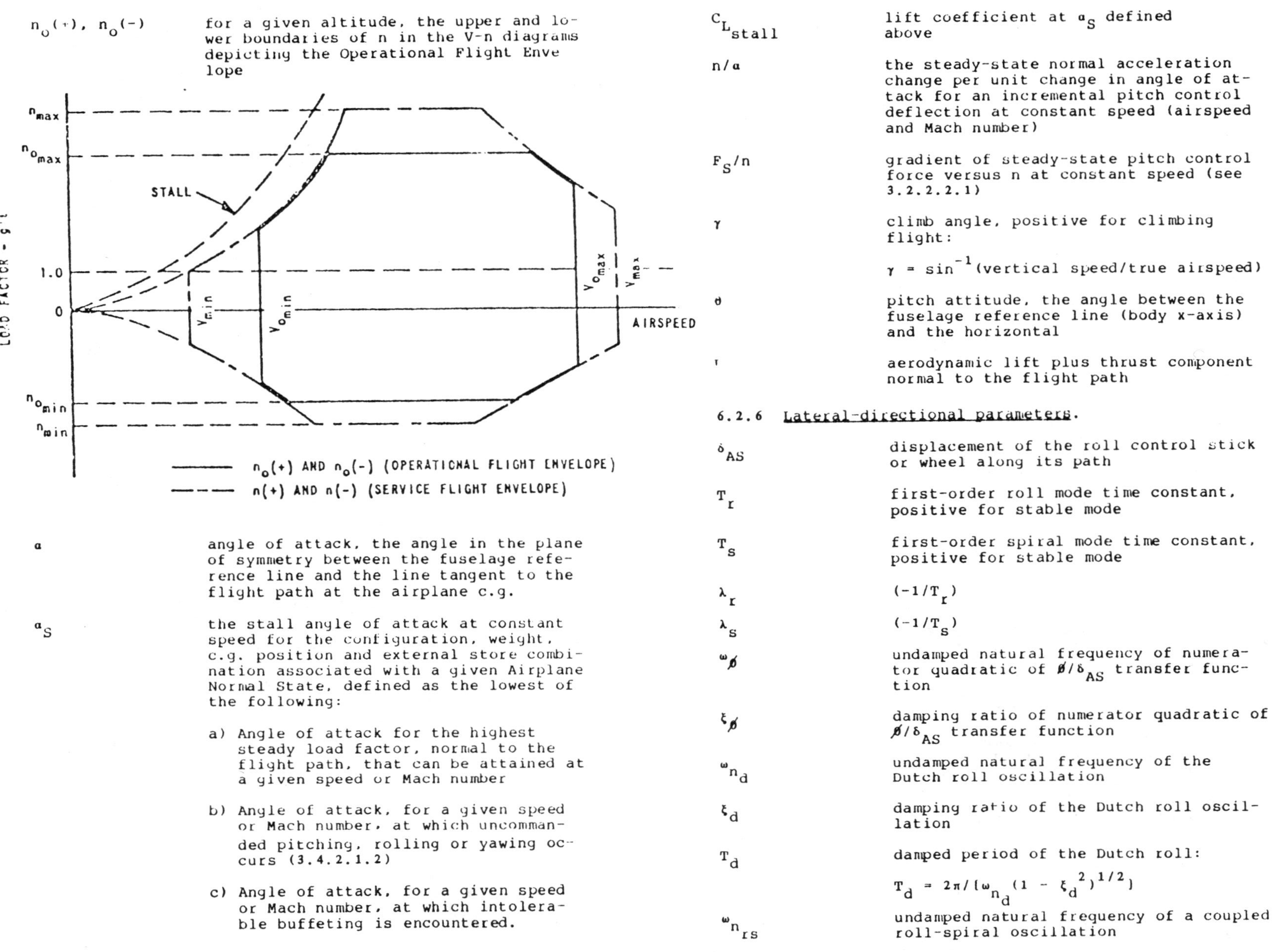

α	angle of attack, the angle in the plane of symmetry between the fuselage reference line and the line tangent to the flight path at the airplane c.g.
α_S	the stall angle of attack at constant speed for the configuration, weight, c.g. position and external store combination associated with a given Airplane Normal State, defined as the lowest of the following:

a) Angle of attack for the highest steady load factor, normal to the flight path, that can be attained at a given speed or Mach number

b) Angle of attack, for a given speed or Mach number, at which uncommanded pitching, rolling or yawing occurs (3.4.2.1.2)

c) Angle of attack, for a given speed or Mach number, at which intolerable buffeting is encountered.

$C_{L_{stall}}$	lift coefficient at α_S defined above
n/α	the steady-state normal acceleration change per unit change in angle of attack for an incremental pitch control deflection at constant speed (airspeed and Mach number)
F_S/n	gradient of steady-state pitch control force versus n at constant speed (see 3.2.2.2.1)
γ	climb angle, positive for climbing flight: $\gamma = \sin^{-1}$(vertical speed/true airspeed)
θ	pitch attitude, the angle between the fuselage reference line (body x-axis) and the horizontal
ı	aerodynamic lift plus thrust component normal to the flight path

6.2.6 Lateral-directional parameters.

δ_{AS}	displacement of the roll control stick or wheel along its path
T_r	first-order roll mode time constant, positive for stable mode
T_s	first-order spiral mode time constant, positive for stable mode
λ_r	$(-1/T_r)$
λ_s	$(-1/T_s)$
ω_ϕ	undamped natural frequency of numerator quadratic of ϕ/δ_{AS} transfer function
ζ_ϕ	damping ratio of numerator quadratic of ϕ/δ_{AS} transfer function
ω_{n_d}	undamped natural frequency of the Dutch roll oscillation
ζ_d	damping ratio of the Dutch roll oscillation
T_d	damped period of the Dutch roll: $T_d = 2\pi/(\omega_{n_d}(1 - \zeta_d^2)^{1/2})$
$\omega_{n_{rs}}$	undamped natural frequency of a coupled roll-spiral oscillation

ζ_{rs}	damping ratio of a coupled roll-spiral oscillation
ϕ	bank angle measured in the y-z plane, between the y-axis and the horizontal (6.2.1)
ϕ_t	bank angle change in time t, in response to control deflection of the form given in 3.3.4
p	roll rate about the x-axis (6.2.1)
p_{osc}/p_{av}	a measure of the ratio of the oscillatory component of roll rate to the average component of roll rate following a yaw-control-free step roll control command:

For $\zeta_d < 0.2$: $p_{osc}/p_{av} = (p_1 + p_3 - 2p_2)/(p_1 + p_3 + 2p_2)$

For $\zeta_d > 0.2$: $p_{osc}/p_{av} = (p_1 - p_2)/(p_1 + p_2)$

where p_1, p_2, and p_3 are roll rates at the first, second and third peaks respectively. (Figures B14 and B15)

ϕ_{osc}/ϕ_{av}	a measure of the ratio of the oscillatory component of bank angle to the average component of bank angle following a pedals-free impulse aileron command:

For $\zeta_d \leqslant 0.2$: $\phi_{osc}/\phi_{av} = (\phi_1 + \phi_3 - 2\phi_2)/(\phi_1 + \phi_3 + 2\phi_2)$

For $\zeta_d > 0.2$: $\phi_{osc}/\phi_{av} = (\phi_1 - \phi_2)/(\phi_1 + \phi_2)$

where: ϕ_1, ϕ_2 and ϕ_3 are bank angles at the first, second and third peaks respectively. (Figures B14 and B15)

β	sideslip angle at the center of gravity, angle between undisturbed flow and plane of symmetry. Positive, or right sideslip corresponds to incident flow approaching from the right side of the plane of symmetry.
$\Delta\beta$	maximum change in sideslip occurring within 2 seconds or one half-period of the Dutch roll, whichever is greater, for a step roll-control command. (Figures B14 and B 15)

k

ratio of 'command roll performance' to 'applicable roll performance requirement' of 3.3.4 or 3.3.4.1, with:

$k = (\phi_t)_{command}/(\phi_t)_{requirement}$

where:

a) 'Applicable roll performance requirement', (ϕ_t) requirement, is determined from 3.3.4 and 3.3.4.1 for the Class, Flight Phase Category and Level under consideration

b) 'Commanded roll performance', (ϕ_t) command, is the bank angle attained in the stated time for a given step roll command with yaw control pedals employed as specified in 3.3.4 and 3.3.4.1

t_{n_β}

time for the Dutch roll oscillation in the sideslip response to reach the nth local maximum for a right step or pulse roll-control command, or the nth local minimum for a left command. In the event a step control input cannot be accomplished, the control shall be moved as abruptly as practical and, for purposes of this definition, time shall be measured from the instant the cockpit control deflection passes through half the amplitude of the commanded value. For pulse inputs, time shall be measured from a point halfway through the duration of the pulse.

ψ_β

phase angle expressed as a lag for a cosine representation of the Dutch roll oscillation in sideslip, where:

$\omega_\beta = -(360/T_d)t_{n_\beta} + (n - 1)360$ deg.

with n as in t_n above.

$\angle(p/\beta)$

phase angle between roll rate and sideslip in the free Dutch roll oscillation. This phase angle is positive when p leads β by an angle between 0 and 180 degrees.

$|\phi/\beta|_d$

at any instant, the ratio of amplitudes of the bank-angle and sideslip-angle envelopes in the Dutch roll mode

Examples showing measurement of roll-sideslip coupling parameters are shown on Figure B14 for right rolls and Figure B15 for left rolls. Since several oscillations of the Dutch roll are required to measure these parameters, and since for proper identification large roll rates and bank angle changes must generally be avoided, step roll control inputs should be small. It should be noted that since Ψ_β is the phase angle for the Dutch roll component of sideslip, care must be taken to select a peak far enough downstream that the position of the peak is not influenced by the roll mode. In practice, peaks occurring one or two roll mode time constants after the aileron input will be relatively undistorted. Care must also be taken when there is ramping of the sideslip trace, since ramping will displace the position of a peak of the trace from the corresponding peak of the Dutch roll component. In practice, the peaks of the Dutch roll component of sideslip are located by first drawing a line through the ramping portion of the sideslip trace and then noting the times at which the vertical distance between the line and the sideslip trace is the greatest. (See the following sketch for Case (a) of Figures B14 and B15; p. 339.)

Since the first local maximum of the Dutch roll component of the sideslip response occurs at t = 2.95 seconds,

$$\Psi_\beta = -(360/T_d)t_{n_\beta} + (n - 1)360 =$$

$$= -(360/3.5)(2.95) = -303 \text{ deg.}$$

Level 1 flying qualities of a Class IV airplane in the approach are under examination, so the roll performance requirement from Table IX upon which the parameter 'k' in the sideslip excursion requirement (Figure B6) is based, is ϕ_t = 30 degrees in 1 second with rudder pedals free (as in the rolls of 3.3.2.4). From the definitions, 'k' for this condition is:

$$k = (\phi_1)_{command}/(\phi_1)_{requirement}$$

Therefore from Figures B14 and B15:

Case (a), k = 9.1/30 = 0.30

Case (b), k = 8.1/30 = 0.27

Case (c), k = 6.8/30 = 0.23

Case (d), k = 6.0/30 = 0.20

6.2.7 <u>Atmospheric disturbance parameters</u>.

j	$(-1)^{1/2}$
Ω	spatial (reduced) frequency (radians per foot)
ω	temporal frequency (radians per sec), where: $\omega = \Omega V$
t	time (seconds)
u_g	disturbance velocity along the x-axis, positive forward (ft/sec)
v_g	disturbance velocity along the y-axis, positive to the pilot's right (ft/sec)
w_g	disturbance velocity along the z-axis, positive down (ft/sec)
	Note: Random u_g, v_g and w_g have Gaussian (normal) distributions
$V_{w/d}$	magnitude of wind over the aircraft carrier deck (ft/sec)
σ, RMS	root-mean-square disturbance intensity, where: $\sigma^2 = \int_0^\infty \phi(\Omega)d\Omega = \int_0^\infty \phi(\omega)d\omega$
σ_u	root-mean-square intensity of u_g
σ_v	root-mean-square intensity of v_g
σ_w	root-mean-square intensity of w_g
L_u	scale for u_g (feet)
L_v	scale for v_g (feet)
L_w	scale for w_g (feet)
$\phi_{u_g}(\Omega)$	spectrum for u_g, where: $\phi_{u_g}(\Omega) = V\phi_{u_g}(\omega)$
$\phi_{v_g}(\Omega)$	spectrum for v_g, where: $\phi_{v_g}(\Omega) = V\phi_{v_g}(\omega)$
$\phi_{w_g}(\Omega)$	spectrum for w_g, where: $\phi_{w_g}(\Omega) = V\phi_{w_g}(\omega)$
v_m	generalized discrete gust intensity, positive along the positive axes, m = x, y, z (ft/sec)
d_m	generalized discrete gust length (always positive), m = x, y, z (feet)
u_{20}	wind speed at 20 feet above the ground

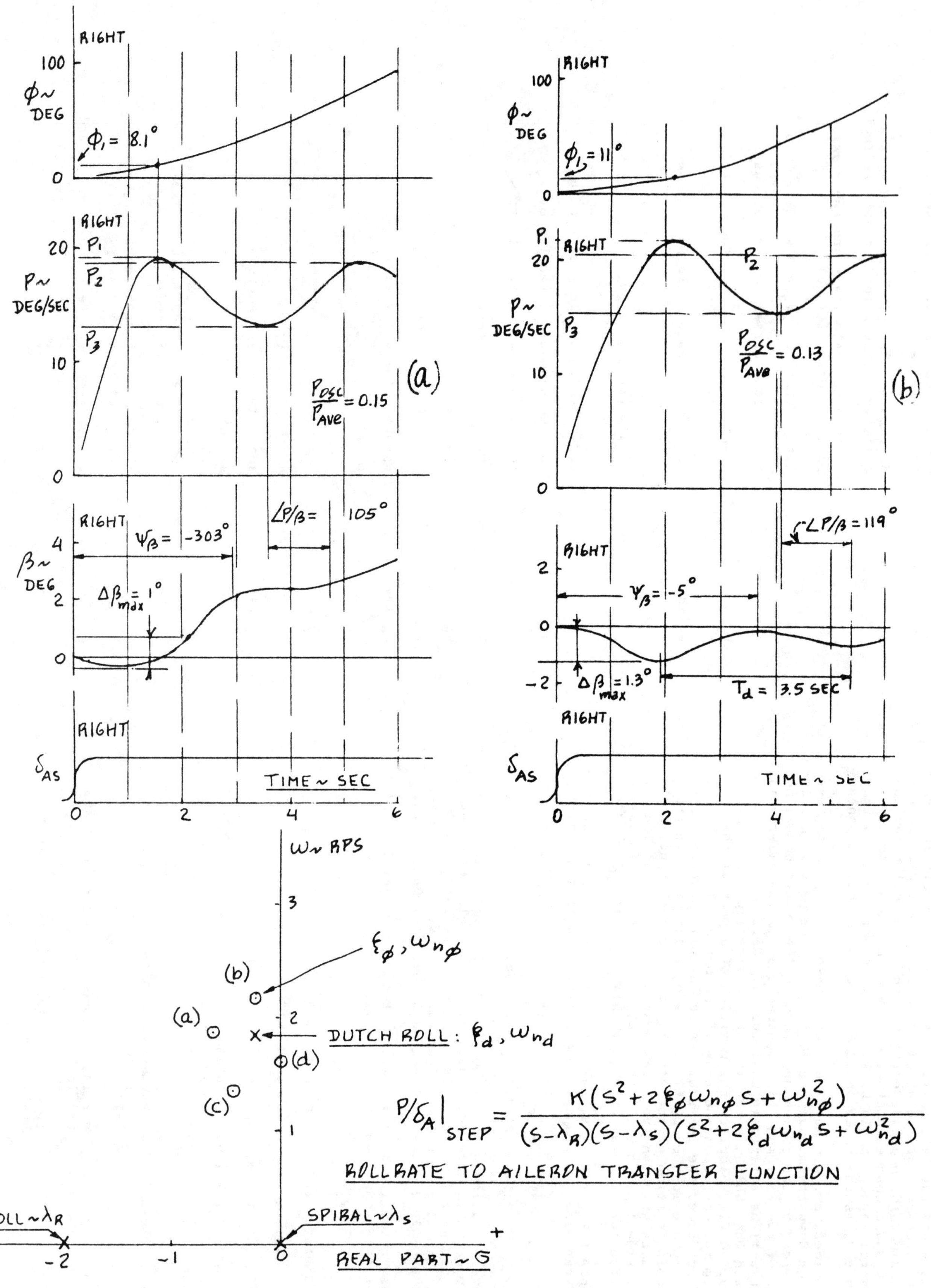

$$P/\delta_A\Big|_{STEP} = \frac{K(s^2+2\xi_\phi\omega_{n\phi}s+\omega_{n\phi}^2)}{(s-\lambda_R)(s-\lambda_s)(s^2+2\xi_d\omega_{n_d}s+\omega_{n_d}^2)}$$

Figure B14 Roll-Sideslip Coupling Parameters: Right Rolls

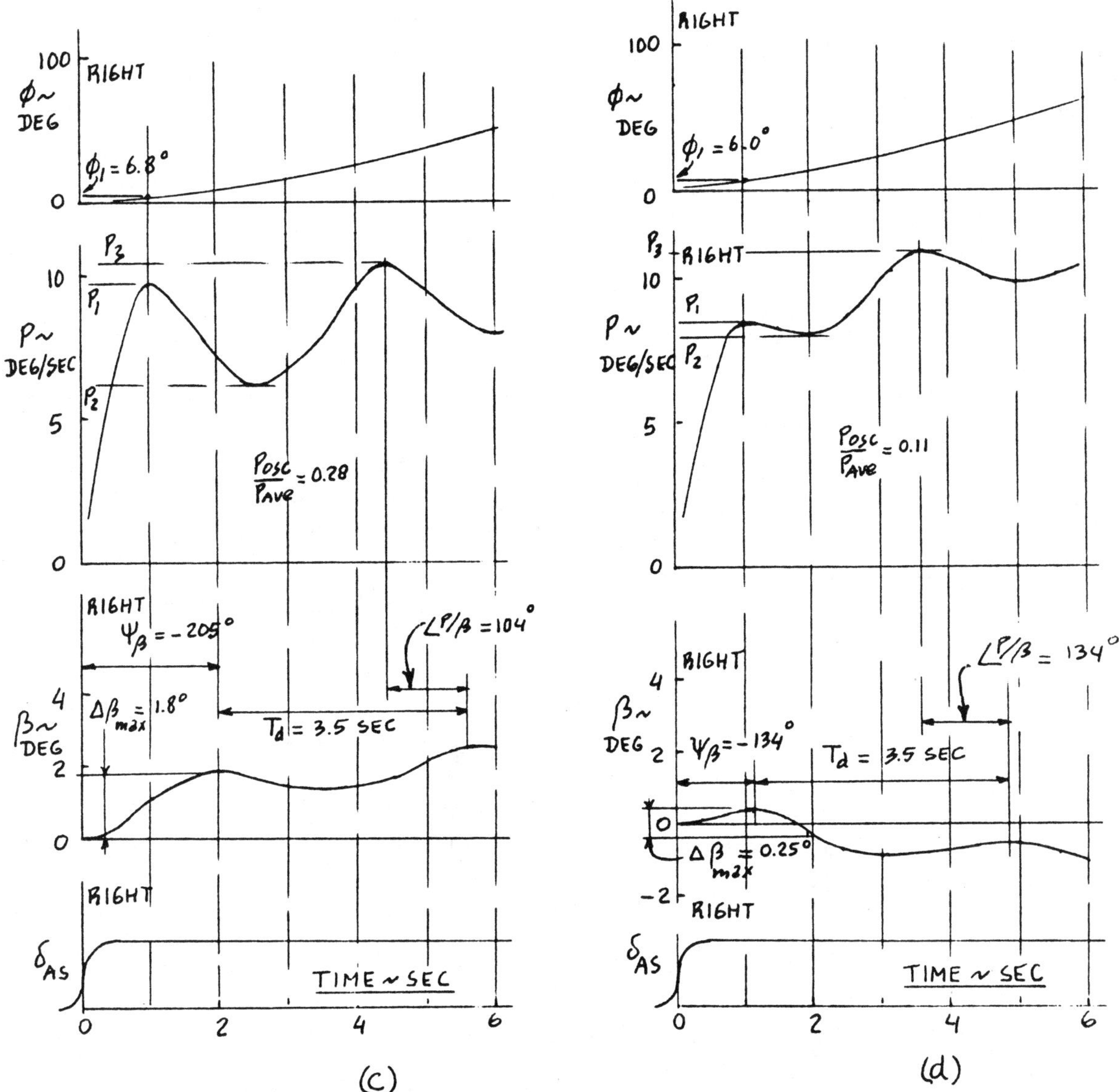

Figure B14 (Cont'd) Roll-Sideslip Coupling Parameters: Right Rolls

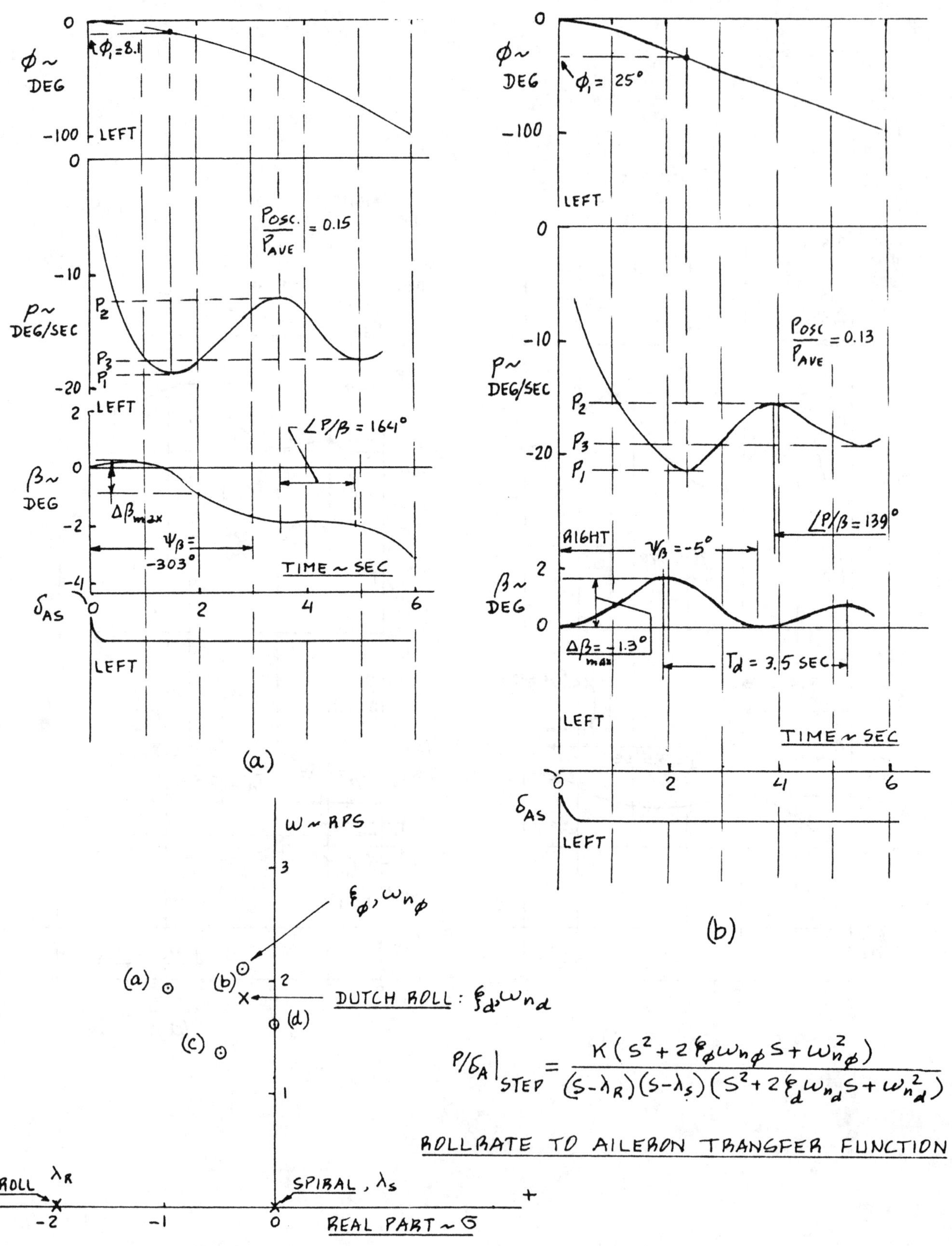

Figure B15 Roll-Sideslip Coupling Parameters: Left Rolls

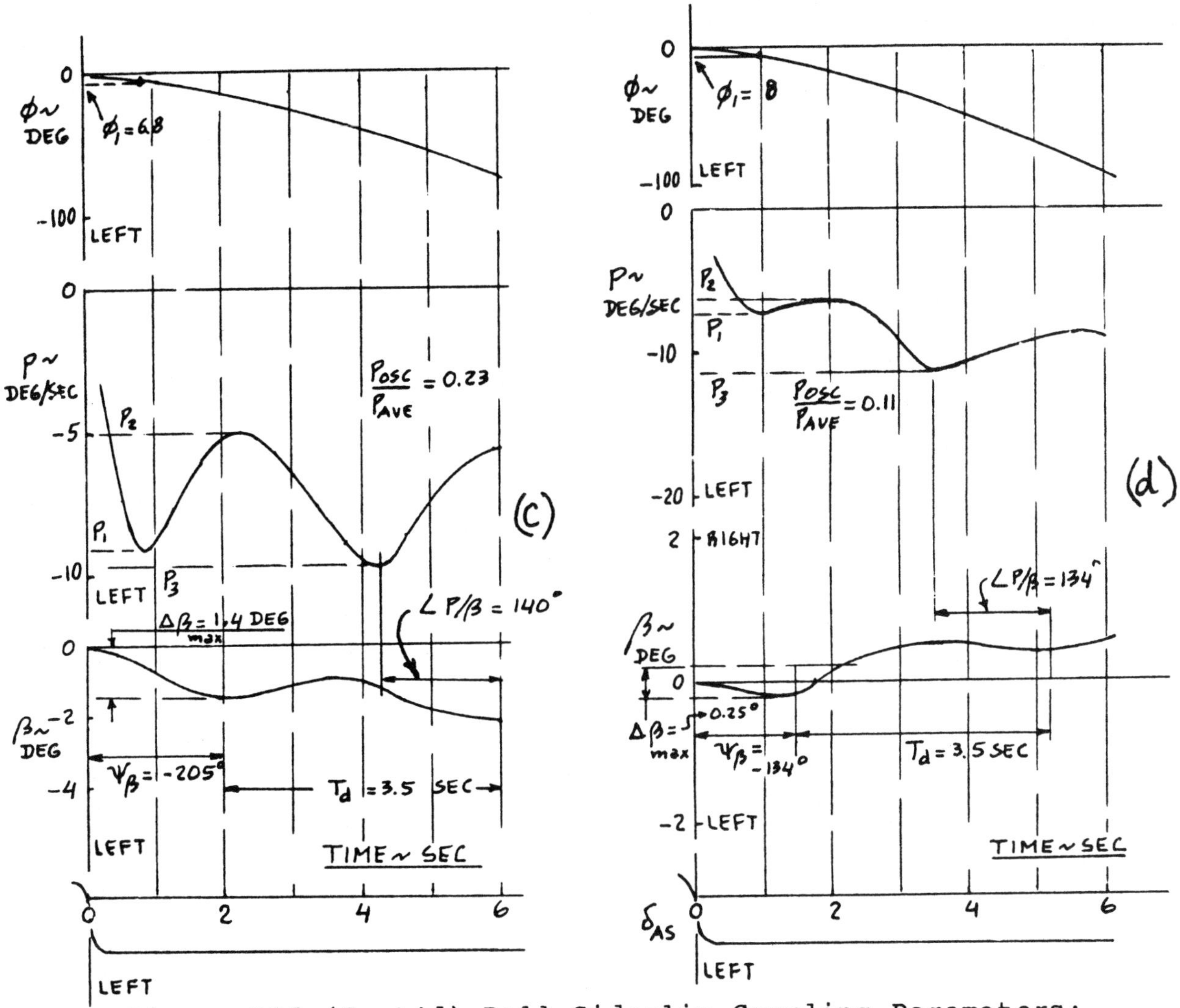

0
ϕ ~ DEG
$\phi_1 = 6.8$
-100
LEFT
0
P ~ DEG/SEC
P_2
-5
P_1
-10
LEFT
P_3
$\frac{P_{OSC}}{P_{AVE}} = 0.23$
(c)
$\Delta\beta_{max} = 1.4$ DEG
$\angle P/\beta = 140°$
0
β ~ DEG
-2
-4
LEFT
$\Psi_\beta = -205°$
$T_d = 3.5$ SEC
TIME ~ SEC
0 2 4 6
LEFT

0
ϕ ~ DEG
$\phi_1 = 8$
-100
LEFT
0
P ~ DEG/SEC
P_2
P_1
-10
P_3
$\frac{P_{OSC}}{P_{AVE}} = 0.11$
-20
LEFT
(d)
2
RIGHT
$\angle P/\beta = 134°$
β ~ DEG
0
$\Delta\beta_{max} = 0.25°$
$\Psi_\beta = -134°$
$T_d = 3.5$ SEC
-2
LEFT
TIME ~ SEC
δ_{AS}
0 2 4 6
LEFT

Figure B15 (Cont'd) Roll-Sideslip Coupling Parameters: Left Rolls

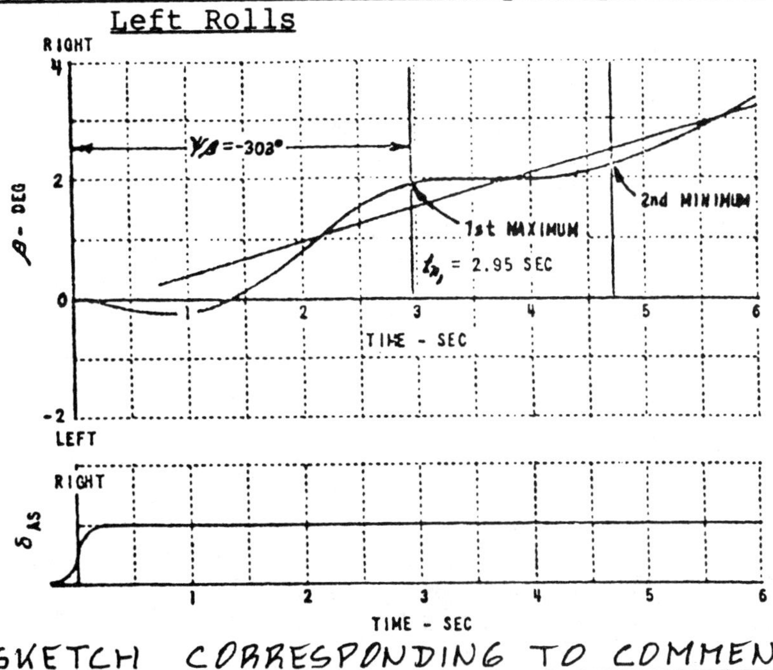

SKETCH CORRESPONDING TO COMMENT ON FIGS B14 AND B15 ON P. 335, LEFT

x	distance from airplane to ship center of pitch, negative aft of ship (feet)
ψ_w	mean wind direction relative to the runway (3.7.3.3)

6.2.8 Terms used in high angle of attack requirements.

Post-stall: The flight regime involving angles of attack greater than nominal stall angles of attack. The airplane characteristics in the post-stall regime may consist of three more or less distinct consecutive types of airplane motion following departure from controlled flight: post-stall gyration, incipient spin, and developed spin.

Post-stall gyration (PSG): Uncontrolled motions about one or more airplane axes following departure from controlled flight. While this type of airplane motion involves angles of attack higher than the stall angle, lower angles may be encountered intermittently in the course of the motion.

Spin: That part of post-stall airplane motion which is characterized by a sustained yaw rotation. The spin may be erect or inverted, flat (high angle of attack) or steep (low, but still stalled angle of attack) and the rotary motions may have oscillations in pitch, roll and yaw superimposed on them. The incipient spin is the initial, transient phase of the motion during which it is not possible to identify the spin mode, usually followed by the developed spin, the phase during which it is possible to identify the spin mode.

6.3 Interpretation of F_s/n limits of Table V. Because the limits on F_s/n are a function of both n_L and n/α, Table V is rather complex. To illustrate its use, the limits are presented on Figure B16 for an airplane having a center-stick controller and n_L = 7.0.

6.4 Gain scheduling. Changes of mechanical gearings and stability augmentation gains in the primary flight control system are sometimes accomplished by scheduling the changes as a function of the settings of secondary control devices, such as flaps or wing sweep. This practice is generally acceptable, but gearings and gains normally should not be scheduled as a function of trim control settings since pilots do not always keep airplanes in trim.

6.5 Engine considerations. Secondary effects of engine operation may have an important bearing on flying qualities and should not be overlooked in design. These considerations are:

a) the influence of engine gyroscopic moments on airframe dynamic motions

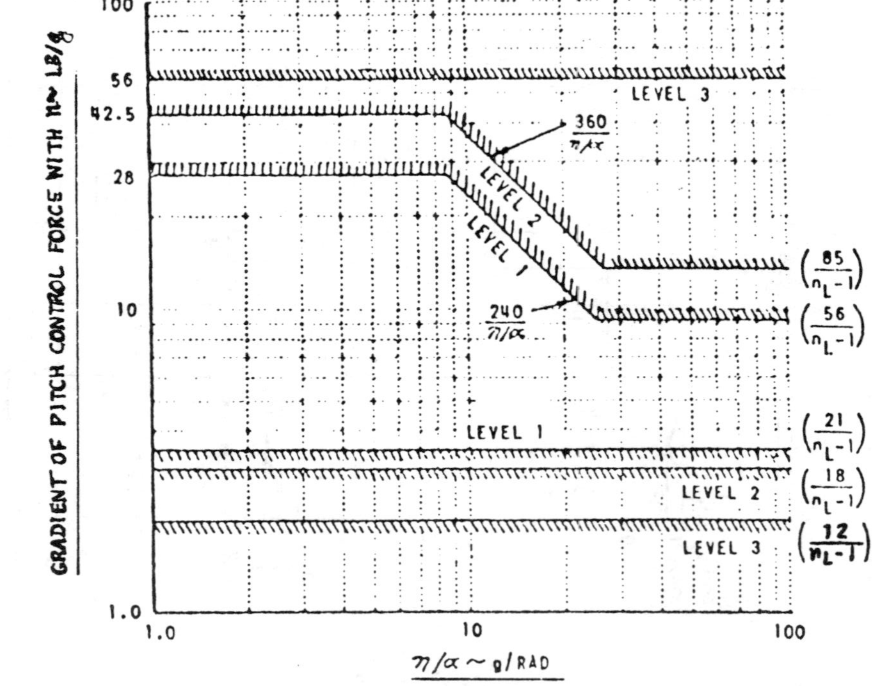

Figure B16 Example of Pitch Maneuvering Force Gradient Limits: Center-stick Controller, n_L = 7.0

b) the effects of engine operation (including flameout and intentional shutdown) on characteristics of flight at high angle of attack (3.4.2)

c) the reduction at low rpm of engine-derived power for operating the flight control system.

6.6 Effects of aeroelasticity, control equipment and structural dynamics. Since aeroelasticity, control equipment and structural dynamics may exert an important influence on the airplane flying qualities, such effects should not be overlooked in calculations or analyses directed toward investigation of compliance with the requirements of this specification.

6.7 Application of Levels. Part of the intent of 3.1.10 is to ensure that the probability of encountering significantly degraded flying qualities because of component or subsystem failure is small. For example, the probability of encountering very degraded flying qualities (Level 3) must be less than specified values per flight.

6.7.1 Level definitions. To determine the degradation in flying qualities parameters for a given Airplane Failure State the following definitions are provided:

a. Level 1 is better than or equal to the Level 1 boundary, or number, specified in Section 3

b. Level 2 is worse than Level 1, but no worse than the Level 2 boundary, or number

c. Level 3 is worse than Level 2, but no worse than the Level 3 boundary, or number.

When a given boundary, or number, is identified simultaneously as Level 1 and Level 2, this means that the flying qualities outside the boundary conditions shown, or worse than the number given, are at best Level 3 flying qualities. Also, since Level 1 and Level 2 requirements are the same, flying qualities must be within this common boundary, or number, in both the Operational and Service Flight Envelopes for Airplane Normal States (3.1.10.1). Airplane Failure States that do not degrade flying qualities beyond this common boundary are not considered in meeting the requirements of 3.1.10.2. Airplane Failure States that represent degradations to Level 3 must, however, be included in the computation of the probability of encountering Level 3 degradations in both the Operational and Service Flight Envelopes. Again, degradation beyond the Level 3 boundary is not permitted regardless of component failures.

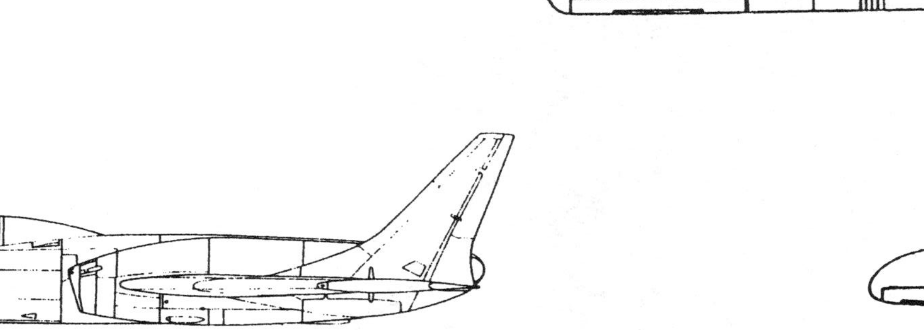

COURTESY: SAAB

APPENDIX C: THE AIRWORTHINESS CODE AND THE RELATIONSHIP BETWEEN FAILURE STATES, LEVELS OF PERFORMANCE AND LEVELS OF FLYING QUALITIES

The purpose of this appendix is to provide airplane designers with a link between the airworthiness regulations, the failure of flight crucial systems and the required level of performance and flying qualities.

LEMMA: It is NOT possible to design an airplane so that the probability of catastrophic failure is zero.

For the airplane designer, the consequence of this Lemma is that:

1. The airplane and all its systems must be designed so that catastrophic failures do not occur above some agreed upon (low) level of probability.

2. The consequences of each flight crucial failure must be understood and the probability of its occurrence must be predicted.

The civil airworthiness code of Figure C1 reflects this design philosophy in a qualitative and quantitative manner. The airworthiness code of Figure C1 reflects the intent of the civil regulations of Appendix A.

The military airworthiness code of Figure C2 reflects this design philosophy in a qualitative and quantitative manner. The airworthiness code of Figure C2 reflects the intent of the military regulations as presented in Appendix B.

There is no formal linkage between the civil and the military airworthiness requirements. However, Figure C2 when compared to Figure C1 infers such a linkage. This inference was made by the author!

The airworthiness codes of Figures C1 and C2 depict the 'level of airplane capability' left, following some failure. The following definitions of capability levels are suggested by the author. They are based on those stated in Appendix B, Section B3:

Level 1: Characteristics clearly adequate for the conduct of the flight.

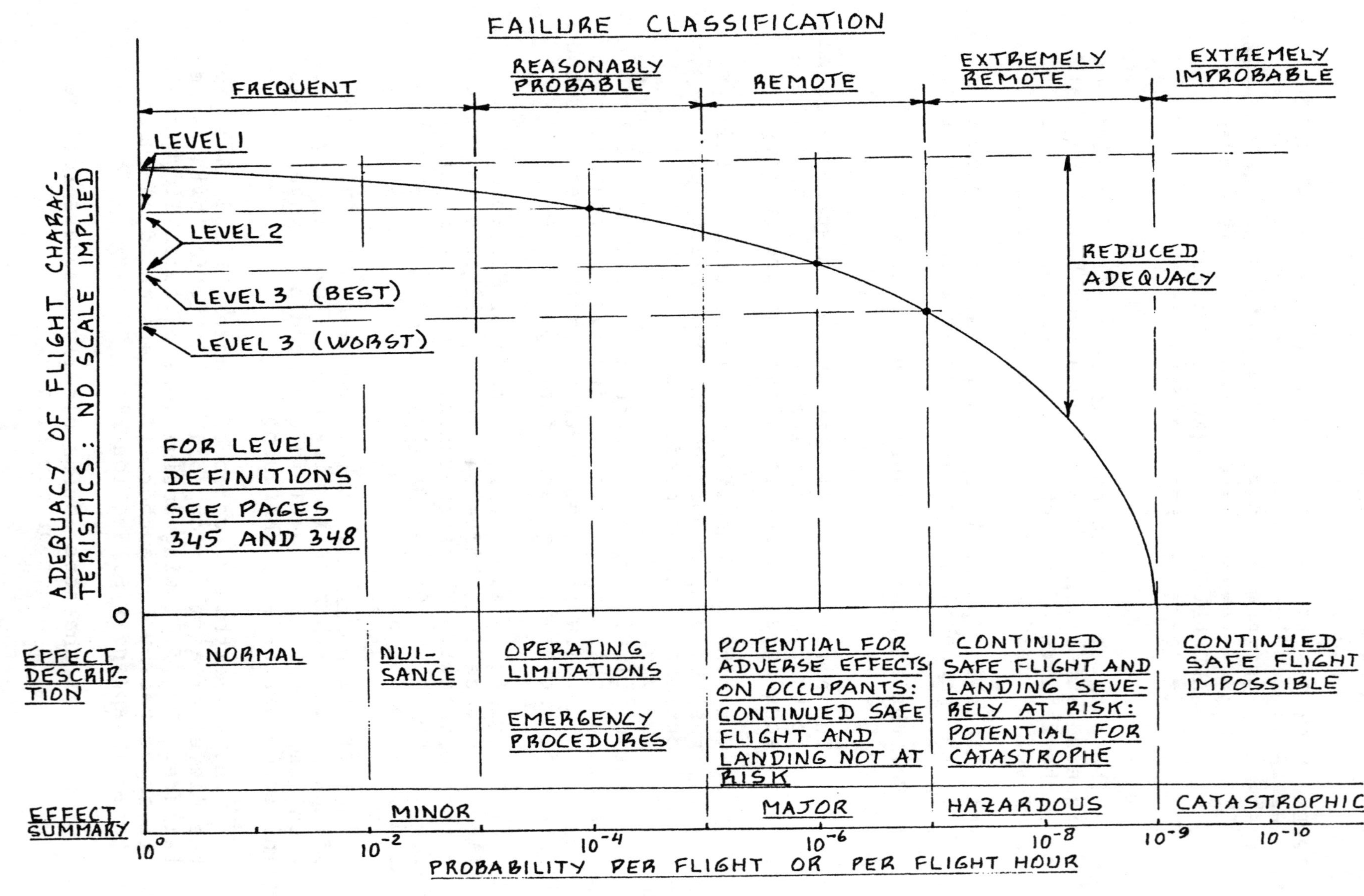

Figure C1 The Civil Airworthiness Code

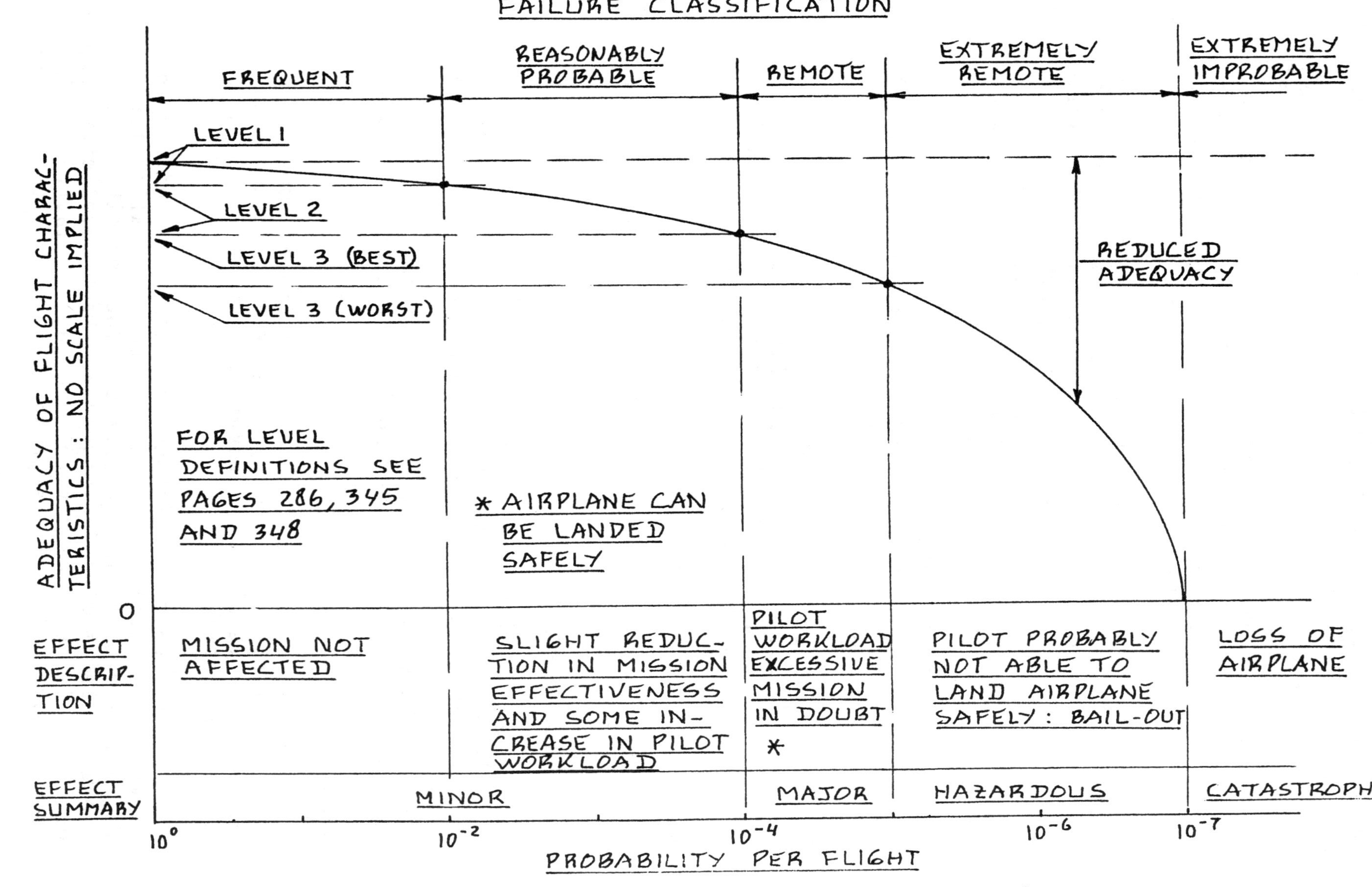

Figure C2 The Military Airworthiness Code

Level 2: Characteristics adequate to conduct the flight, but some increase in pilot workload or some degradation in mission effectiveness, or both, exists.

Level 3: Characteristics such that the flight can be continued and a safe landing conducted, but pilot workload is excessive or mission effectiveness is inadequate, or both.

Note: for flight characteristics worse than Level 3 a catastrophic crash is likely to occur.

The word 'characteristics' as used here implies: performance capabilities and/or flying qualities. Therefore, from a preliminary design viewpoint, two failure aspects are important:

C1: Failures Affecting Performance
C2: Failures Affecting Stability and Control
(i.e. flying qualities to the military and flight characteristics to the civilians)

C1: FAILURES AFFECTING PERFORMANCE

The civil and military performance regulations of Appendices A and B cover three failure situations:

Failure Situation:	Level Definition
1. All engines operating (AEO):	Level 1
2. One engine inoperative (OEI):	Level 2
3. Two or more engines inoperative:	Level 3

The Level association given above is suggested by the author: it is NOT found in any of the regulations.

C2 STABILITY AND CONTROL

The civil regulations for stability and control behavior (flight characteristics) as stated in Appendix A apply to the required characteristics with ALL systems functioning normally.

The military regulations for stability and control (flying qualities) as stated in Appendix B allow for three Levels of flying qualities. The definition of these Levels is given on page 286. Each Level of flying qualities is associated with some failure in the flight control system AND with a probability of occurrence: see

Table II on page 290. Appendix B provides numerical values for all pertinent flying qualities at each flying quality Level and for each phase of flight.

The civil regulations do not formally recognize a link between failures and degradation (Level) in flying qualities. However, industry design practice is to use the military flying quality Levels in design, but with failure probabilities which are typically a factor 100 times better than those allowed by the military.

As seen in Figures C1 and C2, the relative level of failure probability in civil airplanes is a factor 100 lower than that for military airplanes.

With regard to flight control system design, it is suggested to consider the following two extremes:

TYPE 1: Airplanes with reversible control systems and inherent stability.

In these airplanes the assumption should be made that all control system components are purely mechanical so that their probability of failure is equal to the probability of failure in the primary airplane structure. Such airplanes should be designed to Level 1 flying qualities when intended for the military: see Appendix B.

For civil airplanes the regulations of Appendix A should be used where possible. In cases where the civil regulations fail to provide numerical design guidelines, the pertinent military regulation of Appendix B should be used.

TYPE 2: Airplanes with irreversible control systems and inherent instability.

With all systems operating, civil and military airplanes should be designed according to the Type 1 philosophy stated before.

With one or more failures, <u>civil and military</u> airplanes should be designed to the appropriate handling quality levels as stated in Appendix B. The failure probability levels associated with civil airplanes should be at least a factor 100 lower than that associated with military airplanes.

For airplanes which fit in between Types 1 and 2, the design philosophy for Type 2 airplanes should be used.

APPENDIX D: INERTIA TRANSFORMATIONS

The purpose of this appendix is to provide equations for the transformation of airplane moments and product of inertia from one body fixed axis system to another. The two axis systems are shown in Figure D1. Note that both are centered on the airplane center of gravity.

The transformation equations are as follows:

$$\begin{Bmatrix} I_{xx_S} \\ I_{zz_S} \\ I_{xz_S} \end{Bmatrix} = \begin{bmatrix} \cos^2\alpha_1 & \sin^2\alpha_1 & -\sin2\alpha_1 \\ \sin^2\alpha_1 & \cos^2\alpha_1 & \sin2\alpha_1 \\ 0.5\sin2\alpha_1 & -0.5\sin2\alpha_1 & \cos2\alpha_1 \end{bmatrix} \times \begin{Bmatrix} I_{xx_B} \\ I_{zz_B} \\ I_{xz_B} \end{Bmatrix}$$

The angle α_1 represents the steady state angle of attack of the airplane. The subscript 'B' refers to an arbitrarily selected body-fixed axis system. The subscript 's' refers to the so-called stability axis system (its x-axis is aligned with the steady state velocity vector, U_1 of the airplane) which is ALSO a body-fixed axis system!

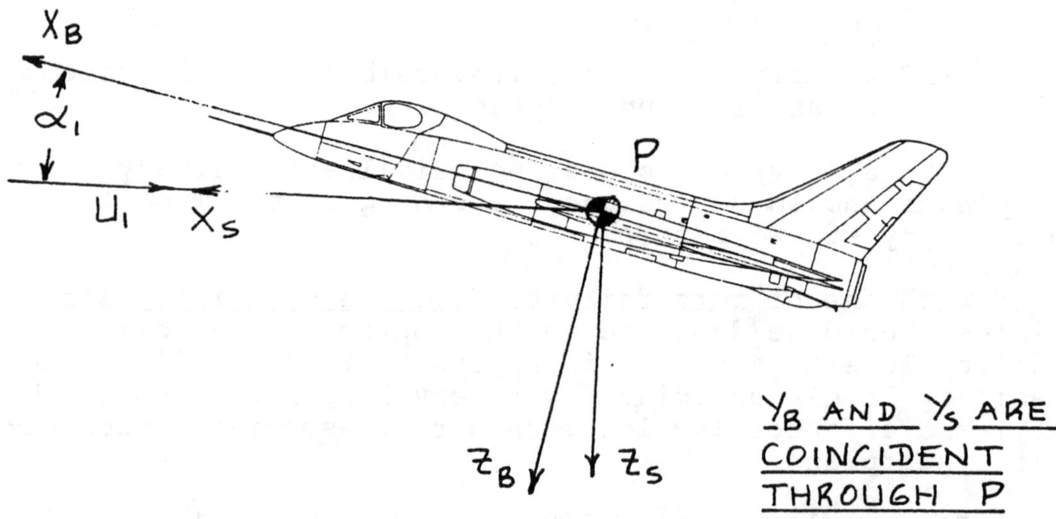

Figure D1 Airplane Axis Systems